Remote Sensing and Digital Image Processing with R

This new textbook on remote sensing and digital image processing of natural resources includes numerous, practical problem-solving exercises and applications of sensors and satellite systems using remote sensing data collection resources, and emphasizes the free and open-source platform R. It explains basic concepts of remote sensing and multidisciplinary applications using R language and R packages, by engaging students in learning theory through hands-on, real-life projects. All chapters are structured with learning objectives, computation, questions, solved exercises, resources, and research suggestions.

Features

- Explains the theory of passive and active remote sensing and its applications in water, soil, vegetation, and atmosphere.
- Covers data analysis in the free and open-source R platform, which makes remote sensing accessible to anyone with a computer.
- Includes case studies from different environments with free software algorithms and an R toolset for active learning and a learn-by-doing approach.
- Provides hands-on exercises at the end of each chapter and encourages readers to understand the potential and the limitations of the environments, remote sensing targets, and process.
- Explores current trends and developments in remote sensing in homework assignments with data to further explore the use of free multispectral remote sensing data, including very high spatial resolution data sources for target recognition with image processing techniques.

While the focus of the book is on environmental and agriculture engineering, it can be applied widely to a variety of subjects such as physical, natural, and social sciences. Students in upper-level undergraduate or graduate programs, taking courses in remote sensing, geoprocessing, civil and environmental engineering, geosciences, environmental sciences, electrical engineering, biology, and hydrology will also benefit from the learning objectives in the book. Professionals who use remote sensing and digital processing will also find this text enlightening.

Remote Sensing and Digital Image Processing with R

Marcelo de Carvalho Alves and
Luciana Sanches

CRC Press
Taylor & Francis Group
Boca Raton London New York

CRC Press is an imprint of the
Taylor & Francis Group, an **informa** business

Designed cover image: © Shutterstock

First edition published 2023
by CRC Press
6000 Broken Sound Parkway NW, Suite 300, Boca Raton, FL 33487-2742

and by CRC Press
4 Park Square, Milton Park, Abingdon, Oxon, OX14 4RN

CRC Press is an imprint of Taylor & Francis Group, LLC

© 2023 Taylor & Francis Group, LLC

ISBN: 978-1-032-35922-9 (hbk)
ISBN: 978-1-032-35982-3 (pbk)
ISBN: 978-1-003-32966-4 (ebk)

DOI: 10.1201/9781003329664

Typeset in Latin Modern font
by KnowledgeWorks Global Ltd.

Publisher's note: This book has been prepared from camera-ready copy provided by the authors.

Contents

About the Authors

Marcelo de Carvalho Alves

Dr. Alves is an associate professor at the Federal University de Lavras, Brazil. His education includes master's, doctoral, and post-doctoral degrees in Agricultural Engineering at Federal University of Lavras, Brazil. He has varied research interests and has published on surveying, remote sensing, geocomputation, and agriculture applications. He has over 20 years of extensive experience in data science, digital image processing, and modeling using multiscale, multidisciplinary, multispectral, and multitemporal concepts applied to different environments. Experimental field sites included a tropical forest, savanna, wetland, and agricultural fields in Brazil. His research has been predominantly funded by CNPq, CAPES, FAPEMIG, and FAPEMAT. Over the years, he has built a large portfolio of research grants, mostly relating to applied and theoretical remote sensing, broadly in the context of vegetation cover, plant diseases, and related impacts of climate change.

Luciana Sanches

Dr. Sanches graduated with a degree in Sanitary Engineering from the Federal University of Mato Grosso, Brazil, a master's degree in Sanitation, Environment, and Water Resources from the Federal University of Minas Gerais, a PhD in Road Engineering, Hydraulic Channels, and Ports from Universidad de Cantabria, Spain, a post-doctorate degree in Environmental Physics, Brazil, and a post-doctorate degree in Environmental Sciences from the University of Reading, United Kingdom. Her education includes postgraduate degrees in Workplace Safety Engineering at Federal University of Mato Grosso, Brazil, and in Project Development and Management for Municipal Water Resources Management at the National Water Agency, Brazil. She is currently an associate professor at the Federal University of Mato Grosso, and worked for more than 20 years in research on atmosphere-biosphere interaction, hydrometeorology in various temporal-spatial scales with interpretation based in environmental modeling and remote sensing. She has been applying remote sensing in teaching and research activities to support the interpretation of environmental dynamics.

Preface

Remote sensing is the science, art, and technology of obtaining information about objects and processes without direct physical contact with remotely observed targets. Remote sensing can be used to monitor geometrical, biophysical, and chemical features of the Earth. These features can be measured and extracted generating remotely sensed big data. Pattern recognition of big data by digital image processing algorithms with machine learning techniques enables us to understand functioning mechanisms and geospatial relationships between ecological variables of agroecosystems and ecosystems, over large areas, repeatedly.

The subjects of the book were chosen so it is possible to learn about the subject's theory, as well as develop practical activities with concrete and objective applications for readers through chapters with remote sensing and digital image processing themes. The chapters were prepared to introduce concepts for each subject followed by computational practices and solved exercises.

The book is designed to support undergraduate and graduate teaching in the physical, natural, and social sciences, with a focus on engineering and technology, such as agricultural engineering, agronomy, environmental engineering, and forestry. The book can be widely used by readers with systematic educational and practical experience in agriculture, geography, geology, hydrology, statistics, geocomputation, physics, chemistry, and applied mathematics. The book can be well applied in 60-hour courses spread over face-to-face or virtual classes over a semester, with weekly activities.

The practical activities in the book are performed in the R software and in virtual libraries of remote sensing data on the internet. R is an open source environment for statistical computing and visualization based on the S language. R is a program used in statistics in a robust, programmable, portable and open computing environment, applicable to the most complex and sophisticated problems, without access or use restrictions. For over two decades, there has been a growing number of packages used for geospatial data manipulation and analysis, from simple analysis to advanced geospatial modeling with machine learning. The codes used in the book, although they can be obtained from numerous books and tutorials on the internet, are designed for reference and as an example for doing similar practical work, with analysis procedures applied to remote sensing big data, from the first to the last chapter. The examples presented can be expanded to a larger number of sensors in future editions to broaden the possibility of using multiple concepts and scientific holism in the area. Professionals working with geoinformation and geospatial data need to know about processing spatial data of vegetation, water, soil, atmosphere, and to be familiar with some basic and advanced digital image processing techniques.

The items covered in the chapters are defined in a form of constructive complexity that allows the student to develop a project using remote sensing and geospatial data, and finally, conclude the studies with a report in the form of a scientific article or scientific review of remote sensing applied to agricultural and environmental analysis. The chapters covered are "Introduction to Remote Sensing and Digital Image Processing with R" (Chapter 1), "Remote Sensing of Electromagnetic Radiation" (Chapter 2), "Remote Sensing Sensors and Satellite Systems" (Chapter 3), "Remote Sensing of Vegetation" (Chapter 4), "Remote Sensing of Water" (Chapter 5), "Remote Sensing of Soil, Rocks, and Geomorphology" (Chapter 6), "Remote Sensing of the Atmosphere" (Chapter 7), "Scientific Applications of Remote Sensing and Digital Image Processing for Project Design"

(Chapter 8), "Visual Interpretation and Enhancement of Remote Sensing Images" (Chapter 9), "Unsupervised Classification of Remote Sensing Images" (Chapter 10), "Supervised Classification of Remote Sensing Images" (Chapter 11), "Uncertainty and Accuracy Analysis in Remote Sensing and Digital Image Processing" (Chapter 12), and "Scientific Applications of Remote Sensing and Digital Image Processing to Enhance Articles" (Chapter 13).

Marcelo de Carvalho Alves and Luciana Sanches, Lavras, June 2023

1

Introduction to Remote Sensing and Digital Image Processing with R

1.1 Learning Questions

The learning questions answered through reading the chapter are as follows:

- What is the importance of remote sensing in studying terrestrial environments?
- How can information obtained by remote sensing generate knowledge about a geographic problem?
- How is geographic information used in the decision-making process of remote sensing?
- What is the definition of remote sensing?
- How has remote sensing been used in history?
- What are the relationships between remote sensing and other scientific disciplines?
- What applications use remote sensing?
- Which professions use remote sensing?
- What are the resolutions used in remote sensing?
- Which remote sensing software can be used?
- How is a scientific investigation with remote sensing started?

1.2 Learning Outcomes

Using the learning outcomes from the chapter, you should be able to do the following:

- Know a brief history of remote sensing.
- Recognize how remote sensing is used in everyday life.
- Understand the scientific importance of remote sensing.
- Know about the geospatial data infrastructure used in remote sensing.
- Understand the need to study geospatial objects and processes with remote sensing.
- Know the difference between raster and vector data used in remote sensing.
- Know in practice the characteristics of a spectral band used in digital image processing.
- Install and use basic functions of the free software used in remote sensing.

1.3 Introduction

The goal of science is to discover universal truths that are the same now, in the past, and in the future. Fortunately, the knowledge gained can be used to protect the environment and improve the quality of human life. Scientists have observed and made measurements to identify universal truths about (Jensen, 2007):

- The physical world, such as the atmosphere, water, soils, and rocks;
- The inhabitants of the planet, such as *Homo sapiens*, flora, and fauna;
- The existing processes, such as erosion, deforestation, and urban sprawl.

Scientists formulate hypotheses in order to systematically accept or reject them in an unbiased way. The data needed to accept or reject a hypothesis can be obtained directly from the field. These data can be referred to as "*in situ* data" or "locality data". This process can be costly, time consuming, and inaccurate (Jensen, 2007).

Remote sensing can be defined as the art, science, and technology of obtaining reliable information about physical objects and environment through the process of recording, measuring, and interpreting images and digital representations of energy patterns derived from non-contact sensor systems (Colwell, 1997).

1.4 Geospatial Data Infrastructure

Remote sensing is used in scientific and technological approaches to provide information on biophysical and hybrid variables to gain knowledge about a particular subject. Chemical, physical and biological variables can be extracted directly from aerial stereoscopic photography, satellite imagery, airborne laser scanner data (LIDAR) or interferometric synthetic aperture radar (IFSAR) imaging (Figure 1.1).

Hybrid variables are created by the systematic analysis of more than one biophysical variable (Table 1.1) (Jensen, 2007).

Table 1.1 Biophysical and hybrid variables used to obtain environmental information in remote sensing.

Variable	Information
Chemical, physical, and biological	Geodetic control x, y, z; topography and bathymetry; public and private geographic boundaries; highways; railroads; airports; vegetation variables; surface temperature (land, water, atmosphere); soils and rocks; soil physicochemical variables; surface roughness; weather variables; water; snow and sea ice; volcanism; urban variables.
Hybrid	Land use; vegetation stress.

Additional information derived from data such as digital elevation model, soil map, geological map, political boundaries and municipal statistics can be used to support the remote sensing process in geographic information systems (Jensen, 2007).

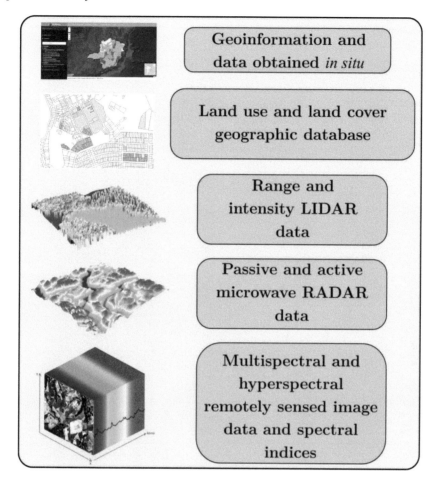

Figure 1.1 Geospatial data infrastructure.

Vector files with Brazilian municipal boundaries can be obtained from the *Instituto Brasileiro de Geografia e Estatística* (IBGE) or in R packages like spData (Bivand et al., 2020), rnaturalearth (South, 2021), raster (Hijmans et al., 2020), brazilmaps (Siqueira, 2017), GADMTools (Decorps, 2021), and geodata (Hijmans, Ghosh, et al., 2022):

- IBGE[1]
- spData[2]
- rnaturalearth[3]
- raster getData[4]
- brazilmaps[5]
- GADM-Spatial database of the World's administrative boundaries[6]
- geodata[7]

---

[1]https://www.ibge.gov.br/geociencias/downloads-geociencias.html
[2]https://cran.r-project.org/web/packages/spData/index.html
[3]https://cran.r-project.org/web/packages/rnaturalearth/
[4]https://www.rdocumentation.org/packages/raster/versions/3.1-5/topics/getData
[5]https://github.com/rpradosiqueira/brazilmaps
[6]https://gadm.org/data.html
[7]https://github.com/rspatial/geodata

1.5   Obtaining Data at the Region of Interest

Data obtained *in situ* can be useful for identifying and delineating objects and processes in the region of interest, and for validating results obtained with digital image processing. Using *in situ* sampling data, environmental features such as soil, water, vegetation, and urban regions can be characterized by interpolating this information to the study area (Figure 1.2).

Figure 1.2 Obtaining data in the region of interest by means of regular or irregular sample meshes georeferenced with a satellite positioning system.

Some essential features for obtaining *in situ* data are:

- The collection plan prepared with georeferenced sampling meshes;
- The direct collection of the variable in the field by the scientist;
- The step can be an expensive, time-consuming and imprecise step;
- Measurement instruments *in situ* must be calibrated;

- The *in situ* data may be called "ground truth", but may contain errors.

In situ data can be obtained from sources on the Internet. For example, meteorological variables at stations with georeferenced locations can be obtained directly from web-based databases, as in the case of the Meteorological Database for Education and Research, Brazil (BDMEP, from Portuguese *Banco de Dados Meteorológicos para Ensino e Pesquisa*), the Hidroweb of the National Water Agency, Brazil (ANA, from Portuguese *Agência Nacional das Águas*), and the Climate Data Online of the National Oceanic and Atmospheric Administration (NOAA):

- BDMEP[8]
- ANA[9]
- NOAA[10]

1.6 Analysis of Data from the Site of Interest

Measurements of environment variables can be made at the locality of interest, i.e., *in situ*, which can be used to (Congalton & Green, 1998):

- Calibrate remote sensing data;
- Evaluate the unbiased accuracy of the final results.

Sampling procedures *in situ* are presented in formal science courses, such as engineering, chemistry, biology, soils, hydrology and meteorology (Jensen, 2007). Most *in situ* data can be collected with geodetic information georeferenced x, y, z of the vertex under study (Jensen & Cowen, 1999), with differential coordinate correction (Alves & Silva, 2016b).

1.7 Radiometric Data

Geospatial raster data is used in the processing of digital remotely sensed images. In R's raster library, there is support for raster data in the classes `RasterLayer` (single layer), `RasterBrick`, and `RasterStack` (multiple layers) (Figure 1.3).

A raster object consists of a raster data variable that includes the number of columns, rows, pixels, extent, spatial resolution, and reference coordinate system (Figure 1.4).

1.8 Vector Data

Geospatial data can also be discrete objects with defined boundaries. Discrete geospatial objects can refer to a river, road, country, city, or research site. Geospatial objects are represented by

---

[8]http://www.inmet.gov.br/portal/index.php?r=bdmep/bdmep
[9]https://www.snirh.gov.br/hidroweb/apresentacao
[10]https://www.ncdc.noaa.gov/cdo-web/

Monochromatic band raster	Raster of stacked bands in R, G, B channels	Color composition of raster bands

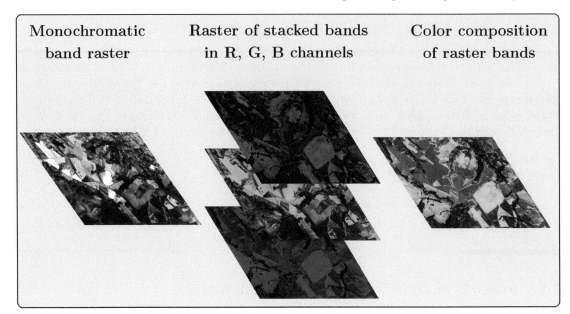

Figure 1.3 Raster representation used in remote sensing image processing.

vector data in the computer. This data describes the geometry or shape of the objects and may include additional variables. For example, a vector dataset might describe the boundaries of farms based on some type of geometry and also store attributes, such as the names and yields of coffee in 2020; or the geometry of rivers in an area, along with their type and name.

The main types of vector data are point, line, polygon and their corresponding multiples of points, lines, polygons, and collection of geometries. In all cases, the geometry of these data structures consists of sets of coordinate pairs (x, y). Points are the simplest case. Each point has one coordinate pair and n associated variables. For example, a point can represent a location where a soil sample was taken and information about the sampling location. It is also possible to combine several points into a multipoint structure with a single attribute record. For example, all soil samples in a field can be considered as a single geometry (Figure 1.5).

The geometry of lines is a bit more complex. A line refers to a set of one or more connected polylines of line segments. Lines are represented as ordered sets of coordinates defined by nodes. The representation of a line is very similar to that of a multipoint structure. The main difference is that the order of the points is important to know which points should be connected. A network is a special type of line geometry in which there is additional information about attributes such as flow, connectivity, direction, and distance.

A polygon consists of a set of closed polylines. The geometry is very similar to that of lines, but to close a polygon, the last pair of coordinates coincides with the first pair. Several polygons can be considered as a single geometry forming together a single multipolygon. Coffee agroecosystems in municipalities in Minas Gerais can be described by multipolygons (Figure 1.6).

Simple features refer to a hierarchical data model representing a wide variety of geometry types. These geometry types are fully supported by the R package sf and also used in GeoJSON files, which is an interchange data format based on JavaScript Object Notation (JSON) (Pebesma et al., 2022). In sf, all common vector geometry types, such as points, lines, polygons, and their respective multi-versions, which group features of the same type into a single feature, can be represented. In sf, there is also support for geometry collections which can contain multiple geometry types in a single object. The R package sp (Pebesma, Bivand, et al., 2021) is also used to

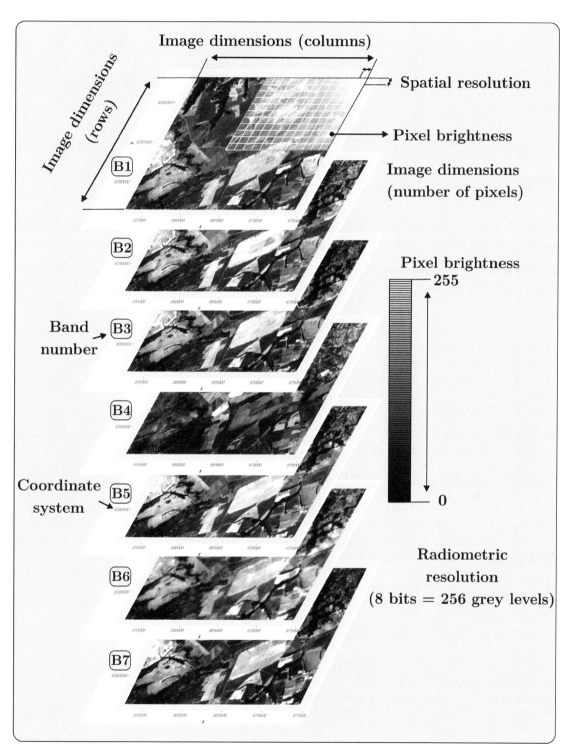

Figure 1.4 Example of multiple raster images used in remote sensing with spatial, spectral, and radiometric resolutions.

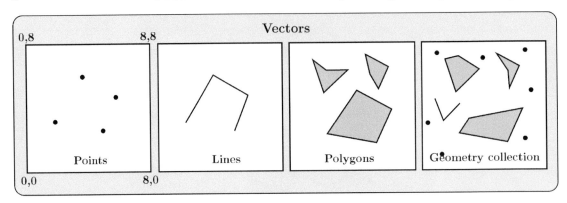

Figure 1.5 Vector representation of point, line, and polygon features.

represent vector geometries. However, sf can replace sp in some situations, since it has improved performance for reading, fast data writing, and plotting.

All geometries are composed of points using coordinates in 2-, 3-, or 4-dimensional space. All points in a geometry have the same dimensionality. The possible dimensions considered are (Pebesma et al., 2022):

- A longitude X coordinate;
- A latitude Y coordinate;
- An altitude Z coordinate;
- A M coordinate denoting some measurement associated with the point.

The possible dimensions in the sf package are (Pebesma et al., 2022):

- Two-dimensional XY points;
- Three-dimensional points XYZ;
- Three-dimensional points XYM;
- Four-dimensional points as $XYZM$.

Each of the geometry types can also be an empty set, containing zero coordinates. Empty geometries can be thought of as being the attributes analogous to missing attributes (NA), NULL values, or empty lists. There are 17 types of vector features that can be used in the sf package (Pebesma et al., 2022):

- POINT <- Zero-dimensional geometry containing a single point;
- LINESTRING <- One-dimensional geometry; sequence of points connected by straight, non-self-intersecting line pieces;
- POLYGON <- Two-dimensional geometry with a positive area;
- MULTIPOINT <- Set of points;
- MULTILINESTRING <- Set of linestrings;
- MULTIPOLYGON <- Set of polygons;
- GEOMETRYCOLLECTION <- Set of geometries except GEOMETRYCOLLECTION;
- CIRCULARSTRING <- Basic curve type. A single segment requires three points, the start, end points and a point on the arc;
- COMPOUNDCURVE <- Continuous curve that has both curved segments and linear segments;
- CURVEPOLYGON <- Example of compound curve in a curve polygon;
- MULTICURVE <- 1-dimensional GEOMETRYCOLLECTION whose elements are curves, including linear strings, circular strings or compound strings;
- MULTISURFACE <- 2-dimensional GEOMETRYCOLLECTION whose elements are surfaces, all using coordinates from the same coordinate reference system;

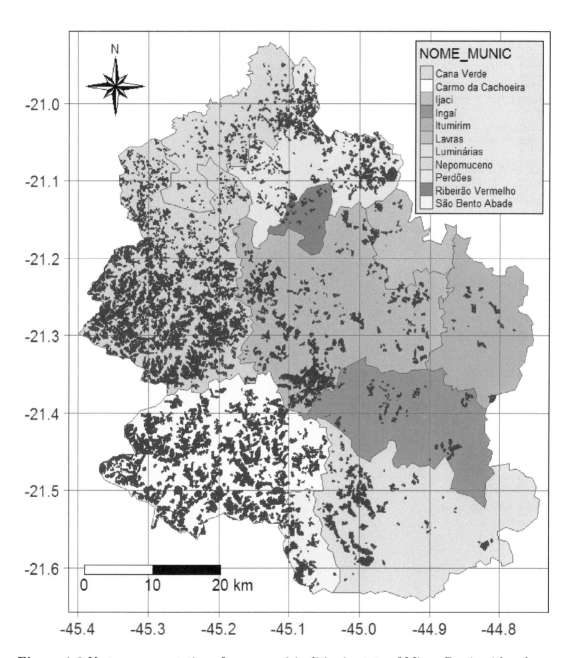

Figure 1.6 Vector representation of some municipalities in state of Minas Gerais with polygons around coffee crop.

- `CURVE` <- 1-dimensional geometric object usually stored as a sequence of points;
- `SURFACE` <- 2-dimensional geometric object;
- `POLYHEDRALSURFACE` <- Contiguous collection of polygons, which share common boundary segments;
- `TIN` <- Polyhedral surface consisting only of triangle patches;
- `TRIANGLE` <- Polygon with 3 distinct, non-collinear vertices and no interior boundary.

Coordinates can be associated with geometries based on a known coordinate reference system (CRS) on the Earth's surface; the CRS can be geodetic such as WGS-84, projected on a two-dimensional Cartesian system such as the Universal Transverse Mercator (UTM), or with three dimensions including time. Similarly, M coordinates need an attribute reference system (Pebesma et al., 2022).

The three classes used to represent simple features are (Pebesma et al., 2022):

- `sf` <- A `data.frame` or `tible` type table with attribute values and geometries;
- `sfc` <- A column is used to record geometries for each feature;
- `sfg` <- Geometry of an individual simple feature.

Some commonly used geometry types are created using the R package `sf` (Pebesma et al., 2022). The `library` function is used to load the `sf` package.

```
library(sf)
```

The `st_point` function is used to create a point of class `sfg` with XY coordinates.

```
p<-c(2.5, 2.5)
(pt<-st_point(p))
#POINT (2.5 2.5)
```

The `st_multipoint` function is used to create multiple points of class `sfg` with XY coordinates. The `rbind` function is used to bind the points into a single object.

```
ps<-rbind(c(0.5,0.5), c(0.5, 2.5), c(2.5,2.5), c(2.5,0.5), c(3.0,3.0), c(3.0,5.0),
          c(5.0,5.0), c(5.0,3.0))
(mp<-st_multipoint(ps))
#MULTIPOINT ((0.5 0.5), (0.5 2.5), (2.5 2.5), (2.5 0.5), (3 3), (3 5), (5 5), (5 3))
```

A line is created with the `rbind` and `st_linestring` functions.

```
s1<-rbind(c(2.5,2.5), c(3.0,3.0))
(ls<-st_linestring(s1))
#LINESTRING (2.5 2.5, 3 3)
```

The s2 and s3 lines are created with the `rbind` function and then transformed into a multilinestring with the `st_multilinestring` function.

```
s2 <-rbind(c(0.5,0.5), c(0.5, 2.5), c(2.5,2.5))
s3 <-rbind(c(3.0,3.0), c(3.0,5.0), c(5.0,5.0))
(mls <- st_multilinestring(list(s1,s2,s3)))
#MULTILINESTRING ((2.5 2.5, 3 3), (0.5 0.5, 0.5 2.5, 2.5 2.5), (3 3, 3 5, 5 5))
```

Polygons are created with the `rbind` function and then converted to `sfg` class polygons.

```
pol1 <-rbind(c(0.5,0.5), c(0.5, 2.5), c(2.5,2.5), c(2.5,0.5), c(0.5,0.5))
pol2 <-rbind(c(3.0,3.0), c(3.0,5.0), c(5.0,5.0), c(5.0,3.0), c(3.0,3.0))
(pol <- st_polygon(list(pol1,pol2)))
#POLYGON ((0.5 0.5, 0.5 2.5, 2.5 2.5, 2.5 0.5, 0.5 0.5), (3 3, 3 5, 5 5, 5 3, 3 3))
```

Two new polygons are created and then converted together with the previous polygons into multipolygons with the `st_multipolygon` function.

```
pol3 <-rbind(c(1.0,3.5), c(1.0,4.5), c(2.0,4.5), c(2.0,3.5), c(1.0,3.5))
pol4 <-rbind(c(3.5,1.0), c(3.5,2.0), c(4.5,2.0), c(4.5,1.0), c(3.5,1.0))
(mpol <- st_multipolygon(list(list(pol1,pol2), list(pol3,pol4))))
#MULTIPOLYGON (((0.5 0.5, 0.5 2.5, 2.5 2.5, 2.5 0.5, 0.5 0.5), (3 3, 3 5, 5 5, 5 3, 3 3)),
#((1 3.5, 1 4.5, 2 4.5, 2 3.5, 1 3.5), (3.5 1, 3.5 2, 4.5 2, 4.5 1, 3.5 1)))
```

The geometry collection is created with the `st_geometrycollection` function.

```
(gc <- st_geometrycollection(list(mp, mpol, ls)))
#GEOMETRYCOLLECTION (MULTIPOINT ((0.5 0.5), (0.5 2.5), (2.5 2.5), (2.5 0.5), (3 3), (3 5),
#(5 5), (5 3)), MULTIPOLYGON (((0.5 0.5, 0.5 2.5, 2.5 2.5, 2.5 0.5, 0.5 0.5),
#(3 3, 3 5, 5 5, 5 3, 3 3)), ((1 3.5, 1 4.5, 2 4.5, 2 3.5, 1 3.5),
#(3.5 1, 3.5 2, 4.5 2, 4.5 1, 3.5 1))), LINESTRING (2.5 2.5, 3 3))
```

Geometries are mapped with the `plot` function (Figure 1.7).

```
par(mfrow=c(3,3), mar=c(2, 2, 1.5, 1.5), mgp=c(1.5, 0.6,0))
plot(pt, main="POINT", lwd=2)
box(col="black")
plot(ls, main="LINESTRING", lwd=2)
box(col="black")
plot(pol, , main="POLYGON", lwd=2)
box(col="black")
plot(mp, main="MULTIPOINT", col="red", lwd=2)
box(col="black")
plot(mls, main="MULTILINESTRING", col="red", lwd=2)
box(col="black")
plot(mpol, , main="MULTIPOLYGON", col="black", border="red", lwd=2)
box(col="black")
plot(gc, main="GEOMETRYCOLLECTION", border="red", lwd=2)
box(col="black")
```

Vector and raster data can be mapped together in order to exploit the large database of available sensor data. For example, one can map the relief variation of municipalities in Minas Gerais, Brazil, using a digital elevation model from NASA's Shuttle Radar Topographic Mission with a spatial resolution of 30 m (Figure 1.8).

Obtaining remote sensing images in raster format is also important for specific projects and vary according to particular objectives. For example, MODIS data with a spatial resolution of 250 m may not be sufficient for mapping small crops. Thus, the following factors should be considered when choosing remote sensing databases:

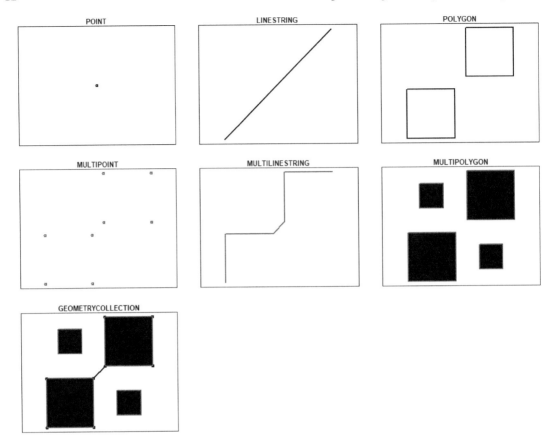

Figure 1.7 Some types of geometries used for vector representation in the `sf` package.

- Spatial resolution or pixel size;
- Date or time of year/season;
- Cloud cover;
- Wavelength used to measure different physical properties;
- Availability of historical data;
- Noise or artifacts in the data (example from Landsat-7 ETM+ sensor).

Therefore, for reliable use, remote sensing data must be calibrated geometrically and radiometrically:

- A remote sensing instrument (sensor) collects information about an object or process within the instantaneous field of view (IFOV) of sensor system without being in direct physical contact with the target.
- The sensor must be located on a ground, suborbital, or orbital (satellite platform) platform.

The amount of electromagnetic radiation, L (W m^{-2}sr$^{-1}\mu^{-1}$) recorded in the IFOV of an optical remote sensing system is a function of:

- Wavelength (λ);
- Location x, y, z of the pixel and its size (x, y);
- Temporal information (t);
- Set of angles between the radiation source and the object of interest on the terrain (θ)

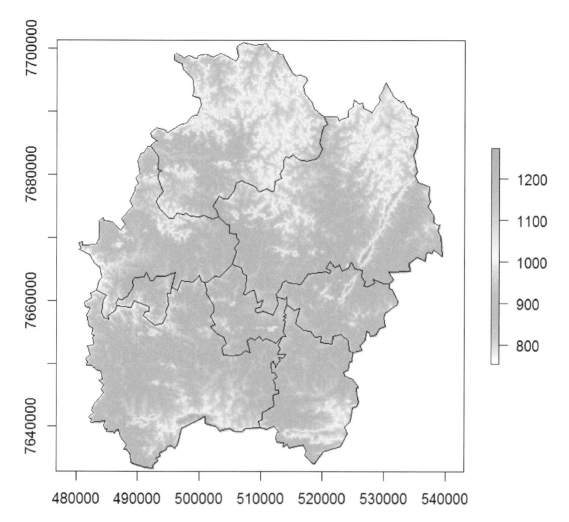

Figure 1.8 Municipalities of southern Minas Gerais state, Brazil, and digital elevation model (SRTM), UTM projection, zone 23S.

- Polarization of the backscattered energy recorded by the sensor (P);
- radiometric information (Ω).

There are different sources of raster data on the Internet. Free remotely sensed images of biophysical and hybrid remotely sensed variables can be obtained from virtual image catalogs from various national and international sources, such as the image catalog of the Space Research Institute, Brazil (INPE, from Portuguese *Instituto de Pesquisas Espaciais*) and the US Geological Survey (USGS):

- INPE[11]
- EarthExplorer[12]
- Nasa Earthdata[13]
- Data Pool USGS[14]

---

[11]http://www.dgi.inpe.br/CDSR/
[12]http://earthexplorer.usgs.gov/
[13]https://search.earthdata.nasa.gov/search
[14]https://lpdaac.usgs.gov/data_access/data_pool

- Scihub Copernicus[15]
- Amazon[16]

Radiometric data can be obtained at different levels of processing. For example, Landsat-5 TM collection 1 level 2 images are processed by the Earth Resources and Science Observation (EROS) Center and made available by the United States Geological Survey (USGS) through the Landsat Ecosystem Disturbance Adaptive Processing System (LEDAPS). This enabled us to estimate surface reflectance in different spectral regions, as if the measurement were obtained at ground level, in the absence of scattering or atmospheric absorption. In this case, radiometric calibration algorithms and atmospheric correction are applied to the Landsat level 1 data (Masek et al., 2006).

Different data distribution collections can be accessed to obtain remote sensing data. To obtain orbital remote sensing data, it is recommended to register on the USGS website before locating the image of interest (USGS, 2021).

In the Earth Explorer website, we should choose a Landsat-4,5 TM C1 Level-2 image in the Landsat Collection 1 Level-2 (On-Demand) option, in order to obtain image information at a higher processing level, considering radiometric, atmospheric and geometric corrections performed on the images. These processing levels have been modified in an attempt to improve the remote sensing data obtained. However, we must evaluate whether the data in higher processing levels really meet the research conducted. The radiance data recorded by the sensor can be used to perform the necessary digital image processing to obtain the surface reflectance in software and routines defined by the scientist himself so that there are no doubts about the image processing method used.

The SRTM and AsterGDEM digital elevation models can be obtained from the same website described in the previous paragraph. In this case, one should look at the metadata of the images to assess whether the date of the survey can be used to represent the region to be studied.

Other options for obtaining remote sensing data can be accessed through virtual interactive remote sensing websites on the Internet (remote sensing virtual libraries), such as:

- Series View INPE[17]
- SATVeg Embrapa[18]
- Google Earth Engine[19]
- AppEEARS - NASA[20]

In the case of virtual interactive remote sensing web sites, the user can work with data at a higher level of processing, without having to go through image preprocessing and postprocessing steps. However, many of the existing platforms have not yet been validated, and further investigation into the reliability of using these data is needed. Virtual platforms can be free, partially free, or paid.

---

[15] https://scihub.copernicus.eu/
[16] https://aws.amazon.com/public-data-sets/landsat/
[17] http://www.dsr.inpe.br/laf/series/
[18] https://www.satveg.cnptia.embrapa.br/satveg/login.html
[19] https://earthengine.google.com/
[20] https://lpdaacsvc.cr.usgs.gov/appeears/

1.9   Radiometric Data Acquisition Platforms

In remote sensing, electromagnetic radiation from an object on Earth is measured and translated into information about the object or object-related processes by means of data collection platforms at different altitudes, i.e., ground, air, and orbital. In the object measurement phase, we must know the source of electromagnetic radiation, the path of the radiation through the atmosphere, the interaction with an object, and the registration of the radiation by the sensor (Curran, 2020). In the phase of obtaining information, there is the transmission, reception and pre-processing of the recorded radiance, interpretation and analysis of remote sensing data and the generation of the final product (Jong et al., 2004) (Figure 1.9).

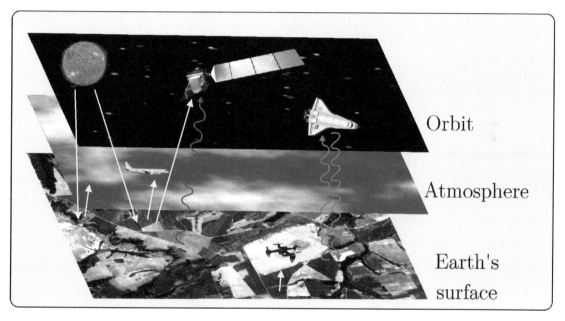

Figure 1.9 Orbital (top) and aerial remote sensing systems of high (middle) and low (bottom) flying altitude of region of municipality of Chapada dos Guimarães, state of Mato Grosso, Brazil.

1.10   Advantages and Limitations of Remote Sensing

There are many advantages and limitations of remote sensing. Among the advantages, it can be highlighted that passive remote sensing does not disturb the object or area of interest because it is non-intrusive; sensors collect data in a systematic way, enabling us to remove sampling bias; it can provide basic biophysical information, including location in x, y, z, temperature, moisture content; it can obtain data from large areas with different multispectral, hyperspectral, ultraspectral, RADAR and LIDAR technologies. As limitations, we highlight that the data obtained in remote sensing can contain human, natural, and instrumental errors; it can be intrusive and affect the investigated phenomenon, besides being of high economic cost of use in some specific cases.

1.10.1   Advantages of remote sensing

The advantages of remote sensing are:

- Aerial perspective on a global, national and regional scale;
- Historical collection of images;
- Perception beyond the human vision;
- Extraction of three-dimensional information on relief, land use, and biophysical variables.

1.10.2   Limitations of remote sensing

The limitations of remote sensing can be:

- High cost;
- Inaccurate;
- Uncalibrated;
- Complex;
- It does not solve all problems.

1.11   Remote Sensing and Other Sciences

Remote sensing works in harmony with other geographic information sciences, including cartography, topography, geographic information systems, and image processing. Geographic information sciences are related to other sub-disciplines, such as mathematics, logic, physical, chemical, biological, and social sciences (Figure 1.10).

1.12   Remote Sensing Societies

The remote sensing societies aim to promote and stimulate the development, study and research in the field of remote sensing and related areas, to bring together people and entities that are dedicated to or interested in the problems, development and applications of remote sensing, and to interact with other technical-scientific societies involved directly or indirectly with this area. Some societies are listed:

- Sociedad Latinoamericana en Percepción Remota y Sistemas de Información Espacial (SELPER[21]);
- Alliance for Marine Remote Sensing (AMRS[22]);
- American Geophysical Union (AGU[23]);
- American Society for Photogrammetry and Remote Sensing (ASPRS[24]);

---

[21] http://www.selperbrasil.org.br/
[22] https://uia.org/s/or/en/1100049641
[23] https://www.agu.org/
[24] http://www.asprs.org/a/society/committees/edupd/

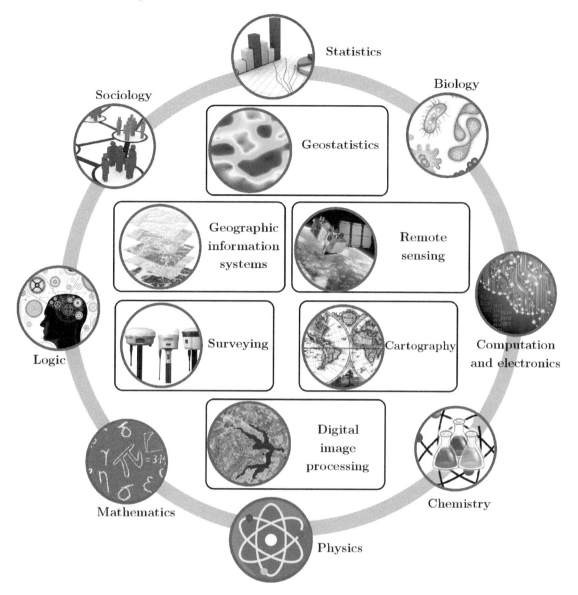

Figure 1.10 Remote sensing and other sciences.

- Canadian Remote Sensing Society (CRSS[25]);
- European Association Remote Sensing Laboratories (EARSel[26]);
- Federation of American Scientists, Image Intelligence[27];
- IEEE Geoscience and Remote Sensing Society[28];
- International Commission on Remote Sensing[29];
- International Society for Photogrammetry and Remote Sensing (ISPRS[30]);

---

[25]https://crss-sct.ca/
[26]https://earsel.org/
[27]https://fas.org/category/intelligence/
[28]https://www.ieee.org/membership-catalog/productdetail/showProductDetailPage.html?product=MEMGR S029
[29]https://iahs.info/Commissions--W-Groups/ICRS-Remote-Sensing.do
[30]https://www.isprs.org/

- National Stereoscopic Association (NSA[31]);
- Remote Sensing & Photogrammetry Society (RSPSoc[32]);
- Remote Sensing Specialty Group, Association of American Geographers[33];
- SPIE The International Society for Optical Engineering[34].

1.13   Remote Sensing Space Agencies

Government agencies and companies work in remote sensing, providing images and thematic maps of the territory and products generated through research. Earth observation and weather forecast satellites have been used to produce science and technology in the areas of space and Earth environment by national and international agencies, such as (Alves & Silva, 2016a):

- Agência Espacial Brasileira[35];
- Instituto Nacional de Pesquisas Espaciais[36];
- Canada Center Remote Sensing[37];
- Centre National d'Etudes Spatiales[38];
- Scientific and Industrial Research for Australia[39];
- European Space Agency[40];
- National Aeronautics and Space Administration[41];
- National Remote Sensing Agency India[42];
- Japan Aerospace Exploration Exploration Agency[43].

1.14   Remote Sensing and Related Journals

Journals in the field of remote sensing are related to the progress of knowledge in the area, in order to facilitate communication among professionals and to update the development of remote sensing science and technology. Some journals can be accessed via the Internet, such as:

- *Advances in Space Research*[44];
- *Applied Geomatics*[45];
- *Atmospheric Research*[46];

---

[31] https://stereoworld.org/
[32] http://www.rspsoc.org.uk/
[33] http://www.aagrssg.org/
[34] https://www.ndt.net/news/spie.htm
[35] https://www.gov.br/aeb/pt-br
[36] www.inpe.br
[37] www.ccrs.nrcan.gc.ca/
[38] www.cnes.fr/
[39] www.csiro.au/
[40] www.esa.int/
[41] www.nasa.gov/
[42] https://www.nrsc.gov.in/
[43] https://global.jaxa.jp/
[44] https://www.journals.elsevier.com/advances-in-space-research
[45] https://www.springer.com/journal/12518
[46] https://www.journals.elsevier.com/atmospheric-research

- *Cartography and Geographic Information Science*[47];
- *Canadian Journal of Remote Sensing*[48];
- *Computers and Geosciences*[49];
- *International Journal of Applied Earth Observation and Geoinformation*[50];
- *GeoInformatics*[51];
- *Geospatial Solutions*[52];
- *GIScience and Remote Sensing*[53];
- *IEEE Transactions on Geoscience and Remote Sensing*[54];
- *International Journal of Photogrammetry and Remote Sensing*[55];
- *Pattern Recognition*[56];
- *Precision Agriculture*[57];
- *Remote Sensing*[58];
- *Remote Sensing of Environment*[59];
- *Photogrammetric Engineering and Remote Sensing*[60];
- *Theoretical and Applied Engineering*[61].

1.15   Remote Sensing History

In 1666, Isaac Newton discovered that white light could be scattered into different spectral components. In 1800, W. Herschel discovered the infrared region. In 1826, the first photograph was taken, by Joseph Nicephore Niepce. In 1855, James Clerk Maxwell postulated the additive theory of color, so that equal proportions of blue, green, and red light superimposed on each other create white light. White light is composed of blue, green, and red light. The complementary colors yellow, magenta and cyan are created selectively by the joint addition of red, blue and red, and blue and green, respectively. In the case of subtractive color theory, equal proportions of cyan, yellow and magenta pigments produce a black surface. A yellow filter absorbs blue light, a magenta filter absorbs green light, and a cyan filter absorbs red light. Around 1860, Maxwell developed the wave electromagnetic theory. In 1867, the term "photogrammetry" was used in a published paper. In 1903 the airplane was invented by the Wright brothers, but Santos Dumont, in 1906, was the first to take off aboard an airplane propelled by an aero engine. From 1914 to 1918 there was photo-reconnaissance in World War I. From 1939 to 1945 there were advances in photo-reconnaissance during World War II. In the 1940s RADAR and jet aircraft were invented. In 1942 Kodak patented the first infra-red false-color film. In 1952 remote sensing in the thermal infrared was realized by the military. In the 1960s, there was a great advance in the area, with the beginning of digital image processing in the USA (Jensen, 2007; Jong et al., 2004). In the 1970s the Landsat series was successfully created, there was a rapid advance in digital image

---

[47]https://www.tandfonline.com/toc/tcag20/current
[48]https://www.tandfonline.com/toc/ujrs20/current
[49]https://www.journals.elsevier.com/computers-and-geosciences
[50]https://www.journals.elsevier.com/international-journal-of-applied-earth-observation-and-geoinformation
[51]https://www.jstage.jst.go.jp/browse/geoinformatics
[52]https://www.scimagojr.com/journalsearch.php?q=28020&tip=sid&clean=0
[53]https://www.tandfonline.com/loi/tgrs20
[54]https://ieeexplore.ieee.org/xpl/RecentIssue.jsp?punumber=36
[55]https://www.journals.elsevier.com/isprs-journal-of-photogrammetry-and-remote-sensing
[56]https://www.journals.elsevier.com/pattern-recognition
[57]https://www.springer.com/journal/11119
[58]https://www.mdpi.com/journal/remotesensing
[59]https://www.journals.elsevier.com/remote-sensing-of-environment
[60]https://www.asprs.org/asprs-publications/pers
[61]http://www.taaeufla.deg.ufla.br/index.php/TAAE/index

processing (Adrien & Baumgardner, 1977) and the beginning of remote sensing activities at INPE (Hammond, 1977a, 1977b). With this came remote sensing applications of agriculture (Idso et al., 1977) and water (Mather et al., 1979). In the 1980s the use of the space shuttle in remote sensing was initiated (Taranik & Settle, 1981). In 1985 land cover classification in Africa was performed with orbital data (Tucker et al., 1985). In 1986 hyperspectral sensors were developed and, in 1990, the first very high spatial resolution sensor systems appeared (Goetz et al., 1985). There were also advances in LIDAR sensing systems in the 1990s. In 2001 a global planialtimetric survey was carried out with the space shuttle (Jensen, 2007). In 2007, Brazil and China launched the CBERS-2B satellite. Currently remote sensing has been used to locate life signs and the chemistry of exoplanets (Seager & Bains, 2015), predict the economy of terrestrial regions (Jean et al., 2016), characterize terrestrial biodiversity (Pecl et al., 2017), locate animals (Kays et al., 2015), and monitor forests (Tyukavina et al., 2017) (Table 1.2).

Table 1.2 Remote sensing history from 1600 to 2020.

Year	Event
1600	Isaac Newton's work with electromagnetic energy
1800	The first photograph
1900	Aircraft
1910	International Society for Photogrammetry
1920	First rockets
1930	Photo-recognition in world war II
1940	RADAR
1950	Infrared; Sputnik and Explorer-1 satellites
1960	Space travel (Yuri Gagarin)
1970	ERTS-1
1980	Space shuttle ; SPOT; Landsat-5
1990	IKONOS
2000	QuickBird
2010	WorldView-2
2020	Nano satellites, drones, cloud computing, geocomputation languages

1.16 Remote Sensing Discipline Development

A search with the keyword "remote sensing" on the Science Direct website (Science Direct, 2019), a web platform with an information base of peer-reviewed journals, articles, book chapters, and open access content, we observed exponential increase in the publication of articles from the 1960s to 2022, agreeing with Jensen (2007), who mentions that remote sensing as a scientific discipline is still at the stage of doubling the number of publications at regular intervals.

In the processing of remote sensing publications data in the R program between 1964 and 2018, the first step is to create the file with time data and publications data. Then model fitting is performed, obtaining model parameters. In this case, adjusted R^2 of 83.1% was obtained. Finally the estimation of the exponential model and graph plotting of the number of publications as a function of time is performed (Figure 1.11).

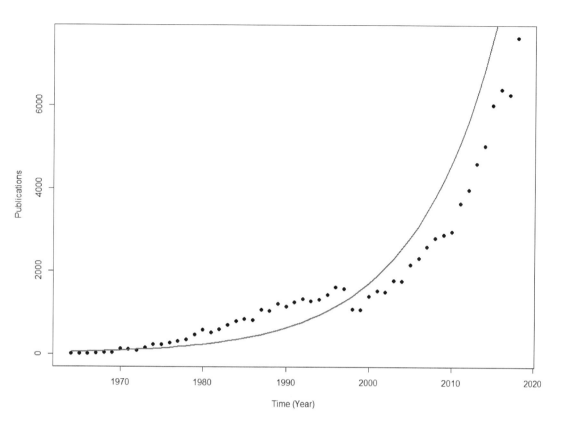

Figure 1.11 Temporal variation of publication of scientific articles with the keyword remote sensing.

1.17 Remote Sensing Resolutions

Remote sensing systems record the reflected, emitted, or backscattered electromagnetic radiation of objects at different resolutions. The following remote sensing resolutions can be used to evaluate the best applicability of a sensor for monitoring an object relative to another sensor:

- Spatial resolution <- Size of the field of view (30 by 30 m, 250 by 250 m, etc.);
- Spectral resolution <- Number and size of the spectral regions in which the sensor record data (blue, green, red, near-infrared, thermal infrared, microwave, etc.);
- Temporal resolution <- Frequency at which the sensor acquires data (daily, every 5 minutes, every 16 days, etc.);
- Radiometric resolution <- The sensitivity of detectors to small differences in electromagnetic energy (8 bits, 11 bits, etc.).

1.18   Remote Sensing Applications

Information about objects and processes occurring on Earth is related to vegetation, soils, minerals, rocks, water, atmosphere, and urban infrastructure (Figure 1.12). Relevant applications of remote sensing are (Schowengerdt, 2006):

- Surveying and monitoring the environment (urban area growth and environmental impact);
- Change detection (global warming, deforestation, ozone layer);
- Agriculture (crop condition, yield prediction, soil erosion);
- Non-renewable mineral resources (minerals, oil, natural gas);
- Renewable natural resources (wetlands, soils, forests, oceans);
- Meteorology (atmospheric dynamics, weather forecasting);
- Mapping (topography, land use, civil engineering);
- Military reconnaissance (strategic policy, tactical determination);
- News and general media (illustrations and analysis).

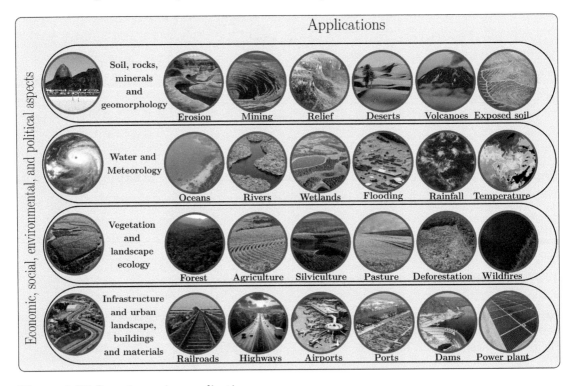

Figure 1.12 Remote sensing applications.

Information obtained from remote sensing of the environment is also useful for modeling the global carbon cycle, ecosystem biology and biochemistry, aspects of the global water and energy cycles, climate variability and prediction, atmospheric chemistry, terrain characteristics, population estimates, and monitoring land use change, and natural disasters (Jensen, 2007; Johannsen et al., 2003) (Figure 1.13).

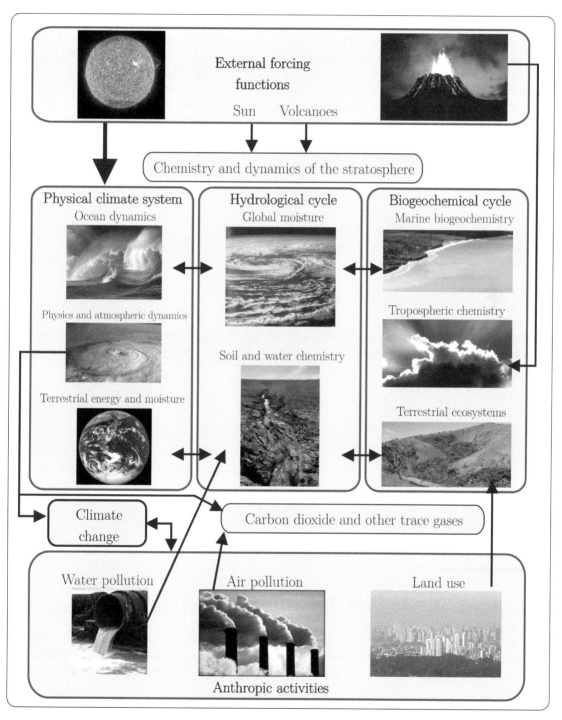

Figure 1.13 Remote sensing applications in a global context.

1.19   Remote Sensing as a Profession

With the advent of satellite positioning technologies and the availability of very high spatial resolution satellite images of much of the Earth via the Internet (Google Earth, Google Maps, MapQuest, Bing Maps), the interest of the general public in geospatial issues has increased. In universities and colleges, geocomputation principles have been addressed in disciplines such as engineering, agriculture, marine sciences, among others. Because remote sensing can be used to make geospatial decisions, perform mapping and various environmental monitoring, jobs in remote sensing may be available in public agencies (national, state and local government; colleges and universities) and private commercial companies. The demand for remote sensing and digital image processing professionals has increased as geospatial data and analysis have become more commonplace. In related job demands such as remote sensing, the following positions have been defined:

- Cartographers and photogrammetry specialists;
- Remote sensing scientists and technologists;
- Remote sensing technicians;
- Surveyors;
- Mapping technicians;
- Surveying technicians.

Job openings in the field of remote sensing and digital image processing can be searched on the Internet at sites to assess the type of skills in demand in the market, typical starting salaries, and other job opportunities:

- Earthworks[62];
- Career in remote sensing[63];
- UNJobs[64];
- Linkedin[65];
- indeed[66];
- researchgate[67];
- glassdoor[68];
- Academic positions[69].

1.20   Remote Sensing and Digital Image Processing Software

Data processing in remote sensing for atmospheric and topographic correction goes beyond the boundaries of remote sensing image processing and geographic information systems. With the use of remote sensing image processing programs, the gap between research and implementation is

---

[62] http://www.earthworks-jobs.com/remotese.htm
[63] https://www.sciencemag.org/careers/2005/08/careers-geoscience-and-remote-sensing
[64] https://unjobs.org/themes/remote-sensing
[65] https://www.linkedin.com/?trk=nav_logo
[66] https://www.indeed.com/q-Remote-Sensing-jobs.html
[67] https://www.researchgate.net/jobs/Remote_Sensing-jobs?page=1&regions=
[68] https://www.glassdoor.com.br/Vaga/remote-sensing-vagas-SRCH_KO0,14.htm?countryRedirect=true
[69] https://academicpositions.com/jobs/remote-sensing-geosciences

closed, in order to obtain new algorithms and processing routines in different applications (Goslee, 2011; Kwok, 2018) (Figures 1.14 and 1.15).

Some free software programs used in remote sensing are:

- R (Example packages: `getSpatialData` (Schwalb-Willmann, 2022), `RStoolbox` (Leutner et al., 2019), `raster` (Hijmans et al., 2020), `sf` (Pebesma et al., 2022), `sp` (Pebesma, Bivand, et al., 2021), `caret` (Kuhn et al., 2020));
- Quantum Gis (QGIS);
- SPRING.

Some commercial software programs used in remote sensing are:

- MATLAB@;
- ArcGIS;
- ENVI;
- Ecognition;
- PCIgeomatics.

It should be noted that due to corporate deals made in the area of commercial software, many programs change their names, making it necessary to update the name of some existing commercial software.

Digital image processing routines   **Command execution screen**

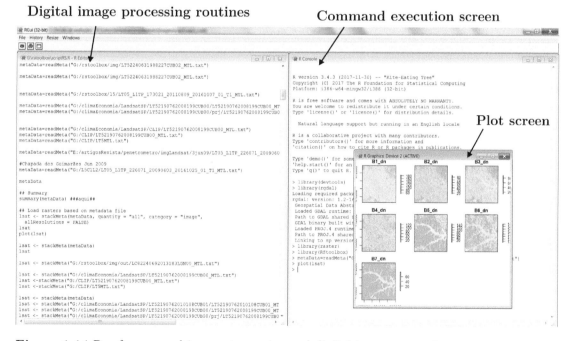

Plot screen

Figure 1.14 R software used in remote sensing and digital image processing.

In remote sensing image processing software, there are options with graphical user interfaces (GUI), such as QGIS software, rather than a command line interface (CLI) typed by keyboard, such as in R software. Reproducibility is a major advantage of command line interfaces, as the same results can be generated by other people through publicly accessible code, leading to profound implications for teaching and science (Pebesma et al., 2012).

Layers with spatial
data models

Access menu to
different applications

Geoprocessing
routines

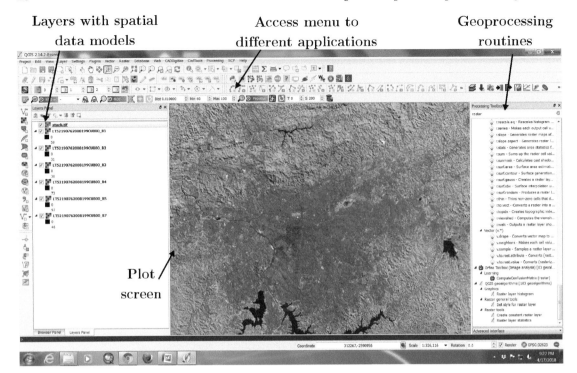

Plot
screen

Figure 1.15 QGIS software used in remote sensing and digital image processing.

1.21   The Future of Remote Sensing

Remote sensing has been important for sustainable economic growth of countries in order to acquire powerful information of the rural, urban, soil, mineral, water and vegetation environment (Paul & Mascarenhas, 1981). High-performance computing systems have become commonplace and cloud computing is available as a commodity. Petabyte-scale remote sensing data are made available by Brazilian, North American, and European government agencies free of charge. Using all the available resources requires expertise and a lot of dedication.

The major difficulties in using information technology are:

- Data acquisition and storage;
- Data format;
- Database management;
- Allocation of machines, CPUs, networks;
- Multiple geoprocessing routines.

Virtual remote sensing libraries can be an alternative to minimize the difficulties of using information technology in the area of remote sensing and digital image processing. Virtual libraries of remote sensing data are readily available catalogs of data and information via a high performance parallel computing service that allow rapid access and visualization of results via an interactive interface on the Internet (Gorelick et al., 2017) (Figure 1.16).

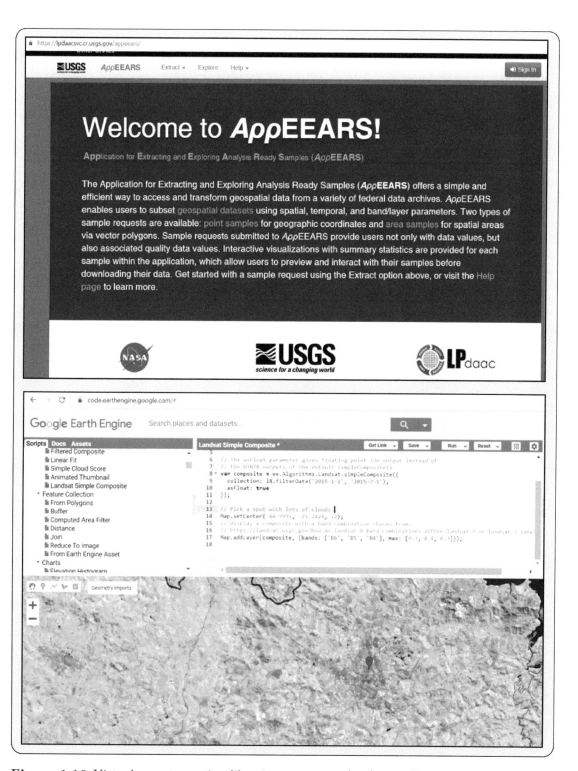

Figure 1.16 Virtual remote sensing libraries, `AppEEARS` (top) and GoogleEarth Engine code (bottom), used for processing digital images and obtaining spatial data infrastructure.

The advantages of remote sensing virtual libraries are:

- Wide repository of geospatial data including airborne and orbital sensor imagery with wavelengths in visible and non-optical regions, climate, socio-economic and relief database;
- High performance data processing;
- Interface based on an interactive Internet environment.

The disadvantages of remote sensing virtual libraries are:

- May depend on product updates on the server;
- Depends on the Internet;
- May require expertise in languages such as Python and Java;
- May lack validation, metadata, and information on data processing details.

Future applications of remote sensing may be related to the mapping of biophysical variables, hybrid and collateral information, using deductive and inductive logics, deterministically and stochastically, to gain knowledge. We can monitor the dynamics of spatial distribution of biodiversity (Kays et al., 2015; Pecl et al., 2017) the richness of regions by combining imagery and processing methods (Jean et al., 2016), as well as research and development of new monitoring satellites (Li & Milliken, 2017) and search for characterization of remote planet environments (Seager & Bains, 2015).

Remote sensing can be used in many medical applications, nondestructive product evaluation, astronomical observations, resource analysis of the Earth's environment, among others. However, the main focus of this book is to present aspects about the art, technology and science of applying remote sensing to extract information about terrestrial resources, mainly focused on the study of vegetation, soils, minerals, rocks, water and urban infrastructure, as well as some atmospheric features and their applications considering economic, social, environmental and political aspects. Therefore, it is expected to contribute to the increase of the knowledge between technicians in remote sensing, image processing, the community of scientists and users.

For example, R and the Earth Engine (ee) can be used to perform night lighting mapping on Earth. In this case, it is necessary to install `rgee` (Aybar et al., 2022) and other packages like `reticulate` (Kalinowski et al., 2022), miniconda (or similar) to install the Python software and APIs needed to connect and use Google Earth Engine with R. Thus, data analysis is performed using R packages and cloud computing via the `rgee` package. The `rgee` is not a native Earth Engine application like JavaScript or Python. With the R package `reticulate`, it is possible to establish perfect interoperability between R and Python. When an Earth Engine request is created in R, reticulate transforms the code into Python. Once the Python code is obtained, the Earth Engine Python API transforms the request into a JSON format. The processing command is received by the Earth Engine platform through a Web REST API (Figure 1.17).

The `library` function is used to load the `rgee` package. The `ee_Initialize` function is used to initialize ee.

```
library(rgee) # Enabling rgee
ee_Initialize(drive = TRUE) # Initialize ee
```

A `createTimeBand` function is created and used to add bands with image dates since 1991.

```
createTimeBand <-function(img) {
  year <- ee$Date(img$get('system:time_start'))$get('year')$subtract(1991L)
  ee$Image(year)$byte()$addBands(img)
}
```

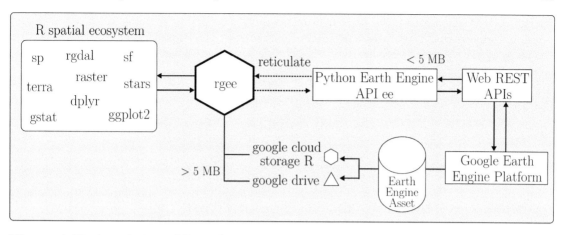

Figure 1.17 Association of R packages with the Google Earth Engine platform via `rgee`, `reticulate`, and APIs.

A Nighttime Lights Time Series Version 4 monitoring product from the Defense Meteorological Program Operational Linescan System (DMSP OLS) is used as an information source for mapping using the `ee$ImageCollection` function.

```
collection <- ee$ImageCollection('NOAA/DMSP-OLS/NIGHTTIME_LIGHTS')$
  select('stable_lights')$map(createTimeBand)
```

The `collection$reduce` function is used to calculate a linear fit over the series of values at each pixel, displaying the y-intercept in green, and positive/negative gradients as red/blue.

```
col_reduce <- collection$reduce(ee$Reducer$linearFit())
col_reduce <- col_reduce$addBands(col_reduce$select('scale'))
ee_print(col_reduce)
#----------------------- Earth Engine Image --
#Image Metadata:
# - Class                  : ee$Image
# - ID                     : no_id
# - Number of Bands        : 3
# - Bands names            : scale offset scale_1
# - Number of Properties   : 0
# - Number of Pixels*      : 194400
# - Approximate size*      : 607.50 KB
#Band Metadata (img_band = scale):
# - EPSG (SRID)            : WGS 84 (EPSG:4326)
# - proj4string           : +proj=longlat +datum=WGS84 +no_defs
# - Geotransform          : 1 0 0 0 1 0
# - Nominal scale (meters) : 111319.5
# - Dimensions            : 360 180
# - Number of Pixels      : 64800
# - Data type             : DOUBLE
# - Approximate size      : 202.50 KB
#----
# NOTE: (*) Properties calculated considering a constant geotransform and data type.
```

An interactive visualization of the night lighting mapping is created by zooming in 5 on a centralized point in Manaus, Brazil, with the `Map$setCenter` function. The `Map$addLayer` function is used in the mapping with specific visualization settings defined in the `visParams` argument.

```
Map$setCenter(-59.89746,-3.25021, 5)
Map$addLayer(eeObject = col_reduce, visParams = list(
    bands = c("scale", "offset", "scale"), min = 0,
    max = c(0.18, 20, -0.18)), name = "stable lights trend")
```

With this we can observe a higher density of nighttime illumination in the coastal regions when compared with the inland regions of the continent, especially in the Amazon region, with large regions with a complete absence of nighttime illumination (Figure 1.18).

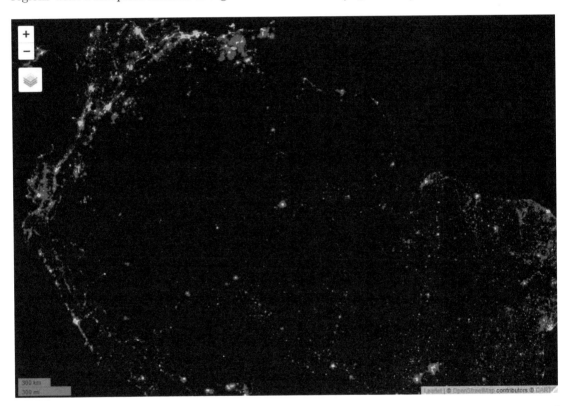

Figure 1.18 Mapping nighttime illumination over part of South America on a composition of Nighttime Lights Time Series Version 4 data from the Defense Meteorological Program Operational Linescan System since 1991.

The study of extraterrestrial targets and the monitoring of other worlds is a future challenge of remote sensing. Images of targets monitored at 500 million light-years (150 Mpc) have been obtained from composites of separate exposures from the James Webb Space Telescope using the MIRI and NIRCam instruments. Various filters are used to sample different wavelength ranges of the electromagnetic spectrum. The color composition of the image presented as an example of this type of monitoring is the result of assigning color tones to each monochrome image, in digital numbers, that is associated with an individual filter. The colors assigned in the color composition are: Red (F444W + F356W), orange (F770W + F1000W + F1280W + F1800W), yellow (F277W), green (F200W) and blue (F150W + F090W). The NIRCam was built by a team at the University of Arizona and Lockheed Martin's Advanced Technology Center. MIRI was built by ESA and NASA, and the instrument was designed and built by the MIRI European Consortium in partnership with JPL and the University of Arizona (Figure 1.19).

Figure 1.19 Cartwheel Galaxy ESO 350-40 AM0035-335 and companion galaxies monitored at 500 million light-years (150 Mpc) by the James Webb Space Telescope with the Near-Infrared Camera (NIRCam), and Mid-Infrared Instrument (MIRI). (Courtesy of NASA, ESA, CSA, STScI, Webb ERO Production Team)

1.22   Computational Practice

R is an open source programming, visualization and data analysis environment originating from the programming language (Lovelace et al., 2019).

1.22.1   Installation of R

The latest 2022 version of R for Windows can be obtained for **download**[70]. Older versions may be more useful if a package used in the data analysis has not yet been updated to the latest version of R. Older versions can be obtained for **download**[71].

R can also be accessed through RStudio, with an interface to R. In RStudio there is a free software version and also a private version, for companies or individuals who need customer support. The latest 2022 version of RStudio for Windows can be obtained for **download**[72]. Older versions of RStudio can be obtained for **download**[73].

1.22.2   Using R with command line

R can be run from an R console or from an RStudio command line environment. We can assign values to objects, such as five numbers to objects x, y with an arrow $(<-)$ or the equal symbol $(=)$ and then perform the sum of the objects at z, with the following code in R:

```
y<-c(1,2,3,4,5) # Create a y database
y # Evaluate y results
```

```
## [1] 1 2 3 4 5
```

```
x=c(1,2,3,4,5) # Create a x database
x # Evaluate x results
```

```
## [1] 1 2 3 4 5
```

```
z<-x+y # Create a z database with the sum of x,y
z # Evaluate z results
```

```
## [1]   2   4   6   8 10
```

A script should be created and saved in R in the case where it is necessary to enter more than a few lines of code as part of the analysis of a project. This makes it easier to retrieve the code to continue the project at another time. Several packages were available in R for analyzing remote sensing data. The search for information about an R package can be performed by keywords on the subject of interest for application in different subject areas, with the R package sos (Graves et al., 2020). To evaluate information about computer programs and R packages used in writing the book, the R package sf (Pebesma et al., 2022) is installed and enabled. In the following, as an example, it is demonstrated how to set up a directory, install and enable packages, and evaluate the version of the operating system and R.

---

[70] https://cran.r-project.org/src/base/R-4/
[71] https://cran.r-project.org/bin/windows/base/old/
[72] https://rstudio.com/products/rstudio/download/
[73] https://www.rstudio.com/products/rstudio/older-versions/

1.22.3   Setting up directory in R

To evaluate the working directory in R, we use the `getwd()` function, and to configure a directory in R, we use the `setwd` function with the address of the new working directory.

```
getwd() # Check the directory used by R
setwd("C:/sr/c1") # Set the directory used by R
```

1.22.4   Installing R packages

The `install.packages` function is used to install the `sf` and `sos` packages in the R console. There are other ways to install packages in R, but this is the most common way. It is necessary to use quotes between the package names to proceed with the installation.

```
install.packages("sf")
install.packages("sos")
```

1.22.5   Enabling R packages

The `library` function is used in the R console to load the `sf` and `sos` packages. The `require` function can also be used to enable packages. It is not necessary to use quotes between the package names to enable use.

```
library(sf)
library(sos)
```

1.22.6   Evaluating information about R and the operating system used

The `sf` package was installed and enabled to evaluate information about computer programs and R packages used in writing the book.

Using the `print(version)` function we can evaluate information about the operating system and version of R used.

```
print(version)
#platform       x86_64-w64-mingw32
#arch           x86_64
#os             mingw32
#system         x86_64, mingw32
#status
#major          4
#minor          0.0
#year           2020
#month          04
#day            24
```

```
#svn rev        78286
#language       R
#version.string R version 4.0.0 (2020-04-24)
#nickname       Arbor Day
```

With the `print(sessionInfo())` function, we get the windows version used, the R base packages, as well as other R packages installed on the computer. In this case, version 3.5.2 (2018-12-20), platform x86_64-w64-mingw32/x64 (64-bit), and Windows 10 x 64 (build 19041) are being used.

```
print(sessionInfo())
#R version 4.0.0 (2020-04-24)
#Platform: x86_64-w64-mingw32/x64 (64-bit)
#Running under: Windows 10 x64 (build 19043)
#Matrix products: default
#locale:
#[1] LC_COLLATE=Portuguese_Brazil.1252  LC_CTYPE=Portuguese_Brazil.1252
#LC_MONETARY=Portuguese_Brazil.1252
#[4] LC_NUMERIC=C                       LC_TIME=Portuguese_Brazil.1252
#attached base packages:
#[1] stats      graphics  grDevices utils     datasets  methods   base
#other attached packages:
#[1] sf_1.0-2
#loaded via a namespace (and not attached):
# [1] tidyselect_1.1.1     xfun_0.25             purrr_0.3.4
#reshape2_1.4.4        splines_4.0.0
# [6] lattice_0.20-41      colorspace_1.4-1      vctrs_0.3.8
#generics_0.1.0        stats4_4.0.0
#[11] htmltools_0.5.2      yaml_2.2.1            utf8_1.1.4
#survival_3.1-12       prodlim_2019.11.13
#[16] rlang_0.4.11         e1071_1.7-8           ModelMetrics_1.2.2.2
#pillar_1.6.2          glue_1.6.2
#[21] withr_2.4.2          DBI_1.1.1             foreach_1.5.0
#lifecycle_1.0.0      plyr_1.8.6
#[26] stringr_1.4.0        lava_1.6.9            timeDate_3043.102
#munsell_0.5.0        gtable_0.3.0
#[31] recipes_0.1.16       codetools_0.2-16      evaluate_0.14
#knitr_1.34           fastmap_1.1.0
#[36] caret_6.0-88         class_7.3-16          fansi_0.4.1
#Rcpp_1.0.7           KernSmooth_2.23-16
#[41] classInt_0.4-3       scales_1.1.1          ipred_0.9-11
#ggplot2_3.3.5        digest_0.6.25
#[46] stringi_1.4.6        bookdown_0.20         dplyr_1.0.7
#grid_4.0.0           tools_4.0.0
#[51] magrittr_2.0.1       proxy_0.4-26          tibble_3.0.1
#crayon_1.4.1         pkgconfig_2.0.3
#[56] ellipsis_0.3.2       MASS_7.3-51.5         Matrix_1.2-18
#data.table_1.14.0    pROC_1.17.0.1
#[61] lubridate_1.7.10     gower_0.2.2           assertthat_0.2.1
#rmarkdown_2.10       iterators_1.0.12
#[66] R6_2.4.1             rpart_4.1-15          units_0.7-2
```

```
#nnet_7.3-13           nlme_3.1-147
#[71] compiler_4.0.0
```

The installation directory of R packages on the computer can be obtained with the `print(.libPaths())` function.

```
print(.libPaths())
#[1] "C:/Users/UFLA/OneDrive/Documentos/R/win-library/4.0"
#"C:/Program Files/R/R-4.0.0/library"
```

The `packageVersion()` function is used to evaluate the version of a specific R package installed on the computer. In this example, with this function we get the version of the `sf` package. The version used for `sf` is 0.7.7.

```
packageVersion("sf")
#[1] '1.0.2'
```

1.22.7 Evaluating the existence of an R package with keywords

Using the `findFn()` function it is possible to perform searches on existing packages on a topic of interest, in this case, with the keywords remote sensing, 100 items were found in 2021.

```
findFn("remote sensing")
```

1.22.8 Performing practice in R with vector data

Different ways of creating polygon-type vector features can be used to define a region of interest, i.e., a spatial subset of remote sensing data. This polygon region can also be used, for example, to define the boundaries of a farm, an urban plot, a reservoir or a coffee agroecosystem. To perform the demonstration, you must install the `raster` (Hijmans et al., 2020), `devtools` (Wickham et al., 2021), `rgdal` (Bivand et al., 2021), `utils` (Bengtsson, 2021), `xROI` (Seyednasrollah et al., 2021), `brazilmaps` (Siqueira, 2017), and `GADMTools` (Decorps, 2021) packages.

```
install.packages("raster")
install.packages("devtools")
install.packages("rgdal")
install.packages("utils")
utils::install.packages('xROI', repos = "http://cran.us.r-project.org" )
devtools::install_github("rpradosiqueira/brazilmaps")
install.packages("dplyr")
install.packages("GADMTools")
install.packages("gridExtra")
```

The packages `raster`, `rgdal`, `sf`, `xROI`, `brazilmaps`, `dplyr`, and `GADMTools` must be enabled to run the computational practice.

```
library(raster)
library(rgdal)
library(sf)
library(xROI)
library(brazilmaps)
library(dplyr)
library(GADMTools)
library(gridExtra)
```

1.22.9   Defining a region of interest with a polygon vector feature

1.22.9.1   Defining a geographic region by coordinates

The simplest way to define a polygon in a rectangle around the region of interest can be accomplished with the extent function. From there, the polygon can be an alternative to defining a subset in remote sensing images with a clipping of the data in the region of interest. In this practice, only the polygon will be created and the cropping will be done later (Figure 1.20):

```
e<-extent(495317.1, 518730.6, 7645542.5, 7666693.4) # Define extent by coordinates
plot(e, col='red') # Map the region
```

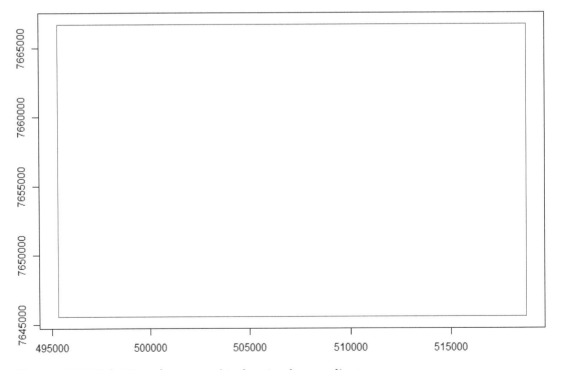

Figure 1.20 Definition of a geographical region by coordinates.

1.22.9.2   Defining a geographic region from a polygon drawn in Google Earth

A polygon created in Google Earth with the KML extension can be imported into R as a vector that is referenced to an object or remotely sensed process defined relative to some location on Earth by creating a polygon drawn on top of the target of interest, as in a satellite image color composite.

A version of Google Earth Pro for Windows can be obtained for **download**[74].

To create a polygon in Google Earth, (1) Open Google Earth. (2) Go to a location on the map. (3) Above the map, click Add Path. (4) To add a shape, click Add Polygon. (5) A New Polygon dialog box will appear. You may have to move it out of the way before proceeding to the next step. (6) To draw the shape you want by connected lines, click a starting point on the map and drag it. (7) Click an end point to close the polygon. In possession of a closed polygon geometry, you can calculate the area of the polygon by going to Tools <- Ruler. However, calculating area is not our goal at this point. (8) Enter a description and properties of the polygon. The polygon will be created as a layer in Google Earth's left menu. (9) Right-click on the created polygon layer and export the file as filename.kml with save place as an option. (10) Click save.

1.22.9.2.1   Obtaining the .kml file from the Internet

The file used in the practical activity was obtained from the Internet and unzipped to perform the practical activity.

```r
# Import from the Internet the vector file (polygon) of the region of interest
download.file(url = "http://www.sergeo.deg.ufla.br/sr/downloads/lavras2.zip",
              destfile = "lavras2.zip")
unzip(zipfile = "lavras2.zip") # Unzip
```

1.22.9.2.2   Importing the .kml file and map in R

The file lavras2.kml was imported into R with the st_read function and then mapped with the plot function (Figure 1.21).

```r
p <- st_read("C:/sr/c1/lavras2.kml") # Import kml
plot(p[1], axes=T, col='grey', title='') # Map the kml
```

1.22.9.2.3   Converting vector file to ESRI shapefile

The st_zm function is used to extract the geometry from the .kml file and add Z and M dimensions of the polygon geometry feature.

```r
pol <- st_zm(p[1], drop=T, what='ZM')
```

---

[74]https://www.google.com/earth/versions/#download-pro

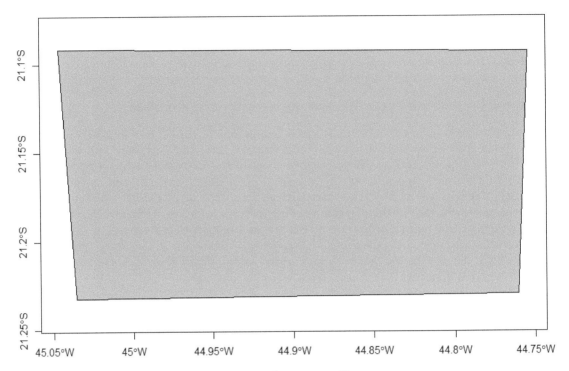

Figure 1.21 Mapping a geographical region from a **kml** file.

1.22.9.2.4   Exporting the polygon as an ESRI shapefile

The polygon p can be exported as a vector file of ESRI Shapefile type for further use, as follows:

```
st_write(pol, dsn= "C:/sr/c1/pol.shp", driver= "ESRI Shapefile", "pol.shp")
```

1.22.9.2.5   Importing and map the polygon shapefile into R

The polygon shapefile *p* is imported into R and then mapped to observe the characteristics of the region studied.

```
p <- st_read("C:/sr/c1/pol.shp")
plot(p, axes=T)
```

1.22.9.2.6   Evaluating file class

The file class is evaluated with the class function.

```
class(p)
#[1] "sf"          "data.frame"
```

1.22.9.2.7   Creating polygon by drawing in R

The operation of creating polygons with the R package xROI (Seyednasrollah et al., 2021) is usually performed by drawing the vectors on top of an image. However, in this example, a polygon is created using as reference the polygon previously created in the region near to the municipalities Lavras and Ijací in Brazil.

Geospatial polygons are created to collect pixel samples. This process must be interactive, drawing the polygon on the image. At the end of editing, close the polygon by accessing the finish button on the plot screen of the polygon creation.

```
# Use xROI to sample pixels
d<-if(interactive()){
drawPolygon()
}
# Perform drawing on the plot with the mouse by creating vertex points
# Create geospatial polygons
 ( p1 <- SpatialPolygons(list(Polygons(list(Polygon(cbind(d))), "1") )) )
# Click finish to close the polygon
# Assign a coordinate system (CRS)
 proj4string(p1) <- CRS("+proj=longlat +datum=WGS84 +no_defs")
# Create a database table to identify the polygons created with ID
 ( p1.df <- data.frame( ID=1:length(p1)) )
 rownames(p1.df)
# Join the polygons with the table
 p1 <- SpatialPolygonsDataFrame(p1, p1.df)
```

1.22.9.2.8   Exporting the geographical region of interest

The geographical region of interest is exported to a directory of interest on the computer. The address must be set according to the computer used. In this case, the address was C:/sr/c1/p1.shp.

```
writeOGR(obj=p1, dsn="C:/sr/c1/p1.shp", layer="p1", driver="ESRI Shapefile")
```

1.22.9.2.9   Importing the geographic region of interest

The geographic region of interest can be imported using the R package rgdal.

```
p1<-readOGR(dsn="C:/sr/c1/p1.shp", layer="p1")
```

1.22.9.2.10   Mapping the geographical region of interest

The result of the classification can be mapped with the plot function (Figure 1.22).

```
plot(p1, col='grey92', axes=T)
```

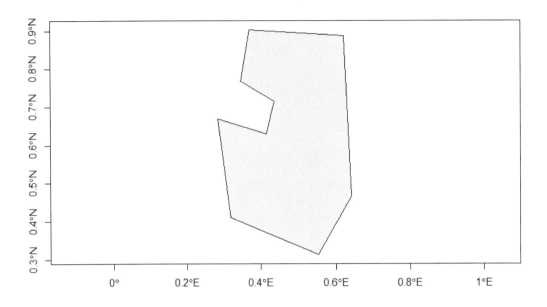

Figure 1.22 Polygon created with interactive drawing using a pre-existing cartographic vector database as reference.

1.22.9.3 Defining a geographical region with a county-level polygon

The get_brmap function is used to locate the county of origin of the rural property with the state number 31 configuration at the Minas Gerais county level.

```
mg <- get_brmap(geo = "City",
                geo.filter = list(State = 31),
                class = "sf")
```

The municipalities are mapped for visual analysis using the plot function (Figure 1.23).

```
plot(st_geometry(mg), col=sf.colors(n=1, alpha=0.3),
     border = 'black', bgc = 'gray92', axes = TRUE)
```

Then, the file characteristics and the coordinate reference system are evaluated using the head function.

```
head(mg)
#Simple feature collection with 6 features and 6 fields
#Geometry type: MULTIPOLYGON
#Dimension:     XY
#Bounding box:  xmin: -47.67975 ymin: -20.45584 xmax: -42.04786 ymax: -17.76667
#CRS:           +proj=longlat +ellps=GRS80 +no_defs
#               nome    City State MicroRegion MesoRegion Region        geometry
```

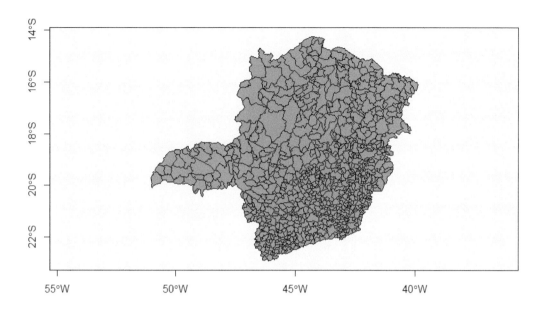

Figure 1.23 IBGE digital municipal mesh mapping for the state of Minas Gerais, Brazil.

```
#1 ABADIA DOS DOURADOS 3100104  31    31019   3105    3 MULTIPOLYGON (((-47.42967 -...
#2               ABAETÉ 3100203  31    31024   3106    3 MULTIPOLYGON (((-45.1393 -1...
#3           ABRE CAMPO 3100302  31    31061   3112    3 MULTIPOLYGON (((-42.31071 -...
#4              ACAIACA 3100401  31    31060   3112    3 MULTIPOLYGON (((-43.02387 -...
#5              AÇUCENA 3100500  31    31039   3108    3 MULTIPOLYGON (((-42.36208 -...
#6             ÁGUA BOA 3100609  31    31036   3108    3 MULTIPOLYGON (((-42.32271 -...
```

A subset is performed in the municipality of Lavras, state of Minas Gerais, to obtain the polygon geometry of just one municipality in the state.

```
lavras = mg[mg$nome == "LAVRAS",]
```

The municipality of Lavras is mapped for geovisualization of the municipal boundaries (Figure 1.24).

```
plot(st_geometry(lavras), graticule = TRUE, col = "grey90", border = 'black',
     axes = TRUE)
```

The lavras polygon is exported as ESRI Shapefile vector file for later use.

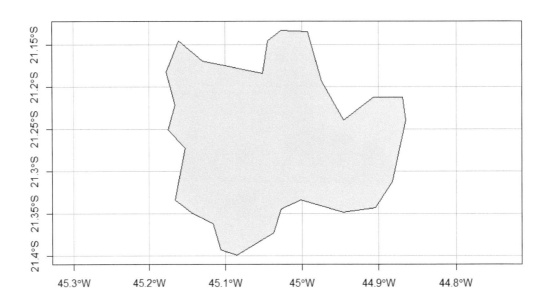

Figure 1.24 Mapping of the municipality of Lavras, state of Minas Gerais, Brazil.

```
st_write(lavras, dsn= "C:/sr/c1/lavras.shp", driver= "ESRI Shapefile", "lavras.shp")
```

1.22.9.4   Defining a geographical region using GADMTools

GADM is a spatial database of world administrative boundaries for use in remote sensing in the class gadm_sf. The administrative areas in this database are countries and lower-level subdivisions such as states, municipalities, and districts. Using the GADM database, we can easily manipulate, assemble, and create subsets of objects, as well as obtain SpatialPolyonsDataFrame and Simple Features shapefile formats (Decorps, 2021). The GADM database, at different levels, can also be obtained for **download**[75] on the Internet in the sf, sp, and KMZ classes.

The gadm_sf_loadCountries function is used to obtain a map with the limits of Brazil. In this case, the argument level=0 is set to obtain only the vector with the limits of the region of interest.

```
br_lim <- gadm_sf_loadCountries("BRA", level=0, basefile = "./")
```

The gadm_plot function is used for mapping the region, including the wind rose and graphic scale on the map with the use of the gadm_showNorth and gadm_showScale functions, respectively (Figure 1.25).

```
gadm_plot(br_lim) %>% gadm_showNorth("tl") %>% gadm_showScale('bl')
#old-style crs object detected; please recreate object with a recent sf::st_crs()
```

---

[75]https://gadm.org/data.html

#old-style crs object detected; please recreate object with a recent sf::st_crs()
#Scale on map varies by more than 10%, scale bar may be inaccurate

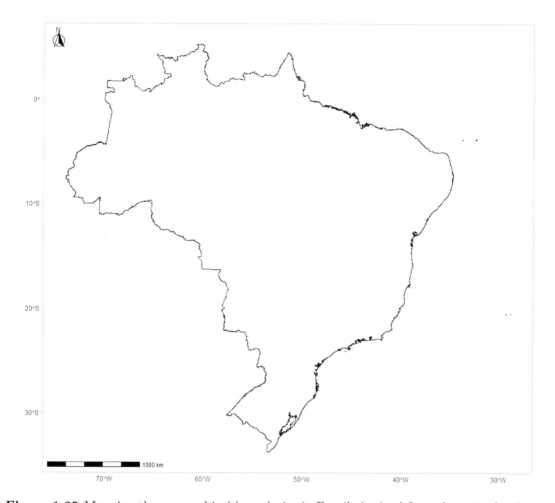

Figure 1.25 Mapping the geographical boundaries in Brazil obtained from the `GADM` database.

The `gadm_sf_loadCountries` function is used to obtain a map with the limits of Brazil, states, municipalities and districts by setting the `level=3` argument.

```
br <- gadm_sf_loadCountries("BRA", level=3, basefile = "./")
```

The states included in the `br` database are listed with the `listNames` function, for a total of 27 states.

```
listNames(br, 1)
#[1] "Acre"     "Alagoas"  "Amapá" "Amazonas" "Bahia"
#[6] "Ceará"    "Distrito Federal" "Espírito Santo" "Goiás" "Maranhão"
#[11] "Mato Grosso" "Mato Grosso do Sul"  "Minas Gerais"  "Pará"  "Paraíba"
#[16] "Paraná"  "Pernambuco"  "Piauí"   "Rio de Janeiro"  "Rio Grande do Norte"
```

```
#[21] "Rio Grande do Sul" "Rondônia"  "Roraima" "Santa Catarina"  "São Paulo"
#[26] "Sergipe"   "Tocantins"
```

The `gadm_subset` function is used to define a subset in the states Espírito Santo, Minas Gerais, Rio de Janeiro, and São Paulo. The same function can also be used to define a subset only in the state of Minas Gerais and in the municipality of Lavras (Figure 1.26).

```
est <- gadm_subset(br, regions= c("Espírito Santo","Minas Gerais","Rio de Janeiro",
                                  "São Paulo"), level=1)
mg <- gadm_subset(br, regions= "Minas Gerais", level=1)
lav <- gadm_subset(br, regions= "Lavras", level=2)
```

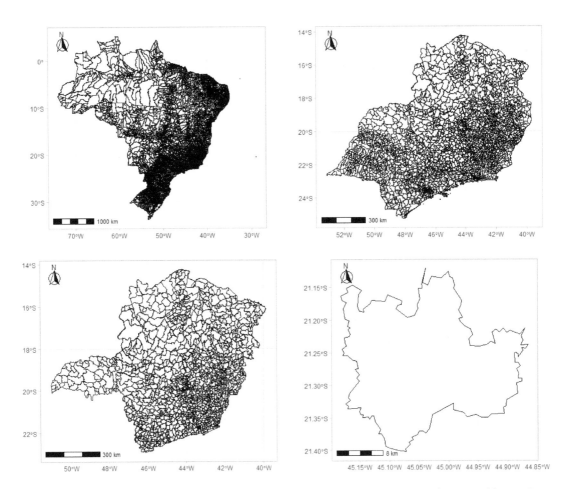

Figure 1.26 Mapping of geographical boundaries of municipalities in Brazil (upper-left), southeast region (upper-right), state of Minas Gerais (lower-left), and municipality of Lavras (lower-right) obtained from the `GADM` database.

The polygons obtained can be exported for later use with the `gadm_exportToShapefile` function. This function creates a directory with the files `name.dbf`, `name.prj`, `name.shp` and `name.shx`. To use GADM files from the `sf` and `sp` packages and import the vectors with the specific function from these packages into R, it is recommended to obtain the files directly from the **GADM** web site[76] and search by country and level of the database of interest in shapefile format. Other options are to export the file in sf format by including $sf in the file to be exported by the st_write function or to import the file exported by the gadm_exportToShapefile function into QGIS and re-export the file in shapefile format. In the latter case, a file in the QPJ extension is required to import the data into R by the sf and rgdal packages and this file is not generated when exporting the vectors from the GADMTools package.

```
gadm_exportToShapefile(br,"br")
#Writing layer `br ' to data source `br' using driver `ESRI Shapefile'
#Writing 10195 features with 7 fields and geometry type Multi Polygon.
```

1.23   Exercises

1.23.1   Define remote sensing and explain a problem that can be studied with the remote sensing process.

1.23.2   Define radiometric data that can be used in the remote sensing process.

1.23.3   Define a variable that can be obtained *in situ* to compare with radiometric data in the remote sensing process.

1.23.4   Explain the advantages and disadvantages of remote sensing.

1.23.5   Name the resolutions used in remote sensing.

1.23.6   Which of these characteristics favors orbital remote sensing over aerial remote sensing?

    a. Spatial resolution.
    b. Cost.
    c. Time resolution.
    d. Stereoscopic view.

1.23.7   Which of these characteristics favors aerial sensing over orbital sensing?

    a. Spatial resolution.
    b. Spectral resolution.
    c. Time resolution.
    d. Stereoscopic view.

---

[76]https://gadm.org/download_country.html

1.23.8   Cite two packages used to import raster and vector data in R.

1.23.9   Cite R functions that can be used to stack bands from the OLI sensor of the Landsat-8 satellite?

1.23.10   What are the basic differences between raster data and vector data in R?

1.23.11   Create a graph representing the temporal variation of publication of scientific articles with the keyword remote sensing.

1.24   Homework

1.24.1   Subject

Definition of geographic region of interest for use in remote sensing.

1.24.2   Assignment

Develop the subject presented with a practical application of remote sensing and digital image processing including the topics Introduction and Objective. Then present the development of the task.

1.25   Resources on the Internet

As a study guide, slides and videos are presented about the subject covered in the chapter as shown in Table 1.3.

Table 1.3 Slide shows and video presentations on introduction to remote sensing with applications.

Guide	Address for Access
1	Remote sensing of Earth resources[77]
2	Advances in remote sensing of the environment with aerial platforms and satellites[78]
3	INPE and remote sensing[79]
4	Virtual classroom on introduction to remote sensing of environments[80]

---

[77] https://youtu.be/IKcLwyxJdIg
[78] https://youtu.be/fVwaxDDt844
[79] https://youtu.be/NpFuRA7hXSo
[80] http://www.sergeo.deg.ufla.br/sr/Presentation/Aula1/presentation.html#/

1.26   Research Suggestion

Activities are proposed for the development of scientific research on remote sensing that can be used or adapted by the student to monitor and identify targets in a specific area of interest (Table 1.4).

Table 1.4 Practical and research activities used or adapted by students using remote sensing.

Activity	Description
1	Selection of the problem to be studied. The problem can be defined in an area between 10 ha to the maximum size of a municipality, where there is vegetation, soil and water and where the analyst has experience of a region previously visited or where data has been collected *in situ*.
2	Get administrative polygons of some region of the world from the GADM[81] website and map the region in R.

---

[81] https://gadm.org/data.html

2

Remote Sensing of Electromagnetic Radiation

2.1 Learning Questions

The learning questions answered through reading the chapter are as follows:

- How is electromagnetic radiation applied in remote sensing science?
- What is the path and energy-matter interactions of electromagnetic radiation between the Sun, Earth, and sensors?
- How are the regions of the electromagnetic spectrum used in remote sensing?
- How is the electromagnetic radiation recorded at the sensor transformed to generate practical remote sensing applications?
- In which models and scientific papers are methods of radiometric correction of the data recorded at the sensor developed?
- How is radiometric correction of data affected by the relief variation in the studied region?
- Which radiometric correction methods are used in different remote sensing systems?
- How is human pollution of the atmosphere monitored by remote sensing?

2.2 Learning Outcomes

Using the learning outcomes from the chapter, you should be able to do the following:

- Use principles of electromagnetic radiation in remote sensing science.
- Know the path and energy-matter interactions of electromagnetic radiation between the Sun, Earth, and sensors.
- Understand how regions of the electromagnetic spectrum are used in remote sensing.
- Know how the electromagnetic radiation recorded in the sensor is used in practical remote sensing applications.
- Know some scientific publications of remote sensing that have been applied to the development of methods for radiometric correction recorded in the sensor.
- Perform correction of radiometric data affected by relief variation.
- Evaluate different radiometric correction methods in different remote sensing systems.
- Understand the applications and sensors used to remotely monitor human pollution of the atmosphere.

2.3   Introduction

Energy can be defined as the ability to do work. In this process, energy is transferred from one body to another or from one place to another by conduction, convection, and radiation. The propagation of energy by electromagnetic radiation is of interest to the science of remote sensing, as it occurs even in vacuum, in the region between the Sun and Earth, as well as in the atmosphere and its interaction with targets on the surface. The energy recorded by sensor systems undergoes various interactions until it reaches the ground, and then is passed from the ground to the sensor. For example, the energy from the Sun (Jensen, 2007) (Figure 2.1):

- Is radiated by atomic particles at the source (the Sun);
- Propagates in the vacuum of space at the speed of light;
- Interacts with the Earth's atmosphere;
- Interacts with the Earth's surface;
- Interacts with the Earth's atmosphere again;
- Reaches the remote sensor with optical systems, filters, emulsions, or detectors.

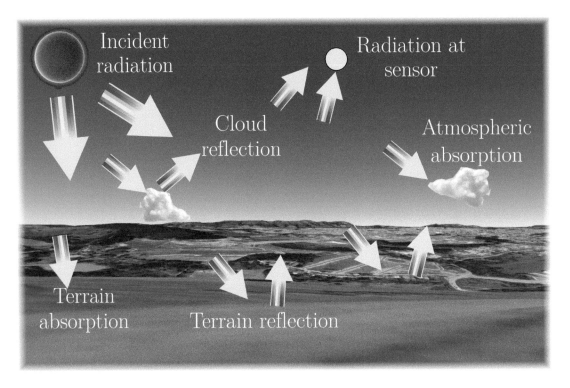

Figure 2.1 Path radiances received by a remote sensing system and their potential effect on the image interpretation process.

To understand how electromagnetic energy was created, its propagation in space, and interaction with other matter the wave and particle models are described.

2.4   Models of Electromagnetic Radiation

Around 1860, J. C. Maxwell observed radiation as an electromagnetic wave moving through space at the speed of light. The electromagnetic wave consists of two fluctuating fields, one electric and the other, magnetic. The two vectors are arranged at right angles to each other and perpendicular to the direction of travel of the wave (Jensen, 2007) (Figure 2.2).

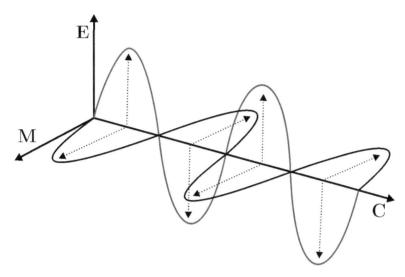

Figure 2.2 Electromagnetic wave composed of electric (E) and magnetic (M) vectors orthogonal to each other traveling at the speed of light (C).

2.4.1   Wave model of electromagnetic radiation

The relationship between the wavelength (λ) (m) and frequency (f) (Hz) of electromagnetic radiation is based on the equation, where c is the speed of light (m s^{-1}) (Jensen, 2007):

$$c = \lambda f \tag{2.1}$$

$$f = \frac{c}{\lambda} \tag{2.2}$$

and

$$\lambda = \frac{c}{f} \tag{2.3}$$

It can be seen that the frequency is inversely proportional to the wavelength. The longer the wavelength, the lower the frequency and vice versa.

Electromagnetic energy can also be described in units of photon energy, such as joules (J) and electron volts (eV).

2.4.2   Particle model

Niels Bohr and Max Planck recognized the discrete nature of radiant energy exchanges and proposed the quantum theory of electromagnetic radiation (Figure 2.3). In this theory, energy is transferred in discrete packets called "quanta" or "photons". The relationship between the frequency of radiation expressed by the wave theory and the quantum theory is:

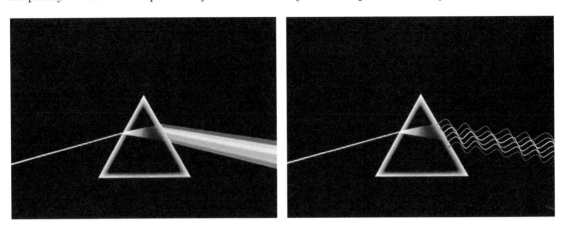

Figure 2.3 Light, a particular kind of matter, is described as electromagnetic energy in terms of wave properties or as discrete packets of energy (quanta) composed of photons, when energy interacts with matter.

$$Q = hf \tag{2.4}$$

where Q is the energy of a quantum measured in joules, h, Planck's constant ($6.626 * 10^{-34}\,\text{Js}$), and f, the frequency (Hz) of the radiation.

Referring to the previous equations, we can multiply the equation $\frac{h}{h}$, or 1, without changing its value:

$$\lambda = \frac{hc}{hf} \tag{2.5}$$

By substituting Q for hf, we can express the wavelength associated with a quantum of energy by:

$$\lambda = \frac{hc}{Q} \tag{2.6}$$

or

$$Q = \frac{hc}{\lambda} \tag{2.7}$$

Thus, the energy of a quantum is inversely proportional to the wavelength. The longer the wavelength, the lower the energy.

The energy that becomes available when an electrically charged electron moves from an excited state to an unexcited state is emitted by the atom as a single packet of electromagnetic radiation with particle behavior, called a "photon". In this case, an electron disappears from its original orbit and reappears in the target orbit by the process called "quantum leap". For example, when you turn on a sodium vapor lamp, thousands of volts of electricity energize the vapor. As a result, the outermost electron in each energized atom of the sodium vapor rises to a higher rung on the energy ladder and then returns down the ladder. The energy released as the electron jumps appears as a photon of yellow light with a wavelength of 0.58 μ with 2.1 eV of energy. By subjecting matter to very high temperatures, electrons become free. When a free electron completes the empty energy level created by the freed electron, radiation of all wavelengths is produced. The intense heat on the surface of the Sun produces a continuous energy spectrum in this same way (Jensen, 2007).

2.5 Thermal Radiation Laws

A blackbody is considered a theoretical entity that absorbs all incident radiation and radiates energy at the maximum possible rate per unit area at every wavelength and temperature. No object in nature is a true black body, but by considering an object as a black body, it is possible to record quantitative information about the total amount of radiant energy at specific wavelengths emanating from the object and the dominant wavelength. For this, it is important to know the Stefan-Boltzmann and Wien displacement laws (Jensen, 2007).

2.5.1 Stefan-Boltzmann's law

According to Stefan-Boltzmann's law, the total spectral radiant exitance (M_b) (W m^{-2}) leaving a black body is proportional to the fourth power of its temperature (T),

$$M_b = \sigma T^4 \tag{2.8}$$

where σ is the Stefan-Boltzmann constant ($5.6697 * 10^{-8}$) m^{-2}K^{-4}, and T, the temperature in Kelvin.

The amount of energy emitted by an object such as the Sun or the Earth is a function of the temperature of the object. The higher the temperature, the greater the amount of energy emanating from the object.

However, in the world there are no radiating black bodies, but bodies selectively radiating and emitting a certain ratio of a black body at the same temperature. The ratio between the actual radiance emitted by a real-world body selectively radiating (M_r) and a black body at the same thermodynamic temperature (M_b) is called "emissivity" (ϵ):

$$\epsilon = \frac{M_r}{M_b} \tag{2.9}$$

All selectively radiating bodies have emissivities between $0 \leq 1$ depending on the wavelengths considered. A gray body has a constant emissivity less than 1 at all wavelengths.

The physicist Kirchoff observed that in the infrared portion of the spectrum, the spectral emissivity of an object is equal to its spectral absorptance, i.e., good absorbers are good emitters and good reflectors are bad emitters. For example, water is a good emitter and has a high emissivity, close to 1, that is, water absorbs almost all the energy and reflects very little. In contrast, a metal roof reflects most of the incident energy and absorbs very little, generating emissivity less than 1. The emissivity of an object is affected by (Jensen, 2007):

- Color;
- Chemical composition;
- Surface roughness;
- Moisture content;
- Soil compaction;
- Field of view;
- Wavelength;
- Angle of view.

When measuring the temperature of soil, water, or vegetation, the goal of remote sensing is to point a radiometer at an object to record the apparent radiant temperature (T_{rad}) equal to the true kinetic temperature (T_{kin}) of the object. However, due to the effects of emissivity, the radiant flux of a real-world object at a given temperature is not equal to the radiant flux of the black body at the same temperature. With this, we can modify the Stefan-Boltzmann law applicable to black bodies (M_b) with adjustment to the spectral radiant flux of real-world materials (M_r):

$$M_r = \epsilon \sigma T_{kin}^4 \tag{2.10}$$

In this equation, the object's temperature and its emissivity are considered for a more accurate estimate of the radiant flux emanating from an object and recorded by a thermal infrared sensor.

Assuming the incorporation of emissivity into the Stefan-Boltzmann equation,

$$M_r = \epsilon M_b \tag{2.11}$$

then,

$$\sigma T_{rad}^4 = \epsilon \sigma T_{kin}^4 \tag{2.12}$$

Therefore, relationships can be established by isolating the radiant temperature, kinetic and emissivity:

$$T_{rad} = \epsilon^{\frac{1}{4}} T_{kin} \tag{2.13}$$

or,

$$T_{kin} = \frac{T_{rad}}{\epsilon^{\frac{1}{4}}} \tag{2.14}$$

or,

$$\epsilon = \left(\frac{T_{rad}}{T_{kin}}\right)^4 \tag{2.15}$$

Empirical determination is also used to determine the true temperature of the object monitored by remote sensing. In this case, measurements of the *in situ* temperature and the remotely measured temperature must be collected simultaneously.

2.5.2 Wien's displacement law

The dominant wavelength (λ_{max}) is determined based on Wien's displacement law used for calculating the total energy emanating from a theoretical blackbody:

$$\lambda_{max} = \frac{k}{T} \tag{2.16}$$

where k is a constant equivalent to 2898 μm K and T, the absolute temperature in Kelvin.

The electromagnetic energy coming from the Sun takes eight minutes to travel the 150 million kilometers in space to Earth. Although the Sun has one dominant wavelength, the continuous spectrum of electromagnetic radiation ranges from very short, high-frequency waves such as gamma and cosmic rays, to low-frequency radio waves.

2.6 Electromagnetic Spectrum

The Earth intercepts a small portion of the electromagnetic energy produced by the Sun. Electromagnetic energy is described not only by wavelength and frequency, but also in units of photon energy, such as joules (J) and electronvolts (eV). In remote sensing, visible light is composed of energy in the blue (B) (0.4-0.5 μm), green (G) (0.5-0.6 μm) and red (R) (0.6-0.7 μm) bands of the electromagnetic spectrum. The infrared region is subdivided into near-infrared (NIR) (0.7-1.3 μm), mid-infrared (SWIR) (1.3-3.0 μm), far (thermal) infrared (TIR) (3-5 μm) and (8-14 μm) of the electromagnetic spectrum. In the microwave region the wavelengths range from 1 mm to 1 m (Jensen, 2007) (Figure 2.4).

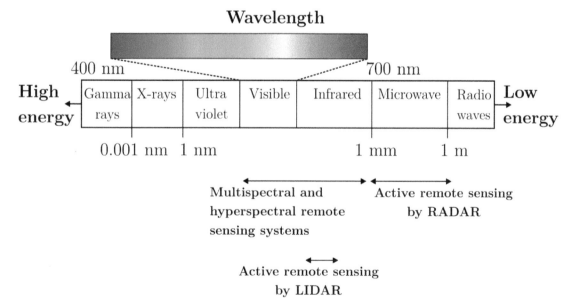

Figure 2.4 The electromagnetic spectrum, the colors obtained in the visible region in order of wavelength size from left to right, and some sensor systems related to each region.

2.7   Energy-Matter Interactions in the Atmosphere

The Earth's atmosphere affects the speed of electromagnetic radiation, wavelength, intensity, and spectral distribution through refraction, scattering, absorption, transmission, and reflection of energy.

2.7.1   Refraction

Refraction shifts the original direction of light when it passes through one medium to another with a different density. For example, the refractive index of the atmosphere and water are 1.0002926 and 1.33, respectively. In other words, light moves more slowly through water than in the atmosphere because of the higher density of water (Jensen, 2007).

2.7.2   Scattering

Atmospheric particles cause radiation scattering. In general, scattering can be of the Rayleigh, Mie, and nonselective types. Rayleigh scattering, or molecular scattering, occurs when the effective diameter of the matter (oxygen and nitrogen) is many times smaller than the wavelength of the incident electromagnetic radiation at an altitude of 2 to 8 km above the ground. Rayleigh scattering determines the blue sky, because the shorter wavelengths of violet and blue are more efficiently scattered than the longer wavelengths of orange and red. Rayleigh scattering also determines the red of the sunset. In this case the sunlight passes through a steeper and longer path at sunset, forming a residue of the poorly scattered wavelengths, as in the case of orange and red. Mie scattering, or non-molecular scattering, occurs when the wavelength of spherical particles (smoke and dust) in lower layers of the atmosphere (up to 4.5 km altitude) have a diameter approximately equal to the wavelength of the incident energy. In this case the smoke and dust remove the violet and blue light, and the longer wavelengths of orange and red light are predominant to the eye. Nonselective scattering occurs when, in the atmosphere, the particles are longer than 10 times the wavelength of the incident electromagnetic radiation. Thus, all wavelengths can be scattered by water droplets and ice crystals that form clouds and fogs, determining white cloud coloration. Scattering also reduces the content of the information recorded by remote sensing making it difficult to differentiate objects due to lack of contrast. Scattering differs from radiation reflection in that the direction associated with scattering is unpredictable, while the direction of reflection is predictable (Jensen, 2007).

2.7.3   Absorption, transmission, and reflection

Electromagnetic energy can be absorbed, transmitted, or reflected by the atmosphere. The incident radiant flux can be reflected by cloud tops and other materials in the atmosphere and back into space. Energy can also be absorbed and converted into other forms of energy. The cumulative effect of absorption by various constituents of the atmosphere, such as water (H_2O), carbon dioxide (CO_2), oxygen (O_2), ozone (O_3), and nitrous oxide (N_2O) can determine the closure of spectral regions without energy being recorded by the remote sensor. The portions of the spectrum where radiant energy is efficiently transmitted are called "atmospheric windows" (Figure 2.5).

With the spread of the coronavirus disease (COVID-19) worldwide, the coronavirus was declared a global pandemic by the World Health Organization. In order to contain the spread of the

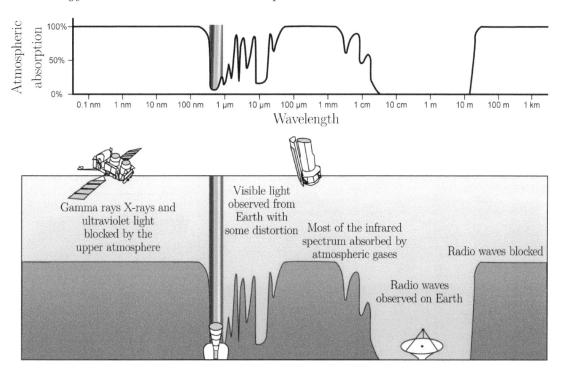

Figure 2.5 Absorption of incident electromagnetic energy from the Sun in the region of 0.1 nm to 1 km.

COVID-19 outbreak, countries implemented strict measures, putting the population of cities and countries into social isolation. This attitude affected the emission of pollutants in regions of the world. Through the Copernicus Sentinel-5P mission of the European Space Agency (ESA), it was possible to monitor nitrogen dioxide from space on a global scale and with satisfactory spatial resolution to detect patterns of variation of nitrogen dioxide (NO_2) in the Earth's atmosphere in different months of the year 2020 (**Earth Engine Apps**[1]) (Google LLC, 2021). With the Sentinel-5 mission's TROPOMI instrument, a multispectral sensor can be used to record wavelength reflectance to measure atmospheric concentrations of ozone, methane, formaldehyde, aerosol, carbon monoxide, nitrogen oxide, and sulfur dioxide, as well as cloud characteristics at a spatial resolution of 0.01 degrees of arc. Comparing the variation of NO_2 in part of South America and neighboring regions on Jan 21, 2020 and Mar 20, 2020, we observed a reduction in the brightness values in the image in the period after the lockdown and used it as evidence of pollution reduction due to the reduced intensity of activities of the population that remained working at home (Figure 2.6).

Sentinel-5P monitoring data can be accessed in the cloud via R and Earth Engine (EE). The geobr (Pereira et al., 2021), sf (Pebesma et al., 2022), rgee (Aybar et al., 2022), and rmapshaper (Teucher et al., 2022) packages are used as examples to establish a workflow for processing and mapping administrative boundaries and atmospheric gases at a location of interest, in this case the Southeast region of Brazil. The packages are enabled with the library function.

```
library(geobr)
library(sf)
```

---

[1]https://dhruvmehrotra3.users.earthengine.app/view/earther-time-series

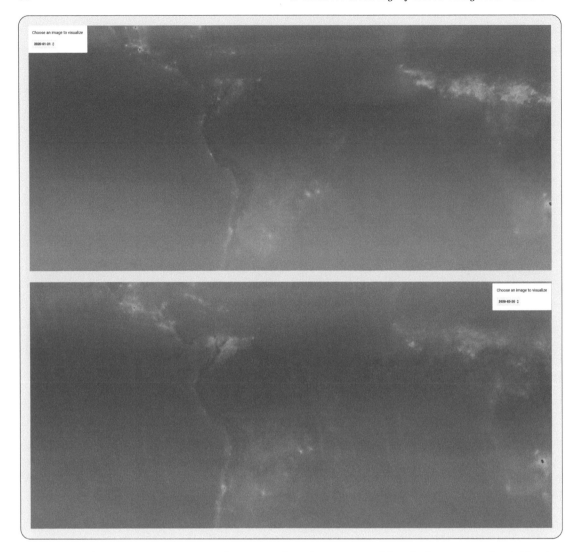

Figure 2.6 Comparative variation of nitrogen dioxide in parts of South America and neighboring regions on Jan 21, 2020 (top) and on Mar 20, 2020 (bottom).

```
library(rgee)
library(rmapshaper)
```

The ee_Initialize function is used to start EE.

```
ee_Initialize(drive = TRUE)
```

The boundaries of Brazilian states are obtained using the read_contry function of the geobr package. The Brazilian boundary data is obtained at scale 1:250,000, using the geodetic reference system SIRGAS2000 and EPSG 4674 and 1.4 MB in size.

```
br<-read_country(year = 2020, simplified = TRUE, showProgress = TRUE)
```

```
#Using year 2020
#Downloading: 1.4 MB
```

The st_transform function of the sf package is used to transform the projection of the data from SIRGAS2000 to WGS-84, using the reference coordinate system with EPSG code 4326 in the transformation.

```
brwgs<-st_transform(br, crs = 4326)
```

A subset is defined in the Southeast region of Brazil with bracket operators and attribute names.

```
se<-brwgs[brwgs$name_region == "Sudeste",]
```

The object.size function is used to evaluate the size of the file after performing the subsetting. This reduces the file to a size of 629896 bytes.

```
object.size(se)
#629896 bytes
```

The ms_simplify function of the rmapshaper package is used to further reduce the file size since this type of mapping does not require much vertex detail at state boundaries. The file is transformed into the sp class and then transformed back into the sf class using the pipe operator.

```
simplepolys <- rmapshaper::ms_simplify(input = as(se, 'Spatial')) %>%
  st_as_sf()
```

This resulted in an object with a size of 33128 bytes. This object with the boundaries of states in the southeast region of Brazil will be used as a reference for mapping the atmospheric variation.

```
object.size(simplepolys)
#33128 bytes
```

The sf_as_ee function is used to convert vectors to multipolygons of class ee.

```
polsee <- simplepolys  %>% sf_as_ee()
```

The polygon fill is removed by using a chunk of ee$Image()$byte() code associated with the paint argument. This facilitates the visualization of Sentinel-5P imagery data within the polygons mapped over the image.

```
empty <- ee$Image()$byte()
outline <- empty$paint(featureCollection=polsee,color=1,width=3)
```

A search period for images in the Earth Engine data collection is set between June 1 and June 6, 2022.

```
startDate = '2022-06-01'
endDate = '2022-06-06'
```

The ee$ImageCollection function is used to obtain Sentinel-5P imaging data over the proposed period. The filtered file consists of 896 images in the size of 16.28 GB and a set of variables on NO_2.

```
collection <- ee$ImageCollection('COPERNICUS/S5P/NRTI/L3_NO2')$
   filterDate(startDate, endDate)
```

The filtered results are displayed with the ee_print function.

```
ee_print(collection)
#------------------- Earth Engine ImageCollection --
#ImageCollection Metadata:
# - Class                    : ee$ImageCollection
# - Number of Images         : 896
# - Number of Properties     : 25
# - Number of Pixels*        : 948326400000
# - Approximate size*        : 16.28 GB
#Image Metadata (img_index = 0):
# - ID                       : COPERNICUS/S5P/NRTI/L3_NO2/
#20220601T005129_20220601T015055_1
# - system:time_start        : 2022-06-01 00:51:23
# - system:time_end          : 2022-06-01 00:56:35
# - Number of Bands          : 12
# - Bands names              : NO2_column_number_density
#tropospheric_NO2_column_number_density
#stratospheric_NO2_column_number_density
#NO2_slant_column_number_density
#tropopause_pressure absorbing_aerosol_index
#cloud_fraction sensor_altitude sensor_azimuth_angle
#sensor_zenith_angle solar_azimuth_angle solar_zenith_angle
# - Number of Properties     : 29
# - Number of Pixels*        : 1058400000
# - Approximate size*        : 18.60 MB
#Band Metadata (img_band = 'NO2_column_number_density'):
# - EPSG (SRID)              : WGS 84 (EPSG:4326)
# - proj4string              : +proj=longlat +datum=WGS84 +no_defs
# - Geotransform             : 0.01 0 176.14539 0 0.01 -71.2054824829102
# - Nominal scale (meters)   : 1113.195
# - Dimensions               : 36000 2450
# - Number of Pixels         : 88200000
# - Data type                : DOUBLE
# - Approximate size         : 1.55 MB
# ---------
# NOTE: (*) Properties calculated considering a constant  geotransform and data type.
```

Parameters for visualization and selection of bands of interest are defined for mapping results centered on the Southeast region of Brazil. A color palette of black, blue, purple, cyan, green, yellow, and red is used for visualization of NO_2 density in the atmospheric column. The Map$addLayer function is used to map the average NO_2 values monitored in the period with the $mean() function.

```
palette <- c('#000000', '#0000FF', '#800080', '#00FFFF', '#00FF00', '#FFFF00', '#FF0000')
imageVisParam <- list(bands = c("NO2_column_number_density"), min = 0, max = 0.0002,
                      palette= palette)
Map$setCenter(-46.58203,-19.80119,6)
Map$addLayer(collection$mean(), imageVisParam, 'S5P NO2', legend = F)+
Map$addLayer(outline, list(palette='#C1CDCD'),'Sudeste region')
```

With this, it is possible to see a greater concentration of NO_2 in lighter tones tending to red around the large capitals located in large urban centers that grow in conurbation, determining greater air pollution in the yellow and red colors referring to the concentration of NO_2 in the atmospheric column with values close to 0.0002 (Figure 2.7).

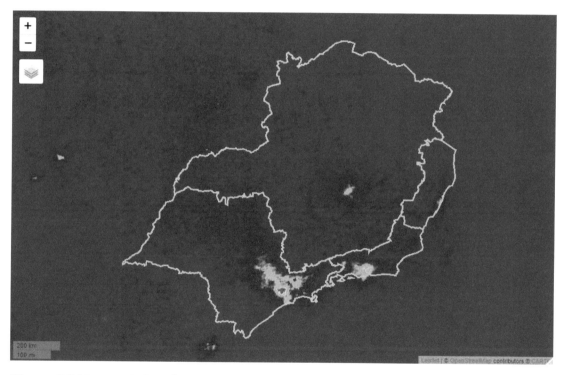

Figure 2.7 Mean variation of nitrogen dioxide in the atmospheric column over southeastern Brazil from June 1 to 6, 2022.

2.7.4 Solar radiation calculation

Solar radiation calculation and determination of related variables can be performed based on location, time, and topographic conditions for surface energy models and estimation of positions and solar components that varied by topography, time, and varying locations. Solar components of the atmosphere, open, diffuse and direct, atmospheric transmittance and diffuse factors, day length, sunrise and sunset, solar azimuth, zenith, altitude, hourly incidence and angles, Earth's declination angle, equation of time and solar constant are calculated through equations (Seyednasrollah et al., 2013; Seyednasrollah, 2021).

2.8   Energy-Matter Interactions on the Ground

The time rate of energy flow toward, away from, or through a surface is called "radiant flux" (ϕ) measured in watts (W). Important information about the terrain can be obtained by monitoring the nature of incident radiant flux at specific wavelengths and its interaction with the terrain. In the energy balance equation, the total amount of radiant flux at specific wavelengths (λ) incident on the ground (ϕ_i) must be balanced by evaluating the amounts of radiant flux reflected (ϕ_ρ), absorbed (ϕ_α), and transmitted from the surface (ϕ_τ)(Jensen, 2007):

$$\phi_{i\lambda} = \phi_{\rho\lambda} + \phi_{\alpha\lambda} + \phi_{\tau\lambda} \tag{2.17}$$

Dividing each of the variables by the original incident radiant flux:

$$\frac{\phi_{i\lambda}}{\phi_{i\lambda}} = \frac{\phi_{\rho\lambda}}{\phi_{i\lambda}} + \frac{\phi_{\alpha\lambda}}{\phi_{i\lambda}} + \frac{\phi_{\tau\lambda}}{\phi_{i\lambda}} \tag{2.18}$$

then,

$$1 = \rho_\lambda + \tau_\lambda + \alpha_\lambda \tag{2.19}$$

where ρ_λ, τ_λ, and α_λ are the hemispherical spectral reflectance, hemispherical spectral transmittance and hemispherical spectral absorptance, respectively.

Considering that most real-world materials are opaque to thermal infrared radiation, little radiant flux passes through objects in the terrain. In this case, $\tau_\lambda = 0$ and emissivity is assumed equal to absorptance. Thus,

$$1 = \rho_\lambda + \epsilon_\lambda \tag{2.20}$$

If the ground does not lose any energy through transmittance, all the energy emanating from the object is accounted for by the relationship between the reflectance and the emissivity of the object.

2.8.1   Reflectance, absorptance, and transmittance

Reflectance is the process in which radiation bounces off an object, such as cloud tops, bodies of water, exposed soil, and vegetation. Spectral reflectance is measured at great distances by means of sensor systems. It is also possible to obtain ground measurements with a spectroradiometer just above the ground. When specular reflection occurs, the surface of the reflected radiation is essentially smooth. On the rough surface, the rays are reflected in many directions by diffuse reflection, depending on the orientation of the smallest reflecting surfaces characterizing a perfectly diffuse surface, called a "Lambertian surface". In this case, the radiant flux leaving the surface is constant for any angle of reflectance normal to the surface (Figure 2.8).

The hemispherical reflectance ($\phi_{i\lambda}$) is the dimensionless ratio of the reflected ($\phi_{i\lambda}$) and incident ($\phi_{i\lambda}$) radiant flux on a surface:

Figure 2.8 Types of reflective surfaces and the nature of specular and diffuse reflectance.

$$\rho_\lambda = \frac{\phi_{\rho\lambda}}{\phi_{i\lambda}} \tag{2.21}$$

The hemispherical transmittance (τ_λ) is the dimensionless ratio of the transmitted ($\phi_{\tau\lambda}$) and incident ($\phi_{i\lambda}$) radiant flux on a surface:

$$\tau_\lambda = \frac{\phi_{\tau\lambda}}{\phi_{i\lambda}} \tag{2.22}$$

Hemispherical absorptance (α_λ) is the dimensionless ratio of absorbed ($\phi_{\alpha\lambda}$) and incident ($\phi_{i\lambda}$) radiant flux on a surface:

$$\alpha_\lambda = \frac{\phi_{\alpha\lambda}}{\phi_{i\lambda}} \tag{2.23}$$

or,

$$\alpha_\lambda = 1 - (\rho_\lambda + \tau_\lambda) \tag{2.24}$$

The net effect of radiation absorption by most objects is the energy converted to heat, causing the object's temperature to rise.

These radiometric quantities are useful for making statements about the reflectance, transmittance, and absorptance of objects and processes on Earth. Percent reflectance is used in remote sensing research to describe the spectral reflectance characteristics of different targets by means of the spectral signature of objects at different wavelengths:

$$\rho_\lambda = \frac{\phi_{\rho\lambda}}{\phi_{i\lambda}} 100 \qquad (2.25)$$

The spectral resolution of most remote sensing systems is described in terms of bands of the electromagnetic spectrum with respect to wavelength and percent reflectance (reflectance response or spectral signature) of monitored objects and processes (Figure 2.9).

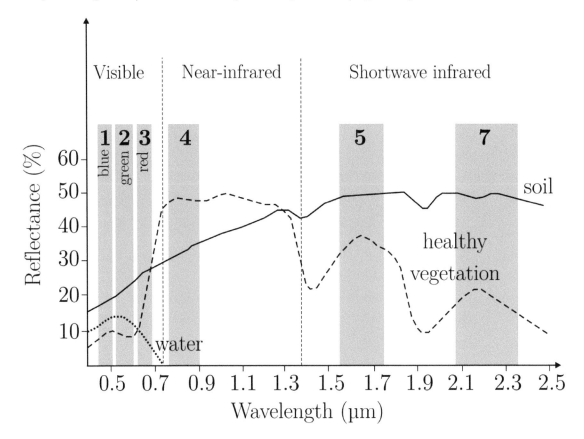

Figure 2.9 Relation between Landsat spectral bands and the electromagnetic spectrum.

2.8.2   Irradiance and exitance

The amount of intercepted radiant flux divided by the area of the planar surface is the average radiant flux density (Figure 2.10). The amount of radiant flux incident on a surface per unit area (A) is called "irradiance" ($E\lambda$) (W m^{-2}):

$$E\lambda = \frac{\phi_{\lambda i}}{A} \qquad (2.26)$$

The amount of radiant flux leaving the surface, per unit area, is called "exitance" $(M\lambda)$ (W m^{-2}):

$$M\lambda = \frac{\phi_{\lambda e}}{A} \tag{2.27}$$

2.8.3 Radiance

Radiance is the most precise radiometric measurement in remote sensing. Radiance (L_λ) is the radiant flux per unit solid angle leaving an area (A) in a given direction (θ) and solid angle (Ω) (W m$^{-2}sr^{-1}$) (Figure 2.10):

$$L_\lambda = \frac{\phi_{\lambda e}}{\frac{\Omega}{A cos\theta}} \tag{2.28}$$

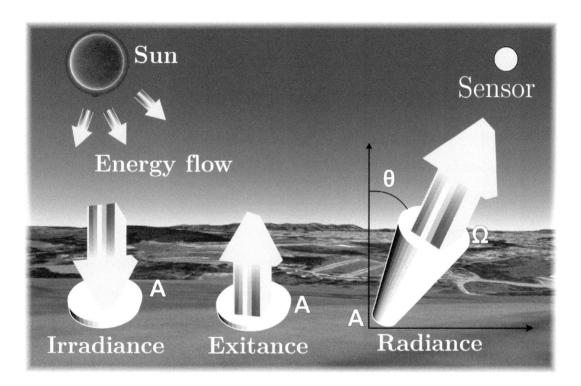

Figure 2.10 Radiant flux density for areas on the Earth's surface represented by irradiance, exitance, and radiance leaving an area, in a specific direction, and at a specific solid angle.

The radiant flux reflected or emitted by the surface re-enters the atmosphere and interacts with gases, water vapor and particulates, under the effect of atmospheric scattering, absorption, reflection and refraction, affecting the energy recorded by the remote sensing system. In digital remote sensing, the radiance reaching a detector is registered according to the number of photons that reach the sensor in spectral regions of specific wavelengths.

2.8.4   Potential irradiance on terrain

The solar irradiation potential over a given area can be calculated using different atmospheric models, digital elevation, latitude, and time of year (Böhner & Antonić, 2009; Oke, 2002; Wilson & Gallant, 2000). The atmospheric components can be calculated based on the height of the atmosphere, vapor pressure, air pressure, water and dust content, atmospheric transmittance, or by the method of Hofierka & Súri (2002).

The packages used in the analysis are enabled with the `library` function.

```
library(rasterVis)
library(raster)
library(RSAGA)
library(gridExtra)
```

The `SAGA 7.3.0` is used for data analysis in R and it is necessary to define the installation location of the software with the `rsaga.env` function.

```
env <- rsaga.env('C:/SAGAGIS/saga-7.3.0_x64/saga-7.3.0_x64/')
```

A digital elevation model of the region surrounding the Funil dam filled with sinks to perform hydrological and morphometric terrain analysis is used as an input file to explore the effect of terrain variation, latitude, and time of year on solar irradiance. The date chosen to evaluate the potential effects of irradiance was October 31, 2022, latitude -21°, and energy unit in kWh m^{-2}.

```
rsaga.pisr2(in.dem="C:/sr/RSAGA/srtmfill.sgrd",
            out.direct.grid="C:/sr/RSAGA/sdirect.sgrd",
            out.diffuse.grid="C:/sr/RSAGA/sdiffuse.sgrd",
            out.total.grid="C:/sr/RSAGA/solrad.sgrd",
            out.ratio.grid="C:/sr/RSAGA/sratio.sgrd",
            out.duration="C:/sr/RSAGA/soldur.sgrd",
            out.sunrise="C:/sr/RSAGA/sunrise.sgrd",
            out.sunset="C:/sr/RSAGA/sunset.sgrd",
            latitude=-21.147769, unit = c("kWh/m2"),
            start.date = list(day = 31, month = 10, year = 2015),
            time.step=0.5, env=env)
```

Some constants are set as defaults in this example, such as a solar constant of 1367 W m^{-2}, height of the atmosphere of 12000 m, atmospheric pressure of 1013 mbar, water content of a vertical strip of the atmosphere of 1.68 cm, dust factor of 100 ppm, and atmospheric transmittance of 70%. It may be necessary to check the obtained results against different versions of RSAGA and SAGA.

The output files after analysis are imported into R with the `raster` function. The `crs` function is used to assign the coordinate system for each raster.

```
alt <- raster("C:/sr/RSAGA/srtmfill.sdat") # Altitude
crs(alt) <- "+proj=utm +zone=23 +south +datum=WGS84 +units=m +no_defs"
sdirect <- raster("C:/sr/RSAGA/Direct Insolation.sdat") # Direct insolation
crs(sdirect) <- "+proj=utm +zone=23 +south +datum=WGS84 +units=m +no_defs"
sdiffuse <- raster("C:/sr/RSAGA/Diffuse Insolation.sdat") # Diffuse insolation
crs(sdiffuse) <- "+proj=utm +zone=23 +south +datum=WGS84 +units=m +no_defs"
```

```
sr_total <- raster("C:/sr/RSAGA/Total Insolation.sdat") # Total insolation
crs(sr_total) <- "+proj=utm +zone=23 +south +datum=WGS84 +units=m +no_defs"
sratio <- raster("C:/sr/RSAGA/Direct to Diffuse Ratio.sdat") # Direct to diffuse ratio
crs(sratio) <- "+proj=utm +zone=23 +south +datum=WGS84 +units=m +no_defs"
soldur <- raster("C:/sr/RSAGA/Duration of Insolation.sdat") # Duration of insolation
crs(soldur) <- "+proj=utm +zone=23 +south +datum=WGS84 +units=m +no_defs"
sunrise <- raster("C:/sr/RSAGA/sunrise.sdat") # Sunrise
crs(sunrise) <- "+proj=utm +zone=23 +south +datum=WGS84 +units=m +no_defs"
sunset <- raster("C:/sr/RSAGA/sunset.sdat") # Sunset
crs(sunset) <- "+proj=utm +zone=23 +south +datum=WGS84 +units=m +no_defs"
```

Spatial variation mapping of altitude (m), direct (kWh m^{-2}), diffuse (kWh m^{-2}), and total (kWh m^{-2}) insolation in the region surrounding the Funil dam is performed with the levelplot and grid.arrange functions (Figure 2.11).

```
a<-levelplot(alt, margin=FALSE, xlab=NULL, ylab=NULL,  par.settings = GrTheme,
             main="Altitude", scales=list(draw=F))
b<-levelplot(sdirect, margin=FALSE, xlab=NULL, ylab=NULL,  par.settings = GrTheme,
             main="Direct insolation", scales=list(draw=F))
c<-levelplot(sdiffuse, margin=FALSE, xlab=NULL, ylab=NULL,  par.settings = GrTheme,
             main="Diffuse insolation", scales=list(draw=F))
d<-levelplot(sr_total, margin=FALSE, xlab=NULL, ylab=NULL,  par.settings = GrTheme,
             main="Total insolation", scales=list(draw=F))
grid.arrange(a, b, c, d, ncol=2)
```

Spatial variation mapping of the direct and diffuse radiation ratio, insolation duration (h), sunrise and sunset (h) in the region surrounding the Funil dam is performed with the functions levelplot and grid.arrange (Figure 2.12).

```
a<-levelplot(sratio, margin=FALSE, xlab=NULL, ylab=NULL,  par.settings = GrTheme,
             main="Direct to diffuse ratio", scales=list(draw=F))
b<-levelplot(soldur, margin=FALSE, xlab=NULL, ylab=NULL,  par.settings = GrTheme,
             main="Duration of insolation", scales=list(draw=F))
c<-levelplot(sunrise, margin=FALSE, xlab=NULL, ylab=NULL,  par.settings = GrTheme,
             main="Sunrise", scales=list(draw=F))
d<-levelplot(sunset, margin=FALSE, xlab=NULL, ylab=NULL,  par.settings = GrTheme,
             main="Sunset", scales=list(draw=F))
grid.arrange(a, b, c, d, ncol=2)
```

The choice of color palette for geovisualization can be interesting to better understand the spatial variation of each variable. Mapping the data in SAGA can facilitate the understanding of each variable by having a proposed color palette for each variable. In this case, the GrTheme color palette is used, but other options such as BTCTheme, and RdBuTheme() can be used as an alternative for scientific geovisualization of the results.

2.8.5   Calibration of Landsat thermal band

Landsat radiance values at the top of the atmosphere L_λ (W m^{-2}srad$^{-1}\mu$ m^{-1}) are converted to top of atmosphere (TOA) radiance by the equation:

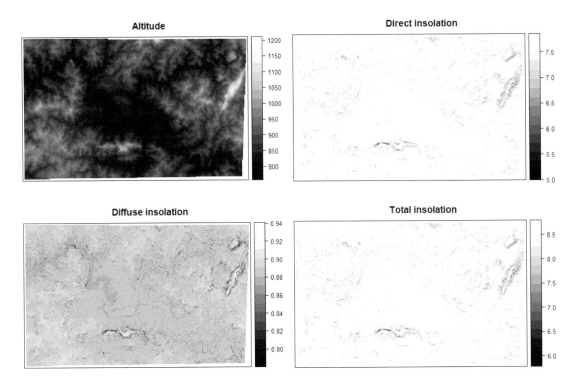

Figure 2.11 Spatial variation of altitude, direct, diffuse and total potential insolation on October 31, 2022 in the region surrounding the Funil dam, state of Minas Gerais, Brazil.

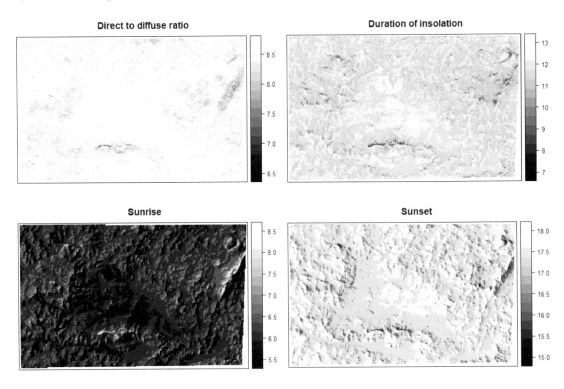

Figure 2.12 Spatial variation of the direct and diffuse ratio, insolation duration, sunrise and sunset on October 31, 2022 in the region surrounding the Funil dam, state of Minas Gerais, Brazil.

$$L_\lambda = M_L Q_{cal} + A_L \tag{2.29}$$

where M_L and A_L are multiplication and addition parameters, respectively, and Q_{cal}, the pixel values in digital numbers.

2.8.5.1   Radiance to brightness temperature conversion at sensor

The thermal band is converted to radiometric temperature (T_{rad}) (brightness temperature) by means of thermal constants:

$$T_{rad} = \frac{K_2}{ln(\frac{K_1}{L_\lambda} + 1)} \tag{2.30}$$

where L_λ is the radiance at the top of the atmosphere (W m^{-2}srad$^{-1}\mu$ m^{-1}), K_1 and K_2, the thermal conversion constants 1 and 2 available in the image metadata file with extension .MTL, respectively.

2.9   Path Radiance of Targets

The radiance (L) recorded by a camera or detector is a function of the radiance emerging from the target on the ground within the sensor's instantaneous field of view (IFOV) at a specific solid angle. In this case, other radiant energies from other trajectories can enter the field of view and introduce noise into the remote sensing process by different situations (Jensen, 2007):

- Attenuation of solar spectral irradiance before illuminating the terrain to the extent captured by IFOV in the sensor system;
- Diffusion of the solar spectral irradiance that did not reach the ground surface as a function of atmospheric scattering;
- Rayleigh, Mie or nonselective scattering of the solar spectral irradiance that also suffered some absorption before illuminating the ground area to the extent captured by the IFOV in the sensor system;
- Reflection or scattering of the solar spectral irradiance into terrain close to the monitored area on the ground and then into the extent captured by the IFOV in the sensor system;
- Reflection of the energy by the nearby terrain to the atmosphere and then reflected back to the area of interest within the extent captured by the IFOV in the sensor system.

Only a small amount of the solar irradiance is reflected by the terrain in the direction of the sensor in the sky or Earth orbit. The total radiance (L_S) recorded by a sensor (W m^{-2} sr^{-1}) is a function of the returned radiance of the target under study in the area of interest (L_T) and an intrusive component called the "path radiance" (L_P) (Jensen, 2007):

$$L_S = L_T + L_P \tag{2.31}$$

2.10 Radiometric Correction

2.10.1 Methods used for image atmospheric correction

There are several methods of removing the unwanted (L_P) component. Radiative transfer models, such as MODTRAN and 6S, are used to predict the trajectory radiance at a particular time and location, and this information can be used to remove the (L_P). This process is called "radiometric correction" or "atmospheric correction" (Goslee, 2011; Leutner et al., 2019). In the case of Landsat mission sensors, the atmospheric correction methods sdos, dos and costz (Chavez, 1989; Chavez, 1996) are used in bands of the reflective spectrum region without affecting the thermal band. The approaches for subtracting dark objects in images rely on estimating atmospheric haze based on dark pixels.

The extra-terrestrial solar irradiation (ESUN) has been required in classical remote sensing image correction approaches. This variable is required to convert and normalize radiance into reflectance and also by simple atmospheric correction approaches as in the dos method.

For Landsat-8, no value for ESUN is provided by NASA. Therefore, these values are derived from a standard reference spectrum published by Thuillier et al. (2003) using the Landsat-8 OLI spectral response functions in DOS-based approaches. The implemented Sun-Earth distances neglected the eccentricity of the Earth. Therefore, a 100-year daily average (1979-2070) is used as a reference (Leutner et al., 2019).

ESUN values obtained from the Thuillier et al. (2003) are recommended by the Committee on Earth Observation Satellites (CEOS) as a standard reference. As an example of the correction performed by the RStoolbox package for Landsat-8 (Barsi et al., 2014; Leutner, 2022), first the reference solar spectrum is obtained. For this, the xlsx (Dragulescu & Arendt, 2020), ggplot2 (Wickham, Chang, et al., 2022), and reshape2 (Wickham, 2020) packages are enabled.

```
library(xlsx)
library(ggplot2)
library(reshape2)
```

The download.file function is used to get the solar irradiance data from the Internet.

```
download.file(
"http://media.libsyn.com/media/npl1/Solar_irradiance_Thuillier_2002.xls",
destfile = "thuillierSolarSpectrum.xls", mode='wb')
```

Data obtained from the Internet is imported into R with the read.xlsx function from the xlsx package.

```
sol <- read.xlsx("thuillierSolarSpectrum.xls", 3)
```

A plot of the Thuillier et al. (2003) irradiance spectrum is produced using the ggplot2 package (Figure 2.13).

```
ggplot(sol, aes(x = nm, y = mW.m2.nm)) + geom_line() +
    ggtitle("Solar Irradiance Spectrum") +
    xlab("Wavelength (nm)") + xlim(0,2400)
```

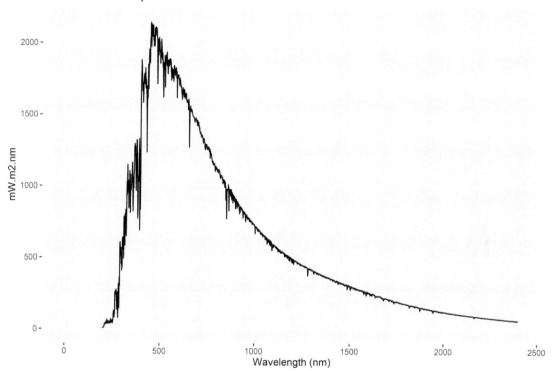

Figure 2.13 Solar irradiance spectrum used for radiometric correction of remote sensing images.

Spectral reflectance curve data for the Landsat-8 OLI bands are obtained from the Internet with the `download.file` function.

```
download.file(
"http://landsat.gsfc.nasa.gov/wp-content/uploads/2013/06/Ball_BA_RSR.v1.1-1.xlsx",
destfile = "landsat8oli.xlsx", mode='wb')
```

A function is created to import the spectral response curve of the OLI bands.

```
bands <- c("CoastalAerosol","Blue","Green","Red","NIR","Cirrus","SWIR1","SWIR2","Pan")
resp <- lapply(bands, function(x){
        data.frame(read.xlsx("landsat8oli.xlsx", sheetName = x)[,1:2])
    })
names(resp) <- bands
```

The `ggplot2` package is used to plot the relative spectral response variation for each wavelength range of the Landsat-8 OLI (Figure 2.13).

```
respDf <- melt(resp, c("Wavelength", "BA.RSR..watts."))
ggplot(respDf, aes( x = Wavelength, y = BA.RSR..watts., colour = L1)) +
    geom_line() + ggtitle("Landsat 8 OLI spectral response")+
    xlab("Wavelength (nm)")+
    ylab("Relative Spectral Response")
```

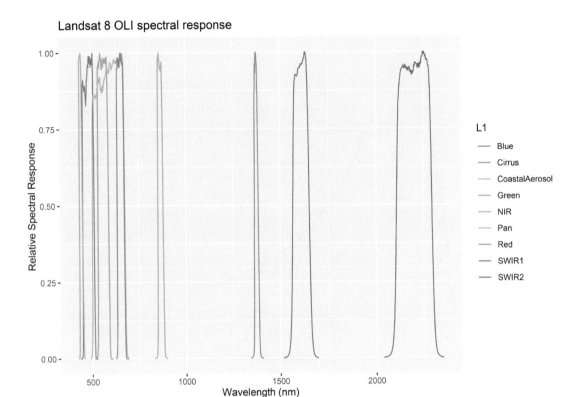

Figure 2.14 Relative spectral variation of Landsat-8 OLI imaging data.

The solar irradiance spectrum is interpolated with 0.01 nm increments for higher accuracy in the ESUN calculation.

```
sora <- range(sol[,1])
xnew <- seq(sora[1],sora[2], 0.01)
ynew <- resamp  <- approx(x = sol[,1], y = sol[,2], xout = xnew)[["y"]]
sol  <- cbind(xnew,ynew)
```

The spectral response curves are recomputed at solar spectrum resolution and the result is normalized so that each band is integrated one by one and used to calculate the weighted sum over the entire spectrum.

```
Esun <- sapply(resp, function(x){
            ## Resample band response to solar spectrum
            resamp  <- approx(x = x[,1], y = x[,2], xout = sol[,1])[["y"]]
            ## Convert to relative weights
            weights <- resamp / sum(resamp, na.rm = TRUE)
```

```
    ## Calculated weighted sum
    sum(sol[,2] * weights, na.rm = TRUE)
})
```

The final ESUN result is rounded to 2 decimal places.

```
round(Esun,2)
#CoastalAerosol Blue  Green  Red  NIR  Cirrus SWIR1 SWIR2 Pan
#1895.33 2004.57 1820.75 1549.49 951.76 366.97 247.55 85.46 1723.88
```

After calculating these values, one can perform the subtraction of dark objects in the Landsat-8 data. In data from previous Landsat missions, radiometric correction is performed against the published ESUN values. There are other ways to calculate ESUN based on min/max radiance calculation and Earth-Sun distance, as implemented in the i.landsat.toar function of the GRASS software. Both calculation approaches are similar but not identical in terms of results obtained (Leutner, 2022).

Currently, sophisticated atmospheric correction products are available, such as those derived from the Second Simulation of a Satellite Signal in the Solar Spectrum vector code (6S) (Vermote et al., 1997). However, there is still a demand for classical approaches for the greater ease, availability and need to perform methodological comparisons (Leutner et al., 2019).

2.10.2 Correction of relief variations

Different methods for topographic correction of images have been developed. Topographical correction, or topographical normalization, refers to the compensation of solar illumination according to the irregularity of the terrain. This effect causes high variation in the reflectance response for similar vegetation types, i.e., shaded areas reflect less than expected, while in sunny areas the effect is the opposite. Therefore, the process of topographic normalization may be critical in areas of rugged terrain, as a preliminary step for digital multispectral and multitemporal classification of vegetation types (Riano et al., 2003).

Information on design, performance, calibration of remote sensing sensor systems can be found in papers published in scientific journal issues (Table 2.1) (Schowengerdt, 2006).

Table 2.1 Information about calibration of some remote sensing systems described in scientific journal issues.

Sensor or Platform	Scientific Dissemination
Aqua	Parkinson (2003)
ASTER	Gillespie et al. (2005); IEEE (2005)
EO-1	Moran et al. (2003)
IKONOS	Goward & Zanoni (2003)
Landsat-4	Palmer (1984); Desachy et al. (1985)
Landsat-5,7	IEEE (2004)
MERIS	Rast et al. (1999)
MODIS	Justice et al. (1998)

2.11　Computational Practice

As a computational practice, functions from the R package RStoolbox (Leutner et al., 2019) are used to explore a metadata file of the Landsat-5 satellite TM sensor. The used image was corrected for illumination based on relief from a digital elevation model obtained by surface monitoring with RADAR with synthetic interferometry from the Shuttle Radar Topography Mission (SRTM) using the space shuttle as the orbital platform for obtaining the data (Goslee, 2011). The digital numbers of optical and infrared spectrum images are converted into radiance (at-sensor radiance), reflectance at the top of the atmosphere (at-sensor reflectance) and surface reflectance (absolute atmospheric correction) by the methods apref, dos and sdos, respectively. It is worth noting that the atmospheric correction methods (sdos, dos) apply to the optical region of the spectrum without affecting the thermal band. In the case of the Landsat-5 image, the radiance at the top of the atmosphere is converted to radiant temperature in Kelvin and degrees Celsius. Radiant temperature is mapped in the municipality of Ijaci, in the region of the Funil dam.

2.11.1　Installing R Packages

The install.packages function is used to install the raster (Hijmans et al., 2020), RStoolbox (Leutner et al., 2019), and rgdal (Bivand et al., 2021) packages in the R console.

```
install.packages("raster")
install.packages("RStoolbox")
install.packages("rgdal")
```

2.11.2　Enabling R Packages

The library function is used to enable the raster, RStoolbox and rgdal packages in the R console.

```
library(raster)
library(RStoolbox)
library(rgdal)
```

2.11.3　Obtaining a Landsat-5 TM image to perform the computational practice

A stacked raster image is obtained in the state of Minas Gerais, near the municipality of Ijaci. The scene information obtained is as follows: ID, LT05_L2SP_218075_20060126_20201008_02_T1; date acquired, Jan 26, 2006; path, 218; row, 075. It should be noted that the image was pre-processed in order to correct the illumination, transform the coordinate system and define a subset in the region of interest. The image with the stacked bands and the metadata file can be obtained **here**[2].

---

[2]http://www.sergeo.deg.ufla.br/sr/downloads/lsat_C.zip

After getting the image from the Internet and unpacking the files into a known directory, the geotiff files are imported into R using the stack function. The names function is used to rename the files for each stacked image.

```
lsat <- stack("C:/bookdown/SRcomR/files/C2/lsat_C.tif")
names(lsat) <- c("B1_dn", "B2_dn", "B3_dn", "B4_dn", "B5_dn", "B6_dn", "B7_dn")
```

2.11.4 Evaluating image metadata

The image metadata described earlier can be checked in R using the readMeta function. The values in the metadata file can be accessed through the summary function or by the name assigned to the metadata file itself. With this, it is possible to evaluate the image metadata to obtain the parameters for transforming the band 6 digital numbers into radiant temperature, if it is of interest to manually perform the conversion of the image digital numbers into brightness temperature.

```
metaData <- readMeta(
"C:/bookdown/SRcomR/files/C2/LT05_L1TP_218075_20060126_20161124_01_T1_MTL.txt")
metaData
summary(metaData)
```

In this case, it will be necessary to record the gain and offset values of Landsat-5 thermal band number 6 and the constants K_1 and K_2 used in the radiometric temperature conversion from mathematical models.

```
$CALRAD
#          offset      gain
#B1_dn -2.28583 0.765830
#B2_dn -4.28819 1.448200
#B3_dn -2.21398 1.044000
#B4_dn -2.38602 0.876020
#B5_dn -0.49035 0.120350
#B6_dn  1.18243 0.055375
#B7_dn -0.21555 0.065551
#$CALBT
#            K1        K2
#B6_dn 607.76 1260.56
```

A more efficient calculation to achieve the same determination goal can be obtained by means of the radColor function used with the use of the metaData file, as follows.

2.11.5 Converting digital numbers to top-of-atmosphere reflectance and brightness temperature

The digital numbers observed in the preprocessed image referring to the solar optical spectrum (bands 1, 2, 3, 4, 5, 7 of the reflective spectrum) are converted to reflectance at the top of the atmosphere. Thermal band number 6 is converted to brightness temperature. The radCor function and the method="apref" parameter are used to achieve this.

```
lsat_ref <- radCor(lsat, metaData = metaData, method = "apref")
```

2.11.6   Mapping the surface temperature in Kelvin and degrees Celsius

Band 6 converted to brightness temperature in Kelvin is mapped, and it is possible to observe the Funil dam in the center of the image and the areas with vegetation with lower brightness temperature, near the municipalities of Ijaci in the center, and Lavras in the southwestern portion of the map (Figure 2.15).

```
plot(lsat_ref$B6_bt, col=rainbow(10))
```

A function is used to convert the temperature Kelvin into degrees Celsius.

```
temp6_celsius <- calc(lsat_ref$B6_bt, fun=function(x){x - 273.15})
```

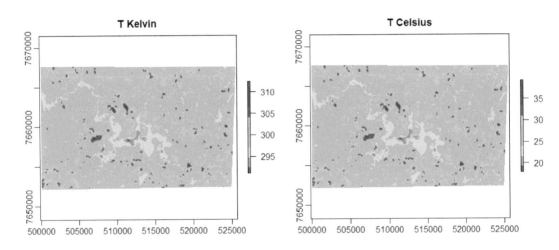

Figure 2.15 Radiant surface temperature in Kelvin and degrees Celsius.

2.11.7   Determining the reflectance of bands in the reflectance spectrum of Landsat-5 TM

The dos and sdos atmospheric correction methods are used comparatively to determine the surface reflectance in bands 1, 2, 3, 4, 5 and 7 of Landsat-5 TM.

The dark object correction method (dos) is used to convert the digital numbers of the images into surface reflectance according to methodology described in Chavez (1989).

```
lsat_dos <- radCor(lsat, metaData = metaData, method = "dos")
```

Another methodology used is the classical dos method, where there is a proposed fog correction in some bands. In this case, the estimateHaze function is used to estimate the presence of haze in bands 1 to 4, at the proportion of dark pixels of 1% (0.01).

```
hazeDN   <- estimateHaze(lsat, hazeBands = 1:4, darkProp = 0.01, plot = TRUE)
```

Then, the simple dark object subtraction method of the image with atmospheric scattering correction is used with the sdos method in order to convert digital numbers of the images into surface reflectance by means of the radCor function, using the results of the previous function to remove the haze in bands 1 to 4 (Figure 2.16).

```
lsat_sdos <- radCor(lsat, metaData = metaData, method = "sdos",
                    hazeValues = hazeDN, hazeBands = 1:4)
```

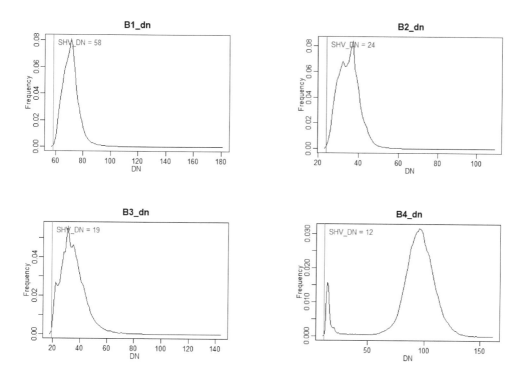

Figure 2.16 Atmospheric correction with haze subtraction in Landsat-5 TM bands 1 to 3.

The hist function is used to compare the results of both the dos and sdos methods in a comparative way. With this, it was possible to observe that the results were similar, with small differences mainly in bands 1, 2 and 3 (Figure 2.17).

```
hist(lsat_dos$B1_sre)
hist(lsat_sdos$B1_sre)
hist(lsat_dos$B2_sre)
hist(lsat_sdos$B2_sre)
hist(lsat_dos$B3_sre)
hist(lsat_sdos$B3_sre)
hist(lsat_dos$B4_sre)
hist(lsat_sdos$B4_sre)
hist(lsat_dos$B5_sre)
hist(lsat_sdos$B5_sre)
```

```
hist(lsat_dos$B7_sre)
hist(lsat_sdos$B7_sre)
```

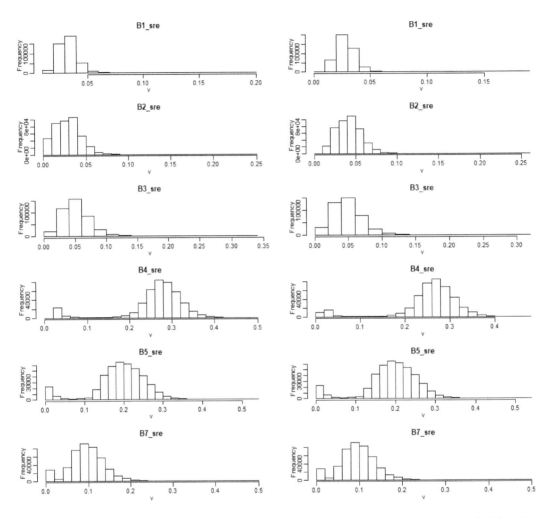

Figure 2.17 Using a histogram to compare the atmospheric correction by the `dos` (left) and `sdos` (right) methods.

The `plot` function is used to comparatively map the results of both methods in space (Figure 2.18).

```
plot(lsat_dos$B1_sre, main="dos-B1")
plot(lsat_sdos$B1_sre, main="sdos-B1")
plot(lsat_dos$B2_sre, main="dos-B2")
plot(lsat_sdos$B2_sre, main="sdos-B2")
plot(lsat_dos$B3_sre, main="dos-B3")
plot(lsat_sdos$B3_sre, main="sdos-B3")
plot(lsat_dos$B4_sre, main="dos-B4")
plot(lsat_sdos$B4_sre, main="sdos-B4")
plot(lsat_dos$B5_sre, main="dos-B5")
plot(lsat_sdos$B5_sre, main="sdos-B5")
```

```
plot(lsat_dos$B7_sre, main="dos-B7")
plot(lsat_sdos$B7_sre, main="sdos-B7")
```

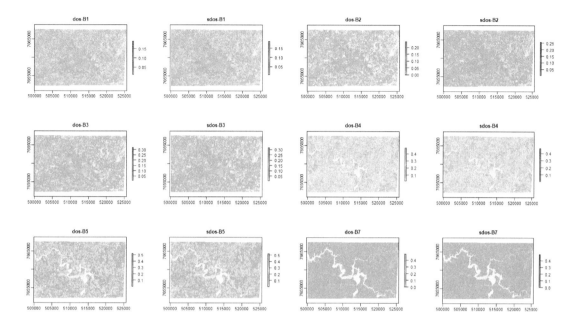

Figure 2.18 Comparative reflectance mapping of Landsat-5 TM bands 1, 2, 3, 4, 5, and 7 by the dos and sdos methods.

The reflectance results from the dos and sdos methods are exported for further use with the writeRaster function. The options="INTERLEAVE=BAND" parameter has been used to export the images of the stacked bands into a single file.

```
writeRaster(lsat_dos, filename="C:/bookdown/SRcomR/files/C2/lsat_dos.tif",
            options="INTERLEAVE=BAND", overwrite=TRUE) #DOS
writeRaster(lsat_sdos, filename="C:/bookdown/SRcomR/files/C2/lsat_sdos.tif",
            options="INTERLEAVE=BAND", overwrite=TRUE) #SDOS
```

2.12 Exercises

2.12.1   Determine the atmospheric transmittance coefficient for two consecutive
days of a location at latitude -21.248488°, longitude -45.001375°, and
altitude 964 m above sea level.

2.12.2   Make a graph of the electromagnetic spectrum.

2.12.3   Arrange the following wavelengths in ascending order: near-infrared,
blue, ultraviolet, radio waves, and X-rays.

2.12.4   An X-ray machine has produced radiation at a wavelength of 1.0 *
10^{-11} m. Determine the frequency of the radiation and the energy.
Consider h = 6.63 * 10^{-34} Js and c = 3.0 * 10^8 m s^{-1}.

2.12.5   A radio transmitter produced waves with a frequency of 1.0 * 10^8 Hz.
Determine the wavelength of the signal in meters. Consider c = 3.0 *
10^8 m s^{-1}.

2.12.6   Determine the solar azimuth and zenith angles in radians from the
angular values in decimal degrees of 61.96° and 40.25°, respectively.

2.12.7   Why is it important to know about emissivity when conducting a
remote sensing survey in the thermal infrared?

2.12.8   Why is knowing the dominant wavelength of an object important to
remote sensing in the thermal infrared?

2.12.9   Define hemispheric reflectance and explain how to use this variable in
the remote sensing process.

2.12.10 Define path radiance and explain its effect on remote sensing data
and image interpretation.

2.12.11 Which of the following variables represents the energy detected by a
sensor system on a satellite?

   a. Irradiance.
   b. Radiance.
   c. Absorptance.
   d. Transmittance.

2.12.12   Reflectance is defined as the ratio between:

    a. Reflected and emitted flux.
    b. Reflected and backscattered flux.
    c. Reflected and incident flow.
    d. Reflected and absorbed flux.

2.12.13   What are objects with similar radiance from different observation angles are:

    a. Backscattered.
    b. Lambertians.
    c. Specular.
    d. Amorphous.

2.12.14   Determine the dominant wavelength of the Sun and Earth (micrometers) considering that these objects approach black bodies at temperatures of 6000 and 300 K, respectively.

2.12.15   Determine the total emissive energy power of the Sun and Earth (W m^{-2}) considering that these objects approach black bodies at temperatures of 6000 and 300 K, respectively.

2.13   Homework

2.13.1   Subject

Monitoring radiant temperature variation in a geographic region of interest with remote sensing data.

2.13.2   Assignment

Develop the subject presented with a practical application of remote sensing and digital image processing including the topics Introduction and Objective. Then present the development of the task.

2.14   Resources on the Internet

As a study guide, slides and illustrative videos are presented about physical principles of remote sensing (Table 2.2).

Table 2.2 Slide shows and video presentations on physical principles of remote sensing.

Guide	Address for Access
1	Slides on physical principles of remote sensing[3]
2	Optical remote sensing principles[4]
3	Interactions of electromagnetic energy and energy transfer[5]
4	Illustrative example on the photoelectric effect[6]

2.15   Research Suggestion

The development of scientific research on remote sensing is stimulated by the activity proposals that can be used or adapted by the student to assess the applicability of the subject matter covered in the chapter (Table 2.3).

Table 2.3 Practical and research activities used or adapted by students using remote sensing.

Activity	Description
1	Define a polygonal boundary of the area of interest by means of an existing shapefile (.shp) vector feature file or a bounding rectangle using the extent function. Use the thermal image provided by the teacher and crop your area of interest. Evaluate the spatial variation of temperature in the region.

---

[3] http://www.sergeo.deg.ufla.br/sr/Presentation/Aula2/presentation.html#/
[4] https://youtu.be/ySY2O5ADjIg
[5] https://youtu.be/1nuZS7kKwH4
[6] https://youtu.be/bnR1syXU5dU

3

Remote Sensing Sensors and Satellite Systems

3.1 Learning Questions

The learning questions answered by reading the chapter are as follows:

- How is the recording of electromagnetic energy by the sensor performed?
- How is the data recorded by the sensor in Earth orbit transferred back to the Earth's surface?
- What types of sensor arrangements are used?
- What types of sensors can be used according to different spatial, spectral, temporal, and radiometric resolutions?
- How can information about sensor resolution be related to a remote sensing application?
- What types of satellite orbits are used?
- What is the relationship between satellite orbit type, sensor resolution, and remote sensing applications?
- How can active and passive remote sensing data be obtained to perform practical applications?

3.2 Learning Outcomes

Using the learning outcomes from the chapter, you should be able to do the following:

- Understand the process of recording electromagnetic energy by the sensor.
- Understand how data recorded in sensors is transmitted to the Earth's surface.
- Understand and describe some types of sensor arrangements.
- Understand the relationships among sensor types, resolutions and remote sensing applications.
- Understand different types of satellite orbits used and their relationship to resolution and remote sensing applications.
- Obtain sensing data to perform practical applications.

3.3 Introduction

Understanding basic information about how remote sensing imagery is acquired can assist in the image processing and interpretation process. In addition, being familiar with satellite missions provides an overview of the information potentially available for different applications (Chuvieco, 2020). Information used in remote sensing can vary depending on the spatial resolution, number and span of bands, spectral bandwidth, temporal observation frequency, signal-to-noise ratio, and radiometric capability of the sensor to detect variations in energy (Jensen, 2007).

The modern era of terrestrial remote sensing from space began with the first Landsat Multispectral Scanner System (MSS), launched in 1972, with 4 spectral bands, each approximately 100 nm wide and 80-m spatial resolution. Today there is great diversity and variety in the performance of remote sensing systems that have made the MSS specifications modest. Almost every part of the electromagnetic spectrum is available in satellite operating systems, with dozens of spectral bands and with pixel sizes, for example, from less than 1 to 1000 m, complemented by many hyperspectral sensors with hundreds of spectral bands, each on the order of 10 nm wide (Schowengerdt, 2006).

3.4   Sensor Energy Registration

The brightness of the reflected and/or emitted energy is converted by the sensor into an image, with the spatial distribution of the brightness. Several important transformations of the radiometric, spatial, and geometric dimensions occur in this phase. Generally, the sensor degrades the signal of interest. From an understanding of the nature of the signal degradation, the image processing algorithms can properly design and interpret the results obtained. In an electrooptical sensor there is scanning operation to convert the radiation at the sensor into a continuous, time-varying optical signal. The optical signal converted into an electronic signal is amplified and further processed by the sensor's electronics. In the analog-to-digital (A/D) converter, the processed signal was sampled in time and quantized into digital number (DN) values representing pixels in the image (Schowengerdt, 2006) (Figure 3.1).

Sensors are classified according to the main mechanism for detecting electromagnetic energy in (Chuvieco, 2020) (Figure 3.2):

- Passive <- Radiation from external sources is registered in the sensor;
- Active <- The sensor system emits its own source of energy at the target and records the energy flux reflected by the target in the area of interest.

The photons of the radiant flux leaving the ground are channeled to the detector of the sensor. In the detector, the radiant energy is converted into an analog electrical signal. The radiant energy is then converted into an analog electrical signal. The greater the number of photons impacting the detector, the greater the signal strength. Infrared detectors are composed of (Jensen, 2007):

- Indium antimonide (In:Sb), with peak sensitivity near 5 μm;
- Mercury-doped germanium (Ge:Hg), with peak sensitivity near 10 μm;
- Cadmium mercury telluride (Hg:Cd:Te), sensitive in the range of 8 to 14 μm.

The detectors are cooled to low temperatures -196°C with liquid helium or liquid nitrogen. The cooling ensures that the radiant energy (photons) recorded by the detectors is relative to the terrain and not to the ambient temperature of the sensor's own objects. The radiant flux recorded by the sensor system is an integration of all the radiant fluxes emitted by the various component materials of the IFOV and any radiant flux scattered by the atmosphere into the IFOV.

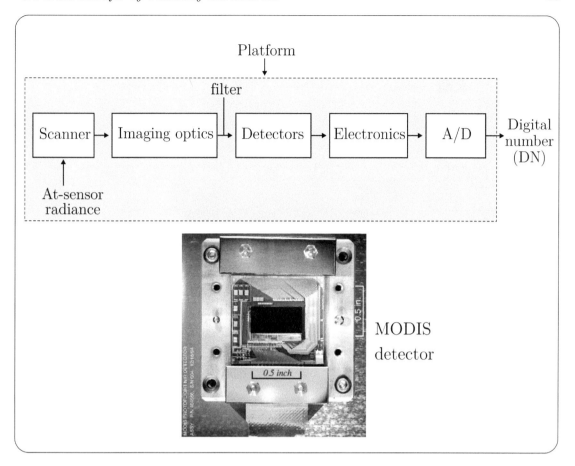

Figure 3.1 The main components of a digital remote sensing system and example of a MODIS NIR focal plane detector.

3.5 Data Transfer by Telemetry and Internet

The energy detected and recorded in the sensor is returned to the Earth when an airborne platform is used, and it is easy to obtain the data from the monitoring performed from a digital data storage device. When an orbital platform is used, data is sent either directly by telemetry to receiving stations on Earth, or indirectly via satellites tracking and sending data. In each situation, it may be necessary to perform radiometric and geometric preprocessing of the digital data to improve the interpretability of the images. Biophysical and land cover information can be extracted from the images and distributed to facilitate decision making by users (Figure 3.3) (Jensen, 2007).

3.6 Types of Passive Sensor Arrangement

The pixel grid that constitutes a digital image is obtained by a combination of scanning in the cross-sectional band direction (orthogonal to the movement of the sensor platform) and by moving

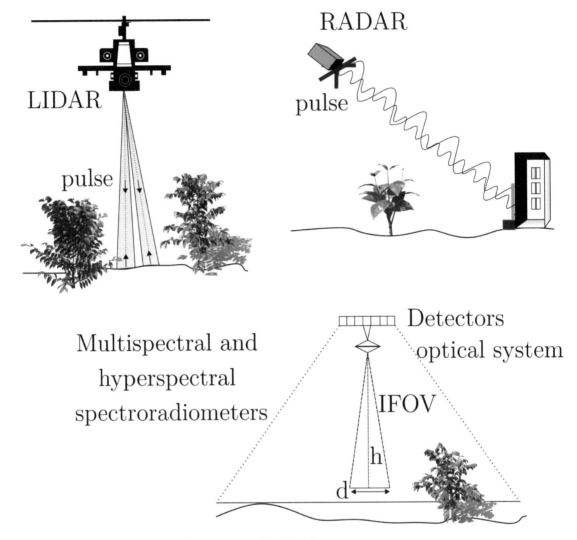

Figure 3.2 Different ways of energy recording by the sensor.

the platform along the terrain. A pixel is created whenever the sensor electronics samples the continuous stream of data provided by the terrain scan. The line scanner uses a single detector element to scan the entire scene. In whiskbroom scanners, such as Landsat TM, multiple detector elements, aligned to the terrain, are used to obtain a parallel scan during each cycle of the scanning mirror. In pushbroom scanners, such as SPOT, a linear array of thousands of detector elements, data is collected in parallel as the platform moves along the terrain. The 2D array pushbroom scanner concept is used in the hyperspectral sensors HYDICE, Hyperion and MERIS. The number of spectral bands is equal to the number of detector elements. All spectral data from one row of pixels must be read out before the sensor moves to the next row (Figure 3.4) (Schowengerdt, 2006).

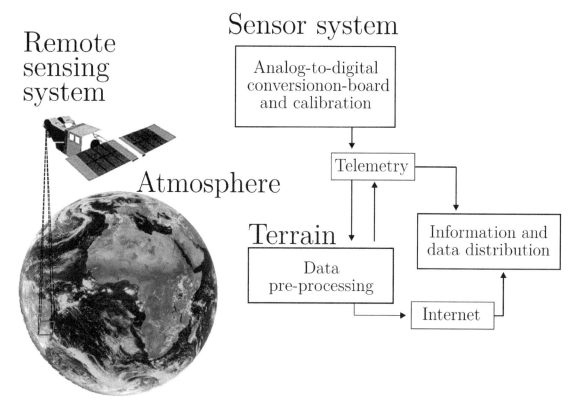

Figure 3.3 Data transfer by telemetry and Internet.

3.7 Spatial Resolution of Electrooptical Sensors

Spatial resolution identifies the smallest object that can be detected in an image and can vary according to the focal length of the electrooptical sensor and the height of the sensor above ground. The spatial resolution of electronic optical sensors varies according to the following factors (Chuvieco, 2020):

- Sensor altitude;
- Number of detectors;
- Focal length;
- System configuration.

The ground distance obtained as a unit of sensor view information (D) is a function of the sensor's instantaneous field of view (IFOV) in radians (β) and the sensor's altitude above ground level (H) (Chuvieco, 2020) (Figure 3.5):

$$D = 2H tan(\frac{\beta}{2}) \tag{3.1}$$

The total field of view (FOV) refers to the area observed by the sensor in a single image. The FOV varies depending on the number of detectors and the optical system. The field of view is also related to the temporal imaging frequency of the sensor. The spatial resolution of the optical electronics is a function of the satellite's orbital altitude, the number of detectors, the focal length,

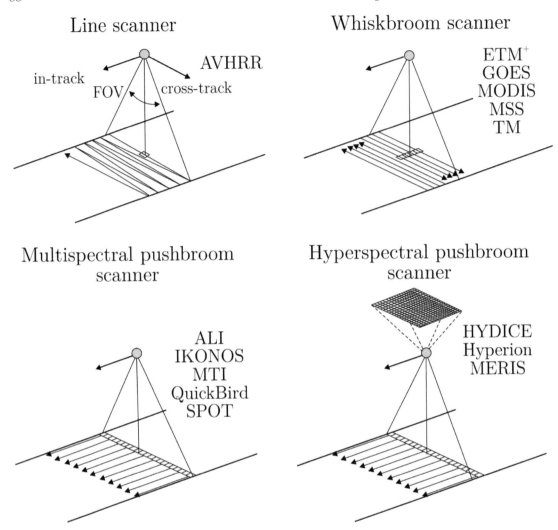

Figure 3.4 Definition of basic scanner parameters and representation of three scanning methods, with specific examples of line, whiskbroom, and pushbroom scanners.

and the configuration of the sensor system. For antenna-type sensor systems, such as RADAR, the spatial resolution is a function of the aperture angle, the platform height, and the wavelength of the RADAR (Chuvieco, 2020).

The terrain imaging swath width (SW) is the extent of the swath remotely imaged by the sensor during a full transverse scan of the scanning system. The SW varies according to the total angular field of view of the sensor system (θ) and the altitude of the sensor system above ground (Jensen, 2007):

$$SW = 2H tan(\frac{\theta}{2}) \tag{3.2}$$

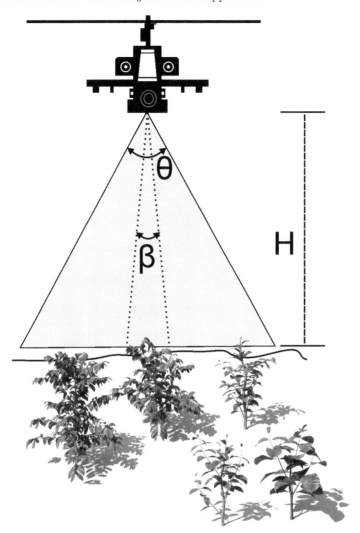

Figure 3.5 Determination of the instantaneous and total field of view of digital sensor systems.

3.8 Sensor Spatial Resolution Trends by Potential Application

In Earth observation sensors there is wide variation of spatial resolution (Figure 3.6). The classification of spatial resolution of remote sensing sensor systems ranges from low to very high-resolution (Table 3.1).

Table 3.1 Sensor classification for spatial resolution.

Class	Resolution (m)	Application
Very high	0.5-4	Urban and detail monitoring
High	4-30	Agricultural and environmental monitoring
Moderate	~ 250	Agricultural and environmental monitoring
Low	~ 1000	Meteorological monitoring

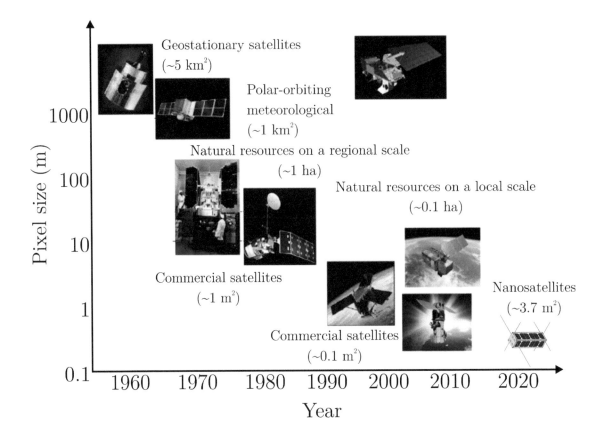

Figure 3.6 Trends in sensor spatial resolution by potential application and time of occurrence.

3.9   Relationship between Pixel Size and Target Discrimination Power

Spatial resolution is useful in image interpretation because it affects the level of detail achieved in imaging. The interpreter can only identify objects several times the pixel size, although smaller features can be detected under sufficient radiometric contrast between the object and its surroundings. The selection of spatial resolution is closely related to the appropriate scale to study a specific problem. In addition, spatial resolution affects the purity of a signal stored in a pixel. The smaller the pixel size, the less likely it is to be a mixture of two or more objects. In a mixed pixel there will likely be an average signal of the land covers present in the IFOV (Figure 3.7) (Chuvieco, 2020).

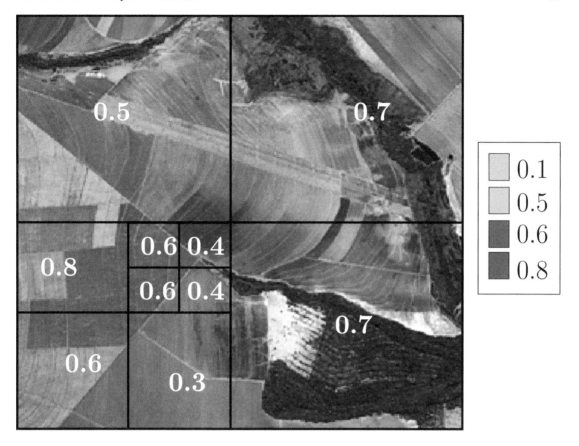

Figure 3.7 Relationship between pixel size and target discrimination power.

3.10   Sensor Temporal Resolution

Temporal resolution refers to the frequency of observation (revisit period) provided by the sensor and varies with the characteristics of the satellite orbit (height, velocity and declination) and sensor FOV (Chuvieco, 2020).

One of the most valuable aspects of polar orbiting remote sensing systems is the repeated coverage of an area of interest. Regular revisits are important for monitoring agricultural plant species, assessing natural, cultural features, and monitoring the atmosphere and oceans (Figure 3.8). On many remote sensing satellites, including Landsat, AVHRR and SPOT monitoring is performed in sun-synchronous orbits. The interval between revisits depends on details of the satellite orbit for sensors with a fixed nadir viewing direction, such as Landsat TM. SPOT systems can be aimed and programmed to point to a cross-sectional range up to 26° from nadir, in order to view the same area more frequently. Very high-resolution commercial satellites, such as IKONOS, QuickBird, and WorldView, can be aimed at a given target in a shorter period of time and obtain two views of the target at angles to form a stereo pair. In manned systems, such as the space shuttle, which carried several experimental synthetic aperture radar (SAR) and other remote sensing systems, and the international space station, the orbits are not polar, and thus the same targets are revisited less regularly. Some examples of revisit times of remote sensing satellites are given in Table 3.2 (Schowengerdt, 2006).

Table 3.2 Revisit time intervals of remote sensing systems.

System	Revisit Interval
AVHRR	1 day (one system), 7 hours (two systems)
GOES	30 minutes
GOES-R	30 seconds to 15 minutes
IKONOS	minutes (same orbit), 1 to 3 days (punctual)
IRS-1A, B	22 days
Landsat (L)	18 days (L1, L2, L3), 16 days (L4, L5, L7, L8)
MODIS	3 hours to 1 day
QuickBird	minutes to 3 days
SPOT	26 days (nadir), 1 to 5 days (punctual)
Sentinel-2	5 days

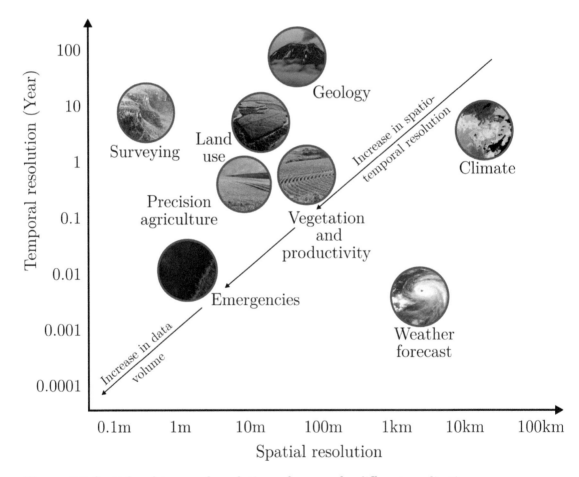

Figure 3.8 Spatial and temporal resolutions of sensors for different applications.

3.11   Spectral Resolution and Sensor Specifications

Spectral resolution refers to the number and width of spectral bands of a sensor. The greater the number of spectral bands, the better the target discrimination. Spectral bands should be narrow enough to identify features of the targets evaluated (Chuvieco, 2020). In multispectral remote sensing systems, data are recorded in multiple bands of the electromagnetic spectrum. In hyperspectral systems, data recording is performed in hundreds of bands. In ultraspectral systems, data recording occurs in thousands of bands. The data are recorded mostly in digital form (Jensen, 2007). Given a three-dimensional continuous space (x, y, λ), defined over the (x, y) coordinate space and spectral wavelength (λ), one can view each pixel in a given image as representing an integration over a relatively small volume element in that continuous space. However, the space (x, y, λ) is not so well partitioned, so that the volume represented by each pixel does not characterize a well-defined cube, considering the overlap in the spatial and spectral dimensions with respect to neighboring pixel cubes (Figure 3.9) (Schowengerdt, 2006).

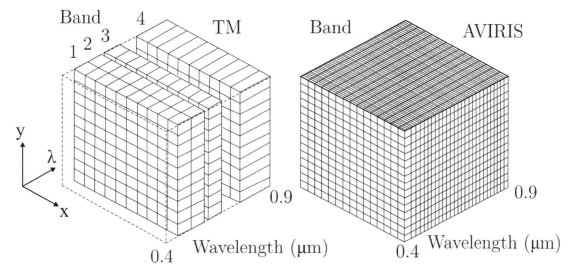

Figure 3.9 Comparison of spatial and spectral sampling from Landsat TM and AVIRIS in the visible and near-infrared spectral bands. Each small rectangular box represents the spatial-spectral integration region of a pixel in an image cube.

The reference spectral regions used in remote sensing of the Earth may vary between different sources, but in general, wavelength ranges from 0.4 μm to 1 m are considered (Schowengerdt, 2006) (Tables 3.3, 3.4, 3.5, 3.6, 3.7, and 3.8).

The selection of the number of bands, width and spectral range measured by the sensor should be related to the objectives that are expected to be achieved (Chuvieco, 2020).

Table 3.3 Characteristics of wavelength, radiation source, and variable of interest for remote sensing.

Name	Wavelength	Radiation Source	Variable of Interest
Visible (V)	0.4-0.7 μm	solar	reflectance
Near-infrared (NIR)	0.7-1.1 μm	solar	reflectance
Shortwave infrared (SWIR)	1.1-1.35 μm 1.4-1.8 μm 2-2.5 μm	solar	reflectance
Mid-wave infrared (MWIR)	3-4 μm, 4.5-5 μm	solar, thermal	reflectance, temperature
Thermal long wave infrared (TIR or LWIR)	8-9.5 μm 10-14 μm	thermal	temperature
Microwave, RADAR (MW)	1 mm - 1 m	thermal (passive), artificial (active)	temperature (passive), roughness (active)

The MODerate Imaging Spectroradiometer (MODIS) is a discrete filter-based system on the Terra and Aqua satellites, with images in 36 spectral bands in the range 0.4 to 14 μm. With this sensor there was satisfactory improvement in the quantity and quality of information collected on the terrestrial environment (Salomonson et al., 1995; Schowengerdt, 2006) (Table 3.4).

Table 3.4 Primary geophysical variables measurable with each spectral band of the EOS MODIS system.

General Application	Specific Application	Band	Spectral Res. (μm)	Spatial Res. (m)
Land boundary	vegetation chlorophyll	1	0.62-0.67	250
Land/cloud boundary	cloud and vegetation	2	0.841-0.876	250
Land/cloud characteristics	differences between soil and vegetation	3	0.459-0.479	500
Land/cloud characteristics	green vegetation	4	0.545-0.565	500
Land/cloud characteristics	leaf and canopy characteristics	5	1.230-1.250	500
Land/cloud characteristics	difference between snow and cloud	6	1.628-1.652	500
Land/cloud characteristics	land and cloud properties	7	2.105-2.155	500
Ocean color	chlorophyll observations	8	0.405-0.420	1000
Ocean color	chlorophyll observations	9	0.438-0.448	1000
Ocean color	chlorophyll observations	10	0.483-0.493	1000
Ocean color	chlorophyll observations	11	0.526-0.536	1000
Ocean color	sediments	12	0.546-0.556	1000
Ocean color	sediments and atmosphere	13	0.662-0.672	1000
Ocean color	fluorescent chlorophyll	14	0.673-0.683	1000

General Application	Specific Application	Band	Spectral Res. (μm)	Spatial Res. (m)
Ocean color	aerosol features	15	0.743-0.753	1000
Ocean color	aerosol features/atmosphere	16	0.862-0.877	1000
Atmosphere/clouds	cloud/atmosphere characteristics	17	0.890-0.920	1000
Atmosphere/clouds	cloud/atmosphere characteristics	18	0.931-0.941	1000
Atmosphere/clouds	cloud/atmosphere characteristics	19	0.915-0.965	1000
Thermal features	sea level temperature	20	3.66-3.84	1000
Thermal features	forest fire/volcano	21	3.929-3.989	1000
Thermal features	surface temperature/clouds	22	3.929-3.989	1000
Thermal features	surface temperature/clouds	23	4.02-4.08	1000
Thermal features	troposphere temperature/cloud fraction	24	4.433-4.498	1000
Thermal features	troposphere temperature/cloud fraction	25	4.482-4.549	1000
Atmosphere/clouds	cirrus clouds	26	1.36-1.39	1000
Thermal features	moisture in the mid troposphere	27	6.535-6.895	1000
Thermal features	moisture in the high troposphere	28	7.175-7.475	1000
Thermal features	surface temperature	29	8.4-8.7	1000
Thermal features	total ozone	30	9.58-9.88	1000
Thermal features	surface/cloud temperature	31	10.78-11.28	1000
Thermal features	surface/cloud temperature	32	11.77-12.27	1000
Thermal features	cloud fraction and height	33	13.185-13.485	1000
Thermal features	cloud fraction and height	34	13.485-13.785	1000
Thermal features	cloud fraction and height	35	13.785-14.085	1000
Thermal features	cloud fraction and height	36	14.085-14.385	1000

The characteristics of the Landsat sensors are described below, and it is possible to obtain collection data from Landsat-4, 5, and 7, 8 and imaging in the current period from Landsat-9 (Tables 3.5, 3.6, and 3.7).

Table 3.5 Characteristics of the spectral bands of the Landsat-4, 5 Thematic Mapper (TM) sensor.

Application	Band Name	Band	Spectral Res. (μm)	Spatial Res. (m)
Analysis of land use, soil and vegetation characteristics; the lower wavelength limit is below the peak transmittance of clear water. The upper limit is the absorption by chlorophyll in the blue for healthy green vegetation. There is penetration into bodies of water and a scattering effect and atmospheric absorption in this spectral region.	blue	1	0.45-0.52	30
There is spectral response of healthy vegetation in the green, and this band is arranged between two chlorophyll absorption bands in the blue and red.	green	2	0.52-0.60	30
Chlorophyll absorption band of healthy green vegetation. It is useful for discriminating vegetation, delineating boundaries of soil classes and rock types. In this spectral band there is reduced effect of atmospheric attenuation when compared to bands 1 and 2. At the upper limit of 0.69 μm the reflectance changes abruptly (red edge).	red	3	0.63-0.69	30
The upper limit of this band is positioned above 0.75 μm (end of red edge). This spectral region is very sensitive to the amount of vegetation biomass and leaf area. It is useful for identifying crops and for highlighting soil/crop and soil/water contrasts in the near-infrared.	NIR	4	0.76-0.90	30
Spectral region sensitive to plant turgidity or water content, crop stress, and plant vigor. Used for discrimination between clouds, snow, and ice.	SWIR1	5	1.55-1.75	30
Measures the amount of infrared radiant energy emitted from the ground. Applications in geothermal activity location, thermal inertia mapping in geology, classification and stress analysis of vegetation, soil moisture, and captures differences in topographic feature in mountainous regions.	TIR	6	10.4-12.5	120
Useful for discriminating geological rock formations and hydrothermal alteration zones of rocks.	SWIR2	7	2.08-2.35	30

Table 3.6 Characteristics of the spectral bands of the Landsat-7 Enhanced Thematic Mapper Plus (ETM+) sensor.

Band Name	Band	Spectral Res. (μm)	Spatial Res. (m)
Blue (B)	1	0.450-0.515	30
Green (G)	2	0.525-0.605	30
Red (R)	3	0.630-0.690	30
Near-infrared (NIR)	4	0.750-0.900	30
Shortwave infrared 1 (SWIR1)	5	1.550-1.750	30
Thermal infrared (TIR)	6	10.400-12.500	60
Shortwave infrared 2 (SWIR2)	7	2.080-2.350	30
Panchromatic (PAN)	8	0.520-0.900	15

Table 3.7 Characteristics of the spectral bands of the Landsat-8 Operational Land Imager (OLI) and Thermal Infrared Sensors (TIRS).

Band Name	Band	Spectral Res. (μm)	Spatial Res. (m)
Coastal aerosol	1	0.435-0.451	30
Blue (B)	2	0.452-0.512	30
Green (G)	3	0.533-0.590	30
Red (R)	4	0.636-0.673	30
Near-infrared (NIR)	5	0.851-0.879	30
Shortwave infrared 1 (SWIR1)	6	1.566-1.651	30
Thermal infrared 1 (TIR1)	10	10.600-11.190	100
Thermal infrared 2 (TIR2)	11	11.500-12.510	100
Shortwave infrared 2 (SWIR2)	7	2.107-2.294	30
Panchromatic (PAN)	8	0.503-0.676	15
Cirrus	9	1.363-1.384	30

Data from the **Sentinel mission**[1] (European Space Agency, or ESA) can be used in a wide variety of applications, given the broad coverage of spectral regions monitored with a Sentinel-2 multispectral sensor (MSI) (Table 3.8), but also RADAR data from Sentinel-1 SAR, studies of ocean variables by Sentinel-3, and atmospheric data monitored by Sentinel-5P TROPOMI (Tables 3.9 and 3.10).

Table 3.8 Characteristics of the spectral bands of the Sentinel-2 multispectral instrument (MSI) sensor (A and B).

Band Name	Band	Spectral Res. (μm)	Spatial Res. (m)
Coastal aerosol	1	~ 0.443	60
Blue (B)	2	~ 0.493	10
Green (G)	3	~ 0.560	10
Red (R)	4	~ 0.665	10
Red edge (RE1)	5	~ 0.704	20
Red edge (RE2)	6	~ 0.740	20

[1]https://sentinels.copernicus.eu/web/sentinel/technical-guides/sentinel-5p/products-algorithms

Band Name	Band	Spectral Res. (μm)	Spatial Res. (m)
Red edge (RE3)	7	~ 0.783	20
Near-infrared (NIR)	8	~ 0.833	10
Narrow NIR	8a	~ 0.865	20
Water vapor	9	~ 0.945	60
Cirrus	10	~ 1.374	60
SWIR	11	~ 1613.7	20
SWIR	12	~ 2202.4	20

Table 3.9 Radiance and irradiance products from TROPOMI Level 1B.

File type	Spectral Region	Spectral Interval (μm)	Description
L1B_RA_BD1	UV	0.270-0.300	Radiance product band 1
L1B_RA_BD2	UV	0.300-0.320	Radiance product band 2
L1B_RA_BD3	UVIS	0.320-0.405	Radiance product band 3
L1B_RA_BD4	UVIS	0.405-0.500	Radiance product band 4
L1B_RA_BD5	NIR	0.675-0.725	Radiance product band 5
L1B_RA_BD6	NIR	0.725-0.775	Radiance product band 6
L1B_RA_BD7	SWIR	2.305-2.345	Radiance product band 7
L1B_RA_BD8	SWIR	2.345-2.385	Radiance product band 8
L1B_IR_UVN	UVN	0.270-0.775	Irradiance product UVN module
L1B_IR_SIR	SWIR	2.305-2.385	Irradiance product SWIR module

Table 3.10 Radiance and irradiance products from TROPOMI Level 1B.

Product Type	Variable
L2_O3	Ozone (O_3) total column
L2_O3_TCL	Ozone (O_3) tropospheric column
L2_O3_PR	Ozone (O_3) profile
L2_NO2	Nitrogen Dioxide (NO_2), total and tropospheric columns
L2_SO2	Sulfur Dioxide (SO_2) total column
L2_CO	Carbon Monoxide (CO) total column
L2_CH4	Methane (CH_4) total column
L2_HCHO	Formaldehyde (HCHO) total column
L2_CLOUD	Cloud fraction, albedo, top pressure
L2_AER_AI	UV Aerosol Index

Product Type	Variable
L2_AER_LH	Aerosol Layer Height (mid-level pressure)
UV product	Surface Irradiance/erythemal dose
L2_NP_BDx, x = 3,	Suomi-NPP VIIRS Clouds
6, 7	
AUX_CTMFC	A priori profile shapes for the NO_2, HCHO and SO_2 vertical column
AUX_CTMANA	retrievals

The CBERS-04A[2] is equipped with cameras for optical observations of the entire globe, in addition to a data collection and environmental monitoring system. The CBERS-04A payloads are all the instruments directly related to the acquisition of scientific data or associated with the satellite's mission:

- Wide-scan multispectral and panchromatic camera (WPM);
- Multispectral camera (MUX);
- Wide-field imaging camera (WFI);
- Image data transmitter (DTS) for the MUX, WFI, and WPM cameras;
- Digital data recorder (DDR);
- Data collection system (DCS);
- Spatial Environment Monitor (SEM).

The WPM camera is the main payload of the CBERS-04A, of Chinese manufacture, with the objective of providing images with panoramic resolution of 2 m and multispectral resolution of 8 m simultaneously in the satellite orbit (Table 3.11).

Table 3.11 Characteristics of the CBERS-04A multispectral and panchromatic wide-scan (WPM) camera.

Characteristic	Specification
Spectral bands	P: 0.45-0.90 μm; B1: 0.45-0.52 μm; B2: 0.52-0.59 μm; B3: 0.63-0.69 μm; B4: 0.77-0.89 μm
Imaged swath width	92 km
Spatial resolution	2 m (panchromatic); 8 m (multispectral)
Side mirror sight	No
Gross data rate	1800.8 Mbps; 450.2 Mbps

In the Advanced Baseline Imager (ABI) sensor of the Geostationary Operational Environmental Satellite (GOES-R) series, 16 spectral bands are obtained, with two in the visible region of the electromagnetic spectrum, four in the near-infrared, and ten in the infrared. GOES-R was launched on November 19, 2016 and became GOES-16 upon reaching geostationary orbit. GOES-16 went into operation on December 18, 2017, at the GOES-East site (Table 3.12) (Schmit et al., 2018).

---

[2]http://www.cbers.inpe.br/sobre/cameras/cbers04a.php

Table 3.12 Approximate central wavelength (μm), number, type, name, and best spatial resolution (km) of spectral bands on the GOES-R ABI sensor.

Central λ	Band	Spectral Region	Band Name	Best Spatial Res. (km)
0.47	1	Visible	Blue	1
0.64	2	Visible	Red	0.5
0.86	3	Near-infrared	Vegan	1
1.37	4	Shortwave infrared	Cirrus	2
1.6	5	Shortwave infrared	Snow/Ice	1
2.2	6	Shortwave infrared	Cloud particle size	2
3.9	7	Mid-wave infrared	Shortwave window	2
6.2	8	Mid-wave infrared	Top-level water vapor	2
6.9	9	Mid-wave infrared	Lower-level water vapor	2
7.3	10	Mid-wave infrared	Upper cloud phase	2
8.4	11	Thermal infrared	Ozone	2
9.6	12	Thermal infrared	Clean long-wave window	2
10.3	13	Thermal infrared	——	2
11.2	14	Thermal infrared	——	2
12.3	15	Thermal infrared	Dirty long-wave window	2
13.3	16	Thermal infrared	CO_2 long-wave	2

In the microwave spectral region, SAR is an imaging technology in which in the face of radiation emitted from a moving sensor, the backscattered component returns from the ground to the sensor and is measured by the sensor. The wavelengths used in active and passive microwave remote sensing are shown in Table 3.13 (Schowengerdt, 2006).

Table 3.13 Microwave wavelengths and frequencies used in remote sensing.

Band	Frequency (GHz)	Wavelength (cm)	Microwave System (frequency in GHz)
Ka	26.5-40	0.8-1.1	SSM/I (37.0)
K	18-26.5	1.1-1.7	SSM/I (19.35; 22.235)
Ku	12.5-18	1.7-2.4	Cassini (13.8)
X	8-12.5	2.4-3.8	X-SAR (9.6)
C	4-8	3.8-7.5	SIR-C (5.3), ERS-1 (5.25), RADARSAT (5.3)
S	2-4	7.5-15	Magellan (2.385)
L	1-2	15-30	Seasat (1.275), SIR-A (1.278), SIR-B (1.282), SIR-C (1.25), JERS-1 (1.275)
P	0.3-1	30-100	NASA/JPL DC-8 (0.44)

ALOS Phased Array type L-band Synthetic Aperture Radar (PALSAR[3]) was used in monitoring from 2006 to 2011, and is one of three instruments of the Advanced Land Observing Satellite-1 (ALOS). PALSAR has two fine-beam modes: single polarization (FBS) and dual polarization (FBD), as well as quad polarization, also known as "polarimetric mode" (PLR). ScanSAR wide beam (WB1, WB2) operates with a considerable loss of resolution. PALSAR cannot observe the areas beyond 87.8° north latitude and 75.9° south latitude when the off-nadir angle is 41.5° (Table 3.14).

---

[3]https://asf.alaska.edu/data-sets/sar-data-sets/alos-palsar/alos-palsar-about/

Table 3.14 Technical description of the ALOS PALSAR.

Characteristic	Fine Resolution		ScanSAR	Polarimetric
Beam mode	FBS, DSN	FBD	WB1, WB2	PLR
Center frequency	L-Band (1.27 GHz)			
Polarization	HH or VV	HH+HV or VV+VH	HH or VV	HH+HV+VV+VH
Spatial resolution	10 m	20 m	100 m	30 m
Swath width	70 km	70 km	250-350 km	30 km
Off-nadir angle	34.3°	34.3°	27.1°	21.5°

The Sentinel-1 mission is the European Radar Observatory for the Copernicus joint initiative of the European Commission (EC) and the European Space Agency (ESA). Copernicus is a European initiative for the implementation of information services dealing with environment and security. Sentinel **data products**[4] are made available systematically and free of charge. All data products are distributed in the Sentinel Standard Archive Format for Europe (SAFE) format. Each mode can potentially produce products at SAR Level-0, Level-1 SLC, Level-1 GRD, and Level-2 OCN. Data products are available in single polarization (VV or HH) for wave mode and dual polarization (VV+VH or HH+HV) or single polarization (HH or VV) for SM, IW and EW modes.

3.12   Sensor Radiometric Resolution

Radiometric resolution characterizes the sensitivity of the sensor, that is, its ability to discriminate small variations in the recorded spectral radiation. Radiometric resolution is more important in digital than visual analysis, since the human eye can distinguish no more than 64 gray levels and 200,000 colors. Radiometric resolution can be useful for discriminating objects with similar spectral characteristics (Chuvieco, 2020).

Radiometric resolution is defined by the number of digital (digital image) or gray (analog photograph) levels recorded in the image or in an analog photographic film. By using radiometric resolution, the amount of data used to encode the input radiance signal or storage bits of the sensor system is defined (Figure 3.10).

In the digitization process, continuous analog data is transformed into discrete digital data. The greater the number of integer values N used in the digitization, the greater the conformity of the digital data to the original analog data. Because of the configuration of computers, the number N is always a power of 2 to the n:

$$N = 2^n \tag{3.3}$$

where n is the number of bits.

---

[4]https://sentinels.copernicus.eu/web/sentinel/missions/sentinel-1/data-products

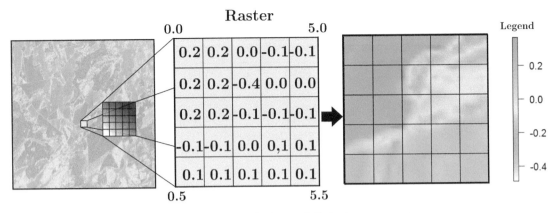

Figure 3.10 Spectral and radiometric resolutions of digital sensor systems.

3.13   Types of Satellite Orbits

Satellite systems can occur in different types of orbits applied in monitoring the environment, called "geostationary" and "polar orbit" (Figure 3.11).

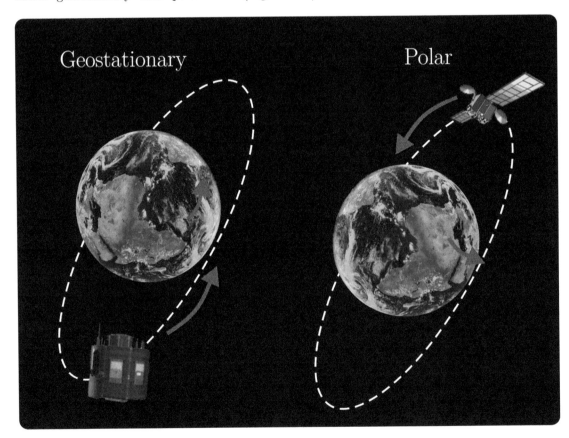

Figure 3.11 Types of satellite orbits.

3.13.1 Geosynchronous or geostationary orbit

Geostationary orbits are arranged at altitudes of approximately 36000 km above the Earth. Satellites in these orbits move in the same direction as the Earth's rotation with speeds adjusted to maintain the satellites' position over a designated point on the Earth. A wide field of view (FOV) is required to record the entire visible hemisphere of the planet in a single image. A network of geostationary satellites of different lengths ensures coverage of the entire Earth. METEOSAT, located on the 0° meridian, is used to acquire images mainly of Europe and Africa.

Another existing option is the two Geostationary Operational Environmental Satellites (GOESs) are located on the 70° and 140° W meridians, monitoring the east and west coasts of America. Similar satellites operate in Asia. On geostationary satellites the temporal resolution is the best possible, ranging from about 15 to 30 min, but at coarse spatial resolutions caused by the high orbit itself (Butler, 1988; Chuvieco, 2020).

The main advantages of a geosynchronous satellite are (Barrett & Curtis, 1999; Butler, 1988):

- More frequent observation of the Earth's region by means of an orbital system;
- Possibility of repeatedly scanning the same point on Earth, generating a series of recorded images;
- Largest area coverage possible from an orbital system;
- Effective use of telecommunications.

The main disadvantages of a geosynchronous satellite are (Butler, 1988):

- Economic and technological difficulties of placing the system in such a high orbit and obtaining adequate performance from the sensors carried on board (e.g., adequate spatial resolution);
- Poor polar coverage.

3.13.2 Sun-synchronous, heliosynchronous or polar orbit

The sun-synchronous orbit is much smaller (about 900 km) than the geosynchronous orbit. The inclination of the orbit, relative to the Equator, is close to 90° (polar or nearly polar) and the satellite (e.g., the Landsat mission) crosses the Equator at the same solar time every day. This means that a specific point on Earth is regularly (depending on the satellite's period) seen at the same time, and is useful for comparative analysis of multi-temporal data. By selecting a specific orbit, it is possible not only to obtain repeated coverage of the entire surface of the Earth, but also to select the interval between observations at a specific location (Butler, 1988).

The number of satellite rotations around the Earth per day (NRS) in polar orbit depends on the time the satellite passes over a particular region of the Earth (TE) relative to the Earth's rotation period (T) (Butler, 1988):

$$NRS = \frac{T}{TE} \tag{3.4}$$

In the case of Landsat, the satellite returns to the same point imaged every 233 revolutions or 16 days, as there is the overlay of adjacent orbits.

Considering that the Earth's circumference at the Equator (CT) is approximately 40000 km it is possible to calculate the distance traveled on the ground (DT) between orbits on the same day (NRS):

$$DT = \frac{CT}{NRS} \tag{3.5}$$

The main advantages of a polar orbit satellite are (Butler, 1988):

- Greater economic and technological ease of placing the system in a low orbit with adequate performance of the on-board sensors to achieve high spatial resolution on the order of tens of meters;
- Possibility of accessing the orbital system with manned space missions.

The main disadvantages of a polar orbit satellite are (Butler, 1988):

- Low repeatability in coverage, but that can be overcome with the proper combination of orbital parameters and sensor imaging characteristics;
- Low-quality terrain imaging due to cloud cover, small imaging area, and low repeatability.

3.14   Data from Remote Sensing Systems

Due to the volume of data and the technical complexity of modern remote sensing systems, it is necessary to perform data preprocessing before the scientific community uses the information obtained. In preprocessing, a consistent and reliable image database is created according to the following procedures (Schowengerdt, 2006):

- Calibration of image radiometry;
- Correction of geometric distortions;
- Removal of some types of sensor noise;
- Formatting for standardized use.

The specific types of preprocessing required depend on the characteristics of the sensor, as the goal is to remove unwanted features in the images and to provide indices derived from processing the spectral bands with different combinations and equations. Several levels of preprocessing are provided as options, for example for Landsat, Sentinel-2 and MODIS systems as shown in Table 3.15. There are products obtained with the MODIS sensor images, for example, MOD09A1, MOD11A1, and MOD13Q1 according to Table 3.16.

Table 3.15 Examples of data processing levels from remote sensing systems.

System	Processing Level	Description
Landsat	Landsat Collection 1 Level 2 Landsat Collection 1 Level 1	Level 2 surface reflectance data products, multispectral OLI and TIRS radiance data.
Sentinel-2	Level 1C, Level 2A	Products with radiometric and geometric correction and reflectance calculation TOA, products with radiometric and geometric correction and reflectance calculation.
MODIS	Level 1, MODIS atmosphere, MODIS ground, MODIS cryosphere, MODIS ocean	Products with raw radiance data, atmosphere products, surface products, snow and ice products, ocean products.

Table 3.16 Example of products obtained with MODIS sensor images.

Product	Variable	Description
MOD09A1	Surface reflectance	Estimated surface spectral reflectance of Earth MODIS bands 1 to 7 corrected for atmospheric conditions such as gases, aerosols and Rayleigh scattering at 500-m spatial resolution.
MOD11A1	Temperature and emissivity of the surface	Temperature and emissivity of the Earth's daily surface at 1-km spatial resolution.
MOD13Q1	Vegetation indices	NDVI and EVI vegetation indices at 250-m spatial resolution.

3.14.1 Geostationary operation environmental satellite (GOES)

GOES data can be visualized in real time and animated on interactive web platforms. In this case, GOES-R bands 7, 8 and 13 are shown as example applications (Jedlovec & Meyer, 2020) (Figures 3.12 and 3.13).

Besides GOES, other geostationary remote sensing systems are used to capture other Earth regions from the Equator. One can observe as an example a full disk of the Earth with the SEVIRI sensor from the METEOSAT 10 satellite (Figure 3.14).

3.14.2 Indian remote sensing (IRS)

Remote sensing techniques are used to quantify forest biomass to extract information necessary for planning, management, and monitoring of natural resources. The Xingu River watershed is located within the Xingu Indigenous Park, in the state of Mato Grosso, Brazil; this area has a low probability of logging or clear-cutting in the short term, in view of the legislation of an environmentally protected area. However, all the headwaters of the rivers that form the Xingu, located outside the indigenous reserve, are subject to the impact of human activities, which can affect the forest communities that inhabit the interior of the indigenous reserve and the surrounding areas. In order to contribute to the knowledge of the forest information present around the Xingu

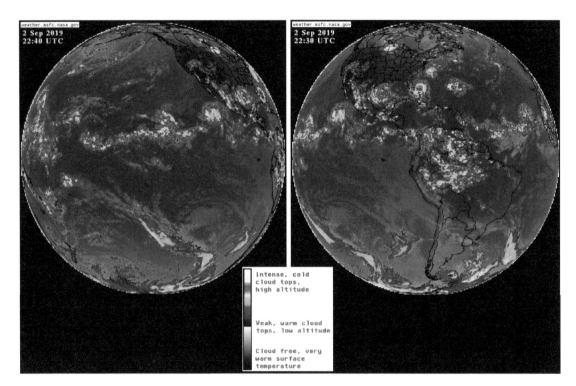

Figure 3.12 Band 13 (10.35 micrometers) of GOES-East (right) and GOES-West (left), with 2-km spatial resolution, used to assess surface temperature and clouds on September 2, 2019.

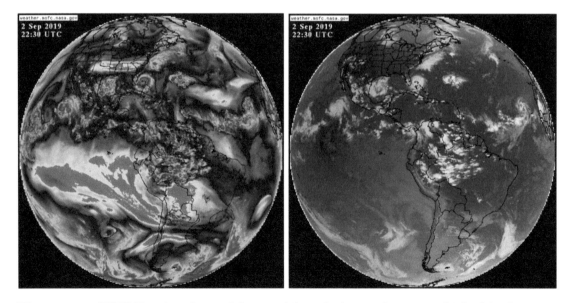

Figure 3.13 GOES-East imaging at 2-km spatial resolution used to assess high-altitude atmospheric water vapor, winds, and rain (Band 8, 6.19 micrometers) (right) and monitoring surface, cloud, night fog, fire, and winds (Band 7, 3.4 micrometers) (left) on September 2, 2019.

Figure 3.14 METEOSAT 10 imagery using the SEVIRI sensor on April 22, 2015.

indigenous reserve in the state of Mato Grosso, images from the AWiFS sensor of the IRS-P6 satellite were used to monitor the Xingu indigenous reserve on June 11, 2010 (Figure 3.15) (Silva et al., 2011).

3.14.3 Moderate resolution imaging spectroradiometer (MODIS)

An example of a global gap-filled albedo image derived from three MODIS reflectance channels. Snow and desert areas are shown at more intense values, while vegetated areas showed higher reflectance in green according to the Figure 3.16 (Chuvieco, 2020).

MODIS surface reflectance imagery is also used to monitor land use in the upper and middle Paraguay basin in Mato Grosso. Vegetation in green in the image as a function of high NIR (band 2) reflectance in these areas can be seen (Figure 3.17).

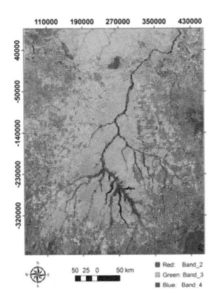

Figure 3.15 Imagery of the Xingu indigenous reserve, state of Mato Grosso, Brazil, using the AWIFS sensor on June 11, 2010 under false-color composition 2R3G4B.

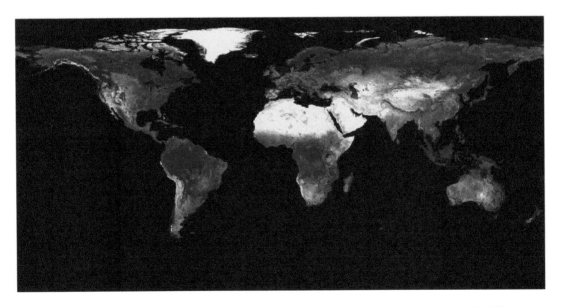

Figure 3.16 Percentage of solar radiation reflected from the terrain detected by the blue, green and red channels of the MODIS sensor on July 12, 2010 (albedo between 0 and 0.25).

Figure 3.17 Surface reflectance of MODIS sensor bands 1, 2 and 3 in false-color composition R1G2B3 from August 13, 2018 of the Upper and Middle Paraguay basin, state of Mato Grosso, Brazil.

Different daily data collections that are produced from imaging **MODIS**[5] are available for cloud computing using Earth Engine and R, such as: MCD43A4.006 MODIS Nadir BRDF-Adjusted Reflectance Daily 500 m, MCD43A3.006 MODIS Albedo Daily 500 m, MCD43A2.006 MODIS BRDF-Albedo Quality Daily 500, MOD09GQ.006 Terra Surface Reflectance Daily Global 250 m, MOD10A1.006 Terra Snow Cover Daily Global 500, MOD11A1.006 Terra Land Surface Temperature and Emissivity Daily Global 1 km, MOD09GA.006 Terra Surface Reflectance Daily Global 1 km and 500, MODOCGA.006 Terra Ocean Reflectance Daily Global 1 km, MOD14A1.006: Terra Thermal Anomalies and Fire Daily Global 1 km, MCD43A1.006 MODIS BRDF-Albedo Model Parameters Daily 500. Other data-derived products are: MCD15A3H.006 MODIS Leaf Area Index/FPAR 4-Day Global 500, MOD09Q1.006 Terra Surface Reflectance 8-Day Global 250 m, MOD09A1.006 Terra Surface Reflectance 8-Day Global 500, MOD11A2.006 Terra Land Surface Temperature and Emissivity 8-Day Global 1 km, MOD14A2.006 Terra Thermal Anomalies and Fire 8-Day Global 1 km, MOD17A2H.006 Terra Gross Primary Productivity 8-Day Global 500,

---

[5]https://developers.google.com/earth-engine/datasets/catalog/modis

MOD16A2.006 Terra Net Evapotranspiration 8-Day Global 500, MOD13Q1.006 Terra Vegetation Indices 16-Day Global 250 m, MOD13A1.006 Terra Vegetation Indices 16-Day Global 500, MOD13A2.006 Terra Vegetation Indices 16-Day Global 1 km, MCD64A1.006 MODIS Burned Area Monthly Global 500, MOD08_M3.006 Terra Atmosphere Monthly Global Product, MCD12Q1.006 MODIS Land Cover Type Yearly Global 500, MOD17A3H.006 Terra Net Primary Production Yearly Global 500, MOD44W.006 Terra Land Water Mask Derived from MODIS and SRTM Yearly Global 250 m.

```
library(rgee)
ee_Initialize()
```

A search period for images in the Earth Engine data collection is set from April 1 to June 2, 2022.

```
startDate = '2022-04-01'
endDate = '2022-06-02'
```

As an example, the MCD43A4 V6 Nadir Bidirectional Reflectance Distribution Function Adjusted Reflectance (NBAR) product can be used to obtain reflectance data from MODIS bands 1 to 7 at 500-m spatial resolution. The imagery data are adjusted using a bidirectional reflectance distribution function to determine values as if they were monitored at the nadir position. The data are produced daily and grouped into 16-day periods, choosing the best representative pixel of the 16-day period.

The ee$ImageCollection and $filterDate codes are used to obtain data from the MCD43A4 collection between April 1 and June 2, 2022. The filtered file consisted of 62 images in the size of 7.81 TB approximate size and a set of variables about nadir reflectance band 1, nadir reflectance band 2, nadir reflectance band 3, nadir reflectance band 4, nadir reflectance band 5, nadir reflectance band 7, BRDF albedo band mandatory quality band 1, BRDF albedo mandatory quality band 2, BRDF albedo mandatory quality band 3, BRDF albedo mandatory quality band 4, BRDF albedo mandatory quality band 5, BRDF albedo mandatory quality band 6, and BRDF albedo mandatory quality band 7.

```
collection <- ee$ImageCollection('MODIS/006/MCD43A4')$
  filterDate(startDate, endDate)
```

The results are displayed with the ee_print function.

```
ee_print(collection)
#------------------- Earth Engine ImageCollection --
#ImageCollection Metadata:
# - Class                    : ee$ImageCollection
# - Number of Images         : 62
# - Number of Properties     : 27
# - Number of Pixels*        : 37476768
# - Approximate size*        : 7.81 TB
#Image Metadata (img_index = 0):
# - ID                       : MODIS/006/MCD43A4/2022_04_01
# - system:time_start        : 2022-04-01
# - system:time_end          : 2022-04-02
# - Number of Bands          : 14
# - Bands names              : Nadir_Reflectance_Band1 Nadir_Reflectance_Band2
```

```
#Nadir_Reflectance_Band3 Nadir_Reflectance_Band4 Nadir_Reflectance_Band5
#Nadir_Reflectance_Band6 Nadir_Reflectance_Band7
#BRDF_Albedo_Band_Mandatory_Quality_Band1 BRDF_Albedo_Band_Mandatory_Quality_Band2
#BRDF_Albedo_Band_Mandatory_Quality_Band3 BRDF_Albedo_Band_Mandatory_Quality_Band4
#BRDF_Albedo_Band_Mandatory_Quality_Band5 BRDF_Albedo_Band_Mandatory_Quality_Band6
#BRDF_Albedo_Band_Mandatory_Quality_Band7
# - Number of Properties      : 6
# - Number of Pixels*         : 604464
# - Approximate size*         : 128.93 GB
#Band Metadata (img_band = 'Nadir_Reflectance_Band1'):
# - EPSG (SRID)  : MODIS Sinusoidal (SR-ORG:6974)
# - proj4string  : +proj=sinu +lon_0=0 +x_0=0 +y_0=0 +datum=WGS84 +units=m +no_defs
# - Geotransform : 463.312716527917 0 -20015109.354 0 -463.312716527917 10007554.677003
# - Nominal scale (meters)    : 463.3127
# - Dimensions                : 1 43176
# - Number of Pixels          : 43176
# - Data type                 : INT
# - Approximate size          : 9.21 GB
#---------
# NOTE: (*) Properties calculated considering a constant  geotransform
#and data type.
```

The `list` function is used to select the bands of interest in the mapping, nadir reflectance band 1, nadir reflectance band 4, and nadir reflectance band 3. The arguments `min`, `max` and `gamma` are set to 0, 4000, and 1.4, respectively.

```
trueColor <- list(bands = c("Nadir_Reflectance_Band1","Nadir_Reflectance_Band4",
                   "Nadir_Reflectance_Band3"), min = 0.0, "max" = 4000,
                   gamma = 1.4)
```

The `Map$addLayer` function is used to map the color composition mosaic with the `$mosaic()` function and the view parameters defined earlier.

```
Map$setCenter(-7.03125, 31.0529339857, 2)
Map$addLayer(collection$mosaic(), trueColor, 'Mosaic')
```

With this it is possible to visualize low cloud fraction in the filtered imagery to obtain better quality pixels from producer MCD43A4 in near-natural color target tones of the global territory with absence of clouds (Figure 3.18).

3.14.4   Landsat-8

Landsat-8 OLI imaging was used for mapping the municipality of Lavras, state of Minas Gerais, in 2013 in natural color composition. With this, it is possible to highlight the road targets, urban area and the rugged relief in the Serra da Bocaina, to the south of the image (Figure 3.19).

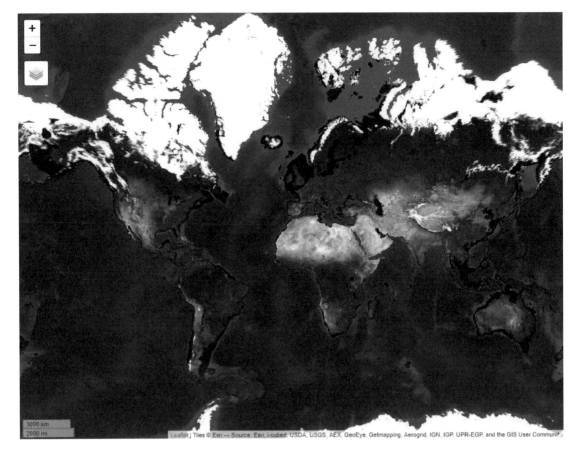

Figure 3.18 Global mosaic of MODIS data collection in color composition bands 1, 4 and 3 between April 1, 2022 and June 2, 2022. The blue tone of the ocean is obtained by the `EsriWorldImagery` template.

3.14.5   Sentinel-2

With the advancement of technology, Sentinel-2 data was applied in monitoring the urban area of Lavras in 2016. In this case, the natural color composition of the reflectance at the top of the atmosphere obtained in the Google Earth Engine program is used for a quick characterization of the region (Figure 3.20).

3.14.6   TRMM microwave imager

The Tropical Rainfall Measuring Mission (TRMM), sponsored by the US and Japanese agencies (NASA/NASDA), studies rainfall in tropical regions and the associated energy release that affects global atmospheric circulation. The TRMM satellite launched on November 27, 1997 contains five instruments (Jensen, 2007):

- Precipitation Radar (PR);
- TRMM Microwave Imager (TMI);
- Visible Infrared Scanner (VIRS);
- Lightning Imaging Sensor (LIS);
- Clouds and Earth's Radiant Energy System (CERES).

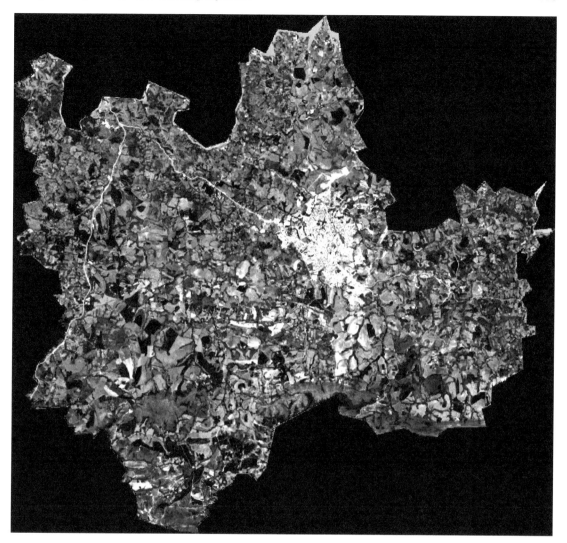

Figure 3.19 Composition of R4G3B2 surface reflectance bands from the OLI sensor under Gram-Schmidt fusion with band 8 from August 25, 2013, municipality of Lavras, state of Minas Gerais, Brazil.

The TMI is a passive microwave sensor with quantitative information about the column-integrated precipitation volume over a bandwidth of 780 km. The radiation intensity is measured at the frequencies 10.7 (45-km spatial resolution); 19.4, 21.3, 37, and 85.5 GHz (5-km spatial resolution). At the 10.7-GHz frequency there is linear response for high rainfall of tropical regions. The data collection initiated by TRMM is continued with the joint NASA/JAXA Global Precipitation Measurement (GPM) mission launched in February 2014 (Jensen, 2007).

3.14.7 Microwave imager AMSR-E

The Advanced Microwave Scanning Radiometer (AMSR-E) is one of six sensors on board the Aqua satellite. The AMSR-E is a dual-polarized, multi-frequency (6.925-, 10.65-, 18.7-, 23.8-, 36.5-, and 89-GHz HV polarization) passive microwave radiometer, with a spatial resolution of 5.4 km at 89 GHz and 56 km at 6.9 GHz and a coverage bandwidth of 1445 km. Geophysical variables can be

Figure 3.20 Reflectance at the top of atmosphere under R4G3B2 band composition of the MSI sensor from the Sentinel-2 satellite, centered on the urban area of Lavras, state of Minas Gerais, Brazil, in 2016.

obtained, such as water vapor, liquid water in clouds, precipitation, sea surface temperature, sea surface wind speed, sea ice concentration, snow water equivalent, and soil moisture (6.925- and 10.65-GHz frequencies) (Jensen, 2007).

3.14.8   Nanosatellites

Cubesat has become an alternative data source for studies requiring high spatio-temporal resolutions. Maciel, Novo, et al. (2020) evaluated the quality of reflectance obtained by PlanetScope's commercial satellite constellation CubeSat in lower Amazon floodplain. There is sufficient radiometric quality for monitoring fine-scale mixing processes between river and lake waters of floodplains.

3.14.9   WorldView-2

With the successful launch of the WorldView-2 satellite, images with very high spatial resolution have been useful for studying spatial and spectral patterns of plant diseases in agroecosystems. In this case, WorldView-2 images are used to detect nematode damage in crotalaria (*Crotalaria ochroleuca* G. Don.). After atmospheric correction, the signals of the pest organisms are evaluated using different band compositions (Alves, 2012) (Figure 3.21).

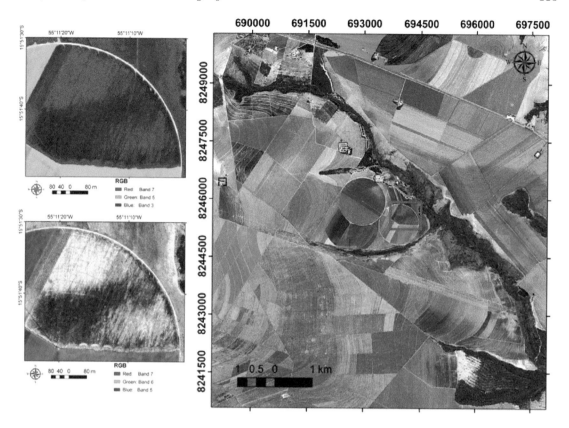

Figure 3.21 Natural color composition (5R3G2B) after WorldView-2 image fusion by the hyperspherical color space resolution merge method of experimental area centered on the image (right) and false-color compositions (R7G5B3 and R7G6B5) of signs of nematode incidence on *Crotalaria ochroleuca* roots in a center pivot-irrigated area on June 12, 2010, municipality of Jaciara, state of Mato Grosso, Brazil.

WorldView-2 images have been acquired to monitor disease progress in coffee crops under different irrigation systems in the municipality of Carmo do Rio Claro, state of Minas Gerais (Figure 3.22).

3.14.10   Drone DJI phantom 4 advanced

The use of drones in agriculture has been applied to monitor coffee cultivars on the Federal University of Lavras campus. The coffee crop is being monitored by natural color composition and vegetation indices over time (Figure 3.23). An approach on this type of monitoring with unmanned aircraft with close distances to the targets and the possible sensor system to be used should be a subject for research on future trends of systems used in drones and similar, as it is a technology focused on individual monitoring and not collective, as in the case of data from orbital sensors freely available to society. In addition, one should carefully observe how to obtain and standardize the data obtained if the survey is carried out by different teams. Depending on the quality required in the monitoring, it may be necessary to use Global Navigation Satellite System (GNSS) (Alves & Silva, 2016b) of very high precision to support the generation of reliable orthomosaics of images. However, because it is a technology focused on the business market, the remote sensing industry has been very active in the use and improvement of this technology applied to the dissemination of results by still images and videos with very high spatial resolution.

| 0 225 450   900 |
| m |

■ Red: Band_5
▨ Green: Band_3
■ Blue: Band_2

Figure 3.22 Natural color composition (5R3G2B) of irrigated and rainfed coffee crops on December 21, 2012, municipality of Carmo do Rio Claro, state of Minas Gerais, Brazil.

3.14.11   RADAR

Topographic mapping by SAR interferometry is based on acquiring data from two different viewing angles. The Space Shuttle Radar Topography Mission (SRTM) of February 11, 2000 was the first to use this type of interferometric coverage. C-band and X-band antennas are installed in the cargo bay and at the end of a 60-m rod. The ellipsoidal altitude of Mato Grosso state is obtained with SRTM v.4 images at 30-m spatial resolution (Alves, Silva, et al., 2016) (Figure 3.24).

3.14.12   LIDAR

LIDAR has become an efficient tool to extract data in forest inventory and also in other forestry studies on board an aircraft (Alves, Oliveira, et al., 2016). However, the Global Ecosystem Dynamics Investigation (GEDI[6]) has developed global ecosystem dynamics investigation from high-resolution surface laser data for the study of ecosystems and terrain morphometry from the International Space Station (ISS). The goal of GEDI is to provide answers to how deforestation contributes to atmospheric CO_2 concentrations, how much carbon will be absorbed by forests,

---

[6]https://gedi.umd.edu/

Figure 3.23 Natural RGB color composition of coffee plantation on the Federal University of Lavras campus, obtained with the DJI Phantom Drone, in 2019.

and how habitat degradation may affect global biodiversity. GEDI data can be used to monitor forests, water resources, carbon cycle science, and weather forecasting (Figure 3.25).

3.14.13   CHIRPS

The Climate Hazards Group InfraRed Precipitation with Station (CHIRPS) data archive is a near-global (50S - 50N) data archive, with 0.05-degree grid resolution, of precipitation time series from 1981 to the current period. Estimates of terrestrial precipitation are available at daily to annual time intervals. In addition to the nearly global extent, subsets of the Western Hemisphere, Africa, and Central American/Caribbean regions are available in various formats (NetCDF, TIFF, BIL, PNG). Two CHIRPS products are produced operationally: a quick preliminary version, and a later final version. The preliminary CHIRPS uses only data from the Global Telecommunication System (GTS) and Conagua (Mexico). The final CHIRPS product is obtained from several other

Figure 3.24 Digital elevation model obtained from the Shuttle Radar Topography Mission (SRTM) of the state of Mato Grosso, in 2001, with 30-m spatial resolution.

Figure 3.25 Platform for obtaining GEDI data from laser measurements obtained from an international space station.

station sources and is complete by the third week of the following month. The final products for all times, domains and formats are calculated in this period (Funk et al., 2014; Sousa et al., 2022).

As an example of obtaining CHIRPS data, the chirps, earth, stars, sf and ggplot2 packages are enabled for analysis.

```
library("chirps")
library("terra")
library("stars")
library("sf")
library("ggplot2")
```

A file with the boundary of the region of interest is imported into R with the vect function.

```
v <- vect("C:/geo/c13/mgwgs.shp")
```

The period of interest between November 15 and 30, 2021 is defined with an atomic vector c() for data.

```
dates <- c("2021-11-15","2021-11-30")
```

The get_chirps function is used to get the data according to the previously defined settings at 0.05° spatial resolution.

```
r3 <- get_chirps(v, dates, server = "CHC", as.raster = TRUE)
```

Images in geotiff format are exported for later use with the writeRaster function from the terra package (Hijmans, Bivand, et al., 2022).

```
terra::writeRaster(r3, "C:/sr/chirps/r3.tif", filetype = "GTiff", overwrite = TRUE)
```

The data exported to a directory of interest is imported back into R with the read_stars function.

```
tif <- read_stars("C:/sr/chirps/r3.tif", package = "stars")
```

The vector file of the area of interest is converted to an object of class sf with the st_as_sf function.

```
lim <- sf::st_as_sf(v)
```

Functions from the ggplot2 package are used to map the results.

```
ggplot() +
    geom_stars(data = tif) +
    scale_fill_viridis_c(limits = c(0,130)) +
    geom_sf(data = lim, fill = NA) +
    coord_sf(datum=st_crs(4326)) +
    facet_wrap( ~ band) +
```

```
labs(fill = "Precip. (mm)") +
theme_void()
```

The CHIRPS data obtained from November 15 to November 30, 2021 in the state of Minas Gerais, Brazil, are used to perform the spatio-temporal mapping of rainfall in order to verify the pattern of rain distribution in this period (Figure 3.26).

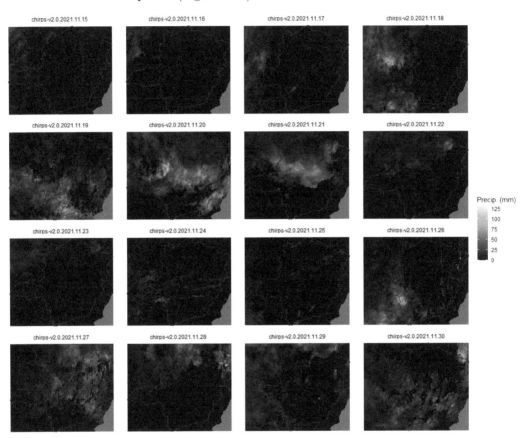

Figure 3.26 Assessment of the spatial-temporal distribution of rainfall in Minas Gerais from November 15 to November 30, 2021.

3.14.14   ALOS PALSAR

The PALSAR L-band synthetic aperture radar (SAR) produced detailed, all-weather, day and night observation and interferometry data between 2006 and 2011. PALSAR data is multi-mode observation with variable polarization, resolution, swath width, and off-nadir angle.

PALSAR was one of three instruments of the Advanced Land Observing Satellite (ALOS), also known as DAICHI, developed to contribute to the fields of cartography, accurate observation of regional land cover, disaster monitoring, and resource surveying. ALOS was a mission of the Japan Aerospace Exploration Agency (JAXA).

A radiometrically geocoded and terrain-corrected GeoTIFF image is obtained from the state of Minas Gerais, Brazil, at the Funil dam near the municipality of Ijaci, on February 20, 2011 (Figure 3.27).

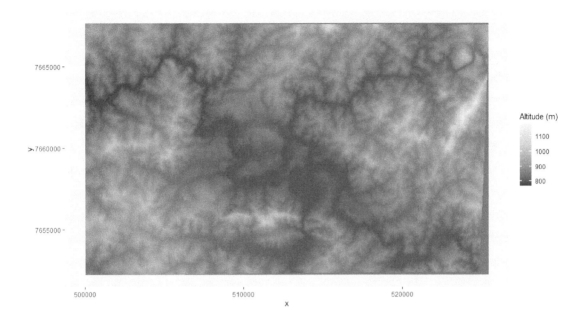

Figure 3.27 Determination of altitude variation in the region of the Funil dam on February 20, 2011.

3.14.15 Sentinel-1

The Sentinel-1 mission comprises a constellation of two polar-orbiting satellites operating day and night with C-band synthetic aperture radar imagery, allowing it to acquire images regardless of weather conditions. Sentinel-1 operates in a pre-programmed mode of operation to avoid conflicts and to produce a consistent long-term data archive built for applications based on long time series. Sentinel-1 is the first of five missions that ESA is developing in the Copernicus program. Each mode can potentially produce products at SAR Level-0, Level-1 SLC, Level-1 GRD, and Level-2 OCN. Data products are available in single polarization (VV or HH) for wave mode and dual polarization (VV+VH or HH+HV) or single polarization (HH or VV) for SM, IW and EW modes.

Sentinel-1, level-1 GRD data in the HV polarization are presented for the Funil dam region on September 20, 2021 (Figure 3.28).

3.14.16 CBERS-04A

The WPM camera is the main payload of the Chinese-made CBERS-04A. Its goal is to provide images with panoramic resolution of 2 m and multispectral resolution of 8 m simultaneously in the satellite's orbit. A fusion of panchromatic and multispectral images by the Brovey method is performed in monitoring completed on July 8, 2020 at the Funil dam in order to make it possible to visualize details of the bridge that connects the municipalities of Ijaci and Macaia (Figure 3.29).

Figure 3.28 Sentinel-1 ground range detected in the Funil dam region on September 20, 2021.

3.14.17 Planet

Planet is capable of obtaining 3-meter resolution images of any location on Earth on a daily basis from hundreds of orbiting satellites. Planet images are acquired by the constellation of 130 Dove satellites with the same type of sensor. The imagery product are images in the visible blue, green, and red bands, and also in the near-infrared (NIR), with 12-bit radiometric resolution. The data are orthorectified and have 3 m of spatial resolution, with a high standard of quality and planimetric accuracy.

Planet data can be accessed and retrieved from an **activation key**[7] obtained from an API. An **account**[8] is created for download management and company contact. Next, the package (Bevington, 2022) can be used in a workflow to obtain images.

A Planet image referring to a UTM-23S total equalized mosaic, SIRGAS 2000 datum, from February 03, 2021 and February 05, 2021, at T11:13:49+00:00 and T13:11:20+00:00, respectively, are mapped in natural color composition in a locality near Vila Nova do Piquiá, state of Pará, Brazil, under suspicion of aerial application of herbicide for dicotyledonous weed control.

---

[7]https://developers.planet.com/quickstart/apis/
[8]https://www.planet.com/account/#/dashboard

Pansharpen (brovey)

Figure 3.29 Brovey fusion used to see details in the Funil dam region, state of Minas Gerais, on July 8, 2020.

3.15 Computational Practice

The remote sensing information used in specific applications of technical papers and scientific articles can be obtained by browsing the web or through commands in R. The following are two ways of obtaining images.

Obtaining remote sensing data directly on Internet platforms can be easier and more practical, requiring registration on the different websites available, such as:

- EarthExplorer[9]
- Copernicus[10]
- AppEEARS[11]
- CBERS-04A[12]
- ALOS-PALSAR[13]

---

[9]https://earthexplorer.usgs.gov/
[10]https://scihub.copernicus.eu/dhus/#/home
[11]https://lpdaacsvc.cr.usgs.gov/appeears/
[12]http://www2.dgi.inpe.br/catalogo/explore
[13]https://search.asf.alaska.edu/#/

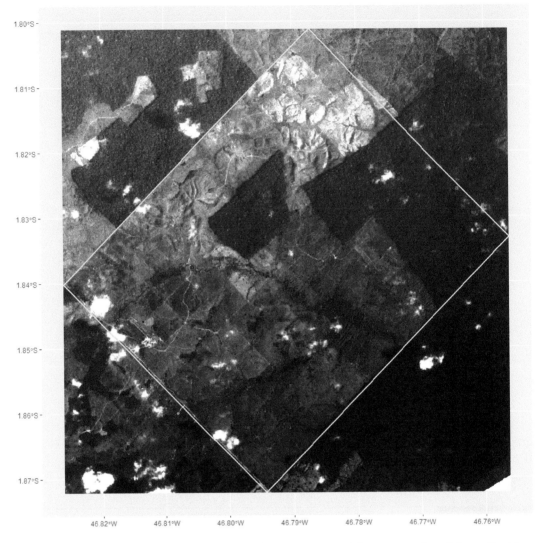

Figure 3.30 Planet imagery to locate details in regions with suspected aerial application of herbicide to control dicotyledonous weeds, state of Pará, Brazil.

- Precipitation CHIRPS[14]
- WorldClim[15]
- Brazil in terrain[16]
- Brazil data cube[17]

---

[14]https://climateserv.servirglobal.net/

[15]https://www.worldclim.org/data/index.html

[16]https://www.cnpm.embrapa.br/projetos/relevobr/

[17]https://brazildatacube.dpi.inpe.br/portal/explore

3.15.1 Obtaining images by browsing the web

3.15.1.1 Accessing the Earth Explorer data catalog

Although it is possible to go to the Earth explorer website and browse for images on the site, it is necessary to register to the data catalog to obtain the data files for analysis in R. The Earth Explorer website is accessed at **EarthExplorer**[18].

3.15.1.2 Registering with the USGS website

To complete the registration it is necessary to confirm the registration in the email forwarded from the Earth Explorer website to the requesting user. To confirm a successful registration, the registered email address should be written on the main catalog page instead of the login option. Registration on the Earth Explorer website is done at **registration**[19]

3.15.1.3 Log in to the USGS website

The log in page of the Earth Explorer website can be accessed at **login**[20].

3.15.1.4 Choose an image from the catalog for practical work

A practical solution for starting remote sensing applications is to use the Landsat satellite for an evaluation of an object or process in the region chosen for doing practical work. In this case, to obtain the radiance and thermal image information, one must use the "Landsat Collection 1 Level-1" option and download the files instantly.

To obtain the information in surface reflectance (atmospheric correction), it is necessary to request the image processing in the cloud by choosing "Landsat Collection 1 Level-2 (On-Demand)". After processing, the requested file is sent in the analyst's email to locate and download the image, as in this example of the Landsat-8 OLI/TIRS image of Ijaci, state of Minas Gerais, with the file name LC08_L1TP_218075_20150119_20170413_01_T1. In this case, there is a higher level of processing in the calculation of the surface reflectance variable (Level-2) at the same orbit point and date as the Landsat Collection 1 Level-1 images (Figure 3.31).

3.15.2 Getting data from R packages

The getSpatialData (Schwalb-Willmann, 2022), an R package used to query, obtain, prepare, and transform various types of geospatial datasets from open sources. There is support for objects in the sf and sp classes when using the getSpatialData package (Kwok, 2018).

With **getSpatialData**[21] you can perform homogeneous and reproducible workflows to query, view, analyze, select, request, and acquire various types of spatial datasets from open sources. Multiple data distributors can be accessed with a common syntax for 159 data products from the Sentinel, Landsat, Terra, Aqua, and Space Shuttle SRTM mission missions. The data services available were ESA Copernicus Open Access Hub, USGS EarthExplorer, USGS EROS ESPA, Amazon Web

---

[18]https://earthexplorer.usgs.gov/
[19]https://ers.cr.usgs.gov/register/
[20]https://ers.cr.usgs.gov/login/
[21]https://www.rdocumentation.org/packages/getSpatialData/versions/0.0.4

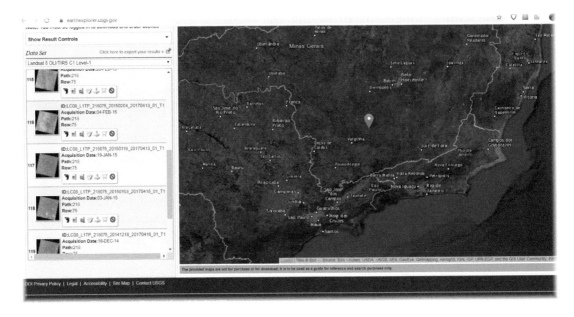

Figure 3.31 Location of Landsat-8 OLI/TIRS image collection in state of Minas Gerais, obtained on January 19, 2015.

Services (AWS), NASA DAAC LAADS, and NASA CMR search. Using `getSpatialData`, it is possible to quickly view the available data catalogs for a location for a specific time period. In addition, one can perform data filtering to automatically select records based on cloud cover and monitoring season. Some products evaluated for implementation in the `getSpatialData` package and sources already accessed are specified below (Table 3.17) (Schwalb-Willmann, 2022).

Table 3.17 Data sources implemented and under evaluation for implementation by the `getSpatialData` package.

Product	Source	Access	Status
Sentinel (-1/-2/-3,-5P, GNSS)	ESA Copernicus	Copernicus open access hub API[22]	Implemented
MODIS	NASA/USGS	ORNL DAAC SOAP MODIS web service, LAADS DAAC SOAP/REST web service[23]	Implemented
Landsat	USGS	USGS EarthExplorer json API[24], USGS-EROS ESPA[25], AWS[26]	Implemented
Global forest change	Hansen et al. (2013)	Analyzing forest change with gfcanalysis[27]	Evaluated
CMIP5/PMIP3 global climate	ecoClimate	ecoClimate r-scripts[28]	Evaluated

[22]https://scihub.copernicus.eu/userguide/5APIsAndBatchScripting
[23]https://ladsweb.modaps.eosdis.nasa.gov/tools-and-services/
[24]https://www.usgs.gov/products/web-tools/apis
[25]https://www.usgs.gov/landsat-missions/landsat-data-access
[26]https://registry.opendata.aws/landsat-8/
[27]http://azvoleff.com/articles/analyzing-forest-change-with-gfcanalysis
[28]https://www.ecoclimate.org/r-scripts/

Product	Source	Access	Status
Copernicus global land products	ESA Copernicus	Copernicus land monitoring service[29]	Evaluated
CHELSA global land climate	Karger et al. (2017)	CHELSA[30]	Evaluated
Global forest cover	EU-JRC	Forest cover and forest cover pattern data by JRC[31]	Evaluated
Global surface dynamics	EU-JRC	Global water dynamics data[32]	Evaluated
Global soil grids	Hengl et al. (2017)	Global soil data: soilgrids[33]	Evaluated
Global urban footprint	Esch et al. (2012)	Global urban footprint[34]	Evaluated
UK urban areas LiDAR	UK Environment Agency	Free LiDAR data for some UK cities[35]	Evaluated
Global human built-up and settlement extent (HBASE)	Wang et al. (2017)	HBASE dataset from Landsat[36]	Evaluated
GIMMS NDVI3g	NASA	Earth science at ames[37]	Evaluated

3.15.3 Installing R packages

The use of the `getSpatialData` (Schwalb-Willmann, 2022), `sf` (Pebesma et al., 2022), `tidyverse` (Wickham & RStudio, 2021), `raster` (Hijmans et al., 2020), `sp` (Pebesma, Bivand, et al., 2021), and `rgdal` (Bivand et al., 2021) packages is suggested to get better functionality to manipulate the image files to be located, manipulated and obtained from the remote sensing data catalogs on the Internet. The `install.packages` function is used in the R console to install most packages. In the case of the `getSpatialData` package, it is suggested to install using the `devtools` package (Wickham et al., 2021) and `install_github` function. At installation time it may be necessary to install other packages needed for the packages to work because of prerequisites defined by the package authors. This may vary depending on what packages have already been installed on the user's computer.

```
devtools::install_github("16EAGLE/getSpatialData")
install.packages("sf")
install.packages("tidyverse")
install.packages("raster")
install.packages("sp")
install.packages("rgdal")
```

[29] http://land.copernicus.eu/
[30] http://chelsa-climate.org/
[31] http://remote-sensing-biodiversity.org/forest-cover-and-forest-cover-pattern-data-by-jrc/
[32] http://remote-sensing-biodiversity.org/global-water-dynamics-data/
[33] http://remote-sensing-biodiversity.org/global-soil-data-soilgrids/
[34] https://www.dlr.de/eoc/desktopdefault.aspx/tabid-9628/16557_read-40454/
[35] http://remote-sensing-biodiversity.org/free-lidar-data-for-some-uk-cities/
[36] http://sedac.ciesin.columbia.edu/data/set/ulandsat-hbase-v1
[37] https://www.nasa.gov/centers/ames/earthscience

3.15.4   Enabling R Packages

The getSpatialData, sf, tidyverse, raster, and sp packages are enabled for use with the library function in the R console.

```
library(getSpatialData)
library(sf)
library(tidyverse)
library(raster)
library(sp)
library(rgdal)
```

3.15.5   Specify a directory for files

A directory for the files is specified using the set_archive function.

```
set_archive("C:/sr/c3")
```

3.15.6   Import the polygon coincident with the area of interest (AOI)

The area of interest (AOI) polygon is obtained from a spatial polygon file with attributes, using the readOGR function.

```
aoi <- readOGR(dsn="C:/sr/c1/pol.shp")
```

To configure the AOI for an image retrieval session in the data catalog, the set_aoi function is used.

```
set_aoi(aoi)
```

Similarly, the region of interest is visualized in interactive mapping with the view_aoi function (Figure 3.32).

```
view_aoi(aoi)
```

To draw an area of interest without the availability of a spatial polygon file with attributes, one can use the set_aoi() function without the vector file argument inside the parentheses. The polygon drawing function must be enabled in the map viewer and vertices must be created by clicking the mouse over the map. After creating four vertices defining the polygon, you must finish editing with finish and then finish the process with done. You can then view the polygon drawn on the map by using the view_aoi() function with no argument inside the parenthesis.

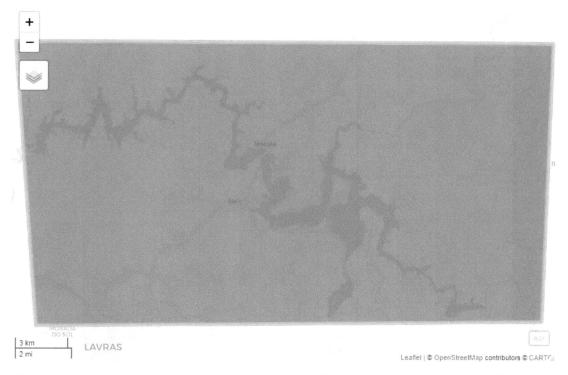

Figure 3.32 Interactive geovisualization of an area of interest to get images by the R package getSpatialData.

3.15.7 Logging in to search catalogs

To access the data catalog, you must register on the Copernicus Open Access Hub website, **registration**[38]. If you have already registered and have the login and password credentials to access the Copernicus Open Access Hub website, enter **login**[39] and test access on the website.

Other data access catalogs required are those for **Earth Explorer**[40] and **AppEEARS - NASA**[41], where registration is also required.

To log in to Copernicus Open Access Hub, Earth Explorer and AppEEARS, three services are used via the login_CopHub, login_USGS and login_earthdata functions, respectively. There may be a login problem if it is the same time as the website maintenance.

```
login_CopHub(username = "insert_login_name") #A pop-up box will ask for the password
login_USGS(username = "insert_login_name") #A pop-up box will ask for the password
login_earthdata(username = "insert_login_name") #A pop-up box will ask for the password
```

The services function is used to evaluate the operation of the service.

```
services()
# * ESA Copernicus Open Hub:  'available'      'Connection successfully established.'
```

---

[38] https://scihub.copernicus.eu/dhus/#/self-registration
[39] https://scihub.copernicus.eu/dhus/#/home
[40] https://ers.cr.usgs.gov/login
[41] https://lpdaacsvc.cr.usgs.gov/appeears/

```
# * ESA Copernicus S5P Hub:   'available'   'Connection successfully established.'
# * ESA Copernicus GNSS Hub:  'available'   'Connection successfully established.'
# * USGS-EROS ESPA:           'available'   'Connection successfully established.'
# * USGS EarthExplorer:       'unknown'     'NA'
# * AWS Landsat 8:            'available'   'Connection successfully established.'
# * NASA DAAC LAADS:          'available'   'Connection successfully established.'
```

The `get_products` function is used to evaluate the available products.

```
get_products()
#[1] "sentinel-1"       "sentinel-2"         "sentinel-3"         "sentinel-5p"
#  [5] "sentinel-1_gnss" "sentinel-2_gnss"    "sentinel-3_gnss" "landsat_8_c1"
#  [9] "lsr_landsat_8_c1" "landsat_ot_c2_l1"  "landsat_ot_c2_l2" "landsat_etm_c1"
# [13] "lsr_landsat_etm_c1" "landsat_etm_c2_l1" "landsat_etm_c2_l2" "landsat_tm_c1"
# [17] "lsr_landsat_tm_c1" "landsat_tm_c2_l1"  "landsat_tm_c2_l2"  "landsat_mss_c1"
# [21] "landsat_mss_c2_l1""modis_mcd64a1_v6"   "modis_mod09a1_v6"  "modis_mod09cmg_v6"
# [25] "modis_mod14_v6"   "modis_mod09ga_v6"   "modis_mod14a1_v6"  "modis_mod09gq_v6"
# [29] "modis_mod14a2_v6" "emodis_global_lst_v6" "modis_mod09q1_v6"  "modis_modocga_v6"
# [33] "modis_myd14_v6"   "emodis"             "modis_modtbga_v6"  "modis_myd14a1_v6"
# [37] "emodis_ndvi_v6" "modis_myd09a1_v6"     "modis_myd14a2_v6"  "emodis_phen_metrics"
# [41] "modis_myd09cmg_v6" "modis_myd09ga_v6"   "modis_myd09gq_v6"  "modis_myd09q1_v6"
# [45] "modis_mydocga_v6" "modis_mydtbga_v6"   "lpcs_modis_mcd12q1" "lpcs_modis_mcd43a3"
# [49] "lpcs_modis_mod09a1""lpcs_modis_mod09ga" "lpcs_modis_mod09gq""lpcs_modis_mod09q1"
# [53] "lpcs_modis_mod11a1""lpcs_modis_mod13a1" "lpcs_modis_mod13a2""lpcs_modis_mod13a3"
# [57] "lpcs_modis_mod13q1""lpcs_modis_myd09a1" "lpcs_modis_myd09ga""lpcs_modis_myd09gq"
# [61] "lpcs_modis_myd09q1""lpcs_modis_myd11a1" "lpcs_modis_myd13a1""lpcs_modis_myd13a2"
# [65] "lpcs_modis_myd13a3" "lpcs_modis_myd13q1" "modis_mcd12c1_v6" "modis_mcd12q1_v6"
# [69] "modis_mcd12q2_v6" "modis_mcd15a2h_v6"  "modis_mcd15a3h_v6" "modis_mcd19a1_v6"
# [73] "modis_mcd19a2_v6" "modis_mcd19a3_v6"   "modis_mcd43a1_v6"  "modis_mcd43a2_v6"
# [77] "modis_mcd43a3_v6" "modis_mcd43a4_v6"   "modis_mcd43c1_v6"  "modis_mcd43c2_v6"
# [81] "modis_mcd43c3_v6" "modis_mcd43c4_v6"   "modis_mcd43d01_v6" "modis_mcd43d02_v6"
# [85] "modis_mcd43d03_v6" "modis_mcd43d04_v6" "modis_mcd43d05_v6" "modis_mcd43d06_v6"
# [89] "modis_mcd43d07_v6" "modis_mcd43d08_v6" "modis_mcd43d09_v6" "modis_mcd43d10_v6"
# [93] "modis_mcd43d11_v6" "modis_mcd43d12_v6" "modis_mcd43d13_v6" "modis_mcd43d14_v6"
# [97] "modis_mcd43d15_v6" "modis_mcd43d16_v6" "modis_mcd43d17_v6" "modis_mcd43d18_v6"
#[101] "modis_mcd43d19_v6" "modis_mcd43d20_v6" "modis_mcd43d21_v6" "modis_mcd43d22_v6"
#[105] "modis_mcd43d23_v6" "modis_mcd43d24_v6" "modis_mcd43d25_v6" "modis_mcd43d26_v6"
#[109] "modis_mcd43d27_v6" "modis_mcd43d28_v6" "modis_mcd43d29_v6" "modis_mcd43d30_v6"
#[113] "modis_mcd43d31_v6" "modis_mcd43d32_v6" "modis_mcd43d33_v6" "modis_mcd43d34_v6"
#[117] "modis_mcd43d35_v6" "modis_mcd43d36_v6" "modis_mcd43d37_v6" "modis_mcd43d38_v6"
#[121] "modis_mcd43d39_v6" "modis_mcd43d40_v6" "modis_mcd43d41_v6" "modis_mcd43d42_v6"
#[125] "modis_mcd43d43_v6" "modis_mcd43d44_v6" "modis_mcd43d45_v6" "modis_mcd43d46_v6"
#[129] "modis_mcd43d47_v6" "modis_mcd43d48_v6" "modis_mcd43d49_v6" "modis_mcd43d50_v6"
#[133] "modis_mcd43d51_v6" "modis_mcd43d52_v6" "modis_mcd43d53_v6" "modis_mcd43d54_v6"
#[137] "modis_mcd43d55_v6" "modis_mcd43d56_v6" "modis_mcd43d57_v6" "modis_mcd43d58_v6"
#[141] "modis_mcd43d59_v6" "modis_mcd43d60_v6" "modis_mcd43d61_v6" "modis_mcd43d62_v6"
#[145] "modis_mcd43d63_v6" "modis_mcd43d64_v6" "modis_mcd43d65_v6" "modis_mcd43d66_v6"
#[149] "modis_mcd43d67_v6" "modis_mcd43d68_v6" "modis_mod11a1_v6"  "modis_mod11a2_v6"
#[153] "modis_mod11b1_v6"  "modis_mod11b2_v6"  "modis_mod11b3_v6"  "modis_mod11c1_v6"
#[157] "modis_mod11c2_v6"  "modis_mod11c3_v6"  "modis_mod11_l2_v6" "modis_mod13a1_v6"
#[161] "modis_mod13a2_v6"  "modis_mod13a3_v6"  "modis_mod13c1_v6"  "modis_mod13c2_v6"
```

```
#[165] "modis_mod13q1_v6"   "modis_mod15a2h_v6"   "modis_mod16a2_v6"   "modis_mod17a2h_v6"
#[169] "modis_mod44b_v6"    "modis_mod44w_v6"     "modis_myd11a1_v6"   "modis_myd11a2_v6"
#[173] "modis_myd11b1_v6"   "modis_myd11b2_v6"    "modis_myd11b3_v6"   "modis_myd11c1_v6"
#[177] "modis_myd11c2_v6"   "modis_myd11c3_v6"    "modis_myd11_l2_v6"  "modis_myd13a1_v6"
#[181] "modis_myd13a2_v6"   "modis_myd13a3_v6"    "modis_myd13c1_v6"   "modis_myd13c2_v6"
#[185] "modis_myd13q1_v6"   "modis_myd15a2h_v6"   "modis_myd16a2_v6"   "modis_myd17a2h_v6"
#[189] "modis_myd21a1d_v6"  "modis_myd21a1n_v6"   "modis_myd21a2_v6"   "modis_myd21_v6"
#[193] "srtm_global_3arc_v003" "srtm_global_1arc_v001"
```

3.15.7.1   Perform record search by mission and period

A query of available records for various products in a given time period is performed for Landsat-5 data. In this case, the search dates and products of interest in January 2006 are specified.

```
records <- get_records(time_range = c("2006-01-01", "2006-01-30"),
                       products = c("landsat_tm_c1")) # Search for Landsat
```

The View function is used to view the obtained records. A table with the records makes it possible to evaluate details about the data, such as the percentage of clouds in the image.

```
View(records)
```

The colnames function is used to check available filter attributes.

```
colnames(records)
```

Interactive image viewing is performed with the view_records function (Figure 3.33).

```
view_records(records)
```

The function plot_records is used to perform a formal mapping of the existing scene to a static mapping (Figure 3.34).

```
plot_records(records)
```

A color composition of the image can be performed with a preview of the image with the get_previews function. Then the mapping is performed with the plot_previews function (Figure 3.35).

```
# Get a color composition of the scene
records <- get_previews(records)

# Map the color composition
plot_previews(records[2:2,])
```

Sentinel-2 data can be obtained and processed with a specific package used in precision agriculture applications. We encourage you to evaluate this package as a complement to the practical activity.

Figure 3.33 Location of the Landsat-5 TM imagery scene in a region near Lavras, state of Minas Gerais, on January 26, 2006.

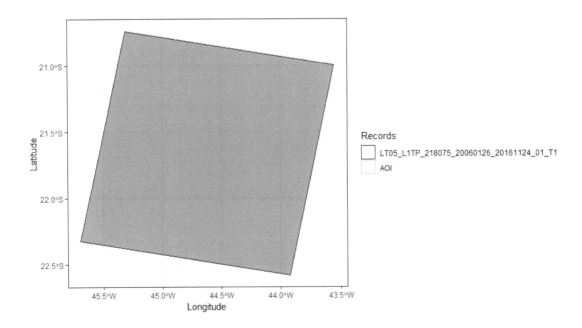

Figure 3.34 Static mapping of Landsat-5 scene available for download.

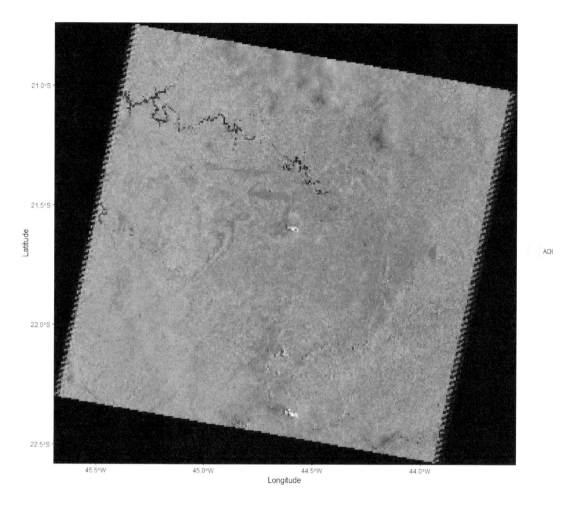

Figure 3.35 Mapping of a Landsat-5 scene color composition available for download.

In this case, it is necessary to install the R package sen2r (Ranghetti & Busetto, 2021) to use the GUI interface that is used by the package from R. The purpose of the functions contained in the package is to provide the tools necessary to easily perform and automate the steps required to build a complete Sentinel-2 processing chain, without the need for any manual intervention, nor the need to manually integrate any external tool (Ranghetti et al., 2020; Ranghetti & Busetto, 2021) (Figure 3.36).

Regarding Sentinel-5P data, the S5Processor is a package used to process Sentinel-5P data from NetCDF format to TIFF at a location of interest. We encourage readers to also evaluate this package as an extension of this hands-on activity (Balthasar, 2020).

3.15.8 Perform data request with the AppEEARS API

The application for extracting and exploring analysis-ready samples (**AppEEARS**[42]) provides a simple and efficient way to access and transform **geospatial data**[43] from a variety of remote

---

[42]https://lpdaacsvc.cr.usgs.gov/appeears/
[43]https://lpdaacsvc.cr.usgs.gov/appeears/products

Figure 3.36 R package `sen2r` interface.

sensing data files into one interface. With AppEEARS, one can access subsets of spatio-temporal data with point and area samples. In addition, one can obtain not only the requested data, but also the quality values associated with the data, as well as perform interactive visualizations with summary statistics in the web interface. Data from the **AppEEARS API**[44] can also be accessed from R. As a prerequisite, an account in **NASA Earthdata Login**[45] is required to log into the AppEEARS API and submit a request. To access comprehensive documentation of the full functionality of the AppEEARS API, see the AppEEARS document **API Documentation**[46]. Further details for performing a point-based search of remote sensing data using R can be obtained from Jami & Krehbiel (2020).

3.15.9   Getting Sentinel-5P data with R and Earth Engine

Sentinel-5P information can be extracted from Earth Engine catalog images using functions created by the Laboratory of Innovation in Health (InnovaLab) of the Institute of Tropical Medicine Alexander von Humboldt, Universidad Peruana Cayetano Heredia.

The `geobr` (Pereira et al., 2021), `sf` (Pebesma et al., 2022), `rgee` (Aybar et al., 2022), `tidyverse` (Wickham & RStudio, 2021), and `InnoVar` (Augusto Sarti, 2022) packages are used as an example to establish a workflow for processing and mapping administrative boundaries and atmospheric gases in a location of interest, in this case, states in the southeast region of Brazil. The packages are enabled with the `library` function.

```
library(geobr)
library(sf)
library(rgee)
```

[44]https://lpdaacsvc.cr.usgs.gov/appeears/api/
[45]https://urs.earthdata.nasa.gov/
[46]https://appeears.earthdatacloud.nasa.gov/api/

```
library(tidyverse)
library(innovar)
```

The ee_Initialize function is used to start EE.

```
ee_Initialize(drive = TRUE)
```

The state boundaries of Brazil are obtained using the read_contry function from the geobr package.

```
br<-read_country(year = 2020, simplified = TRUE, showProgress = TRUE)
#Using year 2020
#Downloading: 1.4 MB
```

The st_transform function of the sf package is used to transform the projection of the data from SIRGAS2000 to WGS-84.

```
brwgs<-st_transform(br, crs = 4326)
```

A subset is defined in the southeast region of Brazil (Sudeste, from Portuguese) with bracket operators and attribute names.

```
se<-brwgs[brwgs$name_region == "Sudeste",]
```

The polygons of the study region are transformed into class ee and simplified while preserving the topology with the use of the pol_as_ee function and argument simplify=1000.

```
region_ee <- pol_as_ee(se , id = 'abbrev_state' , simplify = 1000)
```

The get_no2 function is used to extract time series of nitrogen dioxide in regions of interest. In this case the maximum total NO_2 in a vertical atmospheric column in mol m^{-2} is obtained.

```
data <- region_ee %>% get_no2(
    from = "2021-01-01", to = "2021-12-31",
    band = "NO2_column_number_density", fun = "max")
```

The plot with the time series of the maximum monthly variation of NO_2 in the atmospheric column is performed with functions from the ggplot2 package (Wickham, Chang, et al., 2022).

```
data %>%
    pivot_longer(-abbrev_state, names_to = "month", values_to = "NO2") %>%
    mutate(month, month=gsub("NO2_", "", month)) %>%
    ggplot(aes(x = month, y = NO2, group = abbrev_state, color = abbrev_state)) +
    geom_line(size = 1.5) +
    xlab("Month") +
    ylab(bquote("NO"[2]~(molm^{-2}))) +
    guides(color=guide_legend(title="States"))+
    geom_line() +
    theme_minimal()
```

The states with the highest NO_2 variation in the atmospheric column in 2021 were São Paulo and Minas Gerais, followed by Rio de Janeiro and Espírito Santo (Figure 3.37).

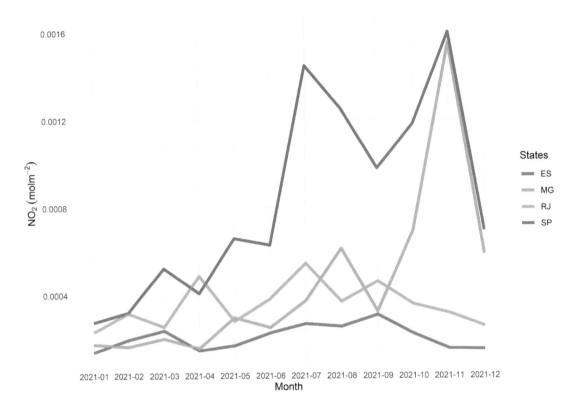

Figure 3.37 Maximum monthly time series of nitrogen dioxide in the atmospheric column in the states of Espírito Santo, Minas Gerais, Rio de Janeiro, and São Paulo, Brazil.

3.16   Exercises

3.16.1   Landsat-4 has an inclination angle of 98.3° and an altitude of 687 km. The satellite passes the Equator every 98.5 minutes. Determine the number of revolutions per day (24 h) (orbits) of the satellite around the Earth.

3.16.2   Determine the distance between polar orbits performed by a satellite considering the Earth's circumference at the Equator is approximately 40000 km and that the platform can complete 14.54 orbits per day.

3.16.3   A coffee crop is mapped using a radiometer with an IFOV of 2.5 mrad at an altitude of 705 km. Determine the spatial resolution of a pixel in the image in meters.

3.16.4   Mapping of rural properties was performed with a radiometer with a full angle of view along a 15° scan line at the altitude of 705 km. Determine the imaging swath width on the terrain in meters.

3.16.5   A soybean crop was imaged using a sensor with a radiometric resolution of 8 bits. Determine how many digital numbers can be registered by the sensor system.

3.16.6   How is the radiometric resolution of a sensor measured?

    a.   Number of spectral bands.
    b.   Pixel size.
    c.   Number of bits per pixel.
    d.   Orbital cycle.

3.16.7   What is the main advantage of a geostationary satellite?

    a.   Temporal resolution.
    b.   Spatial resolution.
    c.   Angular resolution.
    d.   Spectral resolution.

3.16.8   Which of the following variables represents the energy detected by a sensor system on a satellite?

    a.   Irradiance.
    b.   Radiance.
    c.   Absorptance.
    d.   Transmittance.

3.16.9   Which of the following resolutions is the most relevant for urban studies?

a. Spatial.
b. Spectral.
c. Temporal.
d. Radiometric.

3.16.10   Define a problem in remote sensing and a sensor to monitor that problem. Justify the choice.

3.17   Homework

3.17.1   Subject

Monitoring the Earth's surface with free, very high spatial resolution remote sensing data.

3.17.2   Assignment

Develop the subject presented with a practical application of remote sensing and digital image processing including the topics Introduction and Objective. Then present the development of the task.

3.18   Resources on the Internet

As a study guide, we ask you to consult slides and videos on remote sensing sensor systems and satellites (Table 3.18).

Table 3.18 Slide presentation and illustrative video on sensor systems and remote sensing satellites.

Guide	Address for Access
1	Sentinel-1: Radar mission[47]
2	Landsat data in the cloud[48]
3	Introduction to Earth Explorer[49]
4	Set search criteria in Earth Explorer[50]
5	Evaluating the results in Earth Explorer[51]
6	Launch of Brazilian polar orbiting satellite CBERS-4A[52]

[47] https://youtu.be/FJWzLxdSMyA
[48] https://youtu.be/SmG__2t-J__1o
[49] https://youtu.be/eAmTxsg6ZYE
[50] https://youtu.be/CVsgjp9jRyA
[51] https://youtu.be/WLOrtHyLqqA
[52] https://youtu.be/SQyz1CqTICA

Guide	Address for Access
7	Launch of Brazilian geostationary orbiting satellite[53]
8	GOES-R launch[54]
9	GOES-R sensors[55]
10	Landsat-8 anatomy[56]
11	Landsat-8 sensors to get data[57]
12	Landsat-8 targeting coverage[58]
13	5 years of monitoring the Earth with Landsat-8[59]
14	Legacy of 50 years of Landsat missions up to Landsat-9 (part 1)[60]
15	50-year legacy of Landsat missions up to Landsat-9 (part 2)[61]
16	NASA sensors and remote sensing products[62]
17	Version 2 harmonized Landsat and Sentinel-2 (HLS) data are here![63]
18	Slides about sensor systems and remote sensing satellites[64]
19	Brazil data cube - process and analyze time series of images[65]

3.19   Research Suggestion

Activities are proposed for the development of scientific research on remote sensing that can be used or adapted by the student to monitor and identify targets in a specific area of interest (Table 3.19).

Table 3.19 Description of practical activities that can be used or adapted by students with suggested research in remote sensing.

Activity	Description
1	Download a remote sensing image available in a remote sensing catalog. Import the image into R.
2	Import the remote sensing data obtained in R or other software of interest and perform the mapping.

---

[53] https://youtu.be/Lp9HnUjaXiA
[54] https://youtu.be/_c5H6R-M0s8
[55] https://youtu.be/5Ooj-ShktEA
[56] https://youtu.be/1b1q3LHb6-8
[57] https://youtu.be/CooU40t1RZ0
[58] https://youtu.be/xBhorGs8uy8
[59] https://youtu.be/Z2R8nPHdKYA
[60] https://youtu.be/FlRfl7Egexo
[61] https://youtu.be/QoWg68FCjm8
[62] https://youtu.be/rA_VCLzvbvM
[63] https://youtu.be/ZEQKPveOhrk
[64] http://www.sergeo.deg.ufla.br/sr/Presentation/Aula3/presentation.html#/
[65] http://brazildatacube.org/

4

Remote Sensing of Vegetation

4.1 Learning Questions

The learning questions answered by reading the chapter are as follows:

- How is remote sensing science applied in vegetation studies?
- What are the fundamentals of photosynthesis and its relationship to remote sensing?
- How does interaction with electromagnetic radiation occur in a plant leaf?
- How are acquisition and temporal analysis of remotely sensed vegetation vigor data performed?
- How do relief, shade, planting orientation, and cultural treatments affect remote sensing of vegetation?
- Which vegetation indices from different spectral bands are used for different applications?

4.2 Learning Outcomes

Using the learning outcomes from the chapter, you should be able to do the following:

- Apply remote sensing science in vegetation studies.
- Know the basics of photosynthesis and the effect of this biochemical reaction on plants monitored by remote sensing.
- Understand the interaction between electromagnetic radiation and a plant leaf.
- Perform acquisition and temporal analysis of vegetation vigor data obtained by remote sensing.
- Understand how the characteristics of relief, shade, planting orientation and cultural treatments can affect the remote sensing of vegetation.
- Determine and evaluate the vegetation indices from different spectral bands are used for different remote monitoring applications.

4.3 Introduction

A classification system into five kingdoms is proposed based on levels and types of organization that have evolved three main means of nutrition: photosynthesis, absorption, and ingestion. The kingdoms are Monera, Protista (unicellular eukaryotic organisms), Plantae (multicellular green plants and algae), Fungi (multinucleate fungi), and Animalia (multicellular animals) (Whittaker, 1969).

Vegetation is one of the most important components of terrestrial ecosystems. With the available knowledge about vegetation distribution, phenological cycles, physiological and morphological modifications, it is possible to provide information about the edaphic, climatic, geological and physiographic characteristics of an area. With the development of sensors and digital image processing algorithms, biophysical information of different vegetation landscapes is obtained through remote sensing in the following applications (Jensen, 2007):

- Agriculture;
- Native and planted forests;
- Native and planted grasslands;
- Wetlands;
- Urban vegetation.

The media that mainly contribute chemical elements to the composition of plants are air (CO_2), water (H_2O), the essential soil mineral elements (N, P, S, K, Ca, Mg, Fe, Mn, Cu, Zn, Mo, B, and Cl), and global solar radiation (electromagnetic energy). With the analysis of the plant dry matter, it was observed that approximately 90% of the total elements correspond to carbon, oxygen, hydrogen, and the rest from minerals (Malavolta, 1980) (Table 4.1).

Table 4.1 Elemental composition of a dry matter sample of 31 soybeans and soybean plant remains.

Element	Dry Matter (Kg ha^{-1})	Element	Dry Matter (g ha^{-1})
Carbon (C)	3500	Boron (B)	100
Hydrogen (H)	450	Chlorine (Cl)	10000
Oxygen (O)	3300	Copper (Cu)	100
Nitrogen (N)	320	Iron (Fe)	1700
Phosphorus (P)	30	Manganese (Mn)	600
Potassium (K)	110	Molybdenum (Mo)	10
Calcium (Ca)	80	Zinc (Zn)	200
Magnesium (Mg)	35	Cobalt (Co)	5
Sulphur (S)	2	———	———
Aluminium (Al)	138	———	———
Silicon (Si)	138	———	———
Sodium (Na)	138	———	———

One of the most important and challenging problems in remote sensing is to evaluate the spectral characteristics of vegetation. The reflectance properties of a vegetation canopy are complex and are affected by biochemical and biophysical characteristics of the canopy, and by external factors that influence the signal detected by the sensor. A thorough understanding of vegetation reflectance includes notions of leaf biochemistry, plant physiology, structural and morphological characteristics. The leaf biochemical constituents are pigments, lignins, and water. Differences in pigment concentrations determine color change, primarily in the visible part of the spectrum, while leaf moisture content is obtained from energy interactions in the mid-infrared (SWIR) portion of the electromagnetic spectrum. Plant physiology is related to vigor condition, phenology, stress, nutrients, water, and light availability. These factors alter pigment, lignin, and water-related biochemical interactions and affect plant structure. Canopy-level structural properties such as leaf area index, leaf angle distribution, fractional cover of vegetation, plant height, canopy diameter, leaf dry matter, planting geometry, and associations with other shrub, tree, and grass species are also considered. In addition to the vegetation canopy itself, there is also the underlying canopy background composed of soil, rock, litter, water, and snow, with optical properties that contribute an overlying signal to the vegetation canopy. External to the canopy, there is alteration of the signal at the sensor as a function of illumination of the area by the sun, angles of view of the sensor, and variation in the relief such as slope and aspect (Chuvieco, 2020).

4.4 Fundamentals of Photosynthesis

Photosynthesis is the primary means for the normal functioning of civilized society and the maintenance of life, except for some bacteria that extract energy from sulfur salts and other inorganic compounds. Photosynthesis is defined as an energy-storing process that occurs in leaves and other green parts of plants in the presence of light. With the absorption of light energy by the leaf along with carbon dioxide (CO_2) absorbed from the air, and water (H_2O) taken up by the root system, sugar molecules ($C_6H_{12}O_6$) are formed and oxygen gas (O_2) is released. The photosynthetic process begins when sunlight hits the chloroplasts with a green substance called "chlorophyll" (Jensen, 2007):

$$6CO_2 + 6H_2O + solar\ energy = C_6H_{12}O_6 + 6O_2 \tag{4.1}$$

Plants adapt internal and external leaf structure to perform photosynthesis. This structure and its interactions with electromagnetic energy determine the spectral differences of the leaves and the plant canopy recorded by the remote sensing sensor system.

4.5 Interaction between Electromagnetic Radiation and Leaf

4.5.1 Interaction between light and leaf in the visible region of the electromagnetic spectrum

The structure of leaves varies depending on the species and environmental conditions during the growth and development of the plant. The CO_2 in the atmosphere is absorbed into the leaf through pores called "stomata" located mainly in the lower epidermis. In the cells of the outer layer of the upper epidermis there is a cuticular surface that diffuses and reflects little light. Most of the visible and infrared energy is transmitted through the cuticle and the upper epidermis to the mesophyll cells of the palisade and lacunous or spongy parenchyma, where the photosynthesis occurs. Chlorophylls a and b are plant pigments that absorb wavelengths of light in the visible region, with absorption sites in the blue and red. The absorption sites of chlorophyll a and b occur at wavelengths of 0.43 and 0.66 μm, and 0.45 and 0.65 μm, respectively. There is a decrease in light absorption in the green (0.54 μm) region of the electromagnetic spectrum, which makes healthy green leaves look green to human eyes. Other photosynthesizing pigments, such as carotenes and xanthophylls absorb light mainly in the blue region. Phycoerythrins, on the other hand, absorb light predominantly in the green region at 0.55 μm. Phycocyanins absorb light in the red at 0.62 μm. Therefore, the two optimal regions to detect the absorption characteristics of a leaf's chlorophyll are between 0.45 and 0.52 μm, and 0.63 and 0.69 μm (Jensen, 2007).

4.5.2   Interaction between light and leaf in the near-infrared region of the electromagnetic spectrum

The spongy parenchyma located below the palisade is composed of cells and intercellular air spaces where O_2 and CO_2 exchanges occur during photosynthesis and leaf respiration. In the near-infrared region, healthy green vegetation is characterized by high reflectance (40 to 60%), high transmittance (40 to 60%), and low absorptance (5 to 10%). The high near-infrared diffuse reflectance (0.7-1.2 μm) occurs by the internal scattering of light caused by the cell wall and air interfaces within the leaf. Considering the water vapor absorption band between 0.92 and 0.98 μm, the optimal region for remote sensing in the near-infrared occurs between 0.74 and 0.90 μm (Jensen, 2007).

4.5.3   Interaction between light and leaf in the mid-infrared region of the electromagnetic spectrum

Water absorbs energy in the mid-infrared, so the higher the turgidity of the leaves, the lower the reflectance in the mid-infrared. In other words, as the leaf's moisture content decreases, the leaf's reflectance increases in the mid-infrared. The decrease of water in the leaves determines the increase of intercellular air spaces, increased light scattering in the mid-infrared and higher reflectance value in this region. The reflectance in the mid-infrared region and the amount of water in the leaves of a plant canopy have a strong relationship. Liquid water in the atmosphere absorbs electromagnetic energy in the near-infrared to mid-infrared portions of the electromagnetic spectrum 0.97, 1.19, 1.45, 1.94, and 2.7 μm. The water in the plants absorbs the incident energy, causing the reflectance to decrease by 1.3 and 2.5 μm (absorption effect). In this case, the mid-infrared reflectance peaks occur approximately at 1.6 and 2.2, between the two main bands of absorption by water in the atmosphere (Jensen, 2007).

4.5.4   Interaction between light and leaf in the thermal infrared region of the electromagnetic spectrum

Quantitative information about forest canopy structure, biomass, age, and physiological condition is extracted from remote sensing data in the thermal infrared (Jensen, 2007). The plant canopy functions as an aerial array of light-capturing antennae. To achieve maximum yield, each leaf within this array, and the array as a whole must rapidly adjust to naturally occurring fluctuations in light intensity and quality. Excessive light stress triggers the closing of stomata to minimize moisture loss (Devireddy et al., 2018). Similarly, to adapt to moisture gradients in the soil, plants alter their physiology, modify growth and root architecture, and close stomata. These tissue-specific responses modify the flow of cellular signals, resulting in early flowering or stunted growth and reduced productivity. In physiological and molecular analyses of plant *Arabidopsis thaliana*, a phytohormone regulates the response to drought or water deficiency (Gupta et al., 2020).

The opening and closing of stomata in the leaf regulates plant temperature by transpiration. In tomato crops, higher transpiration is observed under higher wind speed. In leaves where stomata naturally open in response to light, lower 5°C temperatures occur in leaves with stomata that remain closed (Cook et al., 1964).

The regulation of gas exchange by stomata is also affected by disease occurrence (Nadeau, 2002). This alters plant temperatures monitored by thermal infrared remote sensing with the death of leaf tissues of plants infected by disease caused by *Phymatotrichum* sp. in cotton *Gossypium hirsutum* L. (Falkenberg et al., 2007). In the coffee crop, using Landsat-8 band 10 TIR images, it is possible to detect increased temperature in the crop in areas with higher incidence of areolate spot (*Pseudomonas syringae* pv. *garcae*) on plant leaves (Marin et al., 2019).

4.6 Spectral Characteristics of Vegetation

The total radiance (L_T) of vegetation recorded by an aircraft- or satellite-embedded sensor is a function of the undesired path radiance (L_P), such as that caused by atmospheric scattering; of the radiance reflected from the leaf surface layer (L_S), the reflected radiance of the subsurface volumetric layer of leaves, twigs, and trunks (L_V), and the reflected radiance of the bottom of the plant canopy under the effect of soil, litter, and weeds (L_B) (Figure 4.1):

$$L_T = L_P + L_S + L_V + L_B \tag{4.2}$$

A healthy green leaf intercepts incident radiant flux (ϕ_i) from the Sun or from diffuse radiation scattered about the leaf. This electromagnetic energy interacts with the pigments, water, and intercellular spaces internal to the plant leaf. The reflected (ϕ_ρ), absorbed (ϕ_α) and transmitted (ϕ_τ) radiant fluxes through the leaf are estimated by the energy balance equation expressed by the second law of thermodynamics (Jensen, 2007; Moreira, 2011):

$$\phi_{i\lambda} = \phi_{\rho\lambda} + \phi_{\alpha\lambda} + \phi_{\tau\lambda} \tag{4.3}$$

Dividing each of the variables by the original incident radiant flux, one has:

$$\frac{\phi_{i\lambda}}{\phi_{i\lambda}} = \frac{\phi_{\rho\lambda}}{\phi_{i\lambda}} + \frac{\phi_{\alpha\lambda}}{\phi_{i\lambda}} + \frac{\phi_{\tau\lambda}}{\phi_{i\lambda}} \tag{4.4}$$

then,

$$i_\lambda = \rho_\lambda + \tau_\lambda + \alpha_\lambda \tag{4.5}$$

where i_λ is the incident energy, and $\rho\lambda$, $\tau\lambda$, and $\alpha\lambda$ are the hemispherical spectral reflectance, hemispherical spectral transmittance, and hemispherical spectral absorptance, respectively.

Many remote sensing systems function in the regions from 0.35 to 3.0 μm measuring mainly the reflected energy of plants according to (Jensen, 2007):

$$\rho_\lambda = i_\lambda - (\alpha_\lambda + \tau_\lambda) \tag{4.6}$$

where the reflected energy from vegetation equals the incident energy minus the energy absorbed directly for photosynthesis or other processes, and the amount of energy transmitted directly through the leaf toward other leaves or the substrate below the plant canopy (Figure 4.1).

The optical characteristics of the canopy of agricultural crops and forests depend on the type of leaves and the underlying soil, and may depend on other parts of the plants, such as the bark of tree branches, flowers, and fruits. The spectral domains of reflectance, absorptance, and transmittance vary according to wavelength and the optical characteristics of the leaves (Guyot, 1990) (Figure 4.2).

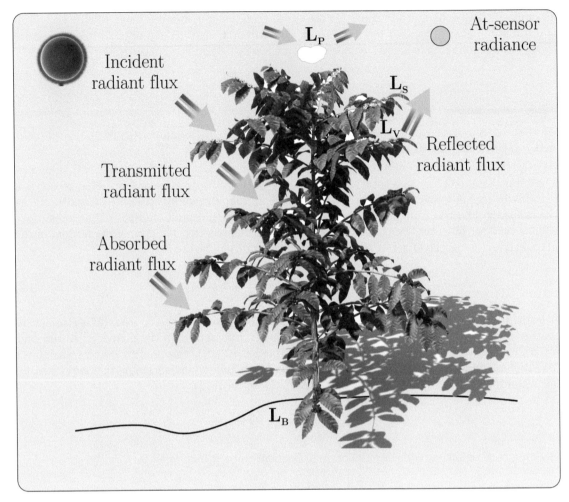

Figure 4.1 Interaction of solar energy with a coffee plant.

4.6.1 Mechanisms of light diffusion through leaves

The leaf reflects 40 to 60% of the incident near-infrared energy as a function of the optical characteristics of the spongy mesophyll. The remaining 45 to 50% of the energy penetrates and is transmitted in the leaf and can be reflected by leaves lower in the plant canopy as a function of additive leaf reflectance. The greater the number of leaf layers in a healthy canopy, the greater the reflectance in the near-infrared. Therefore, there is a direct relationship between leaf spectral response in the near-infrared and biomass-related variables and an inverse relationship between response in the visible, particularly in the red (Guyot, 1990; Jensen, 2007) (Figure 4.3).

4.6.2 Anatomical structure of the leaves

The near-infrared reflectance is affected by the anatomical structure of the leaf. The magnitude of the reflectance depends on the number of cell layers, the size of the cells and the relative thickness of the lacunose parenchyma. Thus, in dicotyledon leaves, the reflectance is higher than in monocotyledon with the same thickness, because the spongy mesophyll is more developed in dicotyledon. The leaves of drought-adapted plants such as olive trees can have very high near-infrared reflectance. Leaves exhibit asymmetry in their optical characteristics: the reflectance

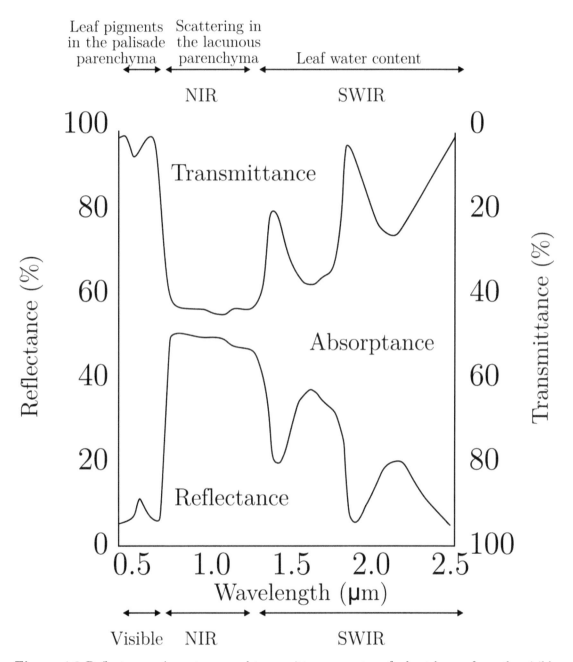

Figure 4.2 Reflectance, absorptance and transmittance spectra of wheat leaves from the visible to the infrared.

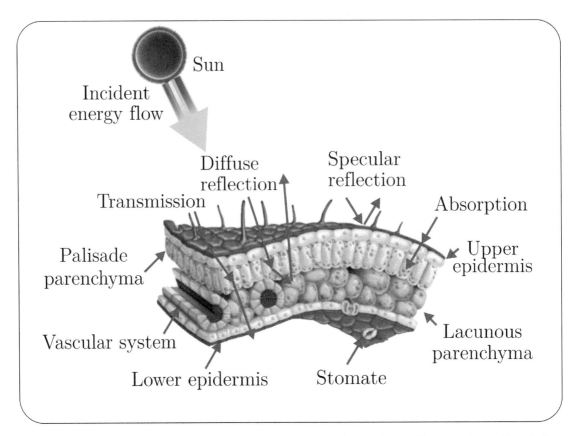

Figure 4.3 Schematic representation of the interaction of incoming radiation with a dicotyledon leaf tissues.

of the underside is generally higher than the reflectance of the upper side of the leaf due to the higher chloroplast density in the palisade parenchyma. In addition, the presence of hairs (trichomes), on the underside of some leaves, or, on both sides, can increase the reflectance in the visible and mid-infrared, but there is little effect on the near-infrared reflectance by the constitution of cellulose and absence of water in these tissues (Guyot, 1990).

4.6.3   Leaf age

The optical characteristics of leaves change during growth stages, plant development, and with the life cycle of the plant species. In forest species, the optical characteristics of leaves are practically constant varying with the seasons and the age of the plant. In the case of annual crops, such as wheat, during senescence of the leaves, chlorophylls disappear and are replaced by brown pigments of degraded chlorophyll. The presence of chlorophyll determines sites of absorption of electromagnetic energy in the blue and red, while in the near-infrared the reflectance increases when the leaf dries and its internal structure is altered. In the mid-infrared, leaf reflectance increases according to increasing dryness (Guyot, 1990) (Figure 4.4).

4.6.4   Leaf water content

The leaf water content directly influences the optical characteristics of leaves in the mid-infrared determining an indirect effect on reflectance in the visible and near-infrared as a function of

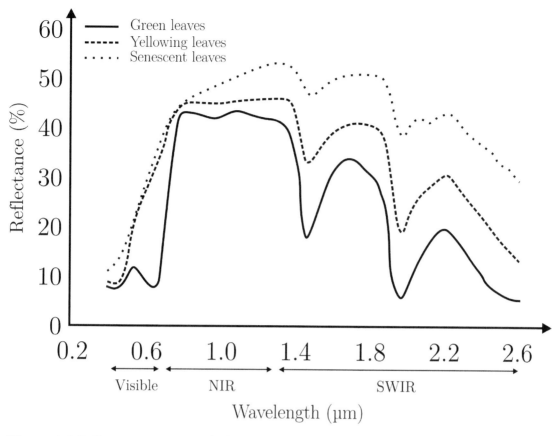

Figure 4.4 Reflectance spectrum of wheat leaves during senescence.

cell turgor. Decreasing water content in the leaves determines increasing reflectance across the spectrum. However, this is greater in the mid-infrared than in the other parts of the spectrum. Under natural conditions, under water stress, the optical characteristics of leaves are affected (Guyot, 1990).

4.6.5 Nutrient deficiency

Nutritional deficiency mainly influences the chlorophyll content and the anatomical structure of the leaves, depending on the severity of the deficiency, determining differentiated signs in deficient leaves compared to healthy ones. Adequate foliar nutrition of the plant increases the chlorophyll content in the leaf by altering the entire reflectance spectrum (YARA, 2020) (Figure 4.5).

4.6.6 Occurrence of pest organisms

The occurrence of pest organisms in plants alters the pigment content of leaves causing yellowing and necrosis. The reflectance of necrotic leaves is similar to the reflectance of senescent leaves. Pest organisms also modify the transpiration rate of leaves, sometimes without changing the optical characteristics, but which can be detected in the thermal infrared (Mesquita et al., 2016) (Figure 4.6).

Figure 4.5 Signs of nutritional deficiency of the coffee tree.

4.7   Solar Elevation and Shading in Crops

The sun's rays penetrate deeper into the plant canopy when they are incident on the less inclined surface. Thus, the proportion of shaded and illuminated surfaces in the area viewed by a radiometer varies with sun elevation, day, year, and latitude (Guyot, 1990) (Figure 4.7).

Other external factors also affect the quality of remotely sensed imagery, such as cloudiness, as a function of cloud cover and atmospheric aerosols.

4.8   Planting Orientation and Reflectance

The reflectance of the plant canopy depends on the percent coverage of the soil optical features varying with planting orientation and solar azimuth. When evaluating the soybean canopy with 60% ground cover and black and white painted plates, one can see variation in reflectance of different targets according to cropping orientation (Guyot, 1990) (Figure 4.8).

Rust

Brown eye spot

Bacterial blight

Mite infestation

Figure 4.6 Signs of pest organisms on the coffee tree.

Figure 4.7 Solar elevation and shading in agricultural crops.

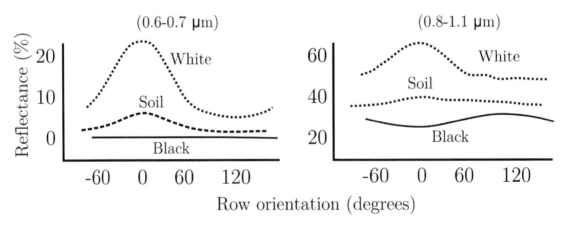

Figure 4.8 Effect of crop row orientation and soil color on soybean reflectance according to the variation of solar azimuth.

4.9   Temporal and Phenological Characteristics of Vegetation

There are seasons that are more suitable than others for identifying different vegetation types or for extracting biophysical information from vegetation using remote sensing. The selection of the most appropriate dates for obtaining radiometric data requires knowledge about the phenological cycle of the plant species (Figure 4.9). Another important temporal factor is the periods of rainfall and cloud cover when the growth and development of agricultural crops or native plant species such as forests, grasslands, and wetlands occurs (Jensen, 2007; Pezzopane et al., 2003).

In areas with mechanized agricultural crops, the application of crop treatments and management is done according to the phenological cycle of the crops. Since not all areas with the same crops are planted during the same month or harvested at the same time, there may be difficulties in identifying crops with remote sensing data (Jensen, 2007).

4.10   Vegetation Indices

Biophysical characteristics of vegetation are extracted from remote sensing data using vegetation indices (Figure 4.10). Vegetation indices are dimensionless radiometric measures that indicate the relative abundance and vigor of vegetation. An ideal vegetation index should (Guyot, 1990; Jensen, 2007):

- Maximize the sensitivity of biophysical plant characteristics in a linear fashion;
- Normalize effects of external variations such as sun angle, angle of view and atmospheric interference enabling spatial and temporal comparisons;
- Normalize the effects of internal variations in the substrate below the canopy, such as relief, soils, senescent vegetation and the presence of woody branches;
- Be coupled with measurable biophysical variables, such as the leaf area index and photosynthetically active radiation, for validation and quality control.

Vegetation indices are functionally equivalent and redundant in terms of information content. The historical development of the major indices provide information on recent advances (Tables 4.2 and 4.3) (Jensen, 2007; Shiratsuchi et al., 2014).

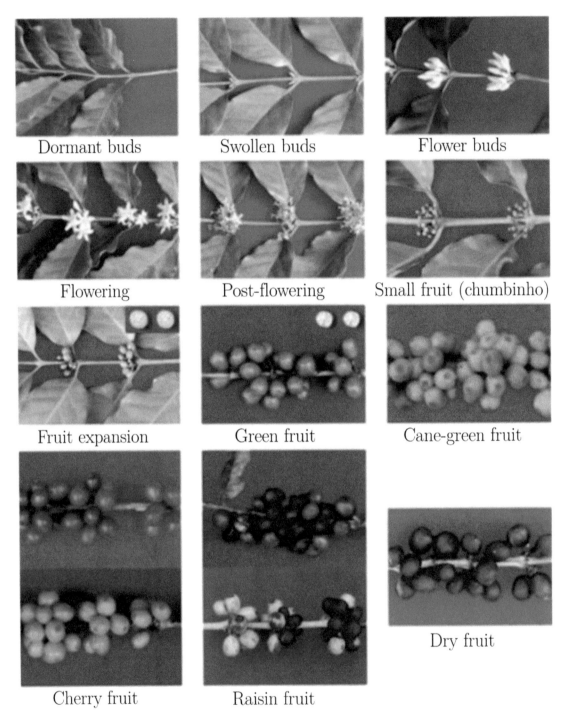

Figure 4.9 Phenological phases of Arabica coffee during 24 months in the tropics of Brazil.

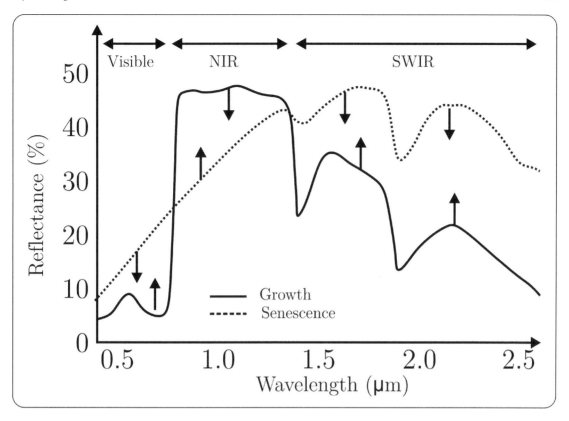

Figure 4.10 Physiological basis for the development of vegetation indices.

Table 4.2 Example of vegetation indices determined using surface reflectance of spectral bands and parameters (C1, C2, L, and G) obtained by remote sensing spectral band data.

Index	Band	Source
NDVI - Normalized Difference Vegetation Index	Red, NIR	Rouse et al. (1974)
SAVI - Soil-Adjusted Vegetation Index	Red, NIR	Huete (1988)
EVI - Enhanced Vegetation Index	Blue, Red, NIR	Huete et al. (1999)
SIPI - Structural Pigment index	Blue, Red, NIR	Peñuelas et al. (1995)
GCI - Green Chlorophyll Index	NIR, Green	Gitelson et al. (2003)
MCARI1 - Modified Chlorophyll Absorption Rate Index 1	NIR, Green	Haboudane (2004)
MCARI2 - Modified Chlorophyll Absorption Rate Index 2	NIR, Green, Red	Haboudane (2004)

Table 4.3 Example of vegetation indices equations.

Index	Equation
NDVI - Normalized Difference Vegetation Index	$\frac{(NIR-Red)}{(NIR+Red)}$
SAVI - Soil-Adjusted Vegetation Index	$\frac{(NIR-Red)(1+L)}{(NIR+Red+L)}$
EVI - Enhanced Vegetation Index	$G[\frac{(NIR-Red)}{(NIR+C1Red-C2Blue+L)}]$
SIPI - Structural pigment index	$\frac{(NIR-Blue)}{(NIR+Red)}$
GCI - Green Chlorophyll Index	$(\frac{NIR}{Green})-1$
MCARI1 - Modified Chlorophyll Absorption Rate Index 1	$1.2[2.5(NIR-Green)-1.3(NIR-Green)]$
MCARI2 - Modified Chlorophyll Absorption Rate Index 2	$\frac{1.2[2.5(NIR-Red)-1.3(NIR-Green)]}{\sqrt{[2(NIR+1)^2-0.5-6(NIR-5\sqrt{Red})]}}$

To determine the vegetation index from sensor spectral bands in the R package `RStoolbox` (Leutner et al., 2019), the band code is identified as shown in Table 4.4.

Table 4.4 Nomenclature of bands used to calculate indices according to the spectral characteristics of the TM sensor of the Landsat-5 satellite and the MSI sensor of the Sentinel-2 satellite by `RStoolbox` package.

Band Code	Description	Wavelength (μm)	Landsat-5 Band	Sentinel-2 Band
vis	Visible	0.40-0.68	1,2,3	2,3,4
red-edge1	Red-edge1	0.68-0.72	——	5
red-edge2	Red-edge2	0.72-0.76	——	6
red-edge3	Red-edge3	0.76-0.80	——	7
nir	Near-Infrared	0.80-1.1	4	8,8a
swir1	Shortwave infrared 1	1.1-1.351	——	9,10
swir2	Shortwave infrared 2	1.4-1.8	5	11
swir3	Shortwave infrared 3	2.0-2.5	7	12
mir1	Thermal mid-infrared 1	3.0-4.0	——	——
mir2	Thermal mid-infrared 2	4.5-5.0	——	——
tir1	Thermal far-infrared 1	8.0-9.5	——	——
tir2	Thermal far-infrared 2	1.0-1.4	6	——

The NDVI vegetation index is used to evaluate the water potential of coffee leaves (ψ_W) based on Landsat-8 OLI images according to the equation (Maciel, Silva, et al., 2020):

$$\psi_W = -8.712 + 17.325(NDVI) - 8.739(NDVI)^2 \quad R^2 = 0.89 \tag{4.7}$$

Time series of vegetation indices and the application of digital image processing functions to extract information about phenological stages of plant species are studied in several R packages as shown in Table 4.5 (Filippa et al., 2020; Forkel & Wutzler, 2015; Kong et al., 2021; Lange & Doktor, 2017; Matias et al., 2020).

Table 4.5 R packages used to extract phenological information from vegetation by digital image processing.

Package	Description	Source
phenopix	Functions to process digital images, describe vegetation index trajectories and extract phenological information.	Filippa et al. (2020)
phenex	Functions for spatial analysis of phenological data sets and satellite observations of vegetation.	Lange & Doktor (2017)
greenbrown	Functions to analyze trends, trend changes and phenological events in time series from satellite observations or climate model simulations.	Forkel & Wutzler (2015)
phenofit	Extraction of vegetation phenology from remote sensing combining TIMESAT and phenopix to eliminate snow, 7 curve fitting methods and 4 phenology extraction methods, model fitting methods with optimization.	Kong et al. (2021)
FIELDimageR	Functions to analyze orthomosaic images of experimental plots in the field with a drone, such as: crop image, remove soil and weeds, rotate image, create plot of SpatialPolygonsDataFrame file, and extract information from each plot to evaluate wavelengths, vegetation indices, stand counts, canopy percentage, and plant height.	Matias et al. (2020)

Remote sensing has revolutionized the collection of agricultural experimentation data with experimental plots in the field based on surveying very high spatial resolution data from low flying altitude aerial platforms. For example, the R package FIELDimageR (Matias et al., 2020) makes it possible to analyze orthomosaics of images, crop and rotate the image, create polygon based on the experimental design, determine the number of plants per plot, percent canopy cover, vegetation indices, and plant height (Tables 4.6, 4.7, and 4.8).

Table 4.6 Example of vegetation indices from the R package FIELDimageR.

Index	Band	Source
BI - Brightness Index	Red, Green, Blue	Richardson & Wiegand (1977)
SCI - Soil Color Index	Red, Green	Mathieu et al. (1998)
GLI - Green Leaf Index	Red, Green, Blue	Louhaichi et al. (2001)
HI - Hue Index of Primary Colors	Red, Green, Blue	Escadafal (1994)
NGRDI - Normalized Difference Index Green Red	Red, Green	Tucker (1979)
SI - Spectral Saturation Index of Slope	Red, Blue	Escadafal (1994)
VARI - Visible Atmospheric Resistance Index	Red, Green, Blue	Gitelson et al. (2002)
HUE - Hue Index	Red, Green, Blue	Escadafal (1994)
BGI - Green Red Pigment Index	Green, Blue	Zarco-tejada et al. (2005)

Table 4.7 Example of vegetation indices and its equations.

Index	Equation
BI - Brightness Index	$\sqrt{\frac{Red^2+Green^2+Blue^2}{3}}$
SCI - Soil Color Index	$\frac{(Red-Green)}{(Red+Green)}$
GLI - Green Leaf Index	$\frac{(2Green-Red-Blue)}{(2Green+Red+Blue)}$
HI - Hue Index of Primary Colors	$\frac{(2Red-Green-Blue)}{(Green-Blue)}$
NGRDI - Normalized Difference Index Green Red	$\frac{(Green-Red)}{(Green+Red)}$
SI - Spectral Saturation Index of Slope	$\frac{(Red-Blue)}{(Red+Blue)}$
VARI - Visible Atmospheric Resistance Index	$\frac{(Green-Red)}{(Green+Red-Blue)}$
HUE - Hue index	$atan[\frac{2(Red-Green-Blue)}{30.5(Green-Blue)}]$
BGI - Green Red Pigment Index	$\frac{Blue}{Green}$

Table 4.8 Example of vegetation indices and its applications.

Index	Application
BI - Brightness Index	vegetation cover and water content
SCI - Soil Color Index	soil color
GLI - Green Leaf Index	chlorophyll
HI - Hue Index of Primary Colors	soil color
NGRDI - Normalized Difference Index Green Red	chlorophyll, biomass, water content
SI - Spectral Saturation Index of Slope	soil color
VARI - Visible Atmospheric Resistance Index	canopy, biomass and chlorophyll
HUE - Hue Index	coil color
BGI - Green Red Pigment Index	chlorophyll, leaf area index

Nowadays, with the possibility of cloud-based remote sensing data processing, R, Python, and Earth Engine can be used in an integrated way to determine vegetation indices. As an example, MODIS sensor data is used to perform animated NDVI mapping between January 1, 2020 and January 1, 2021. For this, the R packages magick (Ooms, 2021), sf (Pebesma et al., 2022), lubridate (Spinu et al., 2021), and rgee (Aybar et al., 2022) packages are enabled with the library function. The ee_Initialize() function is used to initialize the Earth Engine after enabling rgee.

```
library(magick)
library(sf)
library(lubridate)
library(rgee)
ee_Initialize()
```

A polygon with geographic boundaries is used as the regional boundary of animation and mask layers to define a subset with NDVI data in Brazil. The sf_as_ee function is used to convert the sf data.frame class file into the ee class. With the $geometry()$bounds() code, the geometry of the region under analysis is defined.

```
mask <- st_read("C:/sr/S2/BrazilWGS84.shp") %>% sf_as_ee()
region <- mask$geometry()$bounds()
```

MODIS Terra Vegetation Indices 16-Day Global 1 km data are used as a `ee$ImageCollection` dataset. The NDVI variable is selected as indicative of vegetation vigor in the area with the `$select` function.

```
col <- ee$ImageCollection('MODIS/006/MOD13A2')$select('NDVI')
```

The images are grouped into dates between January 1, 2020 to January 1, 2021. A `col` function is created to get dates of interest and then applied with the `$filterDate` code for date selection.

```
col <- col$map(function(img) {
  doy <- ee$Date(img$get('system:time_start'))$getRelative('day', 'year')
  img$set('doy', doy)
})
distinctDOY <- col$filterDate('2020-01-01', '2021-01-01')
```

A `ee$Filter$equals` filter is set to identify which images from the complete collection match the dates of the selected collection.

```
filter <- ee$Filter$equals(leftField = 'doy', rightField = 'doy')
```

A join is defined with the `ee$Join$saveAll` function to convert the resulting `FeatureCollection` with all matching date selections into an `ImageCollection`, with the `ee$ImageCollection(join$apply())` function.

```
join <- ee$Join$saveAll('doy_matches')
joinCol <- ee$ImageCollection(join$apply(distinctDOY, col, filter))
```

A function defined to apply median reduction is performed between the corresponding collections in each month.

```
comp <- joinCol$map(function(img) {
  doyCol <- ee$ImageCollection$fromImages(
    img$get('doy_matches')
  )
  doyCol$reduce(ee$Reducer$median())
})
```

The visualization parameters are set with a `list` function, including color palettes for visualization of the spatial variation of the NDVI.

```
visParams <- list(
  min = 0.0,
  max = 9000.0,
  bands = "NDVI_median",
  palette = c(
```

```
    'FFFFFF', 'CE7E45', 'DF923D', 'F1B555', 'FCD163', '99B718', '74A901',
    '66A000', '529400', '3E8601', '207401', '056201', '004C00', '023B01',
    '012E01', '011D01', '011301'
  )
)
```

A function is defined to create images for use as animation frames in the region of interest.

```
rgbVis <- comp$map(function(img) {
  do.call(img$visualize, visParams) %>%
    ee$Image$clip(mask)
})
```

The display parameters for exporting the image are set to generate an animated file with GIF extension and WGS-84 geodetic projection.

```
gifParams <- list(
  region = region,
  dimensions = 600,
  crs = 'EPSG:4326',
  framesPerSecond = 1
)
```

The month names are obtained from a sequence of codes performed with the %>% operator to get the image dates, select the data start column, get the monthly dates, and perform the abbreviation of month names.

```
dates_modis_mabbr <- distinctDOY %>%
  ee_get_date_ic %>% # Get Image Collection dates
  '[['("time_start") %>% # Select time_start column
  lubridate::month() %>% # Get the month component of the datetime
  '['(month.abb, .) # subset around month abbreviations
```

The ee_utils_gif_creator and ee_utils_gif_annotate functions are used to render the GIF animation and add text to identify each mapped month.

```
animation <- ee_utils_gif_creator(rgbVis, gifParams, mode = "wb")
animation %>%
  ee_utils_gif_annotate(
    text = "NDVI: MODIS/006/MOD13A2",
    size = 15, color = "white",
    location = "+400+6"
  ) %>%
  ee_utils_gif_annotate(
    text = dates_modis_mabbr,
    size = 30,
    location = "+450+450",
    color = "white",
    font = "arial",
```

```
   boxcolor = "#000000"
 )  -> animation_wtxt
```

The animation results are exported with the `.gif` extension for animated mapping with the `ee_utils_gif_save` function.

```
ee_utils_gif_save(animation_wtxt, path = "C:/Aulas/2021_2/SR/raster_as_eebr.gif")
```

In this kind of animated mapping approach, performed based on the darkening of the shades of green on the map, it is possible to see the variation in the intensity of vegetation vigor according to climatic gradients occurring in the country. The vigor of the vegetation is more intense in the Amazon mainly in the winter months. The opposite occurs in the southeast, central and northeast regions of Brazil, where it is possible to note around these regions, from the month of June, a reduction in vigor and a yellowing of the shades of green on the map (Figure 4.11).

4.11 Computational Practice

As a computational practice, functions from the `RStoolbox` (Leutner et al., 2019), `raster` (Hijmans et al., 2020), and `rgdal` (Bivand et al., 2021) packages are used to explore atmospherically corrected images from the Landsat-5 satellite TM sensor. Digital numbers from optical and infrared spectrum images were converted into radiance, reflectance at the top of the atmosphere, and surface reflectance by `dos` and `sdos` methods, referring to monitoring performed on January 26, 2006. The image used was previously corrected for illumination based on relief from a digital elevation model (Goslee, 2011) obtained by surface monitoring with RADAR with synthetic interferometry from the Shuttle Radar Topography Mission (SRTM). The NDVI and EVI vegetation indices are determined in a comparative way to the results of surface reflectance sdos and dos in a mapped geographic region in the municipality of Ijaci, around the Funil dam, state of Minas Gerais, Brazil. The surface reflectance images calculated by the methods `dos` (**download**[1]) and `sdos` (**download**[2]) can be obtained to carry out the practical activity.

4.11.1 Installing R packages

The `install.packages` function is used to install the `raster`, `RStoolbox`, and `rgdal` packages in the R console.

```
install.packages("raster")
install.packages("RStoolbox")
install.packages("rgdal")
```

---

[1] http://www.sergeo.deg.ufla.br/sr/downloads/lsat_dos.zip
[2] http://www.sergeo.deg.ufla.br/sr/downloads/lsat_sdos.zip

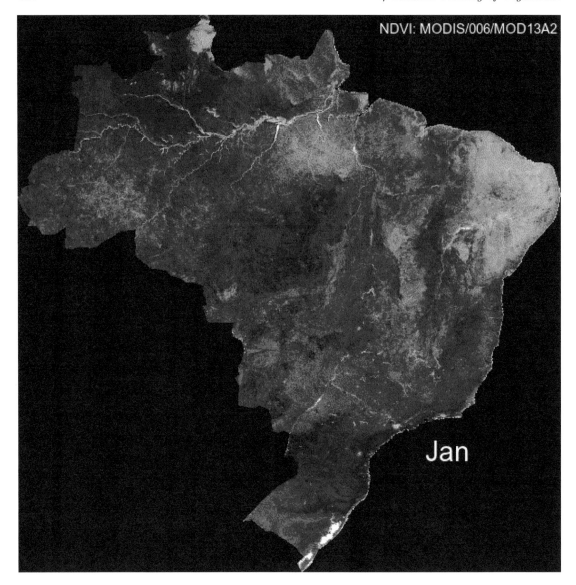

Figure 4.11 Monthly variation of the NDVI vegetation index (MOD13A2) in Brazil, from January 1, 2020 to January 1, 2021.

4.11.2   Enabling R packages

The library function is used to enable the raster, RStoolbox, and rgdal packages in the R console.

```
library(raster)
library(RStoolbox)
library(rgdal)
```

4.11.3   Importing and renaming images

The stack function is used to import the images and the names function to rename the bands used.

```
lsat_dos <- stack("C:/bookdown/SRcomR/files/C2/lsat_dos.tif") # Importar
names(lsat_dos) <- c('blue', 'green', 'red', 'nir', 'swir2', 'tir2', 'swir3')
lsat_sdos <- stack("C:/bookdown/SRcomR/files/C2/lsat_sdos.tif") # Importar
names(lsat_sdos) <- c('blue', 'green', 'red', 'nir', 'swir2', 'tir2', 'swir3')
```

4.11.4 Determining vegetation indices

The NDVI and EVI vegetation indices are determined for the images corrected by the dos and sdos methods with the spectralIndices function.

```
si_dos <- spectralIndices(lsat_dos, blue = "blue", green ="green", red = "red",
  nir = "nir", swir2 = "swir2", tir2 ="tir2", swir3 = "swir3",
  indices = c("NDVI", "EVI"))

si_sdos <- spectralIndices(lsat_sdos, blue = "blue", green ="green", red = "red",
  nir = "nir", swir2 = "swir2", tir2 ="tir2", swir3 = "swir3",
  indices = c("NDVI", "EVI"))
```

4.11.5 Mapping the indices

The indices are mapped comparatively with the use of the plot function (Figure 4.12).

```
si<-stack(si_dos, si_sdos) # Stack results
names(si)<-c("NDVI_dos", "EVI_dos", "NDVI_sdos", "EVI_sdos")
plot(si) # Mapping vegetation indices
```

The brightness values of water mapping showed more homogeneous shades in the central part of the Funil dam for NDVI and EVI determined by the sdos method when compared to dos. Also, in the sdos method there was an increase in the range of NDVI brightness values.

4.11.6 Determine summary statistics

The summary function is used to obtain summary statistics of the results as shown in Table 4.9.

```
summary(si$NDVI_dos)
summary(si$EVI_dos)
summary(si$NDVI_sdos)
summary(si$EVI_sdos)
```

We observed that although not very apparent in the maps, subtle differences were verified to the minimum (Min), first quartile (1st Qu.), median (Median), third quartile (3rd Qu.), and maximum values of the data sets processed by the methods dos and dos. In general, the dos method allows us to increase the amplitude of the distribution of brightness values, and with that, there may be a greater ability to differentiate the targets analyzed in the scene.

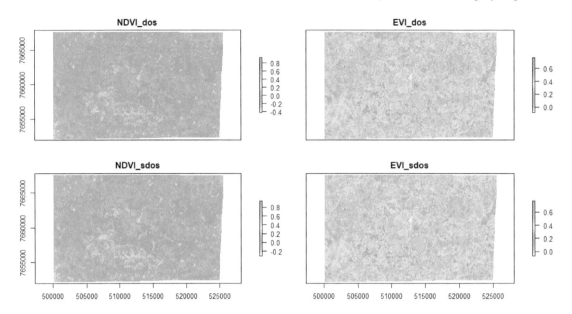

Figure 4.12 Mapping NDVI and EVI vegetation indices on January 26, 2006.

Table 4.9 Summary statistics of NDVI and EVI determined by the dos and sdos methods.

Statistics	NDVI dos	EVI dos	NDVI sdos	EVI sdos
Min.	-0.445	-0.089	-0.313	-0.065
1st Qu.	0.586	0.346	0.607	0.358
Median	0.683	0.416	0.702	0.427
3rd Qu.	0.769	0.478	0.788	0.488
Max.	0.941	0.791	0.958	0.795

4.11.7 Mapping vegetation indices and temperature from MODIS sensor

After consulting the **Earth Explorer**[3] data catalog, data from surface temperature products at 1-km spatial resolution (MOD11A2) and vegetation indices NDVI and EVI at 250-m spatial resolution (MYD13Q1) are used in comparative mapping one day before the imaging performed by the Landsat-5 sensor, in the region analyzed in the previous topic, i.e., on January 25, 2006. The sensor data can be obtained from the NASA LPDAAC Collections item available by choosing the desired sensor mission to obtain the data.

The R package gdalutils (Greenberg, 2000) is used to import the images in the .hdf extension using the get_subdatasets function. The gdal_translate function is used to convert the images from .hdf to geotif. The projectRaster function is used to transform the coordinates from the sinusoidal projection to WGS-84. Finally, the daytime period average surface temperature data in Kelvin and the NDVI and EVI vegetation indices are clipped to the area of interest for a visual comparison of the MODIS sensor monitoring compared to Landsat-5. The EVI and NDVI indices are divided by 100000000 for a better physical interpretation of the vegetation indices (Figure 4.13).

---

[3]https://earthexplorer.usgs.gov/

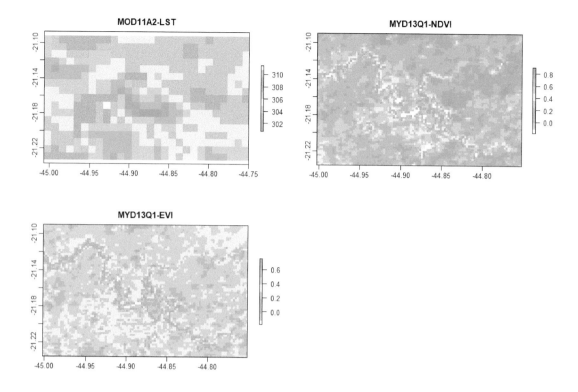

Figure 4.13 Mapping of surface temperature (Kelvin), NDVI and EVI vegetation indices obtained from MODIS surface monitoring on January 25, 2006.

The regions with watercourse are well defined by the vegetation indices according the observed, characterized with low NDVI and EVI values. Regions with higher NDVI and EVI values characterized the regions with higher vegetation vigor around the Funil dam. Despite the difference in spatial resolution between the thermal imaging and the reflective spectrum bands of the MODIS sensor, some regions near the watercourse and with higher vegetation index showed lower temperature values; however, information about the quality of the images in relation to the occurrence of clouds should be evaluated as a criterion for assessing the uncertainty of the results obtained.

4.12   Exercises

4.12.1   Explain how the interaction between visible and infrared radiation occurs in a dicotyledon leaf.

4.12.2   Explain how to calculate the NDVI of vegetation with the Landsat-8 OLI sensor.

4.12.3   Name two factors that can interfere with the spectral response of plants in agricultural crops monitored by multispectral remote sensing.

4.12.4   Justify the monitoring of a vegetation type with an index and how this will be done over time.

4.12.5   Define a remote sensing problem and a sensor to monitor this problem. Justify the choice.

4.13   Homework

4.13.1   Subject

Determination of vegetation index from multispectral remote sensing data.

4.13.2   Assignment

Develop the subject presented with a practical application of remote sensing and digital image processing including the topics Introduction and Objective. Then present the development of the task.

4.14   Resources on the Internet

As a study guide, slides and illustrative videos are presented about the subject covered in the chapter in Table 4.10.

Table 4.10 Slide presentation and illustrative video about remote sensing of vegetation study.

Guide	Address for Access
1	Toolkit mapbiomas v.6 for mapping biomes in JavaScript[4]
2	Video lesson on remote sensing of vegetation[5]
3	Illustrative video on vegetation monitoring and deforestation warning systems in the Amazon[6]
4	Normalized difference vegetation index (NDVI)[7]
5	Use of vegetation indices at different growing seasons for agricultural crops[8]
6	Agricultural monitoring with satellites[9]
7	Remote sensing in precision agriculture[10]
8	Global vegetation change[11]
9	TerraBrasilis - INPE's geographic data visualization platform[12]
10	Study of plant phenology with Landsat[13]
11	Slides about vegetation remote sensing[14]
12	VICAL application for determining vegetation indices with JavaScript language[15]
13	Mapbiomas v.6 legend[16]

4.15 Research Suggestion

Activities are proposed for the development of scientific research on remote sensing that can be used or adapted by the student to monitor and identify targets in a specific area of interest (Table 4.11).

Table 4.11 Description of practical activities that can be used or adapted by students with suggested research in remote sensing.

Activity	Description
1	Determine the EVI using an image of interest and discuss the results obtained.
2	Determine the NDVI using an image of interest and discuss the results obtained.
3	Obtain ready determined vegetation index products from catalogs with remote sensing data collections on the Internet.

---

[4] https://code.earthengine.google.com/?accept_repo=users%2Fmapbiomas%2Fuser-toolkit&scriptPath=users%2Fmapbiomas%2Fuser-toolkit%3Amapbiomas-user-toolkit-lulc.js

[5] https://youtu.be/CDkZgQfptIw

[6] https://youtu.be/Ki_wug5pYxo

[7] https://youtu.be/rxOMhQwApMc

[8] https://youtu.be/1kcUNdyIeaM

[9] https://youtu.be/YsN8ZscTnG4

[10] https://youtu.be/FAnqUs5DktI

[11] https://youtu.be/NgO6crdb9Y0

[12] https://youtu.be/pnB7Yhqk6r0

[13] https://youtu.be/2RN2HMgYfRQ

[14] http://www.sergeo.deg.ufla.br/sr/Presentation/Aula4/presentation.html#/

[15] https://inifapcenidraspa.users.earthengine.app/view/vical

[16] https://mapbiomas-br-site.s3.amazonaws.com/downloads/Colecction%206/Cod_Class_legenda_Col6_MapBiomas_BR.pdf

5

Remote Sensing of Water

5.1 Learning Questions

The learning questions answered by reading the chapter are as follows:

- What physical states of water can be detected with remote sensing?
- How is remote sensing applied to water studies?
- What are the biophysical characteristics of water detected with remote sensing?
- How is remote sensing used to study rainfall, aerosols, clouds, water vapor, and snow?
- How is mathematical modeling of water quality performed using remotely sensed data?
- Which moisture indices are used in studying water at different targets with remote sensing?

5.2 Learning Outcomes

Using the learning outcomes from the chapter, you should be able to do the following:

- Understand how the different physical states of water are detected with remote sensing.
- Apply remote sensing science in water studies.
- Detect biophysical characteristics of water with remote sensing.
- Use remote sensing to study rainfall, aerosols, clouds, water vapor, and snow.
- Perform geospatial mathematical modeling of water quality.
- Use moisture indices in the study of water at different targets with remote sensing.

5.3 Introduction

Water exists on Earth in the form of freshwater, saltwater, water vapor, rain, snow, and ice. It is therefore necessary to monitor and predict the spatial distribution, volume, and movement of water during the hydrologic cycle. Measurements *in situ* are obtained for hydrological variables, such as (Jensen, 2007):

- Surface water area of streams, rivers, lakes, reservoirs, and seas;
- Organic and inorganic constituents of water;
- Depth of water by bathymetry;
- Surface temperature of water;

- Surface area of snow and ice;
- Cloud cover;
- Precipitation;
- Water vapor.

Existing water covers approximately 74% of the Earth. Oceans represented approximately 95% of the water surface area, and lakes, rivers represent only 0.4% of freshwater surface area (Table 5.1) (Campbell & Wynne, 2011). In addition, soil and rocks near the Earth's surface retain significant amounts of freshwater (0.01% by volume of Earth's total water), as does ice and snow from polar regions. Moisture in the form of ice accounts for approximately 5% of the Earth's surface. Melting snow in temperate mountains is an important source of moisture for agricultural regions in arid zones. The physical and chemical properties of water are quite unusual, and these characteristics condition its behavior in the environment. The hydrological cycle is the central concept of hydrology, shipped on a global scale. On a regional scale, there are subcycles, for example, in the precipitated water that make the surface and evaporates, condenses and precipitates again before returning to the ocean.

Table 5.1 Water on the Earth.

Site	Surface Area (%)	Volume (%)
Oceans	94.90	97.1
Rivers and lakes	0.40	0.02
Groundwater	——	0.6
Permanent ice cap	4.69	2.2
Earth atmosphere	——	0.001
Total	99.9	99.9

Remote sensing has been able to understand the complex dynamic patterns of water that can hardly be understood only with point measurements. The relationship between water samples and remotely sensed data helps to study phenomena over large areas and remote regions. With this, patterns can be obtained at scales other than those observed at the surface, recording changes over time and providing data for inaccessible regions (Campbell & Wynne, 2011).

5.4   Biophysical Characteristics of Water Detected by Remote Sensing

5.4.1   Radiance of water

The total radiance (L_T) recorded from water by an aircraft- or satellite-embedded sensor is a function of the unwanted path radiance (L_P), the reflected radiance of the surface water layer (L_S), the reflected radiance of the volumetric subsurface water layer (L_V), and the reflected radiance of the water body bottom (L_B) (Jensen, 2007) (Figure 5.1):

$$L_T = L_P + L_S + L_V + L_B \qquad (5.1)$$

Scientists interested in identifying organic and inorganic constituents in the water column isolate the subsurface volumetric radiance (L_V). Scientists who monitor water depth or bottom features

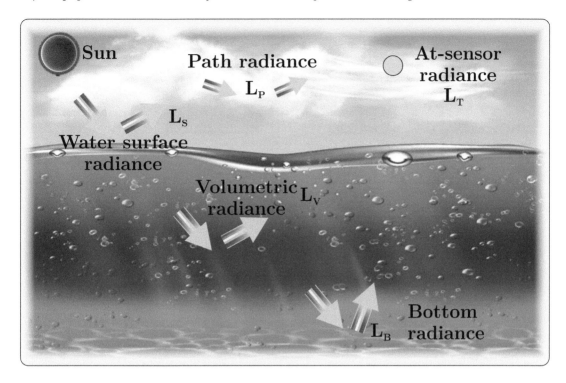

Figure 5.1 Total radiance of a water body for a remote sensor as a function of the atmospheric scattering radiance, water surface radiance, volumetric subsurface radiance, and the bottom radiance of the water body.

(using bathymetry), such as reef structure, isolate the reflected radiance of the water body bottom (L_B).

The volumetric subsurface radiance leaving the water column in the direction of the sensor is a function of the concentration of the clear water (w), the inorganic suspended sediments (SM), the organic chlorophyll a (Chl), the dissolved organic material (DOM), and the total amount of scattering attenuation in the water column in each of these constituents (cλ) (Jensen, 2007):

$$L_V = f[w_{c\lambda}, SM_{c\lambda}, Chl_{c\lambda}, DOM_{c\lambda}] \tag{5.2}$$

Each of these constituents affects the spectral reflectance characteristics of the water column.

5.4.2 Spectral characteristic of water

The molecular scattering of violet and blue light (0.25-0.48 μm) is greater in descending order than the wavelengths of green, yellow, orange, and red (0.52-0.7 μm) in a water column. Therefore, water is visualized in blue color in clear oceanic waters and deep, undisturbed water bodies. The best spectral regions to discriminate areas from clear water are the near-infrared and mid-infrared (0.74-2.5 μm), because almost all of the incident radiant energy flux is absorbed in these regions, especially in deep pure water bodies without sediments and organic matter. However, light can be reflected from the water surface in the near-infrared (sunglint) when the angle of view of the sensor is the same as that reflected, due to the specular characteristic of water. The ground with vegetation and exposed soil, on the other hand, reflects a lot of energy in the near and mid-infrared (Jensen, 2007) (Figure 5.2).

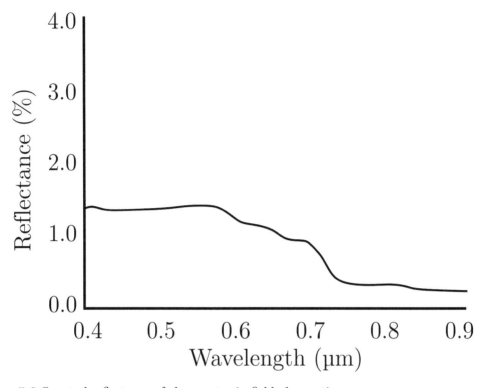

Figure 5.2 Spectral reflectance of clear water in field observation.

5.4.3   Organic and inorganic constituents in suspended water

Many water bodies contain a variety of organic and inorganic constituents, such as chlorophyll *a* from phytoplankton and minerals suspended in the water, respectively, to extract their quantitative information (Jensen, 2007).

5.4.4   Suspended sediments in water

Minerals rich in silicon, aluminum, and iron oxides can occur in suspension sediments in natural water bodies coming from various sources, such as erosion from agricultural areas, weathering of mountainous terrain, coastal erosion caused by waves or boats, ash from volcanic eruptions, and mineral exploration tailings from dam breaches (Jensen, 2007). As an example of tailings from a broken mineral exploration dam, the mouth of the River Doce invaded by mud from ruptured mineral exploration dam tailings flowing into the sea at Regência, state of Espírito Santo, Brazil, on November 23, 2015 (Figure 5.3) (Wikipedia, 2020b).

The transport of suspended sediment load in inland and coastal water bodies influences the spectral reflectance characteristics of the water. The release of sediment load into the water causes silting of water bodies, reducing the useful life of the reservoirs, culminating, in some cases, in the need to dredge the rivers. Sediments influence water quality and consequently its use, especially if it is for human consumption and animal consumption. Sediments can be transporting and storing agents of phytosanitary products, phosphorus, absorbed nitrogen, organic compounds, which can

Figure 5.3 Aerial photograph of the mouth of the River Doce invaded by mud from ruptured mineral exploration dam tailings flowing into the sea at Regência, state of Espírito Santo, on November 23, 2015.

be indicators of pollution. Suspended sediments hinder the transmission of solar radiation and reduce photosynthesis in submerged aquatic vegetation and phytoplankton close to the substrate that makes up the food chain of the aquatic ecosystem.

Remote sensing has been used to monitor suspended sediment concentrations in water bodies (Jensen, 2007). On November 5, 2015, a tailings dam was breached at an iron mine in southeastern Brazil, sending contaminated water sediments down tributaries of the River Doce. Seventeen days after the dam broke, the orange-brown water reached the Atlantic Ocean. The contaminated water continued to flow into the Atlantic on November 30, 2015, when the Operational Land Imager (OLI) sensor on Landsat-8 captured a natural color image of the region (Figure 5.4) (NASA, 2020).

Considering the *in situ* measurements, the spectral reflectance of clear water decreases continuously after 0.58 μm due to the absorption of light by the water column. Adding clay or silt to the water increases the concentration of suspended sediments and, consequently, there is an increase in reflectance at all wavelengths. Silty soil has approximately 10% more reflectance at all wavelengths compared to clay soil. In both cases, the reflectance peak shifts to higher wavelengths in the visible region when more suspended sediment is added to the water. Therefore, in the wavelength range between 0.58 and 0.69 μm it is possible to provide information about suspended sediment types in the water, and the range between 0.71 and 0.88 μm can be useful for determining the amount of suspended sediment (Figure 5.5) (Jensen, 2007).

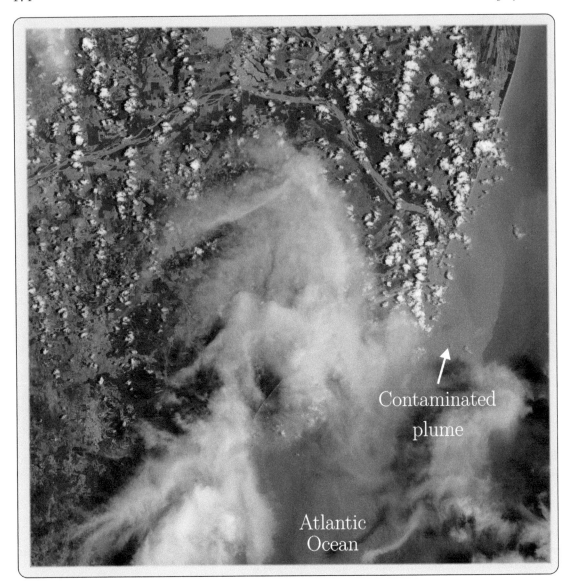

Figure 5.4 Landsat-8 imagery of water contaminated with mud, mercury, arsenic, chromium, and manganese flowing into the sea on November 30, 2015.

5.4.5   Chlorophyll suspension in water

Chlorophyll *a* pigments absorb most of the incident blue light. All phytoplankton in bodies of water contain chlorophyll *a*. When chlorophyll *a* is added to clear water, the spectral reflectance characteristics are changed. When the chlorophyll concentration increases in the water column, there is a decrease in reflected energy at blue and red wavelengths, but an increase in green reflectance. Based on *in situ* spectroradiometer measurements in water with algae, it is possible to observe absorption of blue light by chlorophyll *a* between 0.4 and 0.5 μm, absorption of red light approximately at 0.67 μm, maximum reflectance at approximately 0.55 μm caused by lower absorption of green light by the algae, and peak reflectance in the range between 0.69 and 0.70 μm caused by the interaction of algal cell scattering and minimal absorption by pigment and water (Figure 5.6) (Jensen, 2007).

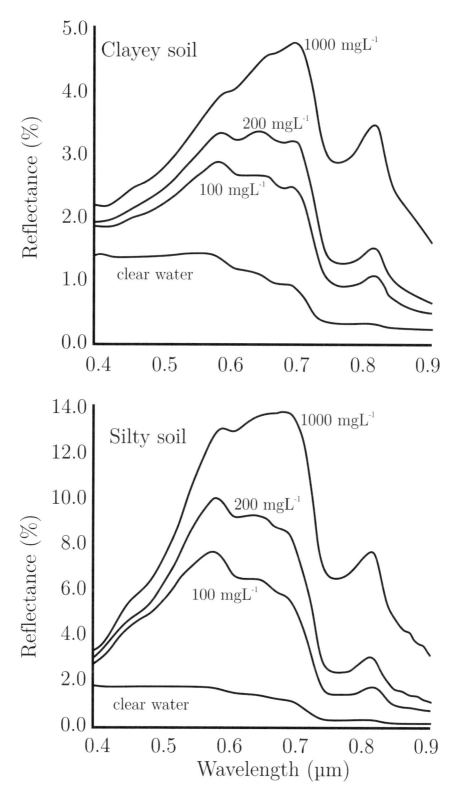

Figure 5.5 Spectral reflectance of clear water with various levels of clay and silty soil sediment concentration.

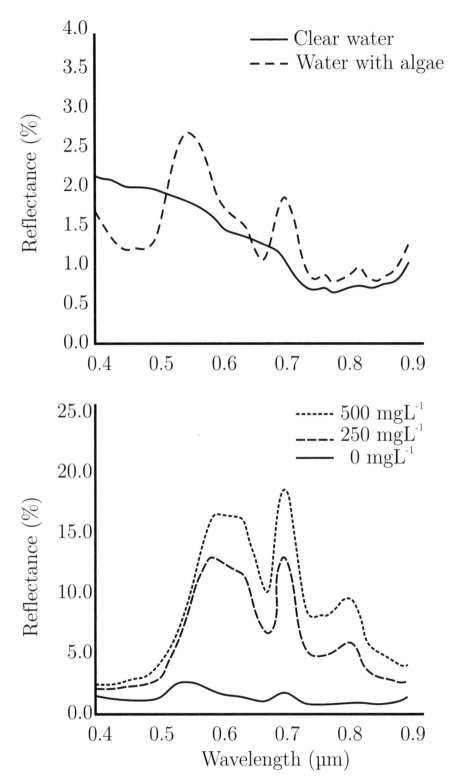

Figure 5.6 *In situ* spectral reflectance of clear water and water with different algae concentrations by spectroradiometer.

5.4.6 Dissolved organic material in the water

In some situations, there may be enough dissolved organic matter in the water to reduce light penetration into the water column. The decomposition of phytoplankton cells produces carbon dioxide, inorganic nitrogen, sulfur, and phosphorus. Humic substances can be produced and dissolved in the water causing a yellowish or gelbstoff appearance. The yellowish-brown color of the water can also come from high concentrations of tannin from mangrove plant species and make the water difficult to identify by remote sensing (Jensen, 2007).

5.4.7 Water bathymetry

Bathymetry of water can be performed by passive optical systems (aerial photography, digital imagery) or active remote sensing (SONAR, LIDAR). In the case of bathymetric mapping of water by passive remote sensing, it is observed that at wavelengths shorter than 0.56 μm, the reflectance of the bottom substrate of a water body increases with increasing water depth from 5 to 80 cm. However, with increasing depth, reflectance in the red and near-infrared decreases by strong absorption by water in a river channel (Figure 5.7) (Legleiter et al., 2004).

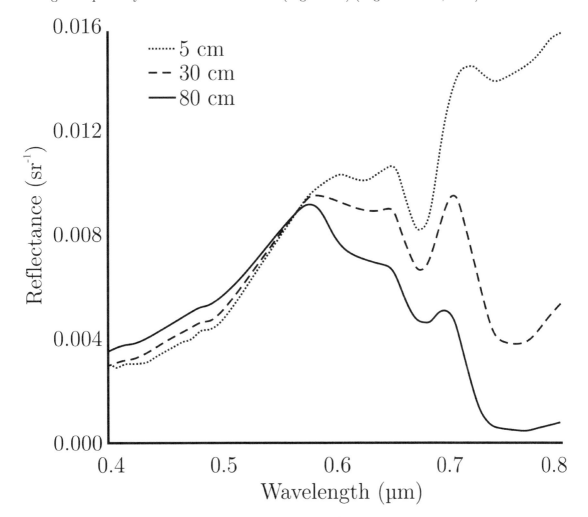

Figure 5.7 Effect of river channel depth on spectral reflectance recorded by remote sensing.

Based on this information, a depth index of a river channel (wd) was developed from the reflectance or radiance of the 0.56 and 0.69 μm bands of a hyperspectral sensor (Legleiter et al., 2004):

$$wd = ln(\frac{X_{0.56}}{X_{0.69}})\tag{5.3}$$

where X is the radiometrically corrected reflectance or radiance obtained from spectral bands at 0.56 and 0.69 μm.

SOund NAvigation and Ranging (SONAR) technology can measure the depth of water bodies by a process called "echo sounding" which consists of sending an acoustic pulse via a transducer to the bottom of the water. With the acoustic pulses reflected from the bottom and received by the transducer, there is a time to send and return the signal echo used to determine water depth by single beam, multiple beam, and side scan SONAR systems (Figure 5.8).

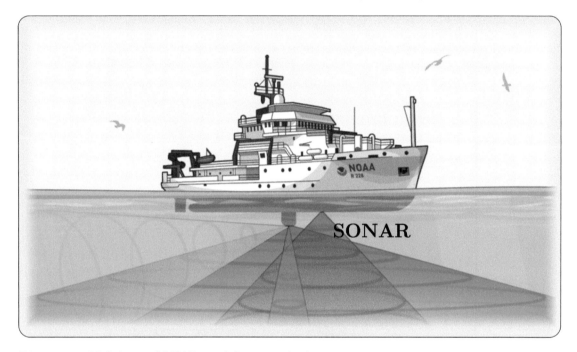

Figure 5.8 Multibeam SONAR used for water bathymetry.

Bathymetric information is also obtained with Light Detection and Ranging (LIDAR) remote sensing. In LIDAR, a laser light pulse in the near-infrared (1.06 μm) and an in the green (0.53 μm) are sent simultaneously toward the water surface. Most of the near-infrared pulse is absorbed by the water, and a certain amount, is reflected back to the LIDAR. A portion of the green pulse is also absorbed by the water column, but a sufficient amount reaches the bottom and is reflected back to the LIDAR. The green light is selected to detect the bottom because it comprises the wavelength that penetrates the water with minimal attenuation and with a maximum penetration depth of 60 m (Figure 5.9)(Jensen, 2007).

Bathymetric mapping by LIDAR and by SONAR can complement each other, because LIDAR is useful for high-resolution bathymetric mapping in shallow water environments, while SONAR, for bathymetric mapping of waters at intermediate and deep depths (Jensen, 2007).

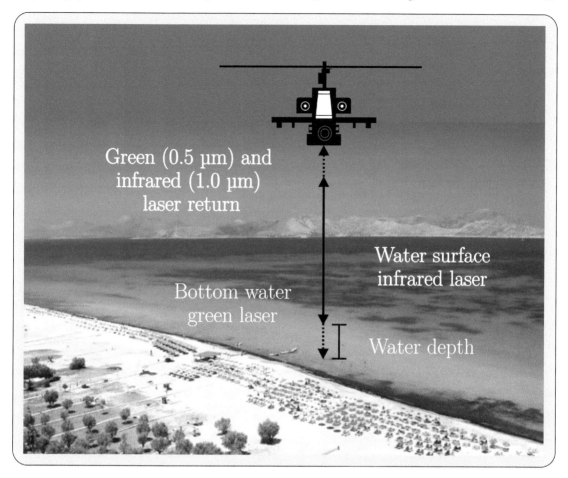

Green (0.5 μm) and
infrared (1.0 μm)
laser return

Bottom water
green laser

Water surface
infrared laser

Water depth

Figure 5.9 Use of airborne LIDAR for bathymetry based on the return time difference between pulses in the green and near-infrared.

5.4.8   Water temperature

The emissivity of water is close to 1, meaning that it allows accurate measurements of water surface temperature because the radiant temperature measurement recorded by the remote sensor is approximately equal to the kinetic temperature. However, the temperature change a few meters below the surface of the water sheet may not be detected by remote sensing in the thermal infrared. Water bodies also have high thermal inertia, meaning that there may be little difference in degrees between daytime and nighttime water surface temperature through caloric energy transferred mainly by convection (Jensen, 2007).

Continuous monitoring of thermal conditions in the surface layer of the oceans is important to know the surface-atmosphere energy balance and heat transport between high and low latitudes. The occurrence of droughts and/or seasonal periods with excessive precipitation in some regions of Brazil are caused by phenomena such as El Niño/La Niña and Atlantic Dipole. These phenomena are determined by anomalous temperature conditions in the Equatorial Pacific and Tropical Atlantic Oceans, respectively. Every two to seven years, the trade winds diminish in the central and western portions of the Pacific Ocean. As a result, ocean currents and winds off the west coast of South America can migrate, bringing heated water to the east, displacing cold nutrient-rich waters that have risen from the ocean depths. Another relevant factor of the sea surface temperature (SST) is the fact that it plays a fundamental role in the genesis, duration, intensity and dissipation of tropical cyclones and also in the flux of moisture from the oceans towards the coast, strengthening or weakening local scale systems, such as sea breezes. Another important contribution of the oceans, under the global climatic point of view, is their natural condition of storing carbon dioxide, and this capacity for carbon dioxide retention is inversely proportional to the variation in temperature at different depth levels. In other words, in warmer oceans there is less capacity to retain the gas and more carbon released into the atmosphere than in colder oceans. NOAA Optimum Interpolation Sea Surface Temperature V2 (NOAA-OI-SST-V2) data from the Physical Sciences Division of the National Oceanic and Atmospheric Administration (NOAA/ESRL/PSD) are used for SST monitoring with spatial resolution of 1°, monthly and biweekly temporal resolution of mean temperature and monthly and biweekly temperature anomaly. The monthly charts are available from January 1982, and the biweekly ones from January 2016, in the climatological reference from 1981 to 2010 (Figure 5.10) (INMET, 2020).

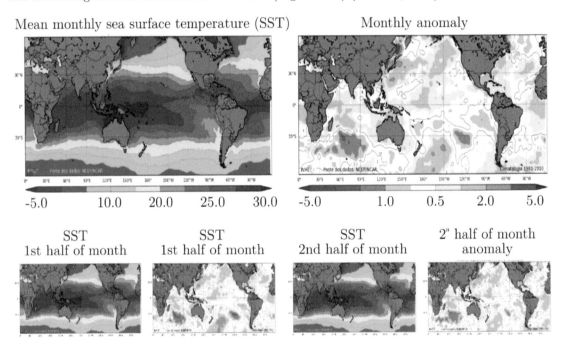

Figure 5.10 Interpolated NOAA-OI-SST-V2 sea surface temperature and monthly and biweekly anomaly charts for January 2020.

5.5 Rainfall

Rainfall is measured on a local or regional scale by active microwave remote sensing with surface fixed meteorological RADAR sensors. By means of the antenna, enclosed in a RADAR dome, water monitoring is performed from the emitted microwave energy beam. The scattered energy, after hitting objects such as water droplets, snowflakes, or hail, is scattered and a small fraction of the energy returns to the RADAR antenna. The strength of the return pulse is analyzed based on the return time and the doppler phase shift. This process of emission and reception of the signal can occur at approximately 1300 times per second, and the maximum range of the RADAR can generally be 400 km (Figure 5.11) (Jensen, 2007).

Raster surfaces of climate variables, including rainfall, can be obtained by WorldClim version 2.1 (Fick & Hijmans, 2017) for the period 1970-2000. This version was released in January 2020

Figure 5.11 Weather RADAR from the National Center for Monitoring and Warning of Natural Disasters (Cemaden), state of São Paulo, Brazil.

but earlier versions are obtainable. Monthly climate data for minimum, average and maximum temperature, precipitation, solar radiation, wind speed, water vapor pressure and total precipitation as well as 19 bioclimatic variables are available at four spatial resolutions, between 30 seconds (~ 1 km^2) and 10 minutes (~ 340 km^2). Historical global monthly meteorological data of mean minimum temperature (°C), mean maximum temperature (°C) and total precipitation (mm) are available for the period 1960-2018, at 2.5-minute spatial resolution (~ 21 km^2). Future CMIP6 climate projections of minimum temperature, maximum temperature, and precipitation were processed for nine global climate models (GCMs): BCC-CSM2-MR, CNRM-CM6-1, CNRM-ESM2-1, CanESM5, GFDL-ESM4, IPSL-CM6A- LR, MIROC-ES2L, MIROC6, MRI-ESM2-0 and for four socioeconomic pathways (SSPs): 126, 245, 370, and 585. Monthly values were available in 20-year average periods (2021-2040, 2041-2060, 2061-2080, 2081-2100) at the spatial resolution of 10, 5, and 2.5 minutes (Fick & Hijmans, 2017; Harris et al., 2014).

Geoprocessing techniques have been used to extract information from precipitation data used in remote sensing. As an example of cloud processing of remote sensing data, R, Python, and Earth Engine are used in an integrated way to study precipitation time series extracted from a polygon vector feature of the **TerraClimate**[1] database (Abatzoglou et al., 2018) between January 1, 2020 and January 1, 2021.

The R packages `sf` (Pebesma et al., 2022), `tidyverse` (Wickham & RStudio, 2021), `ggplot2` (Wickham, Chang, et al., 2022), and `rgee` (Aybar et al., 2022) are enabled with the `library` function. The `ee_Initialize()` function is used to initialize the Earth Engine after enabling `rgee`.

```
library(sf)
library(tidyverse)
library(ggplot2)
library(rgee)
ee_Initialize()
```

---

[1]https://developers.google.com/earth-engine/datasets/catalog/IDAHO_EPSCOR_TERRACLIMATE

A polygon-type vector feature at the border of Brazil with other South American countries is imported into R with the st_read() function.

```
shp1 <- st_read("C:/sr/S2/BrazilWGS84.shp", quiet = TRUE)
```

Rainfall data are obtained from the Terraclimate database with the ee$ImageCollection function. The available data are filtered between the period January 1, 2020 to January 1, 2021.

```
terraclimate <- ee$ImageCollection("IDAHO_EPSCOR/TERRACLIMATE") %>%
  ee$ImageCollection$filterDate("2020-01-01", "2021-01-01") %>%
  ee$ImageCollection$map(function(x) x$select("pr")) %>% # Select only precipitation bands
  ee$ImageCollection$toBands() %>% # from imagecollection to image
  ee$Image$rename(sprintf("PP_%02d",1:12)) # rename the bands of an image
```

Rainfall data are obtained from the Terraclimate database with the ee$ImageCollection function. The available data are filtered from January 1, 2020 to January 1, 2021.

```
ee_nc_rain <- ee_extract(x = terraclimate, y = shp1["name_long"], sf = FALSE)
```

The ggplot2 package is used for graphical mapping of the monthly rainfall variation in Brazil.

```
ee_nc_rain %>%
  pivot_longer(-name_long, names_to = "month", values_to = "pr") %>%
  mutate(month, month=gsub("PP_", "", month)) %>%
  ggplot(aes(x = month, y = pr, group = name_long, color = pr)) +
  geom_line(alpha = 0.8, size = 2.0) +
  xlab("Month") +
  ylab("Precipitation (mm)") +
  theme_minimal()
```

Although rainfall presents variations in rainfall regimes given the large territorial extent of Brazil, and the different biomes and climatic types, on average it is possible to verify the seasonality of rainfall distribution over months of the year (Figure 5.12). Future studies should be carried out to evaluate rainfall time series in smaller polygons and comparatively between regions for a better critical evaluation of the use of data with spatio-temporal variation of rainfall obtained with remote sensing and geoprocessing techniques.

A CHIRPS rainfall mapping approach obtained with cloud processing can also be performed to evaluate the spatial variation of rainfall in a near-global database. These data can be used for both spatio-temporal precipitation trend studies and seasonal drought monitoring (Funk et al., 2015).

The CHIRPS 2.0 database is used as a source to obtain data from **Internet**[2] obtained in this case via the rgee package using the ee$ImageCollection function. The dates of interest are selected with the ee$Filter$date function between May 1 and May 3, 2022.

```
dataset <- ee$ImageCollection('UCSB-CHG/CHIRPS/DAILY')$
              filter(ee$Filter$date('2022-05-01', '2022-05-03'))
```

---

[2]https://developers.google.com/earth-engine/datasets/catalog/UCSB-CHG_CHIRPS_DAILY

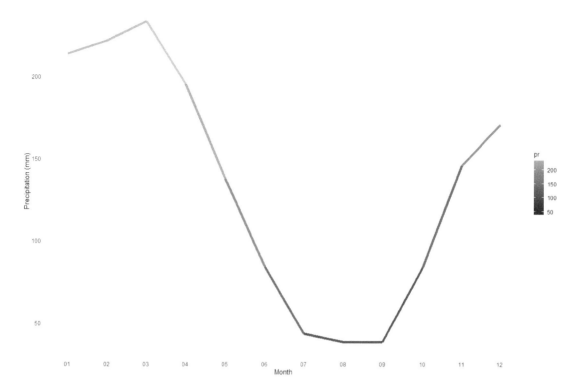

Figure 5.12 Monthly variation of rainfall in Brazil using Terraclimate data from January 1, 2020 to January 1, 2021.

Options for geovisualization of the results are defined by selecting the precipitation band using 5 precipitation color variations with minimum and maximum values between 1 and 17 mm, in order to highlight the regions with the highest rainfall occurrence on the monitoring date, using the `list` function.

```
precipitationVis <- list(bands = c("precipitation"),
  min = 1.0,  max = 17.0,
  palette = c('001137', '0aab1e', 'e7eb05', 'ff4a2d', 'e90000'))
```

The maximum precipitation data in the evaluated period are mapped by applying a `$max()` function to the selected CHIRPS collection selection. The `Map$setCenter` function set a reference center for centering the mapping and the visualization parameters defined earlier are applied to the data collection with the `Map$addLayer` function.

```
Map$setCenter(17.93, 7.71, 2)
Map$addLayer(dataset$max(), precipitationVis, 'Precipitation', legend=TRUE)
```

With this, it is possible to observe a large geographic extent of data availability, besides being possible to observe spatial continuity pattern of precipitation in different tropical and subtropical regions of the globe, including island regions (Figure 5.13). Future studies should be conducted to evaluate advantages and disadvantages of using this information in different monitoring and data analysis applications with geoprocessing methodologies associated with remote sensing big data.

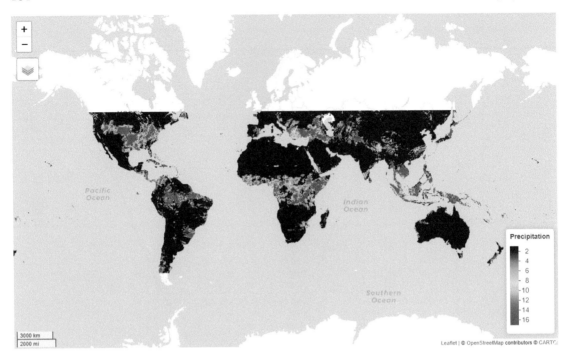

Figure 5.13 Meteorological RADAR from the Monitoring and Warning of Natural Disasters (Cemaden), state of São Paulo, Brazil.

5.5.1   Active and passive microwave techniques

Microwave remote sensing instruments sensitive to the presence of water and ice inside clouds and insensitive to clouds that do not generate immediate precipitation have enabled estimation of rainfall at the global level. The first Microwave Imager (SSM/I) sensor was launched in 1987 with a high-frequency channel at 85.5 GHz, in an orbit of 350 km and inclination of 35°. As ice particles and raindrops reduce the cloud emissivity, the cloud brightness temperature decreases below a nominal reference at which to determine precipitation with reasonable consistency at 15-by 15-km spatial resolution. In November 1997, the Tropical Rainfall Measuring Mission (TRMM) satellite was launched by the National Aeronautics and Space Administration (NASA) of the USA and the National Space Development Agency (NASDA) of Japan, with the Precipitation RADAR (PR), TRMM Microwave Imager (TMI), Visible Infrared Scanner (VIRS), Lightning Imaging Sensor (LIS), and the Clouds and Earth's Radiant Energy System (CERES) sensors. The TMI is a passive microwave sensor designed to provide quantitative information about the amount of precipitation integrated into the column over a 780-kilometer-wide band. The radiation intensity is measured at the frequencies: 10.7 (45-km spatial resolution); 19.4, 21.3, 37, and 85.5 GHz (5-km spatial resolution). At the 10.7-GHz frequency, there is linear response for high rainfall, common in tropical rainfall. By means of PR, the three-dimensional distribution of rainfall is measured over continent and oceans. Through VIRS, high-resolution information on cloud cover, cloud type, and cloud top temperature is recorded with a five-channel spectral cross-scanning radiometer of 0.63, 1.6, 3.75, 10.80, and 12 μm and a spatial resolution of 2.1 km at the nadir and an imaging range of 720 km. With LIS, global ray incidence is measured by an optical sensor at 0.777 μm, spatial resolution of 5 km at nadir, and imaging range of 590 km. With CERES, the radiative energy reflected and emitted by the Earth's surface and the atmosphere is measured in terms of aerosol and cloud constituents by means of a broadband scanning radiometer operating in the visible and infrared spectral ranges (0.3-5.0 μm and 8.0-12.0 μm, respectively). With the combined wavelengths of the TRMM sensors, rainfall was estimated monthly on 500 by 500 km grids to cover tropical latitudes, part of Europe and areas in the northern hemisphere (Jensen, 2007).

Data collection initiated by TRMM continued with the joint NASA/JAXA Global Precipitation Measurement (GPM) mission, launched in February 2014. From the launch of the TRMM to the current GPM mission, there has been evolution in the remotely detected hydrometeorological data. This is reflected in better instrumentation and understanding of water dynamics and their connection in the energy balance, and with the carbon cycle and other elements on Earth. The GPM has enhanced the capabilities of the TRMM in many ways. Although the GPM has only two instruments compared to the five instruments in the TRMM, these two instruments, a dual frequency precipitation RADAR (DPR) and a GPM Microwave Imager (GMI) radiometer, were more advanced for measuring precipitation from space. The DPR is the only dual frequency RADAR in space used to create 3D profiles and estimates of precipitation intensity, ranging from rain to snow and ice (Figure 5.14). There is in GMI a larger frequency range than the TRMM (13 channels versus 9 channels), which allows GPM to measure precipitation intensity and type in all cloud layers using a wider data range. One of the most significant developments in the GPM data is the wider global coverage. While the TRMM collected data in tropical and subtropical regions between approximately 35° north and south latitude, in GPM, data is recorded between approximately 65° north and south latitude. This makes it possible to obtain data from storms that form in the tropics and move into the mid and high latitudes. Another improvement in the GPM data over the TRMM is that it obtains data from a constellation of partner satellites, rather than from a single satellite. Rainfall data from nearly a dozen orbiting US and international satellites are calibrated by the GPM Core Observatory to ensure uniform data structure (Blumenfeld, 2020).

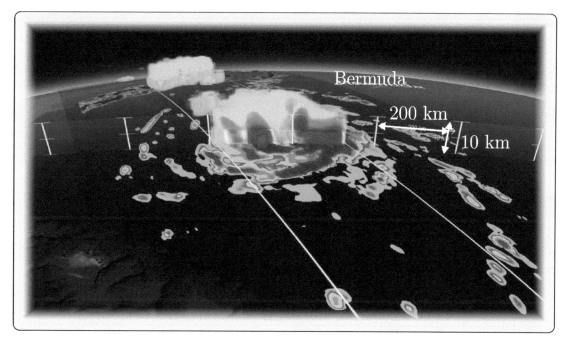

Figure 5.14 3D image of storm structure caused by Hurricane Gonzalo approaching Bermuda on October 16, 2014 created with dual-frequency precipitation RADAR (GPM).

5.5.2   Visible and infrared techniques

The brightness of sunlight reflected by clouds in the visible and near-infrared ranges can indicate the thickness and probability of rainfall. Cloud top temperature can also be used to estimate precipitation. The cooler the cloud top, the greater the probability of rainfall. However, not all clouds with cold tops produce precipitation. Two techniques are used for estimation of rainfall by remote sensing in the visible and infrared as per (Jensen, 2007):

- The use of polar orbit sensors to estimate monthly rainfall through daily estimates of emerging longwave infrared radiation with the AVHRR sensor;
- The use of an index called "GOES Precipitation Index" (GPI) based on thermal infrared data, classifying cloud top temperature pixels $< 235K$ as "rainy" (3 mm h^{-1}). GPI is the standard precipitation product recorded in the tropics and subtropics.

GPI is a model for simple rainfall estimation that relates the fraction of pixels below a given temperature to the precipitation rate (Arkin et al., 1994; Arkin & Meisner, 1987). The cloud top temperature is estimated by the 10.8-μm channel of the GOES satellite and the fraction of pixels with temperatures < 235 K in a 1 by 1 degree area in a time interval between two consecutive images:

$$P = 3FT \tag{5.4}$$

where P is the rainfall (mm), F, the fraction of pixels with $T < 235$ K, T, the time interval between two observations (h), and 3 mm h^{-1}, a constant.

After calculating the cumulative precipitation between a given interval T, the sum of the values in a day is the daily cumulative total.

The hydroestimator is an automatic method that uses an empirical exponential relationship between the precipitation estimated by RADAR and the cloud top brightness temperature extracted from the infrared channel of the GOES satellite to obtain the real-time precipitation rate. Variables such as precipitable water, relative humidity, orography, parallax, and a convective equilibrium level adjustment for hot top events were used to automatically adjust the precipitation rate (Scofield, 2001, 1987). The estimation model implemented is an adaptation of the model used by National Environmental Satellite, Data, and Information Service (NESDIS) (Vicente et al., 2002; Vicente et al., 1998) and adapted for operational implementation in South America (Figure 5.15).

5.6   Aerosols and Clouds

In modeling the Earth's global climate system is necessary to monitor (Jensen, 2007):

- The amount and type of atmospheric particles formed by nature and human activities such as aerosols;
- The amount of, type of, and height of clouds;
- The distribution of land cover and vegetation canopy structure.

5.6.1   Aerosols

Aerosol particles can range in size (0.01 -> 10 μm) and solid or liquid state. With the Multiangle Imaging SpectroRadiometer (MISR) instrument on the Terra satellite, it is possible to locate and quantify the aerosol content. The MISR information is collected from the blue, green, red, and near-infrared spectral bands at nine viewing angles (Jensen, 2007).

Figure 5.15 Estimated rainfall over South America by Hydroestimator on June 12, 2020, at 11:40:00 GMT.

The TROPOMI instrument, on board the Sentinel-5P satellite, is an imaging spectrometer used in the wavelength ranges between the ultraviolet and shortwave infrared. The TROPOMI aerosol index is called the Ultraviolet Aerosol Index (UVAI). The calculation of the UVAI is based on wavelength changes in Rayleigh scattering in the ultraviolet spectral range with low ozone absorption. UVAI can also be calculated in the presence of clouds so that daily global coverage is possible, and is ideal for monitoring aerosol plumes of dust, volcanic ash, and biomass burning (ESA, 2018).

5.6.2   Clouds

Clouds influence the flow of energy in Earth's atmosphere by warming or cooling the Earth depending on their thickness and height above the surface. Low, thick clouds reflect incident solar radiation back into space, causing cooling. High clouds trap the emerging infrared radiation, generating the greenhouse effect. Accurate cloud albedo information, used to generate three-dimensional quantitative information about the height, structure, thickness, shape, and roughness of the cloud tops, can be calculated. Diurnal and nocturnal records of cloud patterns can be obtained through the thermal infrared band. Therefore, with multispectral remote sensing, it is possible to extract information about cloud types and height. High convective cumulonimbus clouds are cold and clear. The sea and the land surface are warm and dark. In possession of the pixel value in the visible and thermal infrared bands, it is possible to identify the nature of the monitored cloud (Jensen, 2007) (Figure 5.16).

The GOES sensor allows us to obtain data in the visible and in the thermal infrared. With visible daytime imagery there is detail of cloud patterns that appear bright in the images, while the continent appears darker. With thermal imagery it is easier to identify the boundary of the frontal systems and distinguish the land-water boundary (Figures 5.17 and 5.18) (Adapted from Jedlovec & Meyer (2020)).

The VIRS sensor from the TRMM satellite, the VIRS, MISR, and CERES instruments from the Terra satellite, and bands 33 to 36 from the MODIS sensor (thermal infrared from 13.185 to 14.385 μm) also provide cloud information.

5.7   Water Vapor

Water vapor is the most important greenhouse gas in the atmosphere and is essential for predicting meteorological processes such as convection, cloud formation, precipitation, and extreme events. Water vapor is mapped based on measurements of water vapor absorption bands around 6.7 μm. At this wavelength, most of the radiation measured by the sensor comes from the atmospheric layer between 300 and 600 km (intermediate layers of the troposphere). The relative humidity is higher in the light areas than in the dark areas in a water vapor image. Upward and downward movements of water vapor can also be identified by light and dark colors, respectively (Adapted from Jensen (2007)) (Figure 5.19).

Atmospheric water vapor can be studied by the MODIS sensor in the 17 (0.89-0.92 μm), 18 (0.931-0.941 μm), and 19 (0.915-0.965 μm) bands (Jensen, 2007).

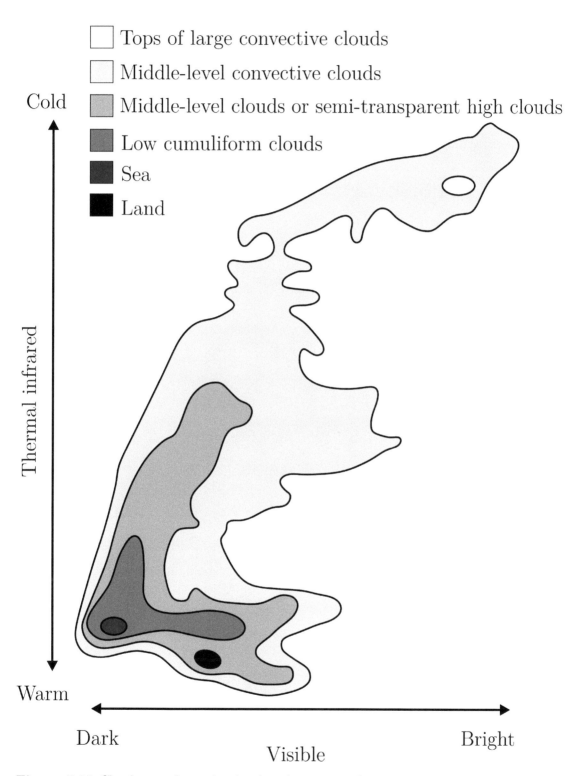

Figure 5.16 Cloud type determination based on spectral measurements in the visible and near-infrared of the electromagnetic spectrum.

weather.msfc.nasa.gov

12 Jun 2020
17:10 UTC

Figure 5.17 GOES-East imagery, channel 2 (0.64 micrometers), at 0.5-km spatial resolution, used for daytime cloud, fog, insolation and wind monitoring

5.8 Snow

The study of snow makes it possible to determine (Jensen, 2007):

- The geographic extent of snow on a seasonal basis;
- The equivalent water content of snow.

The spatial distribution of snow can be realized in visible or near-infrared imagery, because snow is lighter than vegetation, soil, or water not covered by snow. Another evidence for distinguishing snow from cloud is based on the period of observation, because clouds move more frequently than snow. However if, in an image observed on the ground there are clouds and snow, the mid-infrared

Intense, high altitude, cold cloud top

Warm, weak, low altitude cloud top

Cloud-free and very warm surface temperature

Figure 5.18 GOES-East imagery, channel 13 (10.35 micrometers), at 2-km spatial resolution, used for surface and cloud temperature monitoring.

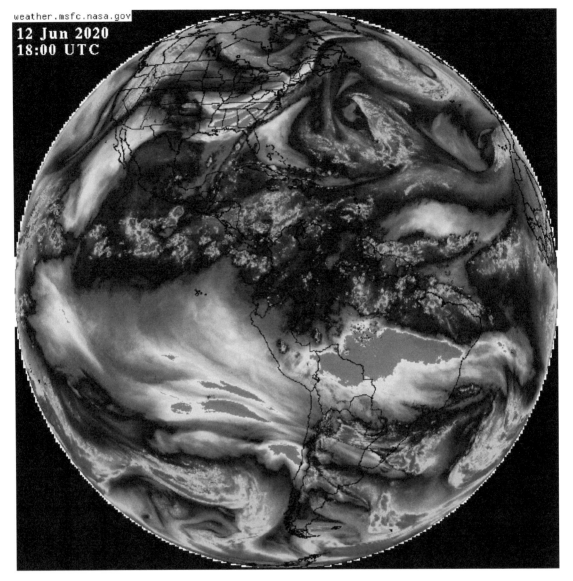

Figure 5.19 GOES-East imagery, channel 8, at 2-km spatial resolution, used for monitoring high-level atmospheric water vapor, wind, and rainfall.

portion of the spectrum is used to distinguish these targets. In the visible and near-infrared spectral regions, clouds and snow reflect roughly equal amounts of radiant flux. In the mid-infrared portion of the spectrum (1.5-2.5 μm), clouds still reflect a lot of energy, while snow's reflectance is approximately zero (Figure 5.20) (Adapted from Jensen (2007)).

Based on these relationships, the Normalized Snow Difference Index (NDSI) (Hall et al., 2002; Jensen, 2007) was developed:

$$Landsat\ TM\ NDSI = \frac{(TM2 - TM5)}{(TM2 + TM5)} \tag{5.5}$$

A threshold of 0.7 can be applied to the NDSI image to separate cloud pixels from cloudless (snow) pixels.

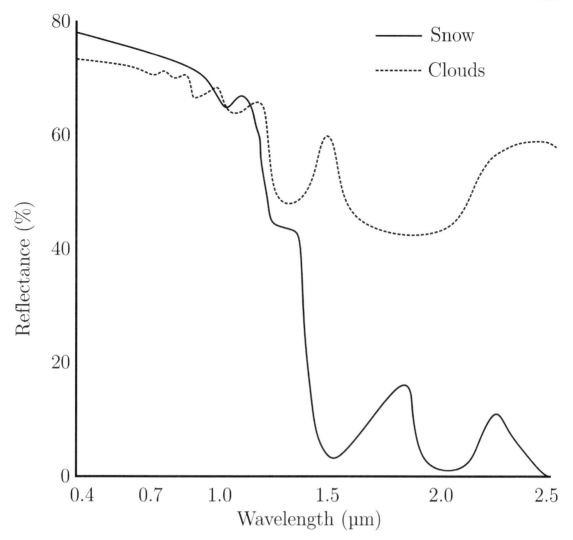

Figure 5.20 Comparative reflectance of cloud and snow according to wavelength variation.

Using MODIS data, bands 4 (0.545-0.565 μm) and 6 (1.628-1.652 μm), the MODIS Normalized Difference Snow Index (Hall et al., 2002) was developed:

$$MODIS\ NDSI = \frac{(MODIS4 - MODIS6)}{(MODIS4 + MODIS6)} \tag{5.6}$$

The microwave spectral region can be used to obtain information for depth estimates, water-equivalent snow, and the presence of liquid water in snow. Clouds are transparent to most microwave frequencies being possible to map surface snow and its properties in regions with clouds in the sky (Jensen, 2007).

5.9   Water Quality Modeling

Traditional techniques of *in situ* measurements associated with modeling techniques in geographic information systems provide useful information about water quality. Biophysical variables measured by remote sensing such as terrain slope, soils, and land use can be used as input data for hydrologic models. Approximately one-third of the model input parameters are obtained from topographic information such as terrain slope, slope length and shape. Soil attributes such as erodibility and texture can be obtained by field sampling. Land use information can be obtained by aerial or orbital imagery (Jensen, 2007).

Pollution originating from urban discharge, construction, hydrologic modification, forestry, mining, agriculture, irrigation return flows, solid waste, atmospheric deposition, river bank erosion, and sewage can cause decreased recreational water use, reduced water storage capacity in rivers, blocked conductors in irrigation canals, excessive water input and sedimentation, problems in determining loss of fish habitat, wildlife, and reduced aesthetic quality of the aquatic environment (Jensen, 2007). Remote sensing data can be used as a standard method for water quality studies. In general, satellite remote sensing provides cheap (or even free) coverage of water bodies in Brazil, such as MERIS/OLCI, MODIS, Landsat-8, Sentinel-2A and 2B. In order to monitor water quality accurately, the R package `waterquality` (Johansen et al., 2020) has been developed with algorithms to detect and quantify chlorophyll *a*, turbidity, and phycocyanin in water. The main function of the package is to convert reflectance images from operational satellite imagery (MODIS, MERIS, Landsat-8, Sentinel-2, and Worldview-2) into water quality indices established for a desired area of interest.

Some R packages provide information about water, as shown in Table 5.2.

Table 5.2 Example of R packages used for water studies.

Package	Description	Source
water	Algorithms for calculating actual evapotranspiration using surface energy balance models.	Olmedo et al. (2018)
waterquality	Satellite water quality detection algorithms. Detection of chlorophyll *a*, blue-green algae (Phycocyanin) and turbidity from WorldView-2, Sentinel-2, Landsat-8, MODIS and MERIS sensor data.	Johansen et al. (2020)
envirem	Generation of bioclimatic data.	Title & Bemmels (2021)
RSAGA	Geoprocessing functions of terrain data for hydrological modeling.	Brenning et al. (2018)
RStoolbox	Remote sensing image processing and analysis, such as spectral index calculation, principal component transformation, unsupervised and supervised classification.	Leutner et al. (2019)
raster	Spatial data analysis and modeling.	Hijmans et al. (2020)

5.10   Moisture Indices

Several water indices can be obtained based on spectral bands from remote sensing as shown in Tables 5.3 and 5.4, for example, Modified Normalized Difference Water Index (MNDWI), Water Index by Normalized Difference (NDWI), Water Index by Normalized Difference 2 (NDWI2), Landsat Albedo, Normalized Drought Difference Index (NDDI), Surface Water Index (LSWI), and Generic Water Mapping.

Table 5.3 Example of moisture indices and variables determined using spectral bands obtained by remote sensing.

Index	Band	Source
MNDWI - Modified Normalized Difference Water Index	green, SWIR2	Xu (2006)
NDWI - Water Index by Normalized Difference	green, NIR	McFeeters (1996)
NDWI2 - Water Index by Normalized Difference 2	NIR, SWIR2	Gao (1996)
Albedo - Landsat Albedo	blue, green, red, NIR, SWIR1, SWIR2	Liang (2001)
NDDI - Normalized Drought Difference Index	NDVI, NDWI	Gu et al. (2007)
LSWI- Surface Water Index	NIR, SWIR3	Chandrasekar et al. (2010)
Water - Generic Water Mapping	NDVI, Albedo	Chemin et al. (2020)

Table 5.4 Moisture indices and its equations.

Index	Equation
MNDWI - Modified Normalized Difference Water Index	(green-SWIR2)/(green+SWIR2)
NDWI - Water Index by Normalized Difference	(green-NIR)/(green+NIR)
NDWI2 - Water Index by Normalized Difference 2	(NIR-SWIR2)/(NIR + SWIR2)
Albedo - Landsat Albedo	0.293blue+0.274green+0.233red+0.156 nir+0.033SWIR1+0.011SWIR2
NDDI - Normalized Drought Difference Index	(NDVI-NDWI)/(NDVI+NDWI) under conditions
LSWI- Surface Water Index	(NIR-SWIR3)/(NIR+SWIR3) under conditions
Water - Generic Water Mapping	NDVI < 0.1; Albedo < 0.1

Indices can be estimated from sensor spectral bands in the R package RStoolbox (Leutner et al., 2019) identified by band code as shown in Table 4.4.

Some indices are based on the variation of relief characteristics. The topographic moisture index can be calculated by the digital elevation model by the geographic information system SAGA GIS in R, through the package RSAGA (Conrad et al., 2015; Lovelace et al., 2019).

Climate and topographic moisture indices, such as the Thornthwaite moisture index, annual evapotranspiration, SAGA topographic moisture index and the terrain roughness index can be obtained by the R package `envirem` (Title & Bemmels, 2018) at different spatial and temporal resolutions.

5.11   Computational Practice

Different computational practices were performed to illustrate water-related studies in decision-making applications from remotely sensed data.

5.11.1   Virtual series view laboratory

The virtual series view laboratory consists of a dataset of over 500 million Enhanced Vegetation Index 2 (EVI2) time series from 16-day MODIS composite data. The EVI2 time series were filtered with auxiliary sensor data and Daubechies Wavelets Transform (Db8) (Freitas, 2011).

An explanatory document on series view applications can be obtained on the Internet for viewing **pdf**[3]. A tutorial at **pdf**[4] can facilitate the use of the platform to obtain orbital remote sensing data interactively with the region of interest.

Rainfall, 3B43V6/TRMM product, and temperature (°C) data from MODIS AQUA and TERRA day and night are available for geovisualization and spreadsheet import from April 2000 to October 2017.

As an example of use of the series view platform, it is proposed to determine the temporal variation of the enhanced vegetation index (EVI), the rainfall obtained from the TRMM, and the day and night temperature from the MODIS sensor in an area with a vegetation mixture of pasture, native forest, and coffee in the southern region of the state of Minas Gerais, Brazil.

Registration and login to the SATVEG website can be done **here**[5].

A county is defined for location in order to demarcate a point in coffee farming, in this case at the following coordinates:

- Longitude: -44.96816°

- Latitude: -21.21154°

The data are presented on a graph after geolocating the EVI2 pixel in the area by defining a point on the map (Figure 5.21).

As a result, the time series of vegetation index and rainfall can be analyzed in relation to the months of the year, exploring the relationship between vegetation and rainfall that can contribute to making crop management decisions (Figure 5.22).

---

[3] http://www.dsr.inpe.br/laf/series/artigos/LAF_INPE_MODIS_EVI2_SeriesTemporais_Portugues.pdf
[4] http://www.dsr.inpe.br/laf/series/tutorial.pdf
[5] http://www.dsr.inpe.br/laf/series/

Figure 5.21 EVI2 pixel defined by a point in the geographical region of interest.

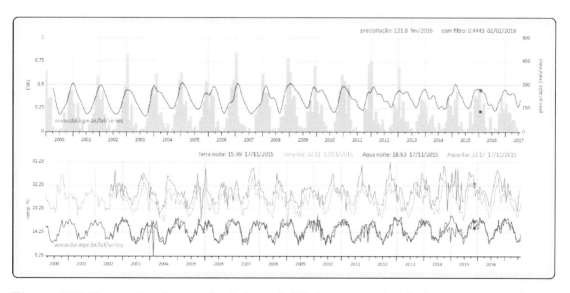

Figure 5.22 Time series of vegetation index, rainfall, daytime, and nighttime temperature from a defined pixel in a coffee plantation, state of Minas Gerais, Brazil.

This type of platform is just one example of how remote sensing data can be democratized for general use by the scientific community; however, political and economic factors can affect the development of this type of readily available information that requires frequent updating and maintenance costs to provide usable data based on scientific knowledge.

Afterward, computational practices are performed to determine the NDVI vegetation index and the moisture indices MNDWI, NDWI, NDWI2 (Leutner et al., 2019). Other indices evaluated are defined from functions used to calculate NDDI, LSWI, albedo and water index, as described in the RemoteSensing package (Laborte et al., 2009). The topographic wetness index is determined using the RSAGA package (Brenning et al., 2018), and calculated based on morphometric relief variables from altitude data from around the Funil dam, state of Minas Gerais, Brazil.

5.11.2   Installing R packages

The install.packages function is used to install the raster (Hijmans et al., 2020), RStoolbox (Leutner et al., 2019), waterquality (Johansen et al., 2020), RSAGA (Brenning et al., 2018), and rgdal (Bivand et al., 2021) packages in the R console.

```
install.packages("raster")
install.packages("RStoolbox")
install.packages("waterquality")
install.packages("RSAGA")
install.packages("rgdal")
```

5.11.3   Enabling R packages

The library function is used to enable the raster, RStoolbox, waterquality, RSAGA, and rgdal packages in the R console.

```
library(raster)
library(RStoolbox)
library(waterquality)
library(RSAGA)
library(rgdal)
```

A Landsat-8 OLI/TIRS image is taken of the region surrounding the Ijaci dam, Minas Gerais, Brazil, for imagery performed on June 28, 2021 on the **Earth Explorer**[6] website. The image used was corrected for illumination based on relief (Goslee, 2011) from Shuttle Radar Topography Mission (SRTM) digital elevation model. The sdos method was used for atmospheric correction in the Landsat-8 bands of the reflective spectrum, with the parameters hazeBands = c(1:8) and darkProp = 0.01. In this case, bands 1 to 7 and 9 are used. The panchromatic band with spatial resolution of 15 m was not stacked. The Landsat-8 image with the calculated surface reflectance data can be obtained for **download**[7] and reproduction of the computational practice.

---

[6]https://earthexplorer.usgs.gov/
[7]http://www.sergeo.deg.ufla.br/sr/downloads/lsat8_sdos.zip

5.11.4 Remote sensing moisture indices

The surface reflectance bands of the Landsat-8 OLI/TIRS image are imported and renamed with the `stack` and `names` functions, respectively.

```
lsat <- stack("C:/sr/c5/lsat8_sdos.tif")
names(lsat) <- c('costal', 'blue', 'green', 'red', 'nir', 'swir2',
                 'swir3', 'swir1', 'tir1', 'tir2')
```

The `spectralIndices` function is used to determine the vegetation vigor index, NDVI, and the moisture indices MNDWI, NDWI, and NDWI2 in the region studied.

```
si <- spectralIndices(lsat, blue = "blue", green = "green", red = "red",
nir = "nir", swir2 = "swir2", swir3= "swir3",
indices = c("NDVI", "MNDWI", "NDWI", "NDWI2"))
```

The `plot` function is used to map the indices determined at Funil dam on June 28, 2021 (Figure 5.23).

```
plot(si)
```

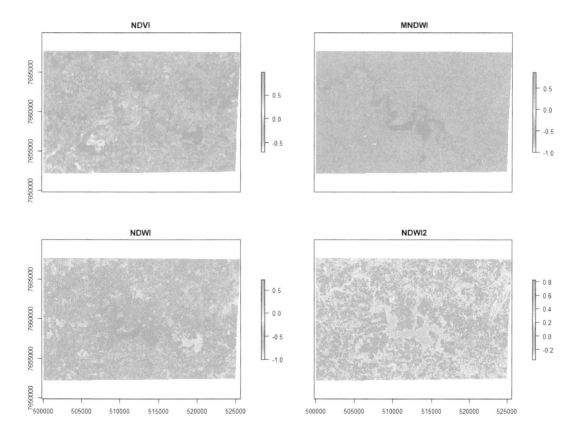

Figure 5.23 Determination of NDVI, MNDWI, NDWI, and NDWI2 indices in the region surrounding the Funil dam, state of Minas Gerais, on June 28, 2021.

The moisture indices NDDI, LSWI, and water around the dam were also determined. As these indices are not implemented in the RStoolbox package, it is necessary to define functions according to the algorithm for determining each index with the function and return functions. Initially a function for normalized index calculation is defined.

```
.normalized_index <- function(x1, x2){
    return((x1-x2)/(x1+x2))
}
```

The function for calculating NDDI is determined with conditionals applied with pixel-by-pixel map algebra between NDVI and NDWI indices, and is called "nddi".

```
nddi <- function(ndvi, ndwi) {
    result<- .normalized_index(ndvi, ndwi)
    result[is.infinite(result)] <- NA
    result[result < 0] <- 0
    result[result > 2] <- 2
    return(result)
}
```

The nddi function is used to calculate the NDDI in the region surrounding the Funil dam, state of Minas Gerais.

```
nddi_lsat <- nddi(si$NDVI, si$NDWI)
```

Similarly, the lswi function is created to determine the LSWI.

```
lswi<-function(nir, swir3) {
    result <- .normalized_index(nir , swir3)
    result[is.infinite(result)] <- NA
    result[result < -1] <- -1
    result[result > 1] <- 1
    return(result)
}
```

Next, the lswi function is applied to determine the LSWI in the region around the Funil dam, state of Minas Gerais.

```
lswi_lsat<-lswi(lsat$nir, lsat$swir3)
```

The albedo is needed to determine the water index by the parameterized albedoLandsat function.

```
albedoLandsat <- function(blue, green, red, nir, swir2, swir3) {
    return(0.293 * blue + 0.274 * green + 0.233 * red +
            0.156 * nir + 0.033 * swir2 + 0.011 * swir2)
}
```

The albedoLandsat function is used to calculate the albedo in the region surrounding the Funil dam, state of Minas Gerais.

```
albedo <- albedoLandsat(lsat$blue,lsat$green,lsat$red,
lsat$nir, lsat$swir2, lsat$swir3)
```

The water function is created to determine the water index using thresholds obtained from the NDVI and albedo results.

```
water<-function(ndvi, albedo) {
    return( (ndvi < 0.1) & (albedo < 0.1) )
}
```

The water function is used to calculate the water index around the Funil dam.

```
water_lsat<-water(si$NDVI, albedo)
```

The indices are stacked with the stack function and then mapped to geovisualization.

```
wsi<-stack(nddi_lsat, lswi_lsat, albedo, water_lsat)
names(wsi)<-c("NDDI", "LSWI", "albedo", "water")
plot(wsi)
```

The plot function is used to map the NDDI, LSWI, albedo, and water indices in the region surrounding the Funil dam. The R package RColorBrewer (Neuwirth, 2022) is used to set a blue color palette to the results using the brewer.pal function (Figure 5.24).

```
plot(wsi, col = RColorBrewer::brewer.pal(n = 9, name = "Blues"))
```

5.11.5   Determine water quality indices

The functions of the R package waterquality are used to determine water quality indices in the surroundings of a dam in Ijaci, southern Minas Gerais. In this case, the water index determined in the previous practice is used as a reference to mask the Landsat-8 image only inside the dam. The mask is determined as a function of water index values greater than 0 that are converted into polygons with the rasterToPolygons function.

```
water <- wsi$water # Rename the water index
pol <- rasterToPolygons(water, fun=function(x){x>0}) # Convert to polygons
```

The mask function is used to crop the image exactly inside the Funil dam region.

```
funnel <- mask(lsat, pol)
```

The resulting brick class raster is converted to the stack class with the stack function.

```
lsat_water<-stack(funnel)
```

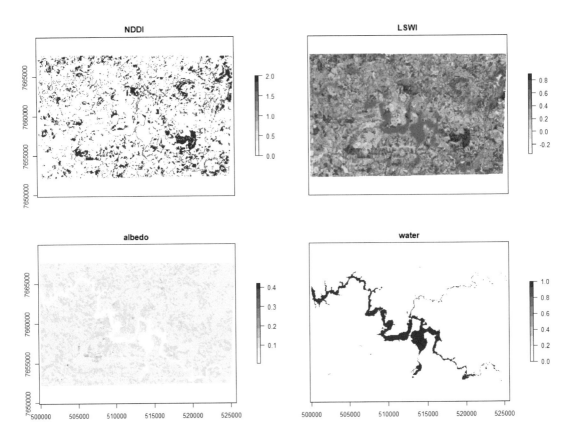

Figure 5.24 Determination of NDDI, LSWI, albedo, and water indices in the region surrounding the Funil dam, state of Minas Gerais, on June 28, 2021.

The raster files in the water mask are exported with the `writeRaster` function and the vector water mask in class `SpatialPolygonsDataFrame` with the `writeOGR` function.

```
writeOGR(pol, dsn="C:/sr/c5/pol.shp"
         "pol", driver="ESRI Shapefile") # Export vector
writeRaster(lsat_agua, filename="C:/sr/c5/lsat_agua.tif",
    options="INTERLEAVE=BAND", format="GTiff", overwrite=TRUE) # Export raster
```

The water quality indices, Al10SABI (Alawadi, 2010), Be16FLHblue, Be16FLHviolet (Beck et al., 2016), Kn07KIVU (Kneubühler et al., 2007), Be16NDTIblue (Beck et al., 2017), Be16NDTIviolet (Beck et al., 2017), Be16FLHBlueRedNIR (Beck et al., 2017), Be16FLHGreenRedNIR (Beck et al., 2017), Be16FLHVioletRedNIR (Beck et al., 2017), TurbBe16GreenPlusRedBothOverViolet (Beck et al., 2017), TurbBe16RedOverViolet (Beck et al., 2017), TurbBow06RedOverGreen (Bowers & Binding, 2006), TurbChip09NIROverGreen (Chipman et al., 2009), TurbDox02NIRoverRed (Doxaran et al., 2002), TurbFrohn09GreenPlusRedBothOverBlue (Frohn & Autrey, 2009), Turb-Harr92NIR (Schiebe et al., 1992), are determined with the `wq_calc` function and calculated based on the reflectance values of Landsat-8 bands 1 to 5.

```
ijaci_All <- wq_calc(lsat_agua, alg = "all", sat = "landsat8")
```

Maps of 16 water quality indices are mapped at the Funil reservoir, state of Minas Gerais (Figure 5.25).

```
plot(ijaci_All, col = RColorBrewer::brewer.pal(n = 9, name = "Blues"))
```

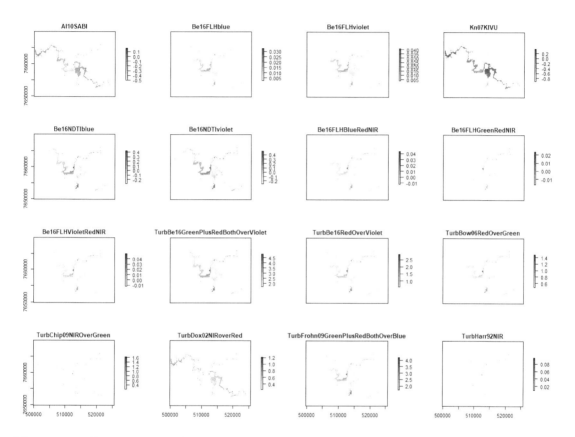

Figure 5.25 Determination of water quality indices in the Funil dam region, state of Minas Gerais, on June 28, 2021.

5.11.6 Determination of altitude and topographic humidity index

Altitude data are obtained to determine the topographic humidity index in the area around the Funil dam, state of Minas Gerais. Altitude data can be obtained with the getData function, specifying the longitude, latitude coordinates of a region of interest. In this case, the SRTM digital elevation model is obtained by specifying the longitude and latitude coordinates of -45° and -21°, respectively.

```
dem <- getData('SRTM', lon=-45, lat=-21, download=TRUE)
```

After returning the digital elevation model in the region surrounding the Ijaci dam, it is necessary to export the raster in SAGAGIS .srgd format to perform the topographic wetness index calculation using algorithms from the GUI program, saga-7.3.0_x64. This program is used as a third-party software to perform the routines for morphometric and hydrologic calculations from R, with the RSAGA package. The rsaga.env function is used to connect the software environments.

```
env <- rsaga.env('C:/SAGAGIS/saga-7.3.0_x64/saga-7.3.0_x64/')
```

The digital elevation model is exported in the .srgd extension using the writeRaster function.

```
writeRaster(dem, filename="C:/sr/C5/srtmprj.sgrd", format='SAGA', overwrite=TRUE)
```

The rsaga.wetness.index function is used to determine the topographic wetness index.

```
rsaga.wetness.index(in.dem = "C:/sr/C5/srtmprj.sgrd"
                    out.wetness.index = "C:/sr/C5/twi.sgrd")
```

The topographic moisture index determined in the .sdat extension is imported and assigned the coordinate reference system for mapping.

```
twi <- raster::raster("C:/sr/C5/twi.sdat") # Import
crs(twi)<-"+proj=utm +zone=23 +south +datum=WGS84 +units=m
+no_defs +ellps=WGS84 +towgs84=0,0,0" # Assign crs
```

The plot function can be used to map the digital elevation model and topographic wetness index defined in the region surrounding the Funil dam (Figure 5.26).

```
par(mfrow = c(1, 2), mar = c(2, 2, 1.5, 1.5), mgp = c(1.5, 0.6, 0))
plot(srtmprj, col = grey.colors(100))
plot(twim, col = rainbow(100))
```

With this it is possible to see the regions of higher topographic humidity according to the relief variation in the region around the Funil dam. The lower regions of the terrain and in places of greater width of the dam's watercourse showed higher values of topographic humidity index with values per $\sim$ 7.5 and altitude of $\sim$ 800 m.

5.11.7 Determination of the temporal variation of water temperature

The variation of water temperature can be related to evaporation linked to latent heat flux but indirectly can relate to aquatic life, macro and micronutrients, and sediments in the water. A practice on the AppEEARS platform is performed to determine the temporal variation of evapotranspiration, at a geographic point in the water of the Funil dam. Day and night surface temperature data are obtained at 1000-m spatial resolution, converted to Kelvin by means of an algorithm applied to thermal band of the MODIS sensor on board the Terra satellite, between January 2018 and December 2019. To do so, the following steps were performed:

(1) Obtain the coordinates of a point in water of the Funil dam. The latitude and longitude coordinates are -21.184055°, -44.866435°.

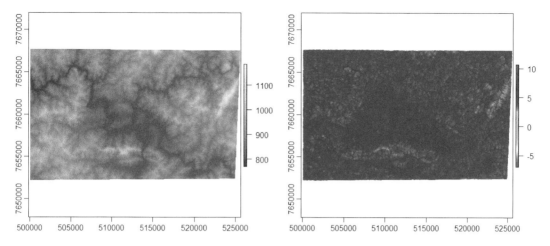

Figure 5.26 Spatial variation of altitude and topographic humidity index in the Funil dam region, state of Minas Gerais.

(2) Log in to **AppEEARS**[8].

(3) After login, from the "Extract" menu, choose the "Point Sample" option.

(4) Identify the sample name as "Temp".

(5) In the field, "Uploaded coordinates (ID, Category, Lat, Long)", enter the coordinates obtained in (1) with (.) in the decimal places, such as: -21.184055° latitude and -44.866435° longitude at the Funil dam, Minas Gerais, Brazil.

(6) In the fields, "Start Date" and "End Date", enter the period of search for day and night surface temperature values from the MODIS sensor, Terra satellite. In this case, choose the dates between January 1, 20020 and September 11, 2021: 01-01-2020 and 11-09-2021, with data every 16 days of temporal resolution.

(7) In the item "Select the layers to include in the sample", it is searched for the remote sensing product "**Earth MODIS Land Surface Temperature & Emissivity (LST&E)** *MOD11A2.006,1000 m, 8day,(2000-02-18 to Present)*". To do this, enter the keyword "temp" in the search field and then select the option of interest to obtain the product.

(8) The following item is added in the "Selected layers" field:

- "LST_Day_1km";
- "LST_Night_1km";
- "QC_Day";
- "QC_Night".

To add the items, you need to click with the left mouse button on the sub-item with the symbol (+), which is instantly added from the field. To remove an item, use the symbol (-), on items already added for the search.

(9) Then access the "Submit" button. The following message is displayed by the system: "The point sample request was successfully submitted. An email notification will be

---

[8]https://lpdaac.usgs.gov/tools/appeears/

delivered once the request is complete. Therefore, it is necessary to wait for the data processing and the email notification in order to manipulate the results (Figure 5.27).

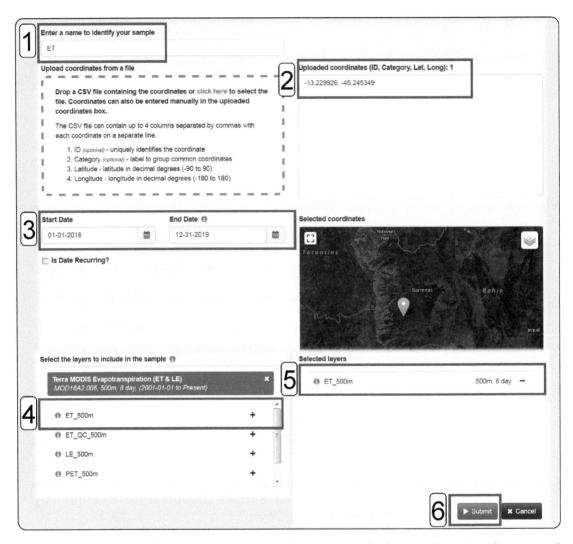

Figure 5.27 Example of setting parameters in the `AppEEARS` platform to determine the temporal variation of remote sensing data at a point with WGS-84 geodetic coordinates.

(10)   The temperature time series can be obtained in point cloud, over the entire period and a comparison of the years 2020 and 2021, or by means of points connected by lines determined using filtering of all pixels with reliable quality based on the imagery quality product obtained from the MOD11A2 product database (Figure 5.28).

Therefore, based on the analysis of reliable remote sensing data of daytime (MOD11A2_006_LST_Day_1km) and nighttime (MOD11A2_006_LST_Night_1km) temperature from the MODIS sensor, it is possible to see, in general, cooler water temperatures in June and warmer in October and January in both years evaluated, and in the nighttime periods there is cooling of the wetland temperature around the Funil dam when compared to the daytime periods between 2020 and 2021.

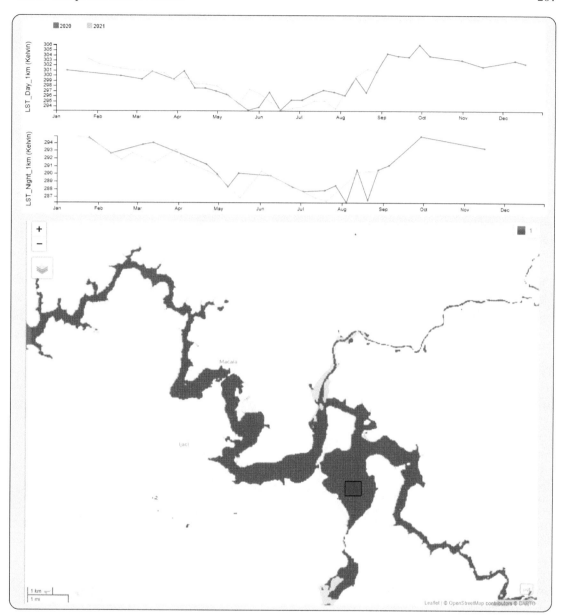

Figure 5.28 Daytime and nighttime MODIS temperature time series between January 1, 2020 and September 11, 2021 at Funil dam, state of Minas Gerais, Brazil.

5.11.8 *In Situ* **Meteorological Data Analysis**

Measurements of environmental variables taken at the site of interest, i.e., *in situ*, are generally used to (Congalton & Green, 1998):

- Calibrate remote sensing data;
- Make non-biased assessment of the accuracy of the final results.

Sampling procedures *in situ* are presented in formal science courses, i.e., engineering, chemistry, biology, soils, hydrology, and meteorology (Jensen, 2007). Most *in situ* data can be collected with georeferenced geodetic information x, y, z of the vertex under study, with differential coordinate correction.

In situ data is used for climate classification of a region. Data of minimum, mean, maximum daily air temperature (°C) and daily rainfall of Lavras, state of Minas Gerais, are obtained from the BDMEP website. The Lavras station is described with the following metadata:

- Latitude: -21.75°;
- Longitude: -45°;
- Altitude: 918.84 m;
- Operating Station: Started operating on February 02, 1911.

The data of minimum, average, maximum daily air temperature (°C) and daily rainfall for Lavras, state of Minas Gerais, from January 1, 1961 to December 31, 2017 were organized in a .csv file for further processing in R. The R package hydroTSM (Zambrano-Bigiarini, 2020) is enabled for analysis with the library function:

```
library(hydroTSM)
```

The *in situ* data analyzed in this activity are available for **download**[9]. The data are imported into R with the read.zoo function.

```
z <- read.zoo("C:/sr/c1/lavras_bdmep1.csv", header = TRUE, sep = ",", dec = ".")
```

The data of rainfall (pcp), minimum temperature (tmn), average temperature (tm), and maximum temperature (tmx) are separated with bracket operation, according to the location of each variable in the data table.

```
pcp <- z[, 1]
tmn <- z[, 3]
tm <- z[, 4]
tmx <- z[, 2]
```

A data window is selected to represent the monthly variation of precipitation in the area between 2004 and 2017 with the window function.

```
pcp<- window(pcp, start=as.Date("2004-01-01"))
tmn<- window(tmn, start=as.Date("2004-01-01"))
tm<- window(tm, start=as.Date("2004-01-01"))
tmx<- window(tmx, start=as.Date("2004-01-01"))
```

The climographic is determined for the station located in Lavras for the period between 2004 and 2017 using the climograph function (Figure 5.29).

```
m <- climograph(pcp=pcp, tmean= tm, tmx=tmx, tmn=tmn, main="Climograph",
                pcp.label="Precipitation (mm)]", tmean.label="Temperature(°C)",
                pcp.col="lightblue", tmean.col="red", na.rm=TRUE)
```

A rainfall matrix can be made to visualize a rectangular representation of the variation of rainfall over the months of the year between 2004 and 2017. Daily data is converted into total rainfall with the daily2monthly function and setting the FUN=sum parameter to perform summation of daily data.

---

[9]http://www.sergeo.deg.ufla.br/sr/downloads/lavras_bdmep1.zip

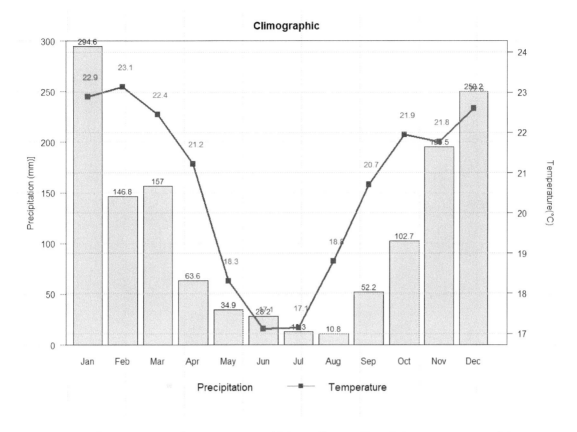

Figure 5.29 Climographic of Lavras, state of Minas Gerais, Brazil, between 1961 and 2017.

```
m <- daily2monthly(x, FUN=sum, na.rm=TRUE)
```

The `matrix` function defines a matrix with monthly values in each column per year, followed with the specification of columns, rows, and time format.

```
M <- matrix(m, ncol=12, byrow=TRUE)
colnames(M) <- month.abb
rownames(M) <- unique(format(time(m), "%Y"))
```

The plot of monthly precipitation values (mm month^{-1}) is performed over the period 2004 to 2017 with the combined function `print(matrixplot())` (Figure 5.30).

```
print(matrixplot(M, ColorRamp="Precipitation",
                 main="Lavras monthly precipitation, [mm/month]"))
```

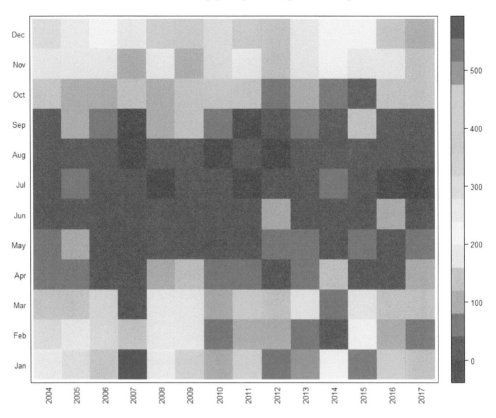

Figure 5.30 Precipitation matrix mapping in Lavras, state of Minas Gerais, Brazil, between 2004 and 2017.

5.12   Exercises

5.12.1   Cite five applications of remote sensing studies of water.

5.12.2   Cite the possible paths of the radiance that reaches a body of water.

5.12.3   Cite four components of the volumetric radiance of water.

5.12.4   Explain how water vapor monitoring can be done in South America and how this information can be used in practice.

5.12.5   Explain how a spectral band ratio remote sensing moisture index can be used to separate water from terrain and to detect the moisture content of the monitored object.

5.13   Homework

5.13.1   Subject

Spatio-temporal monitoring of rainfall from CHIRPS data.

5.13.2   Assignment

Develop the subject presented with a practical application of remote sensing and digital image processing including the topics Introduction and Objective. Then present the development of the task.

5.14   Resources on the Internet

Activities are proposed for the development of scientific research on remote sensing that can be used or adapted by the student to monitor and identify targets in a specific area of interest as shown in Table 5.5.

Table 5.5 Slide presentation and illustrative video about remote sensing of water study.

Guide	Address for Access
1	Landsat helps warn of algae in lakes, rivers[10]
2	Video on remote sensing of water quality with Landsat and *in situ* measurements[11]
3	Video on advanced studies on remote sensing of water and evapotranspiration[12]
4	Video on weather forecast and air quality at INPE[13]
5	Video example of an application used in weather forecasting and climate studies[14]
6	Video example of a GOES-16 monitored storm in Mexico[15]
7	Record-breaking video of the largest lightning storm in Brazil monitored so far in the world with GOES-16[16]
8	Video of GOES-16 monitoring of hurricane Dorian[17]
9	Video about atmospheric river monitoring in California with GOES-17[18]
10	Video of ice monitoring on the Great Lakes with GOES East[19]
11	Slides about remote sensing of water[20]

5.15   Research Suggestion

Activities are proposed for the development of scientific research on remote sensing that can be used or adapted by the student to monitor and identify targets in a specific area of interest (Table 5.6).

Table 5.6 Description of practical activities that can be used or adapted by students with suggested research in remote sensing.

Activity	Description
1	Determine NDWI, NDWI2, and MNDWI moisture indices from multispectral remote sensing imagery.
2	Use the practical example developed by the teacher on the AppEEARS platform to generate time-series graph results for a variable related to remote sensing of water.

---

[10]https://youtu.be/OGawz01Fpk4
[11]https://youtu.be/3fkqLx2wZGo
[12]https://youtu.be/1LMwiloM-Cs
[13]https://youtu.be/5GJzy6WTWvw
[14]https://youtu.be/BeVAUAUOaUo
[15]https://youtu.be/B5SywLlVSy4
[16]https://youtu.be/7l70D9-5Ufw
[17]https://youtu.be/M6Lt6c0IW00
[18]https://youtu.be/HljTWPBoV0M
[19]https://youtu.be/KbnPOratPao
[20]http://www.sergeo.deg.ufla.br/sr/Presentation/Aula5/presentation.html#/

6

Remote Sensing of Soils, Rocks, and Geomorphology

6.1 Learning Questions

The learning questions answered by reading the chapter are as follows:

- What is the relationship between applications of remote sensing and soil taxonomy techniques.
- How is the information about the variation of light under different land use types and conditions, and at different wavelengths, for soil monitoring?
- How is the geology of the terrain studied with remote sensing?
- How is the geomorphology of the terrain detected using remote sensing and mapped with geoprocessing techniques?
- How is the soil index determined from sensor system spectral bands used in remote sensing?

6.2 Learning Outcomes

Using the learning outcomes from the chapter, you should be able to do the following:

- Understand the use of soil taxonomy techniques in the context of monitoring areas using remote sensing.
- Understand the spectral signature of soil types in different uses.
- Understand how the geology of the terrain is monitored with remote sensing.
- Monitor the geomorphology of the terrain with remote sensing and geoprocessing techniques.
- Recognize the soil index from sensor system spectral bands in remote sensing.

6.3 Introduction

Solid ground is composed of rock and weathered rock forming the soil, which has provided support for life on Earth. Remote sensing can be used narrowly in identifying, inventorying, and mapping the surface of soils not covered by dense vegetation. Remote sensing provides information about the chemical composition of rocks and minerals. Absorption bands are available to detect specific rock and mineral types by imaging spectroscopy techniques. With the use of passive or active remote sensing, relief clipping is specific to extract information about lithology, structuring, drainage terrain and geomorphology according to the following applications (Figure 6.1) (Jensen, 2007):

- Mapping exposed soil for agriculture, livestock, and reforestation;
- Identification of texture, organic matter, water content, salinity;
- Modeling erosive processes and hydrology;
- Identifying lithology, structure, drainage patterns and network, geomorphology, watershed, slope, and aspect;
- Soil and water conservation;
- Land planning and agricultural suitability;
- Mining;
- Natural disasters and landslides.

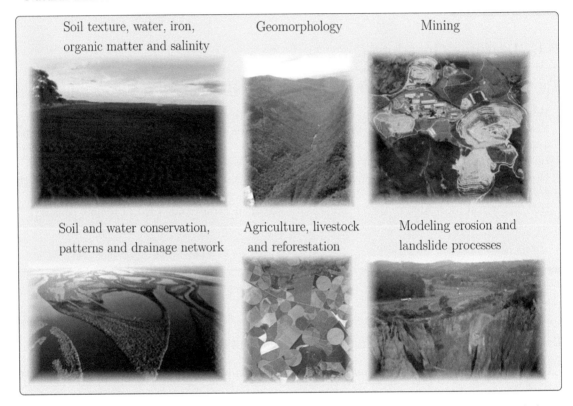

Figure 6.1 Remote sensing applications to obtain information on soils, rocks, and geomorphology.

With knowledge about the location, quality, and abundance of soils, minerals, and rocks, appropriate ecological and socioeconomic decisions can be made in order to best conserve these non-renewable natural resources (Jensen, 2007).

6.4   Soil Characteristics and Taxonomy

A partial equivalence between soil classes at a high categorical level can be obtained theoretically between different soil classification systems. In practice, to have accurate correspondence at classification level, soils must be reclassified in the different systems based on analytical data (IUSS Working Group WRB, 2015; Santos et al., 2011; USDA, 1999, 2014) (Table 6.1).

Table 6.1 Partial equivalence between soil classification at a high categorical level (order) in different systems.

Santos et al. (2011)	IUSS Working Group WRB (2015)	USDA (1999), USDA (2014)
Argisol	Acrisol; Lixisol; Alisol	Ultisol; some oxisols (kandic)
Cambisol	Cambisol	Inceptisol
Chernosol	Phaeozem; Kastanozem Chernozem (few)	Molisol (only the Ta)
Espodosol	Podzol	Spodosol
Gleisol	Gleysol; Stagnosol (some)	Entisol (Aqu-alf-and-ent-ept-)
Gleisol salic	Solonchak	Aridisol; Entisol (Aqu-sulfa-hydra-salic)
Latosol	Ferralsol	Oxisol
Luvisol	Luvisol	Alfisol, Aridisol (argid)
Neosol		Entisol
Neosol fluvic	Fluvisol	Fluvent
Neosol litholic	Leptosol	Lithic orthent; Lithic Psamment
Neosol quartzarenic	Arenosol	Quartzipsamment
Neosol regolithic	Regosol	Psamment
Nitosol	Nitisol; lixisol or alisol	Ultisol, oxisol (kandic), alfisol
Organosol	Histosol	Histosol
Planosol	Planosol	Alfisol
Planosol natric	Solonetz	Natr (ust-ud) alf
Planosol haplic	Planosol	Albaquult, Albaqualf, Plinthaqu(alf-ept-ox-ult)
Plinthosol	Plinthosols	Subgroups of plinthic oxisols; ultisol; alfisol; entisol; inceptisol
Vertisol	Vertisol	Vertisol
Not classified in Brazil	Cryosol	Gelisol
Not classified in Brazil	Anthrosol; technosol	
Not classified in Brazil	Andosol	Andisol
Not classified in Brazil	Umbrisol	Some subgroups of Umbric
Not classified in Brazil	Gypsisol	Large group of aridisol (Gypsi–)
Not classified in Brazil	Durisol	Several large groups dur- of alfisol, andisol, aridisol, inceptisol, molisol, and others
Not classified in Brazil	Calcisol	Several large groups of alfisol, aridisol, inceptisol, molisol, vertisol, and others
Not classified in Brazil	Albeluvisol	Some alb_ gloss_ classes

The geographical distribution of soils in Brazil can be obtained in vector format, according to the Brazilian soil classification system (Figure 6.2) (Santos et al., 2011).

6.4.1 Soil Horizons

Soil originates from unconsolidated material from the Earth's surface being the natural medium for growth, plant development and support for water and nutrient extraction. Soil is defined as weathered material between the Earth's atmosphere and bedrock below the surface with a depth

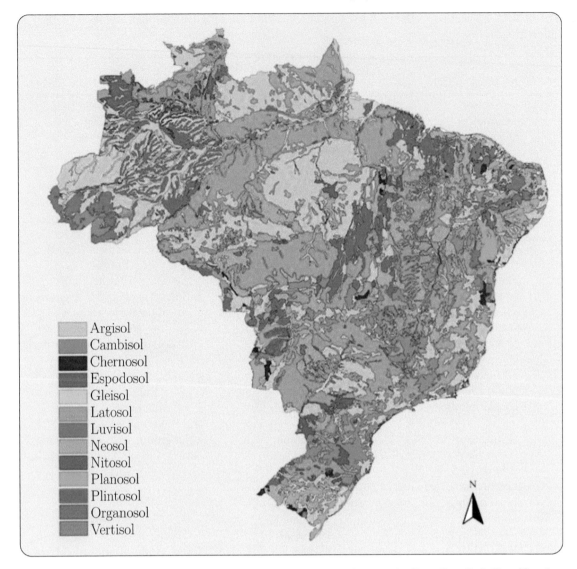

Figure 6.2 Geographical distribution of soils in Brazil according to the Brazilian Soil Classification System at the scale 1:5,000,000.

of approximately 200 cm (Jensen, 2007). According to Santos et al. (2018), soil consists of a collection of natural bodies composed of solid, liquid and gaseous parts. It is three-dimensional, dynamic, and formed by minerals and organic matter existing in most of the surface mantle of the Earth's continental extensions; it is also containing living matter and occasionally modified by anthropic activities. In the tropical and humid climate conditions of Brazil, biological activity and pedogenetic processes can exceed 200 cm.

When soil is examined from the surface, parallel sections are observed and called "soil horizons", or distinct layers of parent material, as a result of additions, losses, translocations and transformations of energy and matter in a natural environment. Pedological changes in soil materials reveal contrast with the rock substrate or its slightly altered residue, expressing pedological differentiation in relation to the pre-existing material. The soil has the atmosphere as its upper boundary. The lateral limits are in contact with neighboring soils, rock outcrops, unconsolidated dendritic materials, landforms, or water mirrors. The lower limit of the soil is the hard rock or saprolitic materials with no signs of animal or vegetal activity or other indications of the presence of biological activity.

The basic study unit of the Brazilian classification system is based on the determination of a soil profile that constitutes the smallest portion of the land surface analyzed, with three dimensions and making up a minimum volume for studying the variability of the attributes, properties and characteristics of the horizons or soil layers (Figure 6.3) (Santos et al., 2011).

Figure 6.3 Example of a soil profile with the O, A, B, C horizons on bedrock (R). In the O horizon, one can see partially decomposed organic matter. In the A horizon, there is destruction of practically all structures of the original rock. In the B horizon, a high clay content is normally observed due to the deposition of materials in the illuvial zone. In the C horizon, the transition to unweathered rock is observed.

6.4.2 Soil formation

Knowledge of soil genesis is useful for understanding soil properties and classification in the landscape. Soil formation (S) and its characteristics of constitution, color, texture, structure vary as a function of environmental factors over time (Figure 6.4) (Resende et al., 2014):

$$S = f(M, O, C, T) \tag{6.1}$$

where M, is the parent material (rock), O, organisms, C, climate, and T, time.

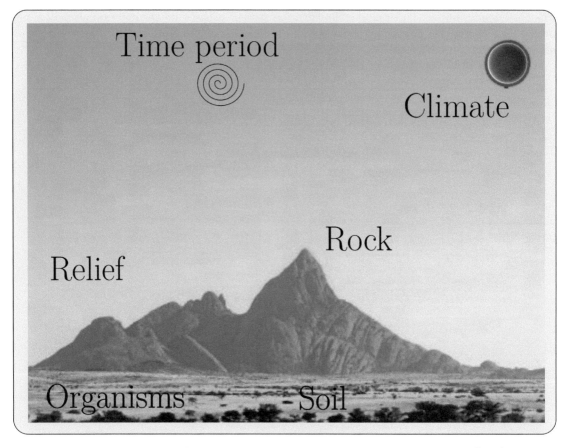

Figure 6.4 Factors in the soil formation process transforming the initial substrate (rock) into soil, over time.

6.4.3 Soil particle size and texture

In general, soil is a mixture of solid particles (mineral and organic) of varying sizes and compositions, making up 50% of its volume. The remaining volume is occupied by liquids and gases in the soil pores. There are three universally used classes of soil grain sizes based on particle diameter: sand (0.05 to 2.0 mm), silt (0.002 to 0.05 mm), and clay (<0.002 mm). Sand particles increase soil drainage by facilitating water percolation in the air spaces between the sandy particles. In the silt and clay particles there is greater capillary water retention of the soil. In the clay particles there are electrical charges that attract and trap dissolved mineral particles (ions), such as potassium and calcium, preventing the leaching of these nutrients that compose the soil fertility. The soil texture triangle makes it possible to identify the percentages of sand, silt, and clay according to different classification systems (Figure 6.5) (Jensen, 2007; Moeys et al., 2018; Santos et al., 2018).

Moeys et al. (2018) performed the soil textural triangle from soil sampling taken across Brazil. In the Southeast Region of Brazil, there was a similar trend in soil texture when compared to data from all of Brazil, as this region contributed 52% of the total samples. However, in the samples from the Southeast Region there was lower silt content when compared to all the data. In the South Region of Brazil, most soils have a clayey textural class, mainly because the parent material is predominantly formed by igneous rocks. Samples with higher silt content also occurred in the South Region due to the low temperature in this region for soil formation. In the Midwest Region, most samples have soil texture classes ranging from sand to clay. The percentage of silt in these soils was low. In this region, there are soils leached by climatic effects, such as ferralsols, derived

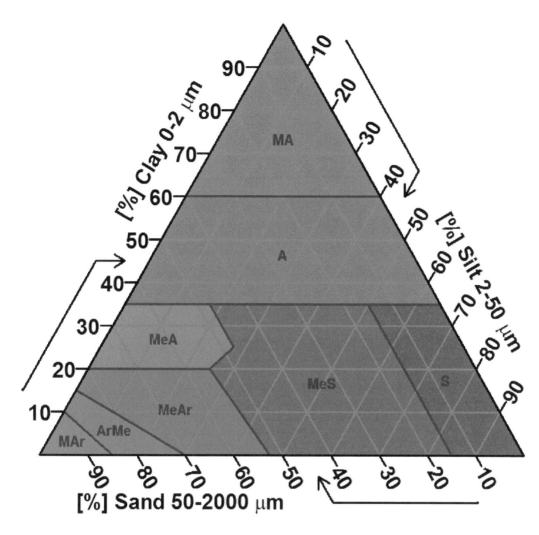

Figure 6.5 Textural triangle of soils based on the Brazilian Soil Classification System, where MA is very loamy texture, A, clayey, S, silty, MeS, medium silty, MeA, medium clayey, MeAr, medium sandy, ArMe, medium sandy, and MAr, very sandy.

from sedimentary and igneous rocks, forming soils with sand and silt, and clayey. In the soils of the North Region there was great textural variation, with lower predictive performance of clay and sand contents in the soils. In the Northeast Region, there wwere many sandy soils that originated from sedimentary materials. The textural variations observed in the textural triangles of each region occur due to geological differences, climate and relief of each region, which determine a large variation of soil types in the country (Figure 6.6) (Demattê et al., 2019).

6.4.4 Soil color

The Munsell Chart is a tool used in agronomy and pedology for identifying the color of a soil, based on Munsell's color system. The Munsell system consists of a notebook with a series of color examples each related to a three-number code of hue, value, and chroma. The hue refers to the ratio of yellow to red color pigments. The value indicates the proportion of the colors white and

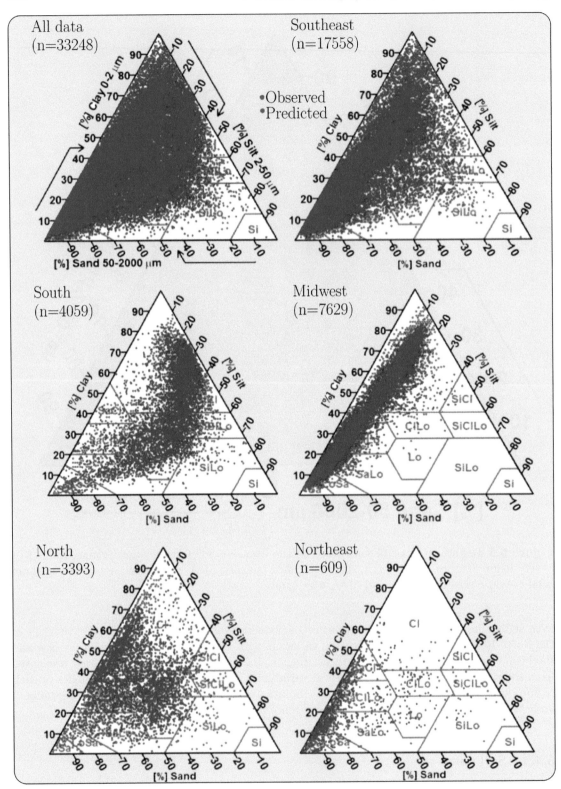

Figure 6.6 Soil textural triangle in the United States Department of Agriculture (USDA) classification system of the entire soil database of Brazil and the Brazilian regions Southeast, South, Midwest, North and Northeast, where, Cl: clay; SiCl: silty clay; SaCl: sandy clay; ClLo: loamy loam; SiClLo: silty clay loam; SaClLo: sandy clay loam; Lo: loam; SiLo: silty loam; SaLo: sandy loam; Si: silt; LoSa: loamy sand; and Sa: sand.

black in the ground, while the chroma refers to the hue's contribution to the coloration. The Munsell Chart method of color identification has been widely used due to its practicality and low cost. However, as this system is based on visual perception, it may present interpretation flaws when comparing a dry soil sample with the colors present in the chart (Figure 6.7) (Kuehni, 2002; Wikipedia, 2020a).

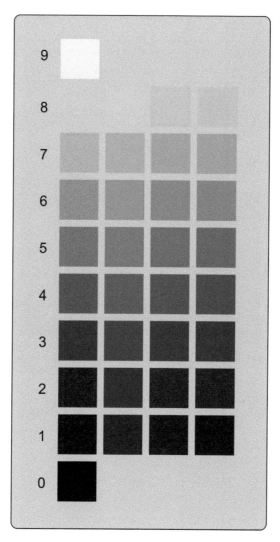

Figure 6.7 Munsell color system used for pedology in Brazil.

6.5   Spectral Characteristics of Soils Detected by Remote Sensing

Optical sensing instruments such as airborne cameras, multispectral and hyperspectral imagers record the spectral reflectance characteristics of the surface of soils not covered by dense vegetation. The total radiance coming from an exposed soil and recorded on a sensor on board a satellite (L_T) is (Jensen, 2007):

$$L_T = L_P + L_S + L_V \tag{6.2}$$

where L_P is the downward radiance from the Sun and atmosphere that never reaches the ground surface, but is recorded by the sensor. L_S is the part of the direct and diffuse solar radiation that reaches the air-soil interface and penetrates at approximately half wavelength depth into the soil, emerges from the soil column by reflection, scattering recorded by the sensor. L_V is the part of the direct and diffuse solar radiation that penetrates a few millimeters to centimeters into the soil column recorded by the sensor (Figure 6.8) (Jensen, 2007).

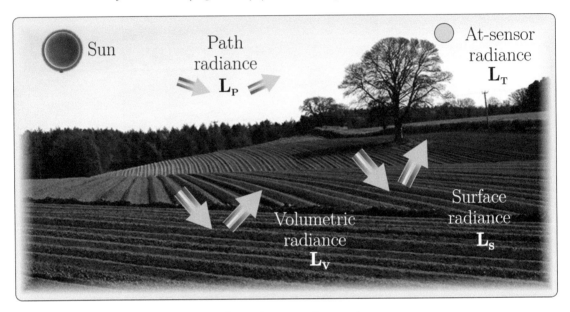

Figure 6.8 Total radiance emerging from the ground towards a remote sensor.

The researcher interested in identifying the organic and inorganic constituents in the upper soil horizons is interested in measuring the integrated surface (L_S) and subsurface (L_V) radiance response (Jensen, 2007):

$$L_S + L_V = L_T - L_P \tag{6.3}$$

i.e., radiometric correction of the data allows removing atmospheric attenuation and separating the individual contribution of L_S and L_V to the reflected radiant flux. As a result, in practice, the scientist improves the soil analysis with the sum of these two radiance constituents.

Soil spectral reflectance characteristics vary as a function of (Jensen, 2007):

- Texture (sand, silt, and clay content);
- Moisture content (dry, wet, saturated);
- Organic matter content;
- Iron oxide content;
- Soil salinity;
- Surface roughness.

In a dry soil with little organic matter, the spectral reflectance curve is relatively simpler than that of water or vegetation. Based on *in situ* spectroradiometer measurement for dry sandy and silty soil, one observes an increase in reflectance with increasing wavelength, mainly in the visible and near-infrared (Figure 6.9) (Jensen, 2007).

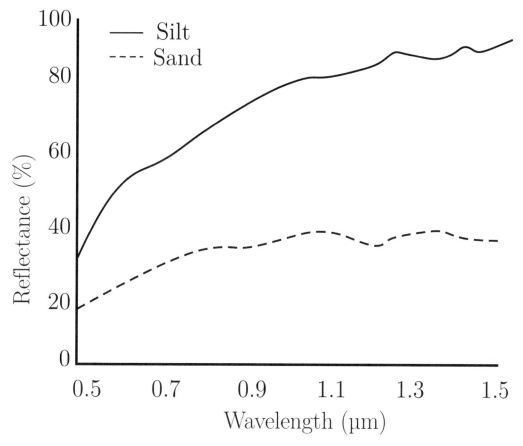

Figure 6.9 Reflectance curves of dry silty and dry sandy soils. Reflectance increases with increasing wavelength along the visible, near-infrared, and shortwave infrared.

With wetting, increased organic matter or oxide in the soil, the spectral curve of the soil can change.

6.5.1 Soil texture and moisture content

In soils with finer clays, the soil particles are arranged closer together with little interstitial air space between them. On the other hand, the sandy particles are large with more interstitial air space. Under rainfall, irrigation or flooding, the individual particles are enveloped by a thin membrane of capillary water that occupies the interstitial air spaces. Clayey soils, more densely packed, can retain a water membrane on their outside and store large amounts of water. Sandy soils with larger air spaces drain and evaporate water faster than clayey soils. Therefore, the higher the soil moisture, the more energy is absorbed and the less light is reflected (Figure 6.10) (Jensen, 2007).

6.5.2 Reflectance of dry and wet soils

Incident radiant energy can be reflected by the dry soil surface after penetrating inside the soil particles and being absorbed or backscattered. Total reflectance is a function of specular reflectance and internal volumetric reflectance of the soil. With increasing soil moisture, each particle can be

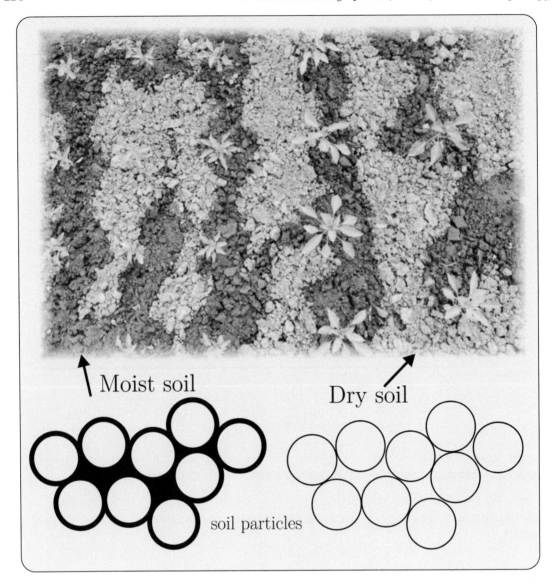

Figure 6.10 Filling the interstitial soil air spaces with water increasing the absorption of the electromagnetic energy incident on the soil by the water and decreasing the soil reflectance.

encapsulated by a thin capillary water membrane and the interstitial air spaces are filled with water. The higher the water content in the soil, the greater the absorption of incident electromagnetic energy and the lower the soil reflectance (Jensen, 2007).

6.5.3   Reflectance of moistened sandy and clay soils

The higher the moisture content in sandy and clayey soil, the lower the reflectance in the visible and near-infrared, especially in the water absorption bands at 1.4, 1.9, and 2.7 μm (Figure 6.11) (Jensen, 2007).

High radiometric and spectral resolution sensors allow differentiating soils with different textures since soils with medium and high clay content exhibit strong hydroxyl absorption bands at 1.4 and

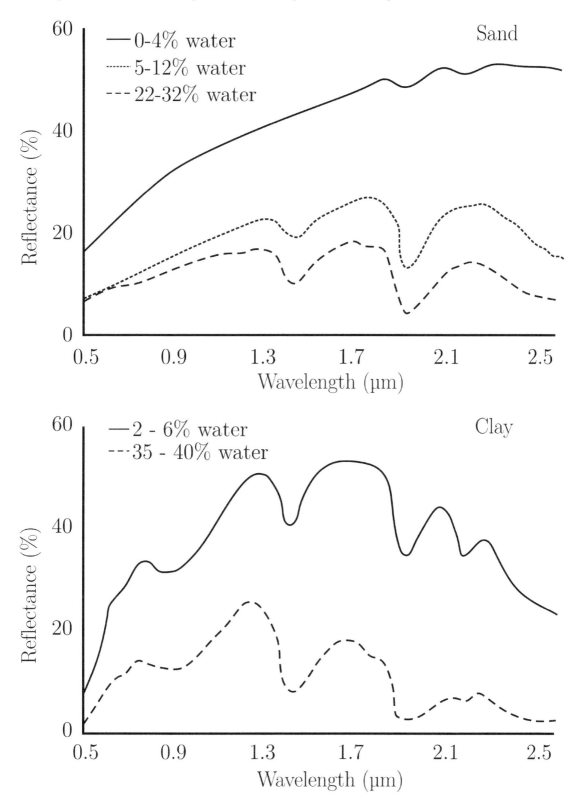

Figure 6.11 The higher the moisture content in sandy and clayey soils, the lower the reflectance along the visible and near-infrared region, mainly in the water absorption bands at 1.4; 1.9; and, 2.7 micrometers.

2.2 μm. In the case of soils with organic matter in the soil, these features can be masked (Jensen, 2007).

Demattê et al. (2019) evaluated the spectral variation of Brazilian soils with a Fieldspec3 spectroradiometer under laboratory conditions, and concluded that the higher sand content in soils from the Northeast region of Brazil determined higher soil reflectance when compared to other regions. On average, the sand content in the Northeast region was 651 g kg^{-1}, while in the South region, it was 264 g kg^{-1}.

6.5.4   Soil organic matter and biological crusts

As animals and plants decompose, organic humus accumulates in the upper portions of soil horizons. The amount of organic matter alters the spectral reflectance characteristics of exposed soil. In sandy soil, the greater the amount of soil organic matter, the greater the absorption of incident energy and the lower the spectral reflectance (Figure 6.12) (Jensen, 2007).

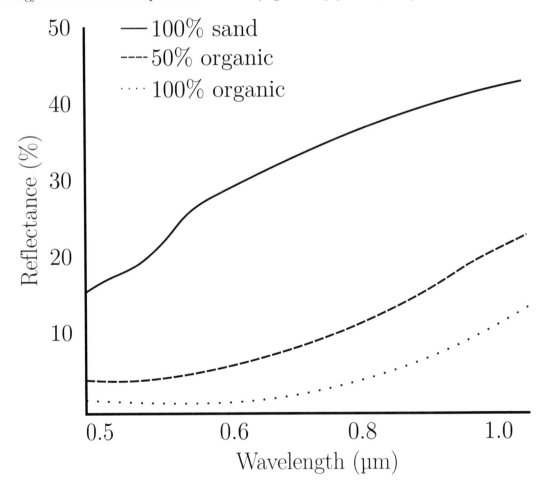

Figure 6.12 Higher levels of organic matter in the soil determine higher absorption of incident energy and lower spectral reflectance.

In Embrapa's digital map of organic carbon of Brazilian soils, mathematical modeling and an *in situ* survey were used to establish a reference of Brazilian soils for several natural resource conservation programs. Available environmental information on soil, relief, parent material, climate, was coupled with modeling to infer information at unmeasured locations. Soil organic carbon maps at different depths can be useful for making decisions about low-carbon agriculture and for targeting greenhouse gas emission reduction practices (Figure 6.13) (Vasques et al., 2017).

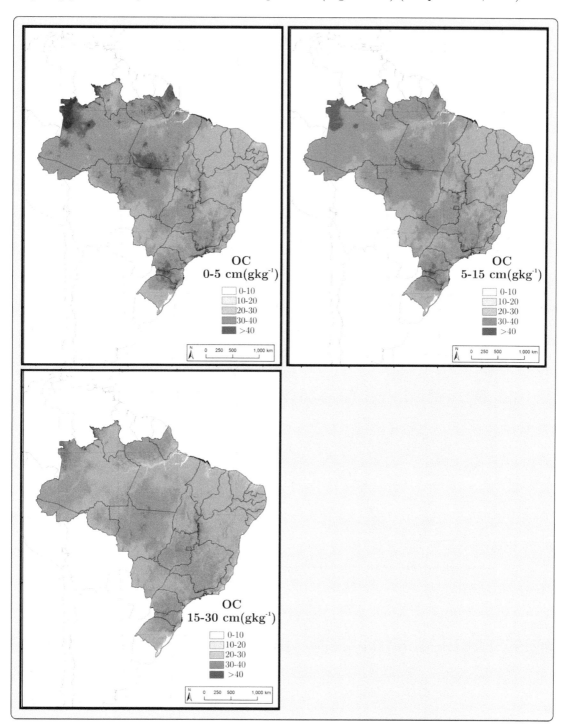

Figure 6.13 Organic carbon (OC) maps of Brazil at depths from 0 to 30 cm.

Crusts and biological material from communities of mosses, lichens, bryophytes, algae, fungi, cyanobacteria, and bacteria can occur in soil often under conditions of drought, extreme temperatures, high pH, and salinity. Biological organisms can be found in deserts and around the world with an important role in desert ecosystems in soil formation, stability, fertility, and erosion prevention (Jensen, 2007).

6.5.5 Iron oxides in soils

The presence of iron oxides in the soil causes color variation with a tendency toward red indicating increased reflectance in the red (0.6-0.7 μm). There is also a decrease in the spectral regions of blue, green and near-infrared (0.85-0.9 μm) in soils with iron oxides when compared to sandy soils without iron oxide (Figure 6.14) (Jensen, 2007).

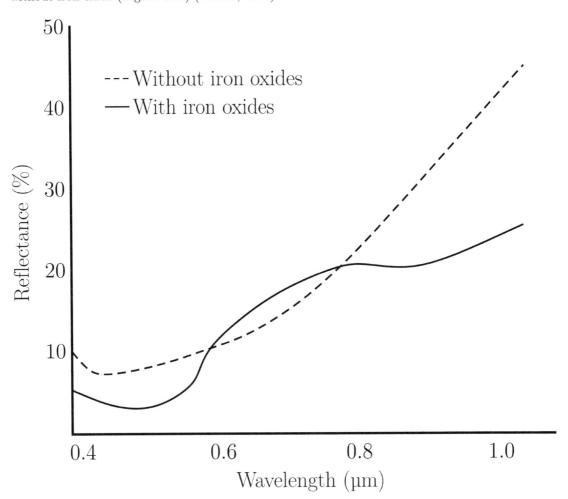

Figure 6.14 Increasing iron oxides in sandy soils increases the red reflectance and decreases the blue, green, and near-infrared reflectance.

6.5.6 Soil salinity

In the surface layers of soils in arid regions and irrigated areas there can be a concentration of salts. The reflectance of saline soils increases with increasing salt concentration in the visible and near-infrared spectral regions, as for example in saline-sodic soils. There can be spectral confusion of saline crusts and light silty soil crusts in the blue and green region (0.45-0.55 μm) (Figure 6.15) (Jensen, 2007).

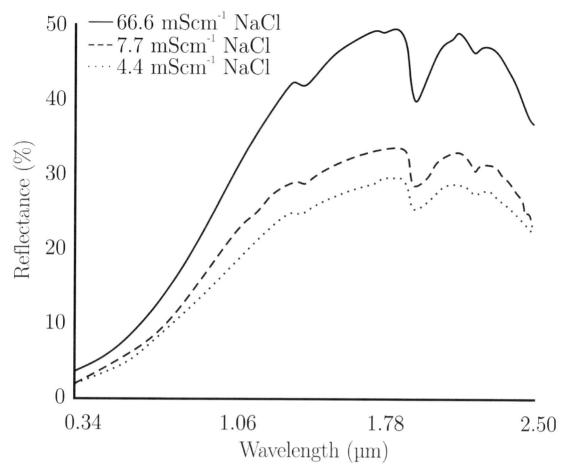

Figure 6.15 Spectroradiometric reflectance measurement of halite (NaCl) at different salt concentrations in soil.

6.5.7   Surface roughness of soil

The lower the relative roughness relative to the size of the incident radiation, the higher the spectral reflectance of the ground. Therefore, comparing the spectral response of soils under different soil roughness conditions, the reflectance can vary as a function of the terrain and making interpretation difficult. Soil surface roughness has been measured using active microwave remote sensing systems (Jensen, 2007).

6.5.8   Rocks and minerals

Rocks are composed of minerals linked together and held together by types of cements, usually silica or calcium carbonate. With the absence of vegetation on the surface, it is possible to differentiate rock types and obtain characteristic information. Through geological surveys, accurate spectral libraries are created using imaging spectroscopy patterns. Remote sensing can capture information about the chemical composition of rocks and minerals on the Earth's surface not fully covered by dense vegetation. Imaging spectroscopy can be used in understanding specific absorption bands associated with particular types of rocks and minerals. In some situations, geochemical information of soils and rocks can be obtained when there are geobotanical relationships in the region studied (Demattê et al., 2019; Jensen, 2007).

Demattê et al. (2019) determined the spectral variation of Brazilian soils according to the variation of the soil parent material with a Fieldspec3 spectroradiometer. In the soils of the southern region of Brazil, where the parent material is predominantly formed under the influence of basalt or related to igneous rocks. Low reflectance values were observed because there were iron oxides and opaque minerals. The low reflectance of soils formed on igneous rocks, such as diabase basalt with high iron content, was correlated with high clay contents. A specific temperate climate was also observed in this region, which favored the preservation of organic matter and determined lower reflectance of the soil samples. In general, in the spectral signatures of igneous rocks, usually rich in calcium and iron, there is low reflectance, while in soils formed in material of metamorphic origin there are high reflectance values. In these soils, the reflectance characteristics are mainly related to orthoclase minerals, quartz and plagioclase (Figure 6.16) (Demattê et al., 2019).

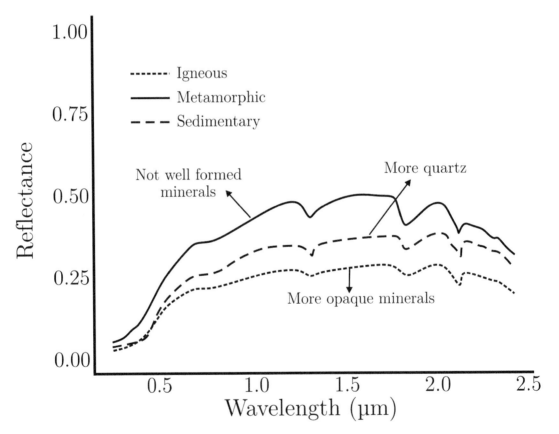

Figure 6.16 Mean spectral reflectance of soil samples according to the geology of igneous, metamorphic, and sedimentary rocks in Brazil.

6.5.9   Soil classes order

The spectral variation of soil classes in Brazil is determined with analysis of soil samples in the laboratory with a Fieldspec3 spectroradiometer according to Demattê et al. (2019). The spectral curve of nitisols shows lower reflectance due to the origin of the soil from mafic rocks, such as basalt and diabase, with high clay, iron oxide, and opaque mineral contents. In the spectral curve of the histosols there is low reflectance in the visible spectral region due to the high organic carbon content in the soil. Podzols have the highest reflectance. In cambisols, rich in quartz, intermediate reflectance is observed. In arenosols, there are high reflectance values due to the higher sand content in the A horizon (Figure 6.17) (Demattê et al., 2019).

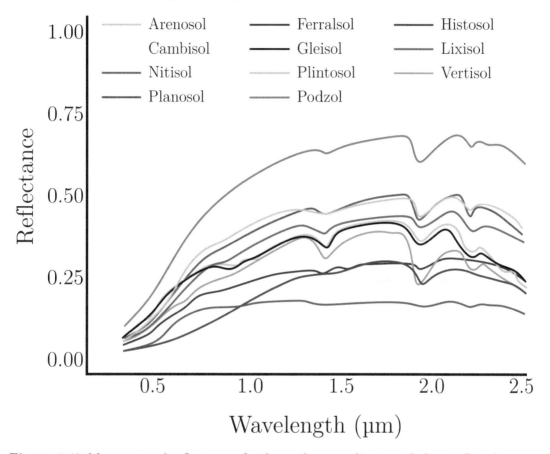

Figure 6.17 Mean spectral reflectance of soil samples according to soil class in Brazil.

6.5.10 Soil in Brazilian biomes

The spectral variation of soils in different biomes in Brazil is determined with analysis of soil samples in the laboratory with a Fieldspec3 spectroradiometer according to Demattê et al. (2019). The soils of the cerrado biome show lower spectral reflectance and specific characteristics at 2.265 μm due to the occurrence of Gibsite. In the Atlantic forest biome there is also low spectral reflectance. Higher reflectance values are observed in the scrub biome due to the predominance of sandy particles in the soils, in addition to high temperatures that accelerate the decomposition of soil organic matter (Figure 6.18) (Adapted from Demattê et al. (2019)).

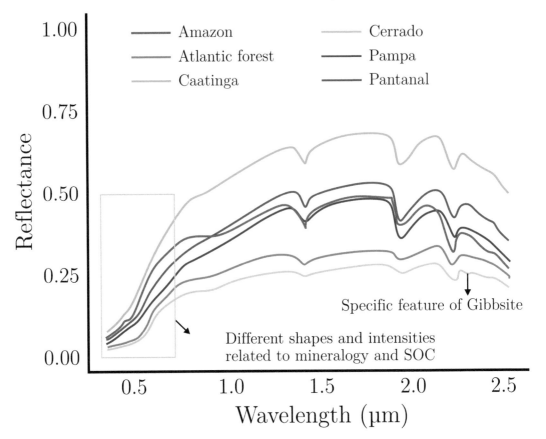

Figure 6.18 Mean spectral reflectance of soil samples according to the occurrence of biomes in Brazil.

6.6   Geology

Geology is defined as the science of rocks used to describe the history of the Earth and its geological formations. Rocks are broken down into sediment through weathering. The sediment is moved by forces of erosion and mass transport and accumulate in new locations. The sediment then consolidated into a new rock type may be buried, heated to the point of melting, flow under pressure to the surface as extrusive lavas, or to an inland location as intrusive magma. As the lava or magma cools, rocks are formed. Weathering begins immediately in extrusive lavas and it can take millennia before the intrusive magma is exposed to the surface where it can be weathered. Much geological information is obtained from detailed *in situ* investigations that have identified thousands of earthquake epicenters around the planet as a result of friction between tectonic plates. Remote sensing has been applied in geology to supplement data obtained with field sampling (Figure 6.19) (Demattê et al., 2019).

6.6.1   Lithology

The lithology of a rock type and its origin are information used to identify rocks *in situ* and by remote sensing. Rocks can be formed by the following processes (Jensen, 2007):

Figure 6.19 Simplified geological map of Brazil.

- Igneous or magmatic rocks <- Formed by molten material (granite, basalt, diabase);
- Sedimentary rocks <- Formed by deposition of particles from pre-existing rocks and by remnants of plants and animals (sandstones, argillites, limestones);
- Metamorphic rocks <- Formed by the application of heat and pressure on previously existing rocks (gneiss, quartzite, shale).

The unconsolidated sedimentary materials are deposited superficially by water and formed alluvial deposits such as alluvial delta, sandbanks, sandbanks, sandbars, and river terraces. If the unconsolidated material is transported by ice, sandy glaciers can form. If there is wind transport, eolian landscapes with sand dunes and glacial deposits may form. Massive material detached from rocks by gravity, can produce slopes or rock mounds visible to remote sensing (Jensen, 2007).

6.6.2   Rock structure

The largest mountain ranges in the world originate from volcanoes or folds. Mountains in oceanic regions are most often volcanic. Basically, continental plates push together causing rocks to be compressed and forced to move in different directions. When a rock is subjected to compression, there can be (Jensen, 2007):

- Elastic deformation <- When the rock returns to its original shape and size after the stress is removed;
- Folding <- In which there is plastic deformation (folding), when the rock is subjected to irreversible compression, i.e., above the elastic limit;
- Fracturing <- In which the plastic limit is exceeded and the rock breaks into pieces, possibly resulting in faults. Joints can occur in the case of rock fracture without apparent displacement as shown in Table 6.2 (Jensen, 2007).

Table 6.2 Compressive rupture of some rocks.

Rock	Mean Fracture Strength (kg cm^{-2})
Basalt	2750
Quartzite	2020
Granite	1480
Slate	1480
Marble	1020
Limestone	960
Sandstone	740

6.6.3   Folds

Compression results in ripples imprinted on the strata that define four basic types of folds (Jensen, 2007):

- Monocline <- Simple fold in a horizontally layered material, appearing as a rounded ramp;
- Anticline <- Upward folded arcs, in which the oldest rocks lie in the center of the convex fold;
- Syncline <- Downward-folded and concave with newer rocks in the center;
- Overturned <- Sedimentary beds are overturned on top of each other.

6.6.4   Rock fractures

Rock fractures are divided into joints and faults. A joint is a crack in the rock in which no significant displacement has occurred. A fault is a crack in rock formed by displacement. With the occurrence of faults, massive blocks of rock can be moved causing earthquakes. The direction and magnitude of displacement can be measured by passive remote sensing.

The main types of displacements on faults are (Figure 6.20) (Jensen, 2007):

- Normal dip-slip <- In which the rock wall is displaced downward exposing a fault scarp;
- Reverse <- In which displacement occurs in the reverse direction;
- Compression <- In which the reverse failure determines the horizontal movement of slabs;
- Graben <- In which a block of material is displaced downward between two normal faults;
- Strike-slip or disconnect <- In which displaced rock material occurs parallel along the fault line;

- Oblique-slip <- In which the displaced rock material occurs oblique with the fault line.

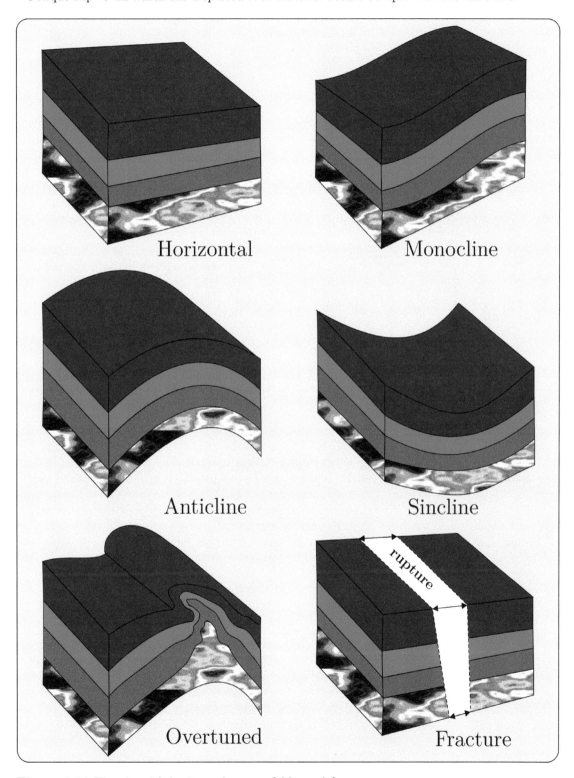

Figure 6.20 Terrain with horizontal strata, folds, and fractures.

6.6.5   Morphometry and drainage patterns

Surface drainage variables measured by remote sensing inform the morphometric characteristics of the drainage as shown in Table 6.3 (Jensen, 2007).

Table 6.3 Drainage morphometric variables measured by remote sensing.

Variable	Equation	Description
Drainage density (D)	$D = \frac{\sum L_i}{A}$	Total length (L) of n channels in a drainage basin divided by the surface area (A) of the basin.
Basin relief (H)	$H = h_{max} - h_{min}$	Vertical distance between the lowest and highest point of a sub-basin.
Roughness index (I_R)	$I_R = HD$	Product of basin relief and drainage density.
Channel frequency (F_C)	$F_C = \frac{N}{A}$	Ratio of the total number of first-order channels to the basin perimeter.
Texture ratio (R_T)	$R_T = N(\frac{1}{P})$	Ratio of the total number of first-order channels to the basin perimeter.
Form factor (F_F)	$F_F = \frac{A}{(L_B)^2}$	Ratio of the basin area to the square of the basin length (L_B).
Elongation ratio (R_E)	$R_E = \frac{2}{L_B}\frac{A}{\sqrt{\frac{A}{\pi}}}$	Ratio between the diameter of the circle that has the same area as the basin and the maximum length of the basin.

The permeability of a soil or rock has a strong correlation with the drainage density. Permeability is inversely proportional to water runoff. In places of low permeability, the water runoff is higher and stream channels can be formed. Weak clays and shales produce the highest drainage density. The drainage patterns visible in remote sensing data can be described as fine, medium or coarse texture. The drainage pattern developed over time provides key information about the bedrock lithology (igneous, sedimentary, metamorphic), topography (slope, aspect), soil texture, materials and permeability, and the type of geomorphology present (alluvial, eolian, glacial). A variety of drainage patterns may occur within a basin, called a "mixed pattern". Where possible, one stratifies the mixed pattern into multiple distinct patterns (Table 6.4) (Jensen, 2007).

Table 6.4 Distinct drainage patterns in survey environments.

Pattern	Description
Dendritic	Tree-like pattern.
Pinnate	Variation of the dendritic pattern with branching similar to a fern plant. Indicates presence of high silt content.
Trellis	Modified dendritic pattern that resembles a trellised vine. Indicates that the underlying rock structure is tilted, folded, or faulted.
Rectangular	Tree-like pattern, but in the main channels there are more abrupt curves at right angles.
Parallel	Pattern with tributaries flowing nearly parallel to each other.
Radial and centripetal	Radial drainage pattern is formed when water flows from a hill or dome. The channels are joined by circles.
Annular	Similar to the radial pattern but the ring-shaped tributaries intersect the radial channels at right angles.

Pattern	Description
Dichotomic	Pattern observed in alluvial fans or deltas at the mouths of channels or rivers.
Braided	Pattern developed on floodplains where deposition of suspended material in interlaced channels has taken place.
Deranged	Drainage pattern between water bodies. Usually swamps, marshes, bogs, and lakes or ponds are presented.
Anastomotic	Mature floodplain drainage pattern in which there are homogeneous sediments and reduced flow velocity. Sand sediments are deposited in the channel increasing its length.
Sinkhole (doline)	Consists of isolated lakes that do not appear to be connected by surface drainage. Channel segments, when present, end abruptly or have disappeared into the relief. Sedimentary limestones ($CaCO_3$) develop in this drainage pattern.

6.7 Geomorphology

Geomorphology is defined as the science of the nature and history of landforms and the processes of weathering, erosion, and deposition that originates the terrain. With geomorphology, the processes of erosion or deposition of materials by movement of water (fluvial), ice (glacial), wind, (eolian) and groundwater are studied. The synoptic view of remote sensing is used to identify and interpret geomorphological features on the Earth's surface. Remote sensing is also used for modeling soil erosion by the universal soil loss equation (USLE) and for applying other hydrological models. The attributes used to classify the terrain forms are (Jensen, 2007):

- Igneous landforms;
- Landforms developed on horizontal strata;
- Landforms developed on folded strata;
- Fault-controlled landforms;
- Fluvial landforms;
- Karst landforms;
- Shoreline landforms;
- Glacial landforms;
- Eolian landforms.

An approach using Earth Engine can be applied via `rgee` (Aybar et al., 2022) for processing cloud remote sensing data for the purpose of terrain study in cloud-intensive region. Data from the **Sentinel-1**[1] mission between June 1, 2020 and October 1, 2020 are used. The Sentinel-1 mission provides data from a dual-polarized C-band synthetic aperture RADAR (SAR) instrument at 5.405 GHz (C-band). This collection includes the S1 Ground Range Detected (GRD) scenes, processed using the Sentinel-1 toolbox to generate a calibrated, orthorectified product. The collection is updated daily. This collection contains all GRD scenes. Each scene has one of 3 resolutions (10, 25 or 40 meters), 4 band combinations (corresponding to the scene polarization) and 3 instrument modes. The possible combinations are single band VV or HH, and dual band VV+VH and HH+HV:

- VV <- Single co-polarization, vertical transmission/vertical reception;
- HH <- Single co-polarization, horizontal transmission/horizontal reception;

---

[1]https://developers.google.com/earth-engine/datasets/catalog/COPERNICUS_S1_GRD

- VV + VH <- Dual-band transverse polarization, vertical transmission/horizontal reception;
- HH + HV <- Dual-band cross-polarization, horizontal vertical transmission/ horizontal reception.

The region studied is called "Pico da Neblina". It is located in the northern Amazonas state, in the Imeri mountain range, and is the highest point in Brazil with an altitude of 2995.30 m (IBGE, 2022). The name of the peak originates from the fact that the top of the mountain is covered by fog most of the time. In turn, the peak gives its name to the Pico da Neblina National Park, where it is located.

The `rgee` (Aybar et al., 2022) package is enabled with the `library` function. The `ee_Initialize()` function is used to initialize the Earth Engine after enabling `rgee`.

```
library(rgee)
ee_Initialize()
```

The Sentinel-1 mission data are obtained from the `ee$ImageCollection` function. Dates of interest in the imagery are filtered between June 1, 2020 and October 1, 2020 with `filterDate` function.

```
sentinel1 <- ee$ImageCollection('COPERNICUS/S1_GRD')$
  filterDate('2020-06-01', '2020-10-01')
```

The Sentinel-1 collection obtained earlier is filtered to obtain dual VV and VH polarization images with the `filter(ee$Filter$listContains())` function. The data is also filtered to obtain Interferometric Wide Swath (IW) mode images with the `filter(ee$Filter$eq())` function.

```
vvVhIw <- sentinel1$
  filter(ee$Filter$listContains('transmitterReceiverPolarisation', 'VV'))$
  filter(ee$Filter$listContains('transmitterReceiverPolarisation', 'VH'))$
  filter(ee$Filter$eq('instrumentMode', 'IW'))
```

The imaging data is separated into orbital images obtained ascending and descending from separate collections with the `filter(ee$Filter$eq())` function.

```
vvVhIwAsc <- vvVhIw$filter(
  ee$Filter$eq('orbitProperties_pass', 'ASCENDING'))
vvVhIwDesc <- vvVhIw$filter(
  ee$Filter$eq('orbitProperties_pass', 'DESCENDING'))
```

Time series means are calculated for different polarizations VH ascending, VH descending, VV ascending and descending, VH ascending and descending in order to make it possible to evaluate different ways of monitoring the terrain for geovisualization. The `$select` and `$mean` functions are used for selecting the polarization of interest and the mean calculation, respectively.

```
# Mean VH ascending.
vhIwAscMean <- vvVhIwAsc$select('VH')$mean()
# Mean VH descending.
vhIwDescMean <- vvVhIwDesc$select('VH')$mean()
# Mean VV for combined ascending and descending image collections.
vvIwAscDescMean <- vvVhIwAsc$merge(vvVhIwDesc)$select('VV')$mean()
# Mean VH for combined ascending and descending image collections.
vhIwAscDescMean <- vvVhIwAsc$merge(vvVhIwDesc)$select('VH')$mean()
```

The result of filtered collections for monitoring the region where Pico da Neblina is located is centralized for mapping with the `Map$setCenter` function. The different polarizations are mapped with the `Map$addLayer` function. The `list` argument is used to set minimum and maximum pixel brightness values for mapping.

```
Map$setCenter(-66.006944, 0.800278, 9)   # Pico da Neblina, Brazil
Map$addLayer(vvIwAscDescMean, list(min = -12, max = -4), 'vvIwAscDescMean') +
Map$addLayer(vhIwAscDescMean, list(min = -18, max = -10), 'vhIwAscDescMean') +
Map$addLayer(vhIwAscMean, list(min = -18, max = -10), 'vhIwAscMean') +
Map$addLayer(vhIwDescMean, list(min = -18, max = -10), 'vhIwDescMean')
```

In both mapped situations it is possible to verify the absence of clouds in the images. With the ascending and descending VV polarization, the drainage network of the region is better differentiated when compared to the ascending and descending VH polarization. Already in the polarizations VH descending and VH ascending it is possible to observe the three-dimensional aspect of the relief in function of the occurrence of terrain shadow to the west or east of the relief, respectively (Figure 6.21).

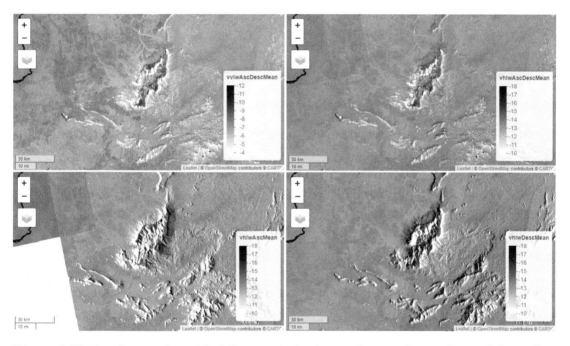

Figure 6.21 Terrain mapping with different polarizations and types of ascending and descending orbits monitored by Sentinel-1.

6.7.1 Geoforms under vegetation canopy

- Aerial laser scanning (LIDAR) has been used for three-dimensional mapping of topographic variables. In archaeological studies, built structures hidden under forest canopies in Guatemala have been detected. Population estimates, measures of agricultural intensification, and evidence of investment in landscape transformation infrastructure are made on the basis of data obtained.

A regionally interconnected network of densely populated towns was observed, supported by a range of agricultural practices that optimized land productivity and interactions between rural and urban communities (Figure 6.22) (Canuto et al., 2018).

Figure 6.22 Representation of the archaeological site of Naachtun, Petén, Guatemala.

6.8   R packages for Soil Study

Several R packages have been developed to study time series of soil indices and the application of digital image processing functions to extract target information as shown in Table 6.5, for example, R packages rnaturalearth (South, 2021), aqp (Beaudette et al., 2021), soiltexture (Moeys et al., 2018), GSIF (Heng et al., 2019), RSAGA (Brenning et al., 2018), gstat (Pebesma & Graeler, 2021), geoR (Ribeiro Jr et al., 2020), raster (Hijmans et al., 2020), FIELDimageR (Matias et al., 2020), and RStoolbox (Leutner et al., 2019).

Table 6.5 Some R packages used to obtain information and map soils.

Package	Description	Source
rnaturalearth	Cultural and physical vector database, such as countries, district, ports, airports, railroads, highways, coastlines, land, ocean, rivers, lakes, glacial regions.	South (2021)
aqp	Functions for quantitative pedology for soil modeling and classification.	Beaudette et al. (2021)
soiltexture	Functions to classify, transform, and display soil texture plots.	Moeys et al. (2018)
GSIF	Functions and databases for digital soil mapping.	Heng et al. (2019)
RSAGA	Geoprocessing and terrain analysis functions.	Brenning et al. (2018)
gstat	Geostatistical soil modeling.	Pebesma & Graeler (2021)
geoR	Model-based geostatistical soil modeling.	Ribeiro Jr et al. (2020)
raster	Obtain information on spatial variation of relief and mapping operations with raster data.	Hijmans et al. (2020)
FIELDimageR	Obtain soil indices on experimental plots.	Matias et al. (2020)

Package	Description	Source
RStoolbox	Remote sensing image processing and analysis, such as spectral index calculation, principal component transformation, unsupervised and supervised classification.	Leutner et al. (2019)

6.9   Remote Sensing Indices for Soil

Some soil indices can be obtained from remote sensing spectral bands (Table 6.6, 6.7) (Diek et al., 2017; Jensen, 2007), for example, Soil Adjusted Vegetation Index (SAVI), Bare Soil Index (BSI), Biological Soil Crusts Index (BSCI), Modified Soil Adjusted Vegetation Index (MSAVI), Modified Soil Adjusted Vegetation Index 2 (MSAVI2), and Soil Adjusted Total Vegetation Index (SATVI).

Table 6.6 Example of indices used to study soils using spectral bands surface reflectance and parameters (L) obtained by remote sensing.

Index	Band	Source
SAVI - Soil Adjusted Vegetation Index	red, NIR	Huete (1988)
BSI - Bare Soil Index	blue, NIR, SWIR3	Rikimaru et al. (2002)
BSCI - Biological Soil Crusts Index	red, green, NIR	Chen et al. (2005)
MSAVI - Modified Soil Adjusted Vegetation Index	red, NIR	Qi et al. (1994)
MSAVI2 - Modified Soil Adjusted Vegetation Index 2	red, NIR	Qi et al. (1994)
SATVI - Soil Adjusted Total Vegetation Index	red, SWIR2, SWIR3	Marsett et al. (2006)

Table 6.7 Example of indices used to study soils and its equations.

Index	Equation
SAVI - Soil Adjusted Vegetation Index	$\frac{(NIR-Red)(1+L)}{(NIR+Red+L)}$
BSI - Bare Soil Index	$\frac{(SWIR3+Red)-(NIR+Blue)}{(SWIR3+Red)+(NIR+Blue)}$
BSCI - Biological Soil Crusts Index	$\frac{1-L[Red-Green]}{[\frac{(Green+Red+NIR)}{3}]}$
MSAVI - Modified Soil Adjusted Vegetation Index	$NIR + 0.5 - (0.5sqrt((2NIR+1)^2 - 8(NIR-(2red))))$
MSAVI2 - Modified Soil Adjusted Vegetation Index 2	$(2(NIR+1)-sqrt((2NIR+1)^2-8(NIR-red)))/2$
SATVI - Soil Adjusted Total Vegetation Index	$(SWIR2-red)/(SWIR2+red+L)(1+L)-(SWIR3/2)$

The R package FIELDimageR (Matias et al., 2020) allows the analysis of soil indices in experimental plots as shown in Tables 6.8, 6.9, and 6.10, for example, Soil Color Index (SCI), Hue Index of Primary Colors (HI), Spectral Saturation Index of Slope (SI), and Hue Index (Hue).

Table 6.8 Example of soil indices from the FIELDimageR package.

Index	Band	Source
SCI - Soil Color Index	red, green	Matias et al. (2020)
HI - Hue Index of Primary Colors	red, green, blue	Escadafal (1994)
SI - Spectral Saturation Index of Slope	red, blue	Escadafal (1994)
Hue - Hue Index	red, green, blue	Escadafal (1994)

Table 6.9 Example of soil indices from the FIELDimageR package and its equations.

Index	Equation
SCI - Soil Color Index	$\frac{(Red-Green)}{(Red+Green)}$
HI - Hue Index of Primary Colors	$\frac{(2Red-Green-Blue)}{(Green-Blue)}$
SI - Spectral Saturation Index of Slope	$\frac{(Red-Blue)}{(Red+Blue)}$
Hue - Hue Index	$atan[\frac{2(Red-Green-Blue)}{30.5(Green-Blue)}]$

Table 6.10 Example of soil indices from the FIELDimageR package and its applications.

Index	Application
SCI - Soil Color Index	soil color
HI - Hue Index of Primary Colors	soil color
SI - Spectral Saturation Index of Slope	soil color
Hue - Hue Index	soil color

Some indices are determined based on relief variation from a digital elevation model using the geographic information system SAGA GIS, with the R package RSAGA (Conrad et al., 2015; Lovelace et al., 2019). The R package raster (Hijmans et al., 2020) is used to determine some morphometric terrain variables without the need to use third-party software, and may be a simpler option for determination in some situations. The SAGA topographic moisture index and the terrain roughness index can be obtained by the R package envirem (Title & Bemmels, 2021) at different spatial and temporal resolutions.

6.10 Computational Practice

Different computational practices have been performed to illustrate soil-related studies in decision-making applications using remote sensing data.

The following are computational practices to determine the indices: SAVI, MSSAVI, MSAVI2, and SATVI, using the RStoolbox package (Leutner et al., 2019). A function is defined to determine the BSI. A demonstration about how to obtain digital elevation model data is performed on a rural property in state of Bahia, Brazil using the AppEEARS (AppEEARS Team, 2020) platform. The raster package (Hijmans et al., 2020) is used to calculate morphometric landform variables from elevation data from around the Funil dam in Minas Gerais, Brazil. The rgdal package (Bivand et al., 2021) is used in map projection transformation of the digital elevation model.

6.10.1 Installing R packages

The install.packages function is used in the R console to install the raster, RStoolbox and rgdal packages.

```
install.packages("raster")
install.packages("RStoolbox")
install.packages("rgdal")
```

6.10.2 Enabling R Packages

The library function is used in the R console to enable the raster, RStoolbox, and rgdal packages.

```
library(raster)
library(RStoolbox)
library(rgdal)
```

6.10.3 Determining spectral indices related to soils

A Landsat-8 OLI/TIRS image is obtained in the region surrounding the Ijaci dam, state of Minas Gerais, Brazil, referring to imaging performed on June 28, 2021 on the **Earth Explorer**[2]. The image used was corrected for illumination based on relief (Goslee, 2011) from Shuttle Radar Topography Mission (SRTM) digital elevation model. The sdos method was used for atmospheric correction in the Landsat-8 bands of the reflective spectrum, with the parameters hazeBands = c(1:8) and darkProp = 0.01. In this case, bands 1 to 7 and 9 are used. The panchromatic band with spatial resolution of 15 m was not stacked. The Landsat-8 image with the calculated surface reflectance data can be obtained for **download**[3] and reproduction of the computational practice.

The surface reflectance bands of the Landsat-8 OLI/TIRS image are imported and renamed with the stack and names functions, respectively.

```
lsat <- stack("C:/sr/c5/lsat8_sdos.tif")
names(lsat) <- c('costal', 'blue', 'green', 'red', 'nir', 'swir2', 'swir3', 'swir1',
                 'tir1', 'tir2')
```

---

[2]https://earthexplorer.usgs.gov/
[3]http://www.sergeo.deg.ufla.br/sr/downloads/lsat8_sdos.zip

The `spectralIndices` function is used to determine the SAVI, MSAVI, MSAVI2, and SATVI indices in the studied region.

```
si <- spectralIndices(lsat, blue = "blue", green = "green", red = "red",
nir = "nir", swir2 = "swir2", swir3= "swir3",
indices = c("SAVI", "MSAVI", "MSAVI2", "SATVI"))
```

The `plot` function is used to map SAVI, MSAVI, MSAVI2, and SATVI indices determined at Funil dam on June 28, 2021 (Figure 6.23).

```
plot(si, col = terrain.colors(100))
```

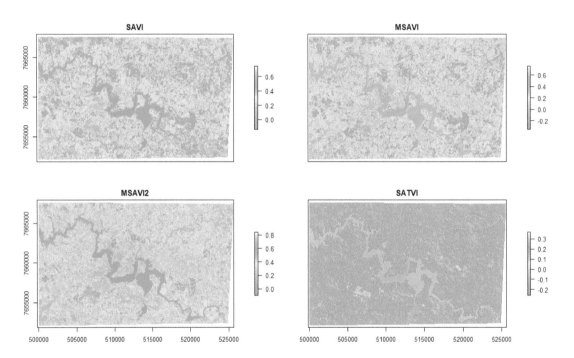

Figure 6.23 Determination of SAVI, MSAVI, MSAVI2, and SATVI indices in the region surrounding the Funil dam, state of Minas Gerais, Brazil, on June 28, 2021.

Since the Bare Soil Index (BSI) is not implemented in the `RStoolbox` package, a `bsi` function is defined for determining this variable in the area of interest.

```
bsi <- function(img, a, b, c, d){
b2 <- img[[a]]
b4 <- img[[b]]
b5 <- img[[c]]
b7 <- img[[d]]
bsi <- ((b7+b4)-(b5+b2))/((b7+b4)+(b5+b2))
return(bsi)
}
```

The `bsi` function is used on the Landsat-8 OLI image to determine the spectral index in the region surrounding the Funil dam.

```
bsi <- bsi(lsat, 2, 4, 5, 7)
```

The BSI mapping is performed with the `plot` function (Figure 6.24).

```
plot(bsi, col = terrain.colors(100))
```

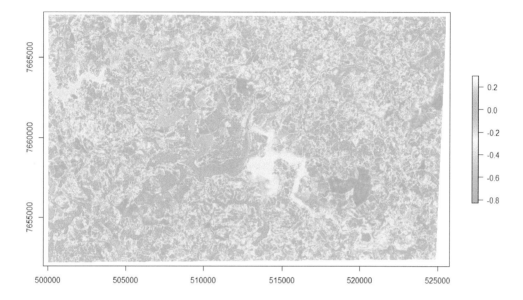

Figure 6.24 Determination of the Bare Soil Index in the region surrounding the Funil dam on June 28, 2021.

6.10.4 Obtaining digital elevation model in **AppEEARS** platform

Information about the altitude variation of a given region can be used to obtain a number of environmental variables, such as slope, aspect, drainage network, topographic moisture index, among other variables. A computational practice to obtain the altitude data of a region of interest, remotely, by the **AppEEARS** platform.

The use of information on relief variation makes it possible to conduct studies to identify morphometry, hydrology, and climate variation in a given geographic region. The **AppEEARS** platform (AppEEARS Team, 2020) is used to determine the altitude variation, in a defined area on rural property, in the state of Bahia, Brazil. The altitude data is obtained at 30-m spatial resolution, determined by means of the SRTM mission.

The file with the boundaries of the rural property in Bahia, Brazil, is used in the practical activity to obtain the altitude data in the studied area. The file with the polygon of the area is provided to **download**[4].

Next, the following steps are performed on the AppEEARS platform:

(1) Log in to the **AppEEARS**[5] platform and, choose the "Launch AppEEARS" option.

(2) After login, in the "Extract" menu (n.1), choose the "Area Sample" option (n.2) (Figure 6.25).

(3) Identify the sample name as "DEM_srtm" (n.3).

(4) Insert the obtained file ("p.zip") with the property boundaries, dragging or locating the directory in which the file is stored on the computer, into the area with the dotted outline of the interface (n.4) (Figure 6.25).

(5) In the fields "Start Date" and "End Date", enter the period for searching altitude values. In this case, the dates from February 1, 2000 to February 29, 2000 (02-01-2000 and 02-29-2000) were chosen (n.5) (Figure 6.25).

(6) In the item "Select the layers to include in the sample", it was searched for the remote sensing product SRTM Elevation (DEM) SRTMGL1_NC.003, 30 m, Static, (2000-02-11 to 2000-02-21"). To do this, the keyword "srtm" was entered into the search field and then the option of interest was selected to obtain the product (n.6) (Figure 6.25).

(7) The following variable was added in the "Selected layers" field (n.7) (Figure 6.25): - SRTMGL1_DEM.

To add the item, it is necessary to click with the left mouse button on the list of sub-items with the symbol (+), choose the variable of interest (product), which was added instantly from the next field (n.8). If necessary, to remove an item from the list in relation to the items already added for the search, click on the symbol (-) in the field beside (Figure 6.25).

(8) In the options for exporting the file, set the geographic projection "datum WGS-84, EPSG:4326, PROJ.4: +proj=lonlat+datum=WGS84+no_defs" (n.9) (Figure 6.25).

(9) Next, place the order using the "Submit" button. The system then displays the following message: "The area sample request was successfully submitted. An email notification will be delivered once the request is complete" (n.10) (Figure 6.25).

Therefore, it was necessary to wait for the data processing and the email notification to manipulate the results. Another option was to enter the "Explore" menu, wait for the request processing on the sample "DEM_srtm" to be completed, and on the icon illustrated with a graph, check the results obtained (Figure 6.26).

(10) The altitude variation at the property is evaluated by means of a boxplot graph. Note that the values in the graph can be obtained interactively by hovering the mouse over the graph (Figure 6.27).

---

[4] http://www.sergeo.deg.ufla.br/sr/downloads/p.zip
[5] https://lpdaac.usgs.gov/tools/appeears/

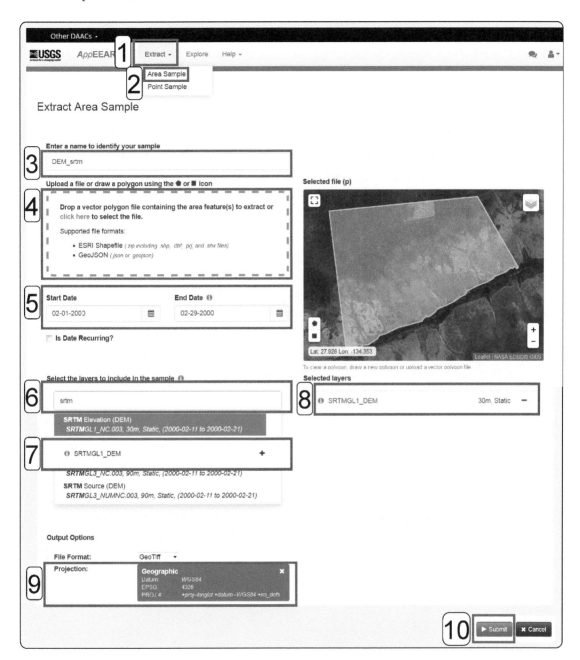

Figure 6.25 `AppEEARS` platform menu used to get data from an area.

Figure 6.26 Explore menu (1) and graphical access option (2) to the results of the `AppEEARS` platform.

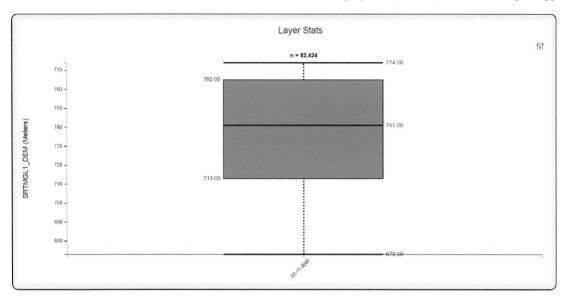

Figure 6.27 Boxplot used to evaluate the variation of altitude (m) above sea level on a rural property.

It was found that 82424 altitude pixels were evaluated every 30 m in the rural property, with the minimum, median, and maximum values of 673, 741, and 774 m, respectively. Based on the first quartile, the threshold of 713 m altitude defined the 25% of the lowest altitude values. Based on the third quartile, the threshold of 765 m defined the 25% highest altitude values observed in the area. It is worth mentioning that the results were obtained based on the 2000 SRTM mission survey and on image processing techniques applied to the RADAR survey data.

The number of pixels evaluated in the rural property was represented in the pixel count graphic (Figure 6.28).

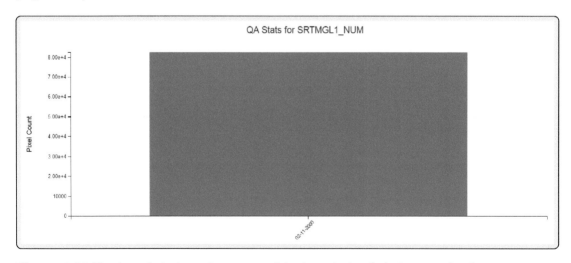

Figure 6.28 Number of pixels used to assess altitude variation (m) above sea level on property at state of Bahia, Brazil.

Raster data can be obtained to map the altitude and perform spatial analysis with the altitude data of the rural property (Figure 6.29).

Figure 6.29 AppEEARS platform interface used to obtain the area data in raster format.

A set of files can be obtained referring to the requested product; however, in this practice, only the raster data with altitude pixels of the area were chosen (Figure 6.30).

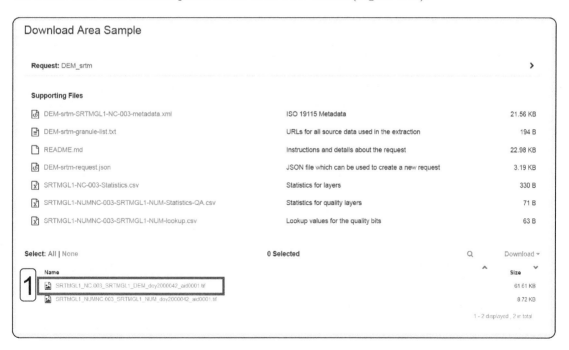

Figure 6.30 AppEEARS platform interface used to obtain the digital elevation model of the area of interest in geotiff format.

Therefore, this practice details how to obtain an area file, referring to a digital elevation model, in the AppEEARS platform and perform the processing of information about the altitude variation in the area.

6.11   Exercises

6.11.1   List five applications of remote soil sensing and explain a situation where monitoring may be limited.

6.11.2   Explain the possible pathways of radiance reaching exposed soil.

6.11.3   List six characteristics that can interfere with the variation in the reflectance of exposed soil.

6.11.4   Explain how soil monitoring can be done based on a digital elevation model and two variables is that can be obtained from altitude.

6.11.5   Explain how to calculate a remote sensing index to study bare soil and what the practical interpretation of this index is.

6.11.6   Which index is not used for soil monitoring with passive sensing?

  a. SAVI.
  b. BSI.
  c. SRTM.
  d. BSCI.
  e. None of the alternatives.

6.11.7   Which mission used to monitor relief for soil studies with active remote sensing?

  a. SAVI.
  b. BSI.
  c. SRTM.
  d. BSCI.
  e. None of the alternatives.

6.11.8 Raster data for an area of interest is obtained from the **AppEEARS** platform with 82424 pixels of altitude at 30-m spatial resolution. Based on this information, what is the size of the total raster area in hectares?

6.11.9 What are the water absorption wavelengths in the reflectance curve of moist sandy soil?

6.11.10 Determine the textural class of the soil in triangle classification.

6.11.11 Map soil organic carbon at different depths and different color options in Brazil.

6.11.12 Map the soil classes of Brazil in order level

6.12 Homework

6.12.1 Subject

Monitoring spatial variation of relief for determining morphometric terrain variables from SRTM data.

6.12.2 Assignment

Develop the subject presented with a practical application of remote sensing and digital image processing including the topics Introduction and Objective. Then present the development of the task.

6.13 Resources on the Internet

Activities are proposed for the development of scientific research on remote sensing that can be used or adapted by the student to monitor and identify targets in a specific area of interest as shown in Table 6.11.

Table 6.11 Slide presentation and illustrative video about remote sensing for soil study.

Guide	Address for Access
1	JavaScript application for monitoring soil erosion vulnerability via the RUSLE method[6]
2	Using remote sensing for digital soil mapping[7]
3	What is a digital elevation model?[8]
4	How do I get a digital elevation model of my study region?[9]
5	Monitoring desert wind erosion with GOES-16[10]
6	Slides about remote sensing of soil and rock[11]

6.14   Research Suggestion

Activities are proposed to develop scientific research on remote sensing, which can be used or adapted by the student to evaluate the applicability of remote sensing (Table 6.12).

Table 6.12 Description of practical activities that can be used or adapted by students with suggested research in remote sensing.

Activity	Description
1	Use the practical example developed by the teacher on the AppEEARS platform to generate the graphical result of the altitude variation in the area of interest where the practical work of the subject will be carried out.
2	Obtaining a digital elevation model of the studied area and determine slope and aspect. Use the Landsat-8 OLI image to determine a Bare Soil Index (BSI) of the studied area.

---

[6] https://soilwatch.users.earthengine.app/view/soilerosionwatch

[7] https://youtu.be/-v5pf9_knTA

[8] https://youtu.be/0UwgPOAkx-c

[9] https://youtu.be/E6sXUr8HWVk

[10] https://youtu.be/SChO_Lby-no

[11] http://www.sergeo.deg.ufla.br/sr/pr/a7/Aula7sr20212.html

7

Remote Sensing of the Atmosphere

7.1 Learning Questions

The learning questions answered by reading the chapter are as follows:

- What is the importance of performing atmospheric monitoring with remote sensing?
- What are the main sources of atmospheric pollution?
- How can the atmospheric composition be monitored by remote sensing?
- What is the energy-matter interaction in the atmosphere?
- How is Sentinel-5P data for practical applications in R obtained?

7.2 Learning Outcomes

Using the learning outcomes from the chapter, you should be able to do the following:

- Understand the importance of performing atmospheric monitoring with remote sensing.
- Understand the main sources of atmospheric pollution.
- Evaluate the atmospheric composition using remote sensing.
- Understand how energy-matter interaction occurs in the atmosphere.
- Use Sentinel-5P data in practical applications in R.

7.3 Introduction

Planet Earth has a gaseous layer that surrounds it and constitutes the atmosphere, with dimensions determined as a function of physicochemical and biological processes developed during geological eras until reaching a dynamic equilibrium in the last 200 million years (Reichardt & Timm, 2004).

The atmosphere surrounds the Earth to a thickness of about 1% of the planet's radius, and is vital to life on Earth. Although air and water share similar physical properties, air is compressible, and water is basically incompressible. The immense reservoir of heat in the surface layer of oceans and the exchanges with the atmosphere are fundamental to understanding climate variability. During the evaporation process, the heat energy of water is transformed into the kinetic energy of water vapor molecules, while subsequent condensation into a cloud or fog releases kinetic energy that returns to the medium as heat energy. Condensation of warm, humid tropical air releases latent heat, increasing the instability of tropical air masses. Thus, warmed air expands, decreases in density and rises, possibly resulting in precipitation, while cold air contracts, increases in density and descends (Barry & Chorley, 2010).

In an equilibrium climate state, the average global solar energy absorbed by the Earth system is balanced by the average global longwave radiation emitted into space. In response to radiative forcing that can cause radiative imbalance at the top of the atmosphere, the system attempts to seek a new equilibrium based on surface warming and cooling, causing global climate change. Radiative imbalances occur from natural processes, such as astronomical effects of incident shortwave solar radiation, volcanic eruption, aerosols, and human action introducing greenhouse gases into the atmosphere (Figure 7.1). Therefore, from knowledge about atmospheric functioning, it is possible to contribute to the understanding of climatic phenomena and global climates (Barry & Chorley, 2010).

7.4   Atmospheric Composition

Atmospheric composition can vary in relation to the main gases and impurities in the air, as well as the vertical distribution and structure of the atmospheric mass (Barry & Chorley, 2010).

7.4.1   Main gases in the atmosphere

Air is a mechanical mixture of gases. Dry air is composed of over 99% nitrogen and oxygen by volume. These gases are mixed in constant proportions up to about 100 km altitude (Barry & Chorley, 2010) (Table 7.1).

Table 7.1 A typical composition of the dry atmosphere below 25 km.

Component	Dry Air Volume (%)	Molecular Weight	Observation
Nitrogen (N_2)	78.08	28.02	——
Oxygen (O_2)	20.95	32.00	——
Argon (Ar)	0.93	39.88	Decay product of potassium and uranium; inert gases
Carbon dioxide (CO_2)	0.037	44.00	——
Neon (Ne)	0.0018	20.18	Inert gases
Helium (He)	0.0005	4.00	Decay product of potassium and uranium; inert gases
Ozone (O_3)	0.00006	48.00	——
Hydrogen (H)	0.00005	2.02	——
Krypton (Kr)	0.00011	——	Inert gases
Xenon (Xe)	0.00009	——	Inert gases
Methane (CH_4)	0.00017	——	At surface

Figure 7.1 Industrial air pollution in São Paulo, Brazil (top), and air pollution from the Cumbre Vieja volcano that devastated the Spanish island of La Palma, in the archipelago of the Canary Islands, on the coast of North Africa, in September 2021 (bottom).

7.5 Greenhouse Gases

The gases of water vapor (H_2O), carbon dioxide (CO_2), methane (CH_4), nitrous oxide (N_2O), ozone (O_3), chlorofluorocarbons (CFC), and hydrogenated halocarbons (HFC, HCFC) are crucial in atmospheric thermodynamics for trapping the radiation emitted by the Earth producing the greenhouse effect (Barry & Chorley, 2010).

Water vapor is the main greenhouse gas that occurs over space and time in a complex global hydrological cycle. CO_2 also occurs in a complex global cycle, being produced by the respiration of biota, soil microbes, burning of fossil fuels, and ocean evaporation. This gas can be dissolved in the oceans and consumed by plant photosynthesis. CH_4 is produced by anaerobic processes in natural and artificial wetlands, as well as by enteric fermentation in animals, coal and oil extraction, biomass burning, and by landfills and dumpsites. N_2O is produced by nitrogen fertilizers, industrial processes, transport, biomass burning, biological mechanisms in oceans and soils, and is destroyed by photochemical reactions in the stratosphere involving the production of nitrogen oxides (NOx). The O_3 is produced by the breakdown of oxygen molecules in the upper atmosphere by the Sun's ultraviolet radiation, and is destroyed by reactions with (NOx) and chlorine (Cl) in the middle and upper atmosphere. The Cl can be generated by CFC, volcanic eruptions, and burning of vegetation. The CFC, represented by $CFCl_3$ and CF_2Cl_2, are anthropogenic gases produced by aerosol propellants, coolant gases in refrigerators, cleaning products and air conditioners. The CFC molecules rise slowly up into the stratosphere and progress towards the Earth's poles, being broken down by photochemical processes into chlorine in an average period of 65 to 130 years. The HFC and HCFC are anthropogenic gases that have increased in the atmosphere in recent decades by replacing CFC with an impact on O_3 destruction (Barry & Chorley, 2010).

7.6 Reactive Gas Species

Nitrogenous, sulfurous gaseous species produced by sulfur, nitrogen, and chlorine cycles are gaseous reactive species determining acid rain and ozone depletion. The nitrogen reactive species are nitric oxide (NO) and nitrogen dioxide (NO_2). The reactive sulfur species are sulfur dioxide (SO_2) and reduced sulfur. Acid deposition can occur in a wet form, by acid rain and snow, as well as by dry particulate deposition (Barry & Chorley, 2010).

7.7 Aerosols

Aerosols occur as suspended particles of sulfate, sea salt, mineral dust, organic matter, and black carbon. These particles are released into the atmosphere from natural and anthropogenic sources in the form of mineral dust particles from dry surfaces, carbon soot from burning coal and biomass, and volcanic dust. Other sources of aerosols are sea salts and organic matter (Barry & Chorley, 2010).

7.8   Atmospheric Variation with Altitude

The variations of water vapor and O_3 are related to altitude. The distribution of these gases interacts with the absorption of solar and terrestrial radiation, affecting the heat balance and the vertical temperature structure of the atmosphere. Water vapor is released to the atmosphere by surface water evaporation and plant transpiration, and is transferred to higher levels by atmospheric turbulence. Turbulence is most effective below 10 to 15 km. The O_3 is mainly concentrated between 15 and 35 km, being formed mainly between 30 and 60 km where collisions between O and O_2 are most likely (Barry & Chorley, 2010).

7.9   Atmospheric Variation with Latitude and Season

Latitude and seasonal variations are important particularly in the case of water vapor and stratospheric O_3. The O_3 content is low over the equator and high at sub-polar latitudes in spring. The water vapor content of the atmosphere is related to air temperature, being highest in summer at low latitudes, with exceptions in desert tropical areas. The CO_2 content of the air also shows seasonal variation according to latitude variation and may be assimilated by the cold polar seas or be transferred throughout the year from low to high latitudes, maintaining equilibrium in the air contents (Barry & Chorley, 2010).

7.10   Atmospheric Variation with the Weather

The amounts of CO_2 and other greenhouse gases and particles in the atmosphere can vary over the long term and affect the Earth's radiation balance. Atmospheric trace gases increased after the start of the industrial revolution around 1750, and the burning of fossil fuels is a major source of these concentrations. The burning of coal and fuel oil releases not only CO_2, but also free nitrogen (NOx), sulfur, and carbon monoxide (CO). Agricultural practices, deforestation, and livestock farming are also actions related to modifying atmospheric composition (Barry & Chorley, 2010).

7.11   Atmospheric Mass

The total mass of the gaseous layer that constitutes the atmosphere corresponds to 0.001% of the total mass of the planet Earth, and is practically concentrated in the first 10 km of altitude above sea level. This layer can be considered very thin when compared to the Earth's radius of approximately 6000 km (Reichardt & Timm, 2004).

7.12   Atmospheric Stratification

The atmosphere has a characteristic vertical structure due to the planet's dimensions, gravitational force, gas density, and heating processes, which determine the characteristic vertical structure (Figure 7.2) (Reichardt & Timm, 2004).

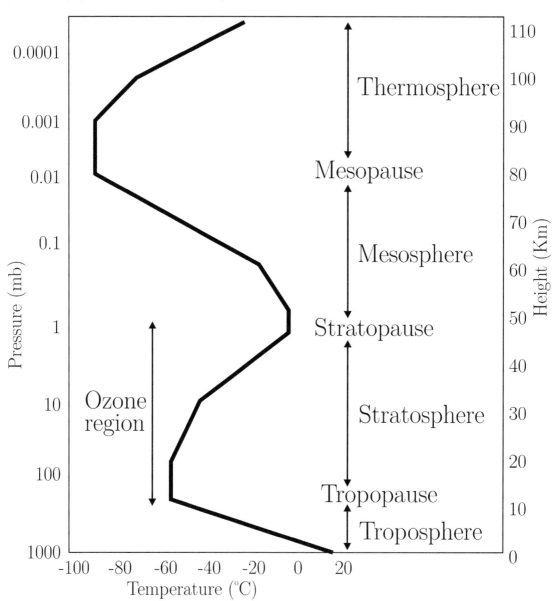

Figure 7.2 Vertical structure of the atmosphere with widespread vertical distribution of temperature and pressure up to 110 km from the Earth's surface.

The atmospheric stratification is defined in several horizontal layers differentiated mainly as a function of temperature. There are three warm layers, near the surface (50 and 60 km) and above 120 km, separated by two cold layers, between 10 and 30 km and 80 to 100 km (Barry & Chorley, 2010). The lowest layer, close to the ground, is called the "troposphere", characterized by decreasing temperature with altitude. In this layer there is 75% of the total mass of the atmosphere influenced by energy transfer at the Earth's surface. These processes determine temperature and pressure gradients that produce atmospheric movements responsible for the transport of water vapor and heat. The thickness of the troposphere is variable, ranging from 16 to 18 km in the tropics and from 2 to 10 km in the polar regions. The tropopause corresponds to the boundary of the troposphere where there is a reduction in atmospheric movements. Above the tropopause is the stratosphere, with an increase in temperature up to 50 km of altitude, with values corresponding to that of the surface. This temperature increase is associated with the absorption of ultraviolet radiation by ozone, in high concentration at an altitude of 20 to 50 km. The stratopause is above the stratosphere, corresponding to a layer of maximum temperature in relation to the stratosphere. The mesosphere occurs above the stratopause, and is characterized by decreasing temperature with increasing altitude. The mesopause corresponds to the region of lowest temperature referring to the upper limit of the mesosphere. Above 80 km, the temperature increases continuously with altitude until it reaches temperatures of approximately 1500 K at 500 km altitude, defining the thermosphere or ionosphere (Reichardt & Timm, 2004).

7.13 Solar Radiation and Global Energy Balance

The amount of energy received at the top of the atmosphere is affected by solar emission, the distance between the Sun and the Earth, the height of the Sun, and the length of the day. The solar radiation is also subject to the absorbing effects of scattering gases and aerosols on the radiation. At the surface, there is an energy balance as a function of additional sensible and latent heat transfers to the atmosphere. Radiation from the sun is predominantly shortwave, while the radiation leaving the Earth is long wave, or infrared. The infrared emission from the surface is less than that of a black body at the same temperature, varying according to an emissivity coefficient. The net effect of energy transfers on the Earth-atmosphere system can be determined with global averages and over an annual period by (Barry & Chorley, 2010):

$$R_n = (Q + q)(1 - \alpha) + L_n \tag{7.1}$$

where R_n is the radiation balance, $Q + q$ the global solar radiation, α, the albedo, and L_n the long wave radiation balance.

The excess radiation is transmitted to the atmosphere by turbulent transfer of sensible heat (H) and latent heat (LE) (Barry & Chorley, 2010):

$$R_n = LE + H \tag{7.2}$$

There is also a ground heat flux that is approximately zero for annual averages.

7.14 Cloud Types

The wide variety of cloud shapes requires a classification for meteorological disclosure purposes based on the general shape, structure, vertical extent, and altitude of clouds. High, cirriform clouds are composed of ice crystals, with a fibrous appearance. Stratiform clouds occur in layers, while cumuliform clouds have a clumped appearance with progressive vertical development. The prefixes high and nimbo are used to describe mid-level and low (thick) clouds, respectively (Figure 7.3) (Barry & Chorley, 2010).

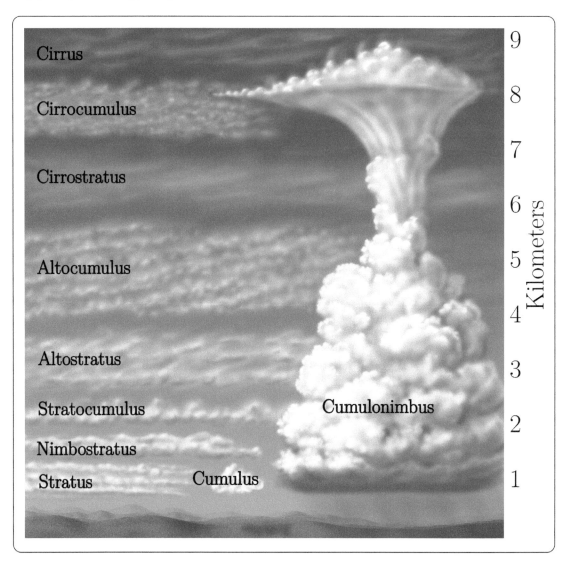

Figure 7.3 Basic cloud groups classified by altitude and shape.

7.15   Interactions between Energy and Matter in the Atmosphere

Radiant energy determines the ability of radiation in a spectral region to do work. Electromagnetic energy propagated from the Sun in a vacuum that penetrates the atmosphere can be affected not only in speed of propagation, but also in wavelength, intensity, and spectral distribution, by effects of refraction, scattering, and absorption (Jensen, 2007).

7.15.1 Refraction

Refraction refers to the deflection of light as it passes from one medium to another with different densities. The refractive index (n) is a ratio between the speed of light in a vacuum (c), and the speed of light in a substance such as the atmosphere or water (c_n), so that the propagation of light is less dense in denser media compared to less dense media (Jensen, 2007):

$$n = \frac{c}{c_n} \qquad (7.3)$$

Refraction can be described by Snell's law, in which the product of the refractive index and the sine of the angle between the ray and the line normal to the interface is constant (Jensen, 2007):

$$n_1 sen\theta_1 = n_2 sen\theta_2 \qquad (7.4)$$

A non-turbulent atmosphere can be seen as a series of layers of gases with different densities, so that every time energy propagates through the atmosphere for a distance at an angle (θ) other than vertical, refraction occurs (Figure 7.4) (Jensen, 2007).

By knowing the refractive index in different mediums and the angle of incidence of the energy in the first medium, it is possible to determine the amount of refraction that will occur ($sen\theta_2$) in the n_2 medium with trigonometric relationships in order to remove localization errors caused by refraction in images formed from energy detected at high altitudes or under very acute angles (Jensen, 2007):

$$sen\theta_2 = \frac{n_1 sen\theta_1}{n_2} \qquad (7.5)$$

7.15.2 Scattering

Scattering of radiation can be determined by atmospheric particles and differs from refraction in that the direction associated with scattering is unpredictable, while the direction of refraction is predictable. The layer subdivisions of the atmosphere and the types of molecules and aerosols in each layer can determine different types of scattering (Figure 7.5) (Jensen, 2007).

The type of scattering can vary depending on the relative size of the wavelength of the incident electromagnetic radiation interacting with gases of varying diameter, such as water vapor and dust. Rayleigh scattering occurs in the atmosphere, from 2 to 8 km altitude, when the effective diameter of matter, such as oxygen and nitrogen in the atmosphere, is many times smaller than the wavelength of the incident electromagnetic radiation. The approximate amount of Rayleigh scattering in the atmosphere at optical wavelengths is inversely related to the fourth power of the wavelength of the radiation. Therefore, shorter wavelengths of violet and blue are more efficiently scattered than the longer wavelengths of orange and red. The Rayleigh scattering cross-section algorithm (τ_m) can be calculated from equation (Jensen, 2007):

$$\tau_m = \frac{8\pi^3(n^2 - 1)^2}{3N^2\lambda^4} \qquad (7.6)$$

where n is the refractive index, N, the number of air molecules per unit volume, and λ, the wavelength.

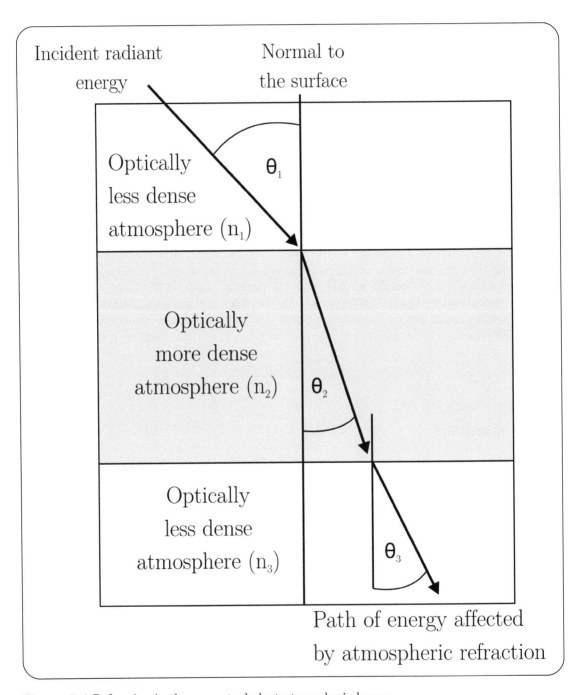

Figure 7.4 Refraction in three non-turbulent atmospheric layers.

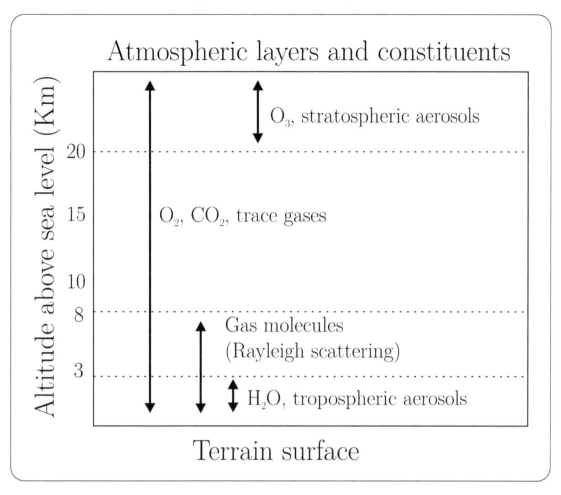

Figure 7.5 Main subdivisions of the atmosphere and types of molecules and aerosols observed in each layer.

Mie scattering occurs in the lower 4.5 km of the atmosphere, determined by the presence of essentially spherical particles with diameters approximately equal to the size of the wavelength of incident energy. The actual size of the particles can range from 0.1 to 10 times the wavelength of the incident energy. The main scattering agents for visible light are dust and other smoke particles in the atmospheric column. The larger amount of smoke and dust particles in the atmospheric column removes the violet and blue light and only the longer wavelengths of orange and red light are observed (Jensen, 2007).

Non-selective scattering occurs in low portions of the atmosphere where there are particles larger than 10 times the wavelength of the incident electromagnetic radiation, such as water droplets and ice crystals that form clouds and fogs, determining the white color of these targets. Non-selective scattering means that all wavelengths are scattered, but not just blue, green or red. Scattering can reduce the information content of remote sensing data causing loss of contrast and difficulty in differentiating one object from another (Figure 7.6) (Jensen, 2007).

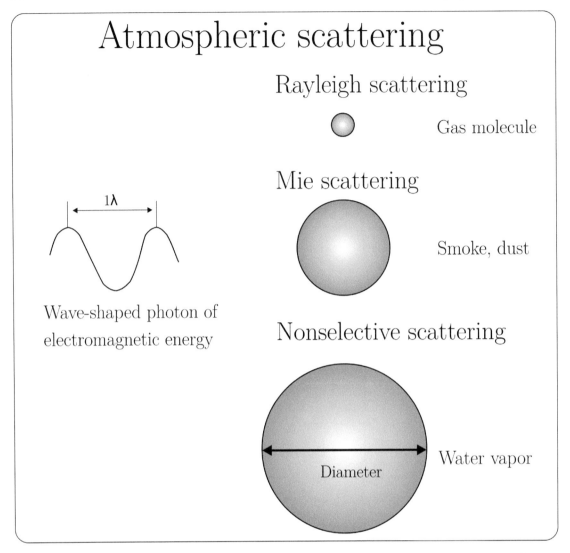

Figure 7.6 Scattering variation as a function of incident radiant energy wavelength and the size of gas molecules and dust particles.

7.15.3   Radiation absorption

Radiation absorption is related to the process in which radiant energy is absorbed and converted into other forms of energy. Incident radiant energy can occur in the atmosphere or on the ground. The cumulative effect of absorption by atmospheric constituents can cause the atmosphere to be impassable ("closed") completely in certain regions of the electromagnetic spectrum. In this case, the energy may be unavailable for recording in a remote sensing system. Portions of the electromagnetic spectrum that efficiently transmit radiant energy are called "atmospheric windows". Absorption occurs when incident energy of the same frequency as the resonant frequency of an atom or molecule is absorbed, producing an excited state, and the energy is transformed into heat at a longer wavelength. In a medium such as air, absorption and scattering are combined into one extinction coefficient, so that transmission is inversely related to the extinction coefficient and the thickness of the layer. The combined effects of absorption, scattering and reflectance in cloud tops can reduce the amount of radiation reaching the Earth's surface at sea level (Figure 7.7) (Jensen, 2007).

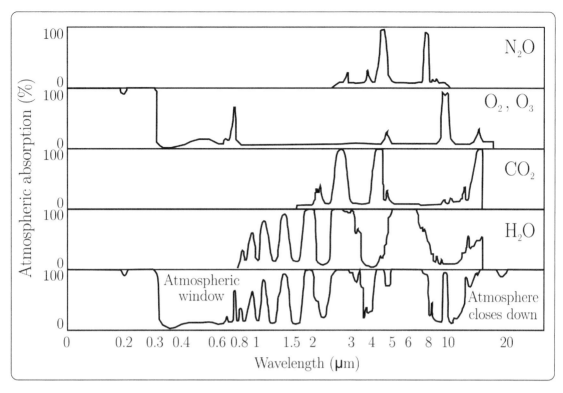

Figure 7.7 Absorption of incident electromagnetic energy from the Sun at different wavelengths at the top of the atmosphere and at sea level.

Absorption of the incident Sun's electromagnetic energy can range in the spectral regions from 0.1 to 30 μm by various atmospheric gases, such as H_2O, CO_2, O_2, O_3, and N_2O (Figure 7.8) (Jensen, 2007). The O_3 almost completely intercepts ultraviolet radiation and in some regions of the infrared. The CO_2 has higher absorption for wavelengths in the infrared, such as at 15 μm. Water vapor (H_2O), despite its low content in the atmosphere, absorbs predominantly from 0.8 to 15 μm (Reichardt & Timm, 2004). The N_2O has higher absorption from 2 up to 9 μm.

A remote sensing and digital image processing approach can be used to determine cloud masking in regions with high cloud frequency throughout the year, as in the north of the state of Pará, Brazil. In this case, Landsat-8 OLI/TIRS imaging data can be used as an alternative for spectral detection of clouds based on the radiometric information of the blue and thermal bands. An iterative approach can be used to sample cloud and shadow pixels in order to establish a threshold value for removing cloud-associated shadow.

A practical solution for starting remote sensing applications is to use the Landsat satellite for an evaluation of an object or process in the region chosen to perform a particular practical job. In this case, to obtain the information in radiance and thermal images, the "Landsat Collection 1 Level-1" can be used as option and the files can be downloaded instantly.

The R packages raster (Hijmans et al., 2020), RStoolbox (Leutner et al., 2019), terra (Hijmans, Bivand, et al., 2022), sf (Pebesma et al., 2022), mapview (Appelhans et al., 2020), dplyr (Wickham, François, et al., 2022), and ggplot2 (Wickham, Chang, et al., 2022), used in this example for cloud monitoring, are enabled with the library function.

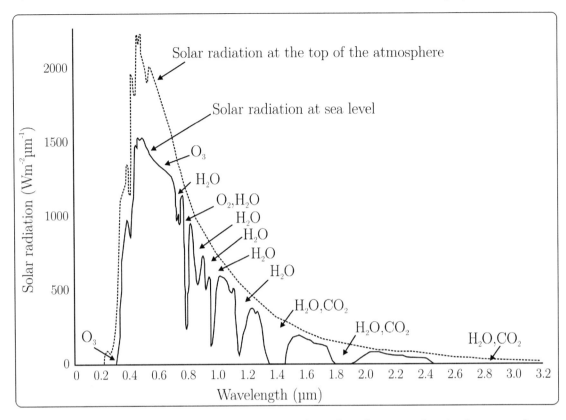

Figure 7.8 Gas absorption characteristics separately and at the same time in the atmosphere.

```
library(raster)
library(RStoolbox)
library(terra)
library(sf)
library(mapview)
library(dplyr)
library(ggplot2)
```

Polygons of interest are created for analysis of the Landsat scene at the location of interest. A rectangular polygon around the Bom Jesus farm is created to crop an extent of interest in the neighborhood of the property. The st_read function is used to import the polygons into R. The st_set_crs function is used to set the coordinate system for each geographic object.

```
bjprj <- st_read("C:/sr/S2/bjprj.shp") # Bom Jesus
bjprj<-st_set_crs(bjprj, "+proj=utm +zone=23 +south +datum=WGS84 +units=m +no_defs")
poprj <- st_read("C:/sr/S2/poprj.shp") # Reg.
poprj<-st_set_crs(poprj, "+proj=utm +zone=23 +south +datum=WGS84 +units=m +no_defs")
```

The sf data.frame class polygons are converted to the SpatVector class for use in mapping by the terra package.

```
bjv<-vect(bjprj) # Bom Jesus
pv<-vect(poprj) # Reg.
```

A Landsat-8 OLI/TIRS collection 1 Level 1 image with metadata is obtained from the image catalog on the Earth Explorer website and used as an example. The compressed file with the bands is decompressed into a directory on the computer to perform data preprocessing.

The list.files function is used to locate the files in the directory of interest. A naming pattern is specified to filter out only bands 1-11.

The sortFilesLandsat function is used to sort the bands from the Landsat-8 imagery.

```
ls8 <- sortFilesLandsat(lsat8)
ls8
#[1]  "LC08_L1TP_222061_20201230_20210311_01_T1_B1.TIF"
#[2]  "LC08_L1TP_222061_20201230_20210311_01_T1_B2.TIF"
#[3]  "LC08_L1TP_222061_20201230_20210311_01_T1_B3.TIF"
#[4]  "LC08_L1TP_222061_20201230_20210311_01_T1_B4.TIF"
#[5]  "LC08_L1TP_222061_20201230_20210311_01_T1_B5.TIF"
#[6]  "LC08_L1TP_222061_20201230_20210311_01_T1_B6.TIF"
#[7]  "LC08_L1TP_222061_20201230_20210311_01_T1_B7.TIF"
#[8]  "LC08_L1TP_222061_20201230_20210311_01_T1_B8.TIF"
#[9]  "LC08_L1TP_222061_20201230_20210311_01_T1_B9.TIF"
#[10] "LC08_L1TP_222061_20201230_20210311_01_T1_B10.TIF"
#[11] "LC08_L1TP_222061_20201230_20210311_01_T1_B11.TIF"
#[12] "LC08_L1TP_222061_20201230_20210311_01_T1_BQA.TIF"
```

A subset of the listed files separating multispectral from panchromatic bands is performed with a bracket operator.

```
l8 <- stack(ls8[c(1:7, 9:11)]) # stack without band 8 (15 m) and BQA
l8p <- raster(ls8[c(8)]) # stack without band 8 (15 m) and BQA
```

The image files are converted in the SpatRaster class with the rast function.

```
lsatmr<-rast(l8) # multi
lsatpr<-rast(l8p) # pan
```

The images are reprojected to the southern hemisphere with the project function. The +south parameter of the crs argument is set. This function may consume computational memory for processing and may take time to complete because of the geographic extent of the Landsat scene. The +proj argument is set to perform the data transformation.

```
utm23s<-"+proj=utm +zone=23 +south +datum=WGS84 +units=m +no_defs"
lsatmrprj<-terra::project(lsatmr,crs(utm23s)) # multi
lsatprprj<-terra::project(lsatpr,crs(utm23s)) # pan
```

Rectangular extensions in space are obtained in the rectangular region of interest and around the Bom Jesus Farm with the extent function.

```
e<-ext(bjv)
e1<-ext(pv)
```

The `e1` extent is used to define a spatial subset and crop the multispectral and panchromatic images with the `crop` function.

```
lsatcrop<-terra::crop(lsatmrprj, e1) # multi
lsatpcrop<-terra::crop(lsatprprj, e1) # pan
```

Image layers are renamed with the `names` function.

```
names(lsatcrop)<-c("B1_dn","B2_dn","B3_dn","B4_dn","B5_dn","B6_dn",
                   "B7_dn","B9_dn","B10_dn","B11_dn") # multi
names(lsatpcrop)<-c("B8_dn") # pan
```

The image data stacked in the `SpatRaster` class is converted to `stack` for use in the `RStoolbox` package.

```
lc8<-stack(lsatcrop)
```

The `cloudMask` function is used to determine the cloud mask based on the blue and thermal (number 10) bands, with argument `threshold` 0.4.

```
cmsk <- cloudMask(lc8, threshold = .4, blue = 2, tir = 9) # bands 2, 10
```

The `ggRGB` and `ggR` functions are used to map the cloud mask (Figure 7.9).

```
ggRGB(lc8, r=5, g=4, b=3, stretch = "lin") +
    ggR(cmsk[[1]], ggLayer = TRUE, forceCat = TRUE, geom_raster = T) +
    scale_fill_manual(values = "red", na.value = NA)
```

The `mask` function is used to remove clouds from Landsat-8 imagery taken around the Bom Jesus property, Pará, Brazil on December 30, 2020.

```
wocl <- mask(lc8, cmsk$CMASK, maskvalue = 1)
```

The functions `viewRGB` and `mapview` are used in mapping the results (Figure 7.10).

```
viewRGB(wocl, r = 4, g = 3, b = 2) +
  mapview(bjprj,alpha.regions = 0.2)
```

As can be seen, only a small region in the center of the property and other sparse regions can be observed in relation to the terrain. The principle of applying the method is that clouds are usually cold in the thermal region and have high reflectance at short wavelengths, such as blue. By calculating a normalized difference index between the two bands and the threshold, a rough cloud mask can be obtained. In the method used by the `RStoolbox` package, before calculating the spectral cloud index or normalized difference thermal cloud index (NDTCI), the thermal band is matched to the same range of values as the blue band.

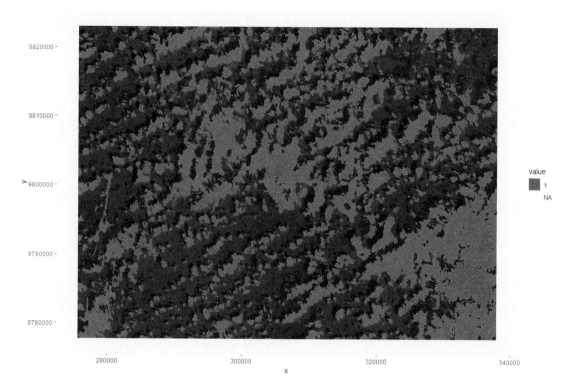

Figure 7.9 Cloud mask obtained by processing Landsat-8 imagery in the state of Pará, Brazil on December 30, 2020.

This cloud masking approach is very simplistic and aims only at coarse removal of potentially cloudy areas, however, it is able to provide satisfactory results. More sophisticated approaches, including cloud shadow detection can be found with the `fmask` software (Zhu & Woodcock, 2012).

Cloud shadow removal can be determined interactively by alternately clicking the mouse button on shadow and cloud, after using the `cloudShadowMask` function (Figure 7.11).

```
shadow <- cloudShadowMask(lc8, cmsk, nc = 2)
```

The `cloudShadowMask` function can also be predefined to estimate the cloud shadow. In this case, a shadow position value x, y, -16 and 6, respectively, is determined.

```
shadow <- cloudShadowMask(lc8, cmsk, shiftEstimate = c(-16, 6))
```

The `merge` function from the `raster` package is used to merge the cloud and shadow cloud values into a single file.

```
csmask <- raster::merge(cmsk[[1]], shadow)
```

The `ggRGB` and `ggR` functions are used to map cloud and shadow cloud from Landsat-8 imagery around the Bom Jesus farm, state of Pará, Brazil (Figure 7.12).

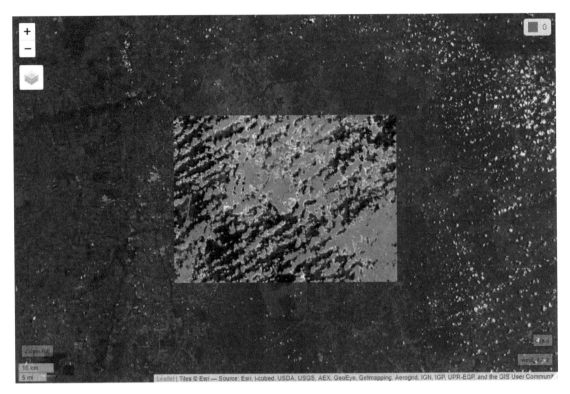

Figure 7.10 Cloud-masked Landsat-8 mapping, state of Pará, Brazil.

Figure 7.11 Using the `cloudShadowMask` function to determine cloud shadow position in the image interactively.

```
ggRGB(lc8,r=4, g=3, b=2, stretch = "lin") +
ggR(csmask, ggLayer = TRUE, forceCat = TRUE, geom_raster = TRUE) +
    scale_fill_manual(values = c("blue", "yellow"),
                        labels = c("shadow", "cloud"), na.value = NA)
```

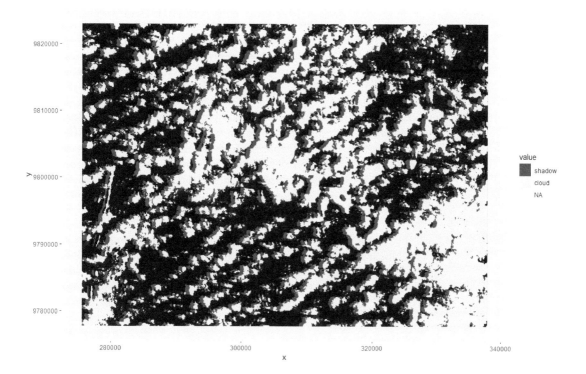

Figure 7.12 Using the `cloudShadowMask` function to determine mask from shadow position (-16, 6) and cloud occurrence in Landsat-8 L1C1 image.

7.16 Atmospheric Circulation and Dynamics

The Earth's atmosphere is made up of a collection of gases bound to the planet by gravitational attraction, and the movement of the air is influenced by the uneven distribution of solar energy and the Earth's rotation. Therefore, the motions of gases are described by the laws of fluid mechanics and thermodynamics. The set of atmospheric movements on a planetary scale determines climate zones and different types of weather in locations around the planet, defining the general circulation of the atmosphere. Thus, there is a balance in the planet's energy balance, since the excess energy in the intertropical zone is transferred by the atmospheric and ocean currents to the temperate and polar zones.

The atmosphere acts as a giant thermal machine, where the temperature difference between the poles and the equator, caused by differential solar heating, drives the planetary atmospheric and oceanic circulation. The conversion of thermal energy into kinetic energy produces both upward and downward air movement, however vertical movements may be less obvious than horizontal ones, which can cover large areas and persist for periods of days to months (Barry & Chorley, 2010).

Wind speed and direction data can be obtained from the Global Forecast System (GFS) of the National Weather Service (**NWS**[1]) of the United States government . Wind data are taken from the NOAA/NCEP Global Forecast System (GFS) Atmospheric Model collection. The geospatial resolution is 0.5 degrees ($\sim$ 50 km), and the wind is calculated for the Earth's surface, 10 m from the ground. More information on metadata can be obtained at the **ERDDAP**[2] website.

The R package `rWind` (Fernández-López et al., 2021) is used to obtain and process wind and ocean current data from the global forecast system. From this data, users can obtain wind/sea current speed and direction layers in order to calculate inter-site connectivity values in a simple workflow (Fernández López & Schliep, 2019).

The wind data are obtained near the Brazilian border in the period from late December 2020 to late February 2021, mapped in static and animated form, in order to detect patterns of variation of this variable in the Brazilian territory. The polygons with the boundaries of Brazilian states and boundaries of indigenous lands (FUNAI, 2022) in the format of spatial polygons with attributes are obtained from the `geobr` package, which contains official spatial data from Brazil, available at various geographical scales and for several years with harmonized attributes, projection and topology (Pereira et al., 2021).

The R software is used as an example, but other programs can be used to accomplish this task at the student's discretion. The `library` function is used in the R console to enable the `sf` (Pebesma et al., 2022), `rgdal` (Bivand et al., 2021), `rWind` (Fernández López & Schliep, 2019; Fernández-López et al., 2021), `lubridate` (Spinu et al., 2021), `fields` (Nychka et al., 2022), `raster` (Hijmans et al., 2020), `geobr` (Pereira et al., 2021), and `gifski` (Ooms & Lesiński, 2022) packages.

```
library(sf)
library(rgdal)
library(rWind)
library(lubridate)
library(fields)
library(raster)
library(geobr)
library(gifski)
```

The boundaries of states and indigenous lands of Brazil were obtained using the `read_contry` and `read_indigenous_land` functions of the `geobr` package. The Brazilian borders data are obtained at scale 1:250,000, using the geodetic reference system SIRGAS2000 and CRS with EPSG value 4674. The dataset of indigenous lands includes all ethnic groups and in different phases of demarcation. The original data comes from the National Indian Foundation (**FUNAI**[3]), for the year 2021. Although the original data is updated monthly, the `geobr` package will only keep the data for a few months each year.

```
br<-read_country(year = 2020, simplified = TRUE, showProgress = TRUE) #Brazil
# Using year 2020
#Downloading: 1.4 MB
ind<-read_indigenous_land(date = 202103, simplified = TRUE,
```

---

[1] https://www.ncei.noaa.gov/products/weather-climate-models/global-forecast
[2] https://pae-paha.pacioos.hawaii.edu/erddap/griddap/ncep_global.graph
[3] http://www.funai.gov.br/index.php/shape

```
                        showProgress = TRUE) # Terras indígenas
#Using year 202103
#Downloading: 1.5 MB
```

The st_transform function of the sf package is used to transform the projection of the data from SIRGAS2000 to WGS-84, using the reference coordinate system with EPSG 4326 in the transformation.

```
brwgs<-st_transform(br, crs = 4326)
indwgs<-st_transform(ind, crs = 4326)
```

The files are stored on the computer for later use with the st_write function.

```
st_write(brwgs, dsn = "C:/sr/S2/brwgs.shp")
st_write(indwgs, dsn = "C:/sr/S2/indwgs.shp")
```

The as_Spatial function is used to convert the polygons in the sp class to spatial polygons with attributes and the crs function is used to set the map projection parameters.

```
brsp<-as_Spatial(brwgs)
crs(brsp)<-"+proj=longlat +ellps=WGS84 +towgs84=0,0,0,0,0,0,0 +no_defs"
indsp<-as_Spatial(indwgs)
crs(indsp)<-"+proj=longlat +ellps=WGS84 +towgs84=0,0,0,0,0,0,0 +no_defs"
```

The lubridate package is used to create a sequence of dates and times every three hours from December 28, 2020 to February 28, 2021 using the seq function.

```
dt <- seq(ymd_hms(paste(2020,12,28,00,00,00, sep="-")),
        ymd_hms(paste(2021,2,28,21,00,00, sep="-")),by="3 hours")
```

The extent function is used to obtain the extent of Brazil in terms of coordinates, in order to get data in the region of interest.

```
extent(brsp)
# class     : Extent
# xmin      : -73.99045
# xmax      : -28.84784
# ymin      : -33.75118
# ymax      : 5.271841
```

The wind.dl_2 function is used to obtain the time series of wind data. The dt object is created using the lubridate package to provide time data input to wind.dl_2. Since it is a large area and many days, it may take some time, so the Sys.time function is used to determine the time used to download the data, a total of 42.7924 minutes.

```
start_time <- Sys.time()
wind_series <- wind.dl_2(dt,-73.99045,-28.84784,-33.75118,5.271841)
# [1] "2020-12-28 downloading..."
```

```
# [1] "2020-12-28 03:00:00 downloading..."
# [1] "2020-12-28 06:00:00 downloading..."
# [1] "2020-12-28 09:00:00 downloading..."
# [1] "2020-12-28 12:00:00 downloading..."
# [1] "2020-12-28 15:00:00 downloading..."
# [1] "2020-12-28 18:00:00 downloading..."
# [1] "2020-12-28 21:00:00 downloading..."
# [1] "2020-12-29 downloading..."
#...
# [1] "2021-02-28 downloading..."
# [1] "2021-02-28 03:00:00 downloading..."
# [1] "2021-02-28 06:00:00 downloading..."
# [1] "2021-02-28 09:00:00 downloading..."
# [1] "2021-02-28 12:00:00 downloading..."
# [1] "2021-02-28 15:00:00 downloading..."
# [1] "2021-02-28 18:00:00 downloading..."
# [1] "2021-02-28 21:00:00 downloading..."
stop_time <- Sys.time()
stop_time - start_time
# Time difference of 42.7924 mins
```

The wind2raster function from the rWind package is used directly over the output of wind.dl_2, and is adapted to work with wind data lists to generate raster layers of wind speed and direction.

```
wind_series_layer <- wind2raster(wind_series)
```

The results are mapped directly into a directory of interest in order to generate a time series of images in .png extension from the static mapping every 3 hours between December 28, 2020 and February 28, 2021.

```
# Wind speed
for (i in 1:length(wind_series_layer)) {
    id <- sprintf("%03d", i)
    png(paste("C:/Aulas/2021_2/SR/img/vel/V",id,".png", sep=""), width=1000, height=890,
        units="px", pointsize=18)
    image.plot(wind_series_layer[[i]]$speed, col=bpy.colors(1000),
            zlim=c(0,18), main =wind_series[[i]]$time[1])
    lines(brsp, lwd=1, col="gray92")
    lines(indsp, lwd=1, col="ForestGreen")
    dev.off()
 }
# Wind direction
for (i in 1:length(wind_series_layer)) {
    id <- sprintf("%03d", i)
    png(paste("C:/Aulas/2021_2/SR/img/wd/WD",id,".png", sep=""), width=1000, height=890,
        units="px", pointsize=18)
    image.plot(wind_series_layer[[i]]$direction, col=bpy.colors(1000),
            zlim=c(0,360), main =wind_series[[i]]$time[1])
    lines(brsp, lwd=3, col="gray92")
    lines(indsp, lwd=2, col="ForestGreen")
```

```
    dev.off()
  }
```

The images generated in the static mapping were animated using the `gifsky` package and the animation created in the `.gif` extension is exported to a folder on the computer (Figures 7.13 and 7.14).

```r
# Wind speed
png_files <- list.files("C:/Aulas/2021_2/SR/img/vel/", pattern = ".*png$",
                        full.names = TRUE)
gifski(png_files, gif_file = "C:/Aulas/2021_2/SR/img/vel/animation.gif", width = 1000,
       height = 890, delay = 1)
# Inserting image 504 at 503.00s (100%)...
# Encoding to gif... done!
# [1] "C:\\Aulas\\2021_2\\SR\\img\\vel\\animation.gif"

# Wind direction
png_files <- list.files("C:/Aulas/2021_2/SR/img/wd/", pattern = ".*png$",
                        full.names = TRUE)
gifski(png_files, gif_file = "C:/Aulas/2021_2/SR/img/wd/animation.gif", width = 1000,
       height = 890, delay = 1)
# Inserting image 504 at 503.00s (100%)...
# Encoding to gif... done!
# [1] "C:\\Aulas\\2021_2\\SR\\img\\wd\\animation.gif"
```

7.17 Computational Practice

Air pollution is a global problem and can result in deaths if exposed to hazardous air pollutants. Satellite data can be used for decision making to define appropriate mitigation strategies for sustainable, inclusive, safe and resilient development.

7.17.1 Sentinel-5P data information

The TROPOspheric Monitoring Instrument (TROPOMI) on board the Sentinel-5P satellite is a hyperspectral sensor with a monitoring bandwidth of 2600 km and recording spectral data in ultraviolet and visible (270-495 nm), near-infrared (675-775 nm) and shortwave infrared (2305-2385 nm) bands at the spatial resolution of up to 5.5 by 3.5 km. The data recorded by the TROPOMI sensor are available as of 2018 and can be used to generate useful information in global coverage on atmospheric measurements of air quality, radiative forcing, ozone, and ultraviolet radiation at temporal resolution of less than 1 day. These data are used to monitor the concentration of trace gases and aerosols that affect air quality and climate, such as CO, NO_2, CH_4, O_3, SO_2, and HCHO, as well as to measure cloud geophysical parameters.

2020-12-28

Figure 7.13 Wind speed mapping (m/s) at 10 m above the ground, in Brazil, from NOAA/NCEP Global Forecast System data every 3 hours at 50-km spatial resolution between December 28, 2020 and February 28, 2021.

7.17.2 Sentinel-5P data access and type

Sentinel-5P data can be obtained from the **Sentinel-5P Pre-Operations Data Hub**[4], with login, s5pguest, and password, s5pguest. Processing levels L1B and L2 are options for obtaining the data, with L2 being the processing level used in computational practice.

Concentrations of NO_2 and other products are provided separately in NetCDF format. NO_2 data for Brazil are used in this practical activity; however, other variables can be obtained in order to perform more complex studies (Tables 7.2 and 7.3).

---

[4]https://s5phub.copernicus.eu/dhus/#/home

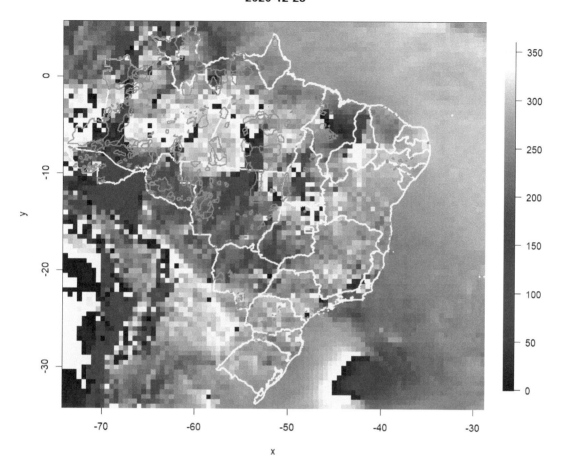

Figure 7.14 Mapping of wind direction (degrees) at 10 m from the ground, in Brazil, from NOAA/NCEP Global Forecast System data every 3 hours at 50-km spatial resolution between December 28, 2020 and February 28, 2021.

Table 7.2 Remote sensing products and variables obtained with the Sentinel-5P monitoring.

Product	Variable
CO	Carbon monoxide total column ($molm^2$)
HCHO	Formaldehyde tropospheric vertical column ($molm^2$)
NO_2	Nitrogen dioxide tropospheric column ($molm^2$)
O_3	Ozone total column ($molm^2$)
SO_2	Sulfur dioxide total column ($molm^2$)
CH_4	Column averaged dry air mixing ratio of methane (parts per billion)
AER_AI_340_380	UV aerosol index from 380 and 340 nm (unitless)
AER_AI_354_388	UV aerosol index from 388 and 354 nm (unitless)
CLOUD_BASE_PRESSURE	Cloud base pressure (pascals)
CLOUD_TOP_PRESSURE	Cloud top pressure (pascals)
CLOUD_BASE_HEIGHT	Cloud base height (meters)

Product	Variable
CLOUD_TOP_HEIGHT	Cloud top height (meters)
CLOUD_OPTICAL_THICKNESS	Cloud optical thickness (unitless)
CLOUD_FRACTION	Effective radiometric cloud fraction (unitless)
dataMask	N/A

Table 7.3 Remote sensing products, magnitude and targets of Sentinel-5P monitoring.

Product	Magnitude	Observation
CO	0-0.1	Certain events (wildfires) may cause these limits to be exceeded
HCHO	0-0.001	Certain events (wildfires) may cause these limits to be exceeded
NO_2	0-0.0003	Peak values for polluted cities may reach two or three times the upper value
O_3	0-0.36	——
SO_2	0-0.01	Explosive volcanic eruptions can exceed 0.35 molm^2 and instrumental noise can produce negative values
CH_4	1,600-2,000	——
AER_AI_340_380	-1-5	——
AER_AI_354_388	-1-5	——
CLOUD_BASE_PRESSURE	1,000-110,000	——
CLOUD_TOP_PRESSURE	1,000-110,000	——
CLOUD_BASE_HEIGHT	0-20,000	——
CLOUD_TOP_HEIGHT	0-20,000	——
CLOUD_OPTICAL_THICKNESS	0-250	——
CLOUD_FRACTION	0-1	——
dataMask	N/A	0-no data, 1-data

Depending on the size of the region, it may be necessary to make a data mosaic for the total coverage of the area of interest, using data obtained on the same day but at different times (Figure 7.15).

7.17.3   Installing R packages

The R package S5Processor (Balthasar, 2020) is used for processing the NetCDF data and converting it to geoTiff, as well as performing cloud masking and avoiding outliers. The product variable qa_value indicates the error probability of the measured values such as by cloud cover or snow. By mixing the two variables and the resulting error, elimination is performed based on the condition qa_value < 0.5 or 0.75 = NoData. With this, the nitrogen dioxide layer is obtained in the unit of NO_2 molecules per cm^2.

The R package devtools (Wickham et al., 2021) is used to install the S5Processor package from the install_github function. The stars (Pebesma, Sumner, et al., 2021), geobr (Pereira et al., 2021), tmap (Tennekes et al., 2020), tmaptools (Tennekes, 2021), gifski (Ooms & Lesiński, 2022), raster (Hijmans et al., 2020), rgdal (Bivand et al., 2021), and sp (Pebesma, Bivand, et al., 2021)

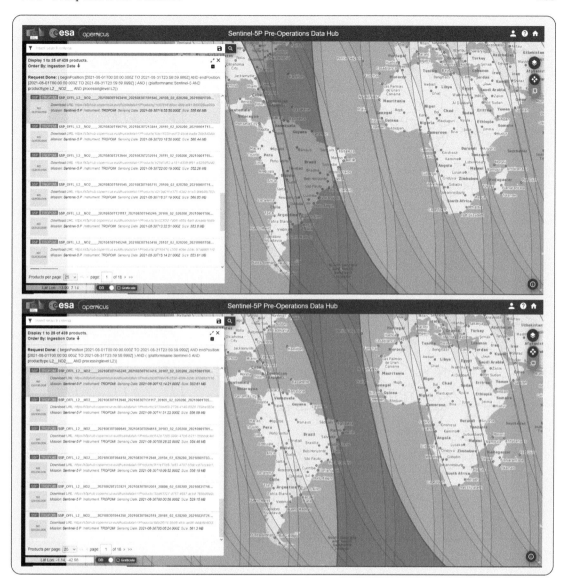

Figure 7.15 Sentinel-5P orbits used to obtain the nitrogen dioxide coverage in Brazil, at 2021-08-30T16:55:50,000Z (top) and 2021-08-30T15:14:21,000Z (bottom).

packages are used for installing and disseminating Sentinel-5P product mapping results. The ggplot2 package (Wickham, Chang, et al., 2022) can also be used as a mapping results alternative. The install.packages function is also used for installing these packages, and you should also check if there are any conflicting versions depending on which version of R is installed on your operating system. As an example, the install.packages and install_github functions are used in the R console to install the stars, geobr, tmap, tmaptools, gifski, raster, rgdal, and S5Processor packages.

```
install.packages("stars")
install.packages("geobr")
install.packages("tmap")
install.packages("tmaptools")
install.packages("gifski")
```

```
install.packages("raster")
install.packages("rgdal")
devtools::install_github("MBalthasar/S5Processor")
```

7.17.4   Enabling R Packages

The library function is used in the R console to enable the stars, geobr, tmap, tmaptools, gifski, raster, rgdal, and S5Processor packages.

```
library(stars)
library(geobr)
library(tmap)
library(tmaptools)
library(gifski)
library(raster)
library(rgdal)
library(S5Processor)
```

The obtained imaging files with the .nc extension are listed in R with the list.files function in the file storage directory with the patter=nc argument to list the data and allow the selection of files used in practice.

```
x <- list.files("C:/sr/S5P", patter="*nc", full.names=TRUE)
#[1]"S5P_OFFL_L2_NO2_20210826T142747_20210826T160916_20050_02_020200_20210828T075540.nc"
#[2]"S5P_OFFL_L2_NO2_20210829T165323_20210829T183453_20094_02_020200_20210831T094759.nc"
#[3]"S5P_OFFL_L2_NO2_20210830T145246_20210830T163416_20107_02_020200_20210901T080228.nc"
#[4]"S5P_OFFL_L2_NO2_20210830T163416_20210830T181545_20108_02_020200_20210901T094243.nc"
```

A vector can be created on the listed files to obtain individual files or to make mosaics from more than one file. In this case, the interest is to obtain the mosaic of files 3 and 4 in order to make a mosaic of the imagery taken on August 30, 2021 at 15:14:21.000Z and 16:55:50.000Z.

```
x1<-c(x[3]) # Select one file
x2<-c(x[4]) # Select one file
x12 <- c(x[3], x[4]) # Selection of two files
```

Polygons with attributes of Brazilian states and Minas Gerais are obtained with the readOGR function in order to mask the data within the area of interest.

```
mg<-readOGR(dsn="C:/geo/c13/brmg1.shp")
br<-readOGR(dsn="C:/geo/GADM/Brazil/gadm36_BRA_1.shp")
```

The S5P_process function is investigated as an example of a basic configuration for viewing the processing options and selecting the variable for the total nitrogen dioxide column, product 39.

```
S5P_1 <- S5P_process(input = x1)
#[1] "Variables checked"
```

```
#[1]  "Receiving product information"
#[1]  "PRODUCT/latitude"
#[2]  "PRODUCT/longitude"
#[3]  "PRODUCT/delta_time"
#[4]  "PRODUCT/time_utc"
#[5]  "PRODUCT/qa_value"
#[6]  "PRODUCT/nitrogendioxide_tropospheric_column"
#[7]  "PRODUCT/nitrogendioxide_tropospheric_column_precision"
#[8]  "PRODUCT/nitrogendioxide_tropospheric_column_precision_kernel"
#[9]  "PRODUCT/averaging_kernel"
#[10] "PRODUCT/air_mass_factor_troposphere"
#[11] "PRODUCT/air_mass_factor_total"
#[12] "PRODUCT/tm5_tropopause_layer_index"
#[13] "PRODUCT/tm5_constant_a"
#[14] "PRODUCT/tm5_constant_b"
#[15] "GEOLOCATIONS/satellite_latitude"
#[16] "GEOLOCATIONS/satellite_longitude"
#[17] "GEOLOCATIONS/satellite_altitude"
#[18] "GEOLOCATIONS/satellite_orbit_phase"
#[19] "GEOLOCATIONS/solar_zenith_angle"
#[20] "GEOLOCATIONS/solar_azimuth_angle"
#[21] "GEOLOCATIONS/viewing_zenith_angle"
#[22] "GEOLOCATIONS/viewing_azimuth_angle"
#[23] "GEOLOCATIONS/latitude_bounds"
#[24] "GEOLOCATIONS/longitude_bounds"
#[25] "GEOLOCATIONS/geolocation_flags"
#[26] "DETAILED_RESULTS/processing_quality_flags"
#[27] "DETAILED_RESULTS/number_of_spectral_points_in_retrieval"
#[28] "DETAILED_RESULTS/number_of_iterations"
#[29] "DETAILED_RESULTS/wavelength_calibration_offset"
#[30] "DETAILED_RESULTS/wavelength_calibration_offset_precision"
#[31] "DETAILED_RESULTS/wavelength_calibration_stretch"
#[32] "DETAILED_RESULTS/wavelength_calibration_stretch_precision"
#[33] "DETAILED_RESULTS/wavelength_calibration_chi_square"
#[34] "DETAILED_RESULTS/wavelength_calibration_irradiance_offset"
#[35] "DETAILED_RESULTS/wavelength_calibration_irradiance_offset_precision"
#[36] "DETAILED_RESULTS/wavelength_calibration_irradiance_chi_square"
#[37] "DETAILED_RESULTS/nitrogendioxide_stratospheric_column"
#[38] "DETAILED_RESULTS/nitrogendioxide_stratospheric_column_precision"
#[39] "DETAILED_RESULTS/nitrogendioxide_total_column"
#[40] "DETAILED_RESULTS/nitrogendioxide_total_column_precision"
#[41] "DETAILED_RESULTS/nitrogendioxide_total_column_precision_kernel"
#[42] "DETAILED_RESULTS/nitrogendioxide_summed_total_column"
#[43] "DETAILED_RESULTS/nitrogendioxide_summed_total_column_precision"
#[44] "DETAILED_RESULTS/nitrogendioxide_slant_column_density"
#[45] "DETAILED_RESULTS/nitrogendioxide_slant_column_density_precision"
#[46] "DETAILED_RESULTS/nitrogendioxide_slant_column_density_stripe_amplitude"
#[47] "DETAILED_RESULTS/ozone_slant_column_density"
#[48] "DETAILED_RESULTS/ozone_slant_column_density_precision"
#[49] "DETAILED_RESULTS/oxygen_oxygen_dimer_slant_column_density"
#[50] "DETAILED_RESULTS/oxygen_oxygen_dimer_slant_column_density_precision"
#[51] "DETAILED_RESULTS/water_slant_column_density"
```

```
#[52]  "DETAILED_RESULTS/water_slant_column_density_precision"
#[53]  "DETAILED_RESULTS/water_liquid_slant_column_density"
#[54]  "DETAILED_RESULTS/water_liquid_slant_column_density_precision"
#[55]  "DETAILED_RESULTS/ring_coefficient"
#[56]  "DETAILED_RESULTS/ring_coefficient_precision"
#[57]  "DETAILED_RESULTS/polynomial_coefficients"
#[58]  "DETAILED_RESULTS/polynomial_coefficients_precision"
#[59]  "DETAILED_RESULTS/intensity_offset_coefficients"
#[60]  "DETAILED_RESULTS/intensity_offset_coefficients_precision"
#[61]  "DETAILED_RESULTS/cloud_fraction_crb_nitrogendioxide_window"
#[62]  "DETAILED_RESULTS/cloud_radiance_fraction_nitrogendioxide_window"
#[63]  "DETAILED_RESULTS/chi_square"
#[64]  "DETAILED_RESULTS/root_mean_square_error_of_fit"
#[65]  "DETAILED_RESULTS/degrees_of_freedom"
#[66]  "DETAILED_RESULTS/air_mass_factor_stratosphere"
#[67]  "DETAILED_RESULTS/air_mass_factor_cloudy"
#[68]  "DETAILED_RESULTS/air_mass_factor_clear"
#[69]  "DETAILED_RESULTS/nitrogendioxide_ghost_column"
#[70]  "DETAILED_RESULTS/cloud_selection_flag"
#[71]  "O22CLD/o22cld_cloud_fraction_crb"
#[72]  "O22CLD/o22cld_cloud_fraction_crb_not_clipped"
#[73]  "O22CLD/o22cld_cloud_fraction_crb_precision"
#[74]  "O22CLD/o22cld_cloud_pressure_crb"
#[75]  "O22CLD/o22cld_cloud_pressure_crb_not_clipped"
#[76]  "O22CLD/o22cld_cloud_pressure_crb_precision"
#[77]  "O22CLD/o22cld_cloud_height_crb"
#[78]  "O22CLD/o22cld_cloud_height_crb_precision"
#[79]  "O22CLD/o22cld_cloud_albedo_crb"
#[80]  "O22CLD/o22cld_scene_albedo"
#[81]  "O22CLD/o22cld_scene_albedo_precision"
#[82]  "O22CLD/o22cld_apparent_scene_pressure"
#[83]  "O22CLD/o22cld_apparent_scene_pressure_precision"
#[84]  "O22CLD/o22cld_chi_square"
#[85]  "O22CLD/o22cld_continuum_at_reference_wavelength"
#[86]  "O22CLD/o22cld_continuum_at_reference_wavelength_precision"
#[87]  "O22CLD/o22cld_polynomial_coefficient"
#[88]  "O22CLD/o22cld_polynomial_coefficient_precision"
#[89]  "O22CLD/o22cld_ring_coefficient"
#[90]  "O22CLD/o22cld_ring_coefficient_precision"
#[91]  "O22CLD/o22cld_nitrogendioxide_slant_column_density"
#[92]  "O22CLD/o22cld_nitrogendioxide_slant_column_density_precision"
#[93]  "O22CLD/o22cld_oxygen_oxygen_dimer_slant_column_density"
#[94]  "O22CLD/o22cld_oxygen_oxygen_dimer_slant_column_density_precision"
#[95]  "O22CLD/o22cld_oxygen_oxygen_dimer_slant_column_density_correction_factor"
#[96]  "O22CLD/o22cld_ozone_slant_column_density"
#[97]  "O22CLD/o22cld_ozone_slant_column_density_precision"
#[98]  "O22CLD/o22cld_surface_albedo"
#[99]  "O22CLD/o22cld_wavelength_calibration_irradiance_offset"
#[100] "O22CLD/o22cld_wavelength_calibration_offset"
#[101] "O22CLD/o22cld_wavelength_calibration_offset_precision"
#[102] "O22CLD/o22cld_wavelength_calibration_stretch"
#[103] "O22CLD/o22cld_wavelength_calibration_stretch_precision"
```

```
#[104] "FRESCO/fresco_cloud_fraction_crb"
#[105] "FRESCO/fresco_cloud_pressure_crb"
#[106] "FRESCO/fresco_scene_albedo"
#[107] "FRESCO/fresco_apparent_scene_pressure"
#[108] "FRESCO/fresco_cloud_albedo_crb"
#[109] "FRESCO/fresco_surface_albedo"
#[110] "INPUT_DATA/surface_altitude"
#[111] "INPUT_DATA/surface_altitude_precision"
#[112] "INPUT_DATA/surface_classification"
#[113] "INPUT_DATA/instrument_configuration_identifier"
#[114] "INPUT_DATA/instrument_configuration_version"
#[115] "INPUT_DATA/scaled_small_pixel_variance"
#[116] "INPUT_DATA/eastward_wind"
#[117] "INPUT_DATA/northward_wind"
#[118] "INPUT_DATA/surface_pressure"
#[119] "INPUT_DATA/surface_albedo_nitrogendioxide_window"
#[120] "INPUT_DATA/surface_albedo"
#[121] "INPUT_DATA/cloud_pressure_crb"
#[122] "INPUT_DATA/cloud_fraction_crb"
#[123] "INPUT_DATA/cloud_albedo_crb"
#[124] "INPUT_DATA/scene_albedo"
#[125] "INPUT_DATA/apparent_scene_pressure"
#[126] "INPUT_DATA/snow_ice_flag"
#[127] "INPUT_DATA/aerosol_index_354_388"
#[128] "QA_STATISTICS/nitrogendioxide_stratospheric_column_histogram_bounds"
#[129] "QA_STATISTICS/nitrogendioxide_stratospheric_column_pdf_bounds"
#[130] "QA_STATISTICS/nitrogendioxide_tropospheric_column_histogram_bounds"
#[131] "QA_STATISTICS/nitrogendioxide_tropospheric_column_pdf_bounds"
#[132] "QA_STATISTICS/nitrogendioxide_total_column_histogram_bounds"
#[133] "QA_STATISTICS/nitrogendioxide_total_column_pdf_bounds"
#[134] "QA_STATISTICS/nitrogendioxide_tropospheric_column_histogram"
#[135] "QA_STATISTICS/nitrogendioxide_stratospheric_column_histogram"
#[136] "QA_STATISTICS/nitrogendioxide_total_column_histogram"
#[137] "QA_STATISTICS/nitrogendioxide_tropospheric_column_pdf"
#[138] "QA_STATISTICS/nitrogendioxide_stratospheric_column_pdf"
#[139] "QA_STATISTICS/nitrogendioxide_total_column_pdf"
#Enter an integer for product selection: 39
#[1] "Getting values from file 1 of 1"
#[1] "Convert data frame to spatial points"
#[1] "Calculate number of rows and columns for raster file"
#[1] "Create raster file from points"
#[1] "===================== Done! ====================="
#[1] "Total processing time: 16.0754241943359 seconds"
#[1] "Total vertical column of nitrogen dioxide derived from the total slant column and
#TM5 profile in stratosphere and troposphere in the unit mol m-2"
#[1] "Multiplication factor to convert to molecules per cm2: 60221399743430918144"
```

In this case, the total processing time was 16.0754241943359 seconds with the total vertical column of nitrogen dioxide being derived from the total oblique column and TM5 profile in the stratosphere and troposphere in the unit mol m^{-2}. The data are converted to mol cm^{-2} with the conversion factor 60221399743430918144 (Figure 7.16).

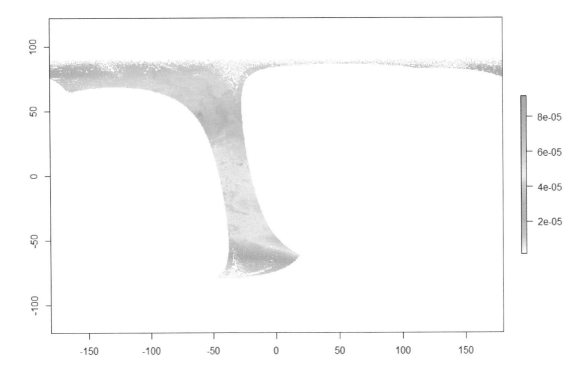

Figure 7.16 Total vertical column of nitrogen dioxide in the stratosphere and troposphere obtained by Sentinel-5P on September 30, 2021 T16:55:50.000Z.

Another processing option can be performed by masking the data in the region of interest. As an example, the processing of the nitrogen dioxide mosaic in Minas Gerais is performed. In this case, the spatial resolution is set to 20000 m and the argument `my_aoi=mg` is used to define the region in Minas Gerais (Figure 7.17).

```
NO2mg <- S5P_process(input = x12, my_res = 20000,
                     product = 39, my_aoi = mg,
                     extent_only = FALSE,
                     apply_scale_factor = T)
#[1] "Variables checked"
#[1] "Receiving product information"
#[1] "Getting values from file 1 of 2"
#[1] "Getting values from file 2 of 2"
#[1] "Convert data frame to spatial points"
#[1] "Crop points to aoi"
#[1] "Calculate number of rows and columns for raster file"
#[1] "Create raster file from points"
#[1] "Mask final raster to aoi"
#[1] "====================== Done! ======================"
#[1] "Total processing time: 9.44579911231995 seconds"
#[1] "Total vertical column of nitrogen dioxide derived from the total slant column and
#TM5 profile in stratosphere and troposphere"
#[1] "Data has been converted from mol m-2 to molecules per cm2 by multiplying with the
#factor 60221399743430918144"
```

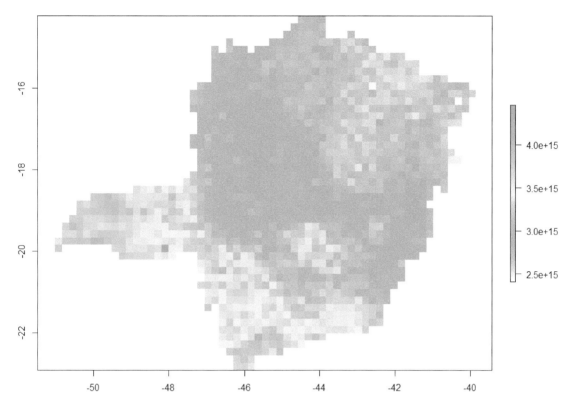

Figure 7.17 Sentinel-5P data mosaic to map the spatial variation of nitrogen dioxide in state of Minas Gerais, Brazil, on August 30, 2021.

7.17.5 Processing Sentinel-5P imagery in Google Earth Engine

Remote sensing virtual libraries can be an alternative to minimize the difficulties of using information technology in the area of remote sensing and digital image processing of Sentinel-5P (Gorelick et al., 2017).

The **Google Earth Engine**[5] code editor can be accessed to perform nitrogen dioxide mapping around a point centered in the southeastern region of Brazil at the geodetic coordinates of longitude and latitude -45.38°, -22.69°. A chunk of code in JavaScript language is used to perform the imaging from September 1 to 6, 2021 (Figure 7.18).

```javascript
var collection = ee.ImageCollection('COPERNICUS/S5P/NRTI/L3_NO2')
   .select('NO2_column_number_density')
   .filterDate('2021-09-01', '2021-09-06');
var band_viz = {
  min: 0,
  max: 0.0002,
  palette: ['black', 'blue', 'purple', 'cyan', 'green', 'yellow', 'red']
};
Map.addLayer(collection.mean(), band_viz, 'S5P N02');
Map.setCenter(-45.38, -22.69, 4);
```

---

[5]https://code.earthengine.google.com/

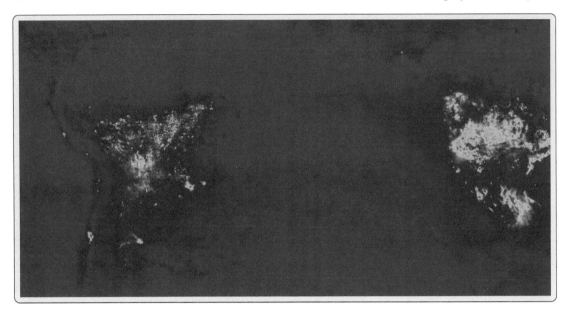

Figure 7.18 Mapping nitrogen dioxide in Google Earth Engine, with coordinate center in southeast Brazil, between September 1 and 6, 2021.

7.17.6   Spatio-temporal mapping of Sentinel-5P images in R

The R package `geobr` is used in this case to obtain the geometry of municipalities for the year 2020.

The `read_municipality` function is used to obtain the municipalities of Minas Gerais, referring to the year 2020.

```
muni <- read_municipality(code_muni= "MG", year=2020) # Municipalities
mg <- read_state(code_state="MG", year=2020) # MG state
```

The coordinate reference system (CRS) in the GRS-1980 system is transformed to the WGS-84 system with the `st_transform` function.

```
muniwgs <- st_transform(muni, crs = 4326)
mgwgs <- st_transform(mg, crs = 4326)
```

The municipalities and contour of Minas Gerais are exported to a directory of interest for later use with the `st_write` function.

```
st_write(mgwgs, dsn = "C:/sr/c7/lavrasshp/mgwgs.shp")
st_write(muniwgs, dsn = "C:/sr/c7/lavrasshp/muniwgs.shp")
```

Vector files with municipalities and contour of Minas Gerais can be imported into R with the `st_read` or `readOGR` functions. The use of these files according to the specific class is according to the package used.

```
mgwgs<-st_read("C:/sr/c7/lavrasshp/mgwgs.shp") #Contorno sf
mgwgsp<-readOGR(dsn="C:/sr/c7/lavrasshp/mgwgs.shp") #Contorno sp
muniwgs<-st_read("C:/sr/c7/lavrasshp/muniwgs.shp") #Municípios sf
muniwgsp<-readOGR(dsn="C:/sr/c7/lavrasshp/muniwgs.shp") #Municípios sp
```

Sentinel-5P imaging files obtained with the .nc extension are listed in R with the list.files function in the file storage directory with the patter=nc argument to list the data and allow the selection of files used in practice.

```
x <- list.files("C:/sr/S5P/tempo", patter="*nc", full.names=TRUE)
x
#[1]"S5P_OFFL_L2_NO2_20210901T155601_20210901T173730_20136_02_020200_20210903T084455.nc"
#[2]"S5P_OFFL_L2_NO2_20210902T153653_20210902T171822_20150_02_020200_20210904T084741.nc"
#[3]"S5P_OFFL_L2_NO2_20210903T151745_20210903T165914_20164_02_020200_20210905T082008.nc"
#[4]"S5P_OFFL_L2_NO2_20210903T165914_20210903T184044_20165_02_020200_20210905T102325.nc"
#[5]"S5P_OFFL_L2_NO2_20210904T145837_20210904T164007_20178_02_020200_20210906T080021.nc"
#[6]"S5P_OFFL_L2_NO2_20210904T164007_20210904T182136_20179_02_020200_20210906T100037.nc"
#[7]"S5P_OFFL_L2_NO2_20210905T162059_20210905T180228_20193_02_020200_20210907T093847.nc"
#[8]"S5P_OFFL_L2_NO2_20210906T160151_20210906T174320_20207_02_020200_20210908T090843.nc"
#[9]"S5P_OFFL_L2_NO2_20210907T154243_20210907T172412_20221_02_020200_20210909T090039.nc"
#[10]"S5P_OFFL_L2_NO2_20210908T152335_20210908T170504_20235_02_020200_20210910T082102.nc"
#[11]"S5P_OFFL_L2_NO2_20210908T170504_20210908T184634_20236_02_020200_20210910T101748.nc"
#[12]"S5P_OFFL_L2_NO2_20210909T150427_20210909T164556_20249_02_020200_20210911T080932.nc"
#[13]"S5P_OFFL_L2_NO2_20210909T164556_20210909T182726_20250_02_020200_20210911T094024.nc"
#[14]"S5P_OFFL_L2_NO2_20210910T162648_20210910T180818_20264_02_020200_20210912T094441.nc"
#[15]"S5P_OFFL_L2_NO2_20210911T160740_20210911T174910_20278_02_020200_20210913T091431.nc"
#[16]"S5P_OFFL_L2_NO2_20210912T154832_20210912T173001_20292_02_020200_20210914T084650.nc"
#[17]"S5P_OFFL_L2_NO2_20210913T152924_20210913T171053_20306_02_020200_20210915T084309.nc"
#[18]"S5P_OFFL_L2_NO2_20210913T171053_20210913T185223_20307_02_020200_20210915T101142.nc"
#[19]"S5P_OFFL_L2_NO2_20210914T151016_20210914T165145_20320_02_020200_20210916T080345.nc"
#[20]"S5P_OFFL_L2_NO2_20210914T165145_20210914T183314_20321_02_020200_20210916T094740.nc"
#[21]"S5P_OFFL_L2_NO2_20210915T163237_20210915T181406_20335_02_020200_20210917T092944.nc"
#[22]"S5P_OFFL_L2_NO2_20210916T161328_20210916T175458_20349_02_020200_20210918T085957.nc"
```

A vector is created on the listed files to obtain individual files or to make mosaics from more than one file. In this case, the interest is to obtain the mosaic of files 3 and 4 in order to make a mosaic of the imagery taken on August 30, 2021 at 15:14:21.000Z and 16:55:50.000Z.

```
x1<-c(x[1])
x2<-c(x[2])
x3 <- c(x[3], x[4])
x4<-c(x[5], x[6])
x5<-c(x[7])
x6 <- c(x[8])
x7 <- c(x[9])
x8 <- c(x[10], x[11])
x9 <- c(x[12], x[13])
x10 <- c(x[14])
x11 <- c(x[15])
x12 <- c(x[16])
x13 <- c(x[17], x[18])
```

```
x14 <- c(x[19], x[20])
x15 <- c(x[21])
x16 <- c(x[22])
```

The S5P_process function is investigated as an example of a basic setup for viewing the processing options and selecting the variable for the total nitrogen dioxide column, product 39.

Processing is performed by masking the data in the region of interest. As an example, the processing of the nitrogen dioxide mosaic in municipalities of Minas Gerais is accomplished. In this case, the spatial resolution is set to 20000 m and the argument my_aoi=mgwgsp is used to define the region in Minas Gerais. The processed data are for the period September 1-16, 2021.

After processing the data, the total vertical column of nitrogen dioxide in the stratosphere and troposphere in the unit mol m^{-2} are obtained. The data are converted to mol cm^{-2} by multiplying by the factor 60221399743430918144.

The file dates are created to perform the mapping of the results according to each date.

```
dates <- c("NO2_2021-09-01","NO2_2021-09-02","NO2_2021-09-03","NO2_2021-09-04",
           "NO2_2021-09-05","NO2_2021-09-06","NO2_2021-09-07","NO2_2021-09-08",
           "NO2_2021-09-09","NO2_2021-09-10","NO2_2021-09-11","NO2_2021-09-12",
           "NO2_2021-09-13","NO2_2021-09-14","NO2_2021-09-15","NO2_2021-09-16")
```

The data with nitrogen dioxide mapping results are stacked and renamed with the stack and names functions, respectively.

```
NO2mg <- stack(NO2mg1,NO2mg2,NO2mg3,NO2mg4,NO2mg5,NO2mg6,NO2mg7,NO2mg8,NO2mg9,NO2mg10,
               NO2mg11,NO2mg12,NO2mg13,NO2mg14,NO2mg15,NO2mg16)
names(NO2mg) <- dates
```

The stacked file is converted to the stars class with the st_as_stars function and exported to a directory of interest with the write_stars function.

```
x <- st_as_stars(NO2mg)
write_stars(x, "C:/sr/c7/NO2mg.tif")
```

The read_stars function is used to import the file with the nitrogen dioxide data for mapping.

```
tif <- read_stars("C:/sr/c7/NO2mg.tif", package = "stars")
```

The ggplot2 package is used to perform static mapping of nitrogen dioxide in Minas Gerais (Figure 7.19).

```
ggplot() +
geom_stars(data = tif) +
scale_fill_viridis_c(limits = c(2e+15,1.5e+16),option = "inferno") +
geom_sf(data = mgwgs, fill = NA) +
coord_sf(datum=st_crs(4326)) +
facet_wrap( ~ band) +
```

```
labs(fill=expression(NO[2]~molecules~cm^-2)) +
theme_void()
```

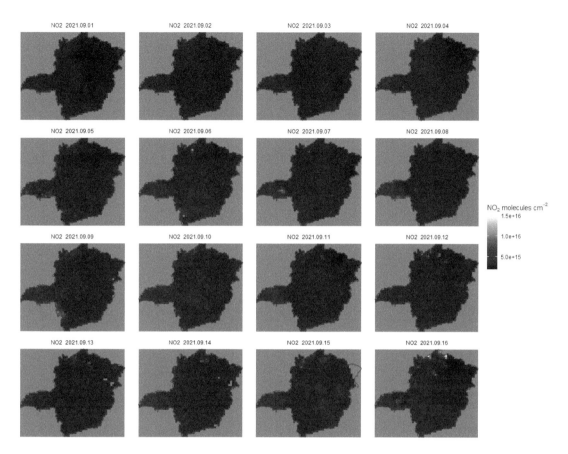

Figure 7.19 Sentinel-5P data mosaic to map the spatial variation of nitrogen dioxide in Minas Gerais on September 1-16, 2021.

In order to perform animated mapping, it is necessary to install the ImageMagick program on the computer and then set the PATH location of where the program was installed. The Sys.setenv function is used to set the ImageMagick installation directory on the computer.

```
Sys.setenv(PATH = paste("c:/Arquivos de Programas/ImageMagick-7.0.10-Q16-HDRI",
                        Sys.getenv("PATH"), sep = ";"))
```

A color palette with shades of red is defined to colorize the maps to represent a gradient of variation of nitrogen dioxide in Minas Gerais using the tmaptools package.

```
reds <- get_brewer_pal("Reds", n = 9)
```

The outline of Minas Gerais is used as the boundary line of the results in the region of interest.

```
outline <- tm_shape(mgwgs) + tm_borders()
```

Raster objects are mapped by `tmap` with different options for configuring the mapping.

```
NO2_plots <- tm_shape(NO2mg) + # object with rasters
tm_grid(lines = FALSE) + # grid
tm_raster(title = expression("NO"[2]*~"molecules"~"cm"^"-2"),
palette = reds,
style = "cont") +
tm_facets(nrow = 1, ncol = 1) + # show only 1 map at a time
tm_layout(panel.labels = dates) # map names
```

The edge maps in vector format and the nitrogen dioxide rasters are combined.

```
combined_plot <- NO2_plots + outline
```

The `tmap_animation` function is used to generate the combined vector and boundary animated mapping (Figure 7.20).

```
NO2_animation <- tmap_animation(combined_plot, "NO2_animation.gif", delay = 160)
```

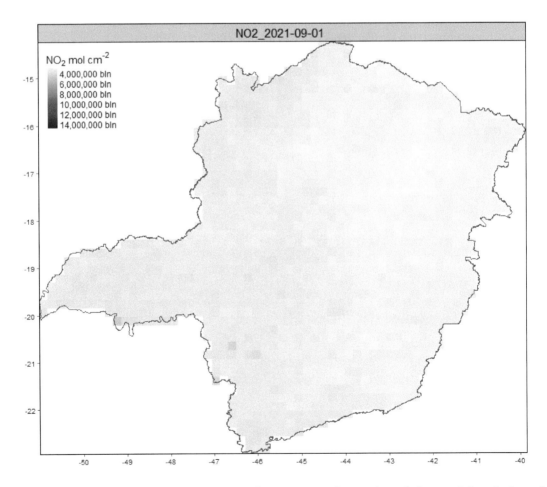

Figure 7.20 Sentinel-5P data mosaic to perform animated mapping of the spatial variation of nitrogen dioxide in Minas Gerais on September 1-16, 2021.

7.18 Exercises

7.18.1 How can remote sensing of atmosphere be useful to society?

7.18.2 What is the mean composition of the dry atmosphere below 25 km?

a. 99% nitrogen and oxygen.
b. 99% hydrogen and oxygen.
c. 99% hydrogen and ozone.
d. 99% carbon dioxide and ozone.
e. None of the alternatives.

7.18.3 Which mission is a passive remote sensing mission used to monitor the concentration of trace gases and aerosols that affect air quality and climate is obtained by satellite?

a. Landsat-8 TIRS.
b. TRMM.
c. Sentinel-5P.
d. SRTM.
e. None of the alternatives.

7.18.4 Which option is an R package specializes in processing and mapping Sentinel-5P data in a region of interest?

a. gstat.
b. S5Processor.
c. glcm.
d. geoR.
e. None of the alternatives.

7.19 Homework

7.19.1 Subject

Planetary-scale cloud fraction monitoring with Sentinel-5P remote sensing data.

7.19.2 Assignment

Develop the subject presented with a practical application of remote sensing and digital image processing including the topics Introduction and Objective. Then, present the development of the task.

7.20 Resources on the Internet

Activities are proposed for the development of scientific research on remote sensing that can be used or adapted by the student to monitor and identify targets in a specific area of interest as shown in Table 7.4.

Table 7.4 Slide presentation and illustrative video about remote sensing of atmosphere study.

Guide	Address for Access
1	Video on monitoring with the TROPOMI sensor[6]
2	Sentinel-5P processing workflow in SNAP[7]
3	Download Sentinel-5P data for air quality assessment[8]
4	Introducing Sentinel-5P[9]
5	Sentinel-5P services[10]
6	Global carbon monoxide measured by Sentinel-5P[11]
7	*In situ* air quality monitoring[12]

7.21 Research Suggestion

Activities are proposed for the development of scientific research on remote sensing that can be used or adapted by the student to monitor and identify targets in a specific area of interest (Table 7.5).

---

[6]https://dlmultimedia.esa.int/download/public/videos/2017/07/025/orig-1707_025_AR_EN.mp4
[7]https://youtu.be/G8tVNbdu8-A
[8]https://youtu.be/If-5QDw-RWE
[9]https://youtu.be/doqsNc8vC00
[10]https://youtu.be/8DGC6enV4-8
[11]https://youtu.be/wIlcXnUvNdc
[12]https://youtu.be/_QD61Y9iaqs

Table 7.5 Description of practical activities that can be used or adapted by students with suggested research in remote sensing.

Activity	Description
1	Use the practical example developed by the teacher and monitor a region of interest with Sentinel-5P data.
2	Evaluate Sentinel-5P data processing in SNAP software and highlight differences observed when processing the same data in R.
3	Process Sentinel-5P data in Google Earth Engine and determine advantages and disadvantages.

8

Scientific Applications of Remote Sensing and Digital Image Processing for Project Design

8.1 Learning Questions

The learning questions answered by reading the chapter are as follows:

- What are the scientific applications of remote sensing?
- What is the relationship between remote sensing applications and scientific practice?
- How are problems in remote sensing objectively solved objectively?
- How is scientific research planned in remote sensing?

8.2 Learning Outcomes

Using the learning outcomes from the chapter, you should be able to do the following:

- Understand practical applications of remote sensing information.
- Understand applications of remote sensing as science.
- Identify hypotheses in scientific studies involving remote sensing.
- Write a simplified scientific project in the area of remote sensing.

8.3 Introduction

Remote sensing systems are used in a variety of applications for monitoring natural resources and the Earth's environment. The science of remote sensing provides innovative and fundamental scientific information about biotic and abiotic data of the environment, such as positional location, elevation or depth, biomass estimation, temperature and moisture content of targets. The use of remote sensing provides basic information for scientific research in other sciences such as Geomatics and Geographic Information Systems. With the use of remote sensing, data can be obtained systematically for points or geographic areas in order to model natural processes such as estimation of water supply, eutrophication and pollution, population estimates and terrain variations in agricultural and urban areas with digital elevation modeling (Jensen, 2007).

The synergy of combining scientific knowledge with the analyst's real-world experience to better understand scientific principles, the increased field experience in observing landscape objects and geographic areas, and the ability to synthesize scientific principles and experience to derive logical and correct conclusions (Jensen, 2007).

Some everyday uses of remote sensing applications are highlighted:

- Effectiveness in decision making, such as agricultural management;
- Application in diverse areas, such as socioeconomics and environment;
- Application in mapping, measuring, managing, monitoring, and modeling operations;
- Measurable economic return from different industries;
- Combinations with other sciences and technologies, such as geomatics and geoprocessing.

The factors that determine the use of remote sensing in society are:

- Availability of Internet and local networks for data access and sharing;
- Relative reductions in the price of digital image processing hardware and software;
- Increased awareness of the population to include spatial, temporal, radiometric and spectral geographic aspects in decision making;
- Availability of data processing in GUI environments and geocomputation algorithms;
- Technology supporting applications to visualize, manage data and analysis, as well as linking to third-party software;
- Availability of satellite positioning systems to orthorectify images and locate points and areas under imagery
- Availability of free, user-friendly applications;
- Accumulated experience in using remote sensing applications.

8.4   Context of Geospatial Data Infrastructure

In addition to active and passive remote sensing imagery data, ancillary data are used in the remote sensing process, such as digital elevation model, soil maps, geological maps, vector files with political boundaries database, and population statistics. With the use of remote sensing, two classes of variables are obtained, the biophysical and the hybrid. The fundamental biological or physical information refers to biophysical variables, such as (Jensen, 2007):

- Geodetic location;
- Topography and bathymetry;
- Vegetation;
- Soils and rocks;
- Water;
- Snow and sea ice;
- Volcanism;
- Surface temperature of land, water and atmosphere;
- Surface roughness;
- Radiance and reflectance of targets.

Hybrid variables are created by systematically analyzing more than one biophysical variable, such as (Jensen, 2007):

- Land use;

- Vegetation vigor;
- Water quality;
- Exposed soil index.

8.5   Remote Sensing Process

The procedures for collecting and analyzing remote sensing data are applied to terrestrial resources and implemented in a systematic way, through the remote sensing process. In this case, a hypothesis must be defined and tested to solve a given problem of soil, water, atmosphere, vegetation, rural or urban environments. Then, complementary and *in situ* data may need to be obtained to calibrate and evaluate the remote sensor data according to geometric, radiometric and thematic characteristics. By processing passively or actively collected remote sensor data, along with *in situ* data and supplementary information, the processed images can be visualized in n-dimensions and by modeling. Finally, the generated results must be analyzed and interpreted by means of images, graphs, statistical tables, databases in geographic information systems, and spatial decision support systems in order to generate knowledge about the geographic problem (Jensen, 2007). Therefore, data collection and analysis procedures of terrestrial resources are implemented in a systematic way, and represent the procedure called the "remote sensing process" (Figure 8.1).

8.5.1   Determination of rainfall on the UFLA campus

The determination of rainfall time series on the Federal University of Lavras campus between the years 2018 and 2022 is performed with climate data from Terraclimate (Abatzoglou et al., 2018) and the rgee package (Aybar et al., 2022).

8.5.1.1   Enable packages

The library function is used to enable the rgee (Aybar et al., 2022), sf (Pebesma et al., 2022), tidyverse (Wickham & RStudio, 2021), ggplot2 (Wickham, Chang, et al., 2022), and gridExtra (Auguie & Antonov, 2017) packages. The ee_Initialize function is used to start the Earth Engine.

```
# Carregar os pacotes utilizados
library(rgee)
library(sf)
library(tidyverse)
library(ggplot2)
library(gridExtra)
ee_Initialize()
```

8.5.1.2   Get polygon feature

A polygon-type vector feature on the UFLA boundary is imported into R with the st_read() function.

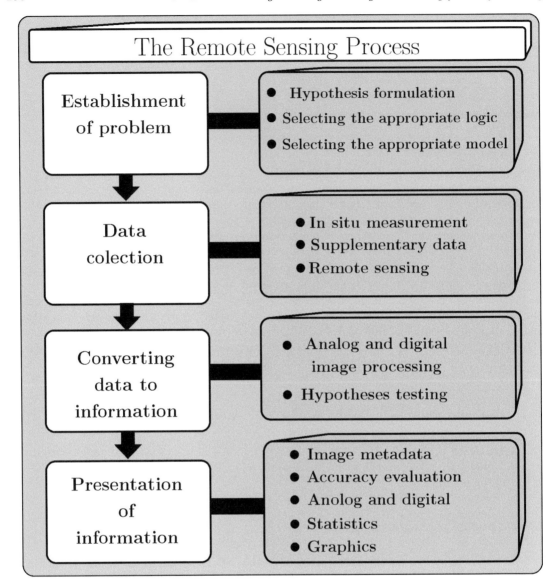

Figure 8.1 Remote sensing process used to implement data collection and analysis procedures, in a systematic way, in surveying environments.

```
shp1 <- st_read("C:/sr/ufla/uflabordawgs.shp", quiet = TRUE)
```

8.5.1.3   Obtain climate data

Rainfall data is obtained from the **Terraclimate**[1] database with the ee$ImageCollection code. A data filtering is performed between the period January 1, 2018 to January 1, 2022, separating the data from the collection year by year.

---

[1] https://developers.google.com/earth-engine/datasets/catalog/IDAHO_EPSCOR_TERRACLIMATE

```
terraclimate18 <- ee$ImageCollection("IDAHO_EPSCOR/TERRACLIMATE") %>%
  ee$ImageCollection$filterDate("2018-01-01", "2019-01-01") %>%
  ee$ImageCollection$map(function(x) x$select("pr")) %>%
  ee$ImageCollection$toBands() %>%
  ee$Image$rename(sprintf("PP_%02d",1:12))
terraclimate19 <- ee$ImageCollection("IDAHO_EPSCOR/TERRACLIMATE") %>%
  ee$ImageCollection$filterDate("2019-01-01", "2020-01-01") %>%
  ee$ImageCollection$map(function(x) x$select("pr")) %>%
  ee$ImageCollection$toBands() %>%
  ee$Image$rename(sprintf("PP_%02d",1:12))
terraclimate20 <- ee$ImageCollection("IDAHO_EPSCOR/TERRACLIMATE") %>%
  ee$ImageCollection$filterDate("2020-01-01", "2021-01-01") %>%
  ee$ImageCollection$map(function(x) x$select("pr")) %>%
  ee$ImageCollection$toBands() %>%
  ee$Image$rename(sprintf("PP_%02d",1:12))
terraclimate21 <- ee$ImageCollection("IDAHO_EPSCOR/TERRACLIMATE") %>%
  ee$ImageCollection$filterDate("2021-01-01", "2022-01-01") %>%
  ee$ImageCollection$map(function(x) x$select("pr")) %>%
  ee$ImageCollection$toBands() %>%
  ee$Image$rename(sprintf("PP_%02d",1:12))
```

8.5.1.4   Extract rainfall values on a polygon feature

The ee_extract function is used to extract monthly precipitation values from the Terraclimate ImageCollection from the geometry defining the boundaries of the UFLA campus.

```
ee_nc_rain18 <- ee_extract(x = terraclimate18, y = shp1["FID"], sf = FALSE)
ee_nc_rain19 <- ee_extract(x = terraclimate19, y = shp1["FID"], sf = FALSE)
ee_nc_rain20 <- ee_extract(x = terraclimate20, y = shp1["FID"], sf = FALSE)
ee_nc_rain21 <- ee_extract(x = terraclimate21, y = shp1["FID"], sf = FALSE)
```

8.5.1.5   Time series analysis

The ggplot2 package is used in graphical mapping of the variation of monthly rainfall at UFLA between 2018 and 2021.

```
p1<-ee_nc_rain18 %>%
  pivot_longer(-FID, names_to = "month", values_to = "pr") %>%
  mutate(month, month=gsub("PP_", "", month)) %>%
  ggplot(aes(x = month, y = pr, group = FID)) +
  geom_bar(stat="identity", fill="steelblue") +
  geom_text(aes(label=pr), vjust=-0.2, color="black", size=3.5) +
  xlab("") +
  ylab("Precipitation (mm)") +
  ggtitle("2018") +
  ylim(0, 390) +
  theme_minimal()
p2<-ee_nc_rain19 %>%
```

```
  pivot_longer(-FID, names_to = "month", values_to = "pr") %>%
  mutate(month, month=gsub("PP_", "", month)) %>%
  ggplot(aes(x = month, y = pr, group = FID)) +
  geom_bar(stat="identity", fill="steelblue") +
  geom_text(aes(label=pr), vjust=-0.2, color="black", size=3.5) +
  xlab("") +
  ylab("") +
  ggtitle("2019") +
  ylim(0, 390) +
  theme_minimal()
p3<-ee_nc_rain20 %>%
  pivot_longer(-FID, names_to = "month", values_to = "pr") %>%
  mutate(month, month=gsub("PP_", "", month)) %>%
  ggplot(aes(x = month, y = pr, group = FID)) +
  geom_bar(stat="identity", fill="steelblue") +
  geom_text(aes(label=pr), vjust=-0.2, color="black", size=3.5) +
  xlab("Month") +
  ylab("Precipitation (mm)") +
  ggtitle("2020") +
  ylim(0, 390) +
  theme_minimal()
p4<-ee_nc_rain21 %>%
  pivot_longer(-FID, names_to = "month", values_to = "pr") %>%
  mutate(month, month=gsub("PP_", "", month)) %>%
  ggplot(aes(x = month, y = pr, group = FID)) +
  geom_bar(stat="identity", fill="steelblue") +
  geom_text(aes(label=pr), vjust=-0.2, color="black", size=3.5) +
  xlab("Month") +
  ylab("") +
  ggtitle("2021") +
  ylim(0, 390) +
  theme_minimal()
grid.arrange(p1, p2, p3, p4, ncol=2)
```

Thus, it is possible to observe that precipitation is variable year after year, but with a certain distribution pattern with higher rainfall values from October to March and lower values from April to September. In the year 2021 there was less rainfall when compared to previous years (Figure 8.2).

8.5.2 Determination of vegetation index at UFLA campus

NOAA's Climate Data Registry (CDR) for the Normalized Difference Vegetation Index (NDVI) derived from the AVHRR sensor contains daily grid-based NDVI derived from the NOAA AVHRR surface reflectance product. This index provides a grid-based measurement of surface vegetation cover activity at a resolution of 0.05° and calculated globally over the Earth's surface. The orbital drift of N-19 (the last NOAA satellite carrying the AVHRR sensor) began to severely degrade the quality of the retrieved product. Thus, VIIRS is now the primary sensor to be used for these products from 2014 to the present. For more details, access the **website**[2] with the data source.

---

[2]https://developers.google.com/earth-engine/datasets/catalog/NOAA_CDR_AVHRR_NDVI_V5

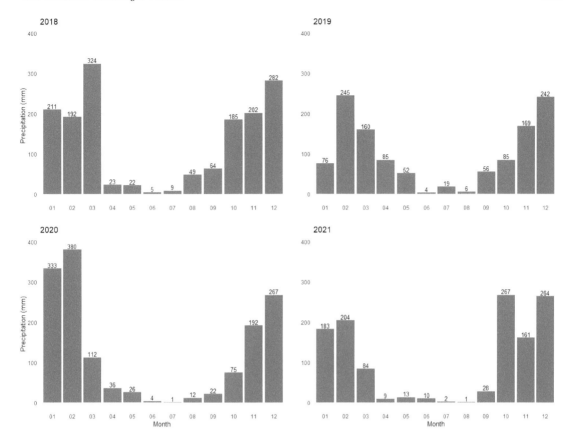

Figure 8.2 Monthly rainfall between 2018 and 2021 on the Federal University of Lavras campus, state of Minas Gerais, Brazil.

The packages used in the analysis are enabled with the `library` function. The Earth Engine is initialized with the `ee_Initialize` function.

```
library(rgee)
library(raster)
library(tidyverse)
library(sf)
library(ggplot2)
ee_Initialize(drive = TRUE)
```

The region of interest is obtained from a polygon with the UFLA boundaries in an `sf` class file. The `st_read` function imports the file into R and the `st_geometry` and `sf_as_ee` functions are used to obtain a `geometry` object from Earth Engine.

```
ee_roi <- st_read("C:/sr/ufla/uflabordawgs.shp") %>%
  #summarise() %>%
  st_geometry() %>%
  sf_as_ee()
```

NOAA CDR AVHRR Normalized Difference Vegetation Index (NDVI), version 5 data are obtained with the `ee` and `ImageCollection` functions.

```
avhrr <- ee$ImageCollection("NOAA/CDR/AVHRR/NDVI/V5")
```

The quality filter types are defined to perform atmospheric correction of the data by filtering the image collection.

```
bit1 <- ee$Number(2)$pow(1)$int() # Pixel is cloudy
bit2 <- ee$Number(2)$pow(2)$int() # Pixel with cloud and shadow
```

A filter to obtain atmospheric-quality image data is created from a function to extract the NDVI band from the collection, extract the band with quality information, select pixels for masking, and mask pixels with a value of zero.

```
qaFilter <- function(img) {
  ndvi <- img$select("NDVI")
  qa <- img$select("QA")
  qa_mask <- qa$bitwiseAnd(bit1)$eq(0)$
    And(qa$bitwiseAnd(bit2)$eq(0))
  ndvi$updateMask(qa_mask) %>% return()}
```

The quality filter is applied to NOAA imagery data.

```
ndvi_mask <- avhrr$map(qaFilter)
```

The time series of interest is set between 2015 and 2022 to extract the mean NDVI values in the area of interest.

```
period <- seq(as.Date("2015-01-01"), as.Date("2022-01-01"), by = "1 month")
```

A function is defined to extract the time series of data with the dates of interest and to print the dates obtained in the period if interested.

```
ts_extract <- function(date, images, roi) {
  #print(date)
  year <- str_sub(date, 1, 4) %>% as.numeric()
  month <- str_sub(date, 6, 7) %>% as.numeric()
  ndvi <- images$
    filter(ee$Filter$calendarRange(year, year, "year"))$
    filter(ee$Filter$calendarRange(month, month, "month"))$
    median()
data <- ee_extract(ndvi, roi, fun = ee$Reducer$mean(), scale = 5000)
if (ncol(data) == 0) { data <- data.frame(NDVI = rep(NA, nrow(data))) }
  return(data) }
```

The time series is extracted with the `sapply` function.

```
ts <- sapply(period, FUN = ts_extract, images = ndvi_mask, roi = ee_roi)
```

A `data.frame` is created to rename the data and get values with the unit of interest.

```
df <- t(as.data.frame(ts)) %>%
  as_tibble() %>%
  rename("value" = "V1") %>%
  mutate(period, value = value * .0001)
```

The time series is plotted with functions from the `ggplot2` package.

```
ggplot(df, aes(period, value)) +
  geom_line() +
  geom_point() +
  geom_text(aes(label=period), vjust=-0.2, color="black", size=3.5) +
  labs(y = "NDVI") +
  scale_x_date(
    limits = c(as.Date("2015-01-01"), as.Date("2020-02-01")),
    date_breaks = "1 year",
    date_labels = "%b%Y", expand = expansion(mult = c(.02, 0))
  ) +
  scale_y_continuous(
    breaks = seq(-.1, 1, .1)
  ) + theme_minimal()
```

Thereby, note that there was a continuous time series recorded between 2015 and 2019. Thereafter, only a few points were obtained (Figure 8.3).

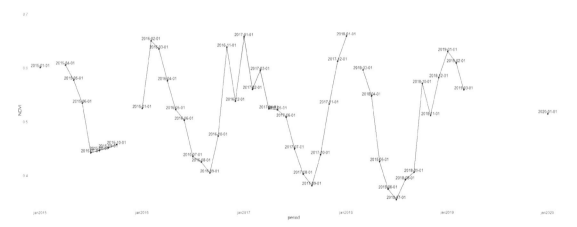

Figure 8.3 Time series of quality NDVI values obtained from the AVHRR NOAA sensor on the Federal University of Lavras campus, between the years 2015 and 2022.

8.6 Scientific Applications of Remote Sensing

Earth remote sensing data collection and analysis procedures are systematically implemented in the remote sensing process (Table 8.1) (Jensen, 2007).

Table 8.1 Systematic scientific process of sequential steps used to extract information from remote sensing data.

Step	Description
Geographic problem	Hypothesis formulation. Selection of appropriate logic (inductive, deductive, technological). Selection of appropriate model (empirical deterministic, knowledge-based deterministic, process-based deterministic or stochastic).
Data collection	*In situ* measurements with GNSS, biomass, reflectance, leaf area index, laboratory results. Complementary data with digital elevation models, soil maps, geology, population. Passive digital remote sensing, multispectral, hyperspectral. Active remote sensing, microwave (RADAR), laser (LIDAR), acoustic (SONAR).
Data to information conversion	Visual analysis of images with elements of interpretation. Digital image processing with radiometric and geometric correction, enhancement, machine learning, classification and segmentation of images. Hypothesis testing.
Information presentation	Metadata with details of collection, image processing and processing steps. Evaluation of the accuracy of results in terms of geometry, radiometry, thematic class and change detection. Orthorectified images of variables and color compositions, thematic maps, animations, simulations, database, graphs, tables and charts.

In designing scientific applications of remote sensing, some fundamental concepts are used to clarify any conceptual doubts about science, scientist, research, experiment, and hypothesis (Table 8.2).

Table 8.2 Fundamental concepts used in scientific applications of remote sensing.

Term	Meaning
Science	Know and solve geographic problems critically and with theoretical and practical foundations.
Scientist	Any person who generates knowledge.
Research	Set of activities oriented towards the search for a certain knowledge.
Experiment	Activity planned to obtain new facts, confirm results of previous experiments, generate or validate technologies.
Hypothesis	Testable proposition in the experiment that involves the solution to the problem
Methodology	Use of experimental procedures.

The hypothesis to be tested in remote sensing is defined based on a specific type of logic, inductive or deductive, and by an appropriate processing model, deterministic or stochastic (Jensen, 2007).

8.7   Elaboration of Scientific Projects in Remote Sensing

In the remote sensing process, the steps of problem selection, data collection in a systematic way, with evaluation and interpretation methodology, are addressed to obtain the necessary knowledge to make decisions about solving a problem with science according to the following steps (Jensen, 2007):

- Problem selection;
- Formulation of research hypotheses;
- Observation and experimentation;
- Interpretation of data;
- Outlining the conclusions.

The complete contents of known digital libraries are used to perform keyword searches and to search for topics of interest relative to the selected remote sensing problem (Arvanitou et al., 2021):

- Web of science[3];
- ScienceDirect[4];
- IEEExplore[5];
- ACM[6];
- Scopus[7];
- Google scholar[8].

In the preparation of the scientific project in the area of remote sensing, some topics should be written with the verb in the future, as the methods section, because the text is prepared in the perspective of presenting a proposition to study and generate relevant scientific conclusions about an object or process of remote sensing. The following topics are contemplated in the preparation of a scientific research proposal (Table 8.3).

Table 8.3 Meaning of section topics used in the development of scientific projects in remote sensing.

Topic	Meaning
Title	Should be brief, containing a few words describing what you intend to accomplish with the project.
Author	Project proponent, usually the project coordinator. Provides information on the call for proposals to which the project will be submitted.
Abstract and keywords	Include index words for the abstract that are not already mentioned in the title.
Introduction	Go straight to the point, highlighting the problem, generating demand, and indicating the diagnosis of the problem, and possible resolution. Get information about what is already done in other work on a similar subject.
Hypothesis	Write in affirmative form, in order to elucidate the testable proposition of the project.
Objectives	Write in a way that leaves no doubt about what you want to achieve in the project.
Literature review	Recent scientific articles published in high impact journals on the researched subject.

---

[3]https://www.periodicos.capes.gov.br/?option=com_pcollection&mn=70&smn=79&cid=81
[4]https://www.sciencedirect.com/
[5]https://ieeexplore.ieee.org/Xplore/home.jsp
[6]https://dl.acm.org/
[7]https://www.scopus.com/home.uri
[8]https://scholar.google.com.br/

Topic	Meaning
Material and methods	Present as many details as possible, but without exaggeration. Ex: Variable studied, date when the radiometric data is obtained, analysis performed on the data.
Expected results	Present the results obtained based on the data analysis.
Execution schedule	Time schedule in which the project will be conducted.
Diffusion of technology	Teaching, research and extension activities associated with the project.
Budget	Include only what is essential to develop the project, such as permanent material, costs, and research grants.
Team	Team of researchers, with information on affiliations, institution, and how they work on the project.
References	Include the bibliographical references used.

8.8   Practice for Project Writing

In the project writing practice, an abstract is developed as an example of writing a scientific project abstract in the area of remote sensing and digital image processing.

8.8.1   Project Abstract

The title, abstract and keywords of the project are elaborated as follows:

Morphometric characterization and remote visual interpretation of rural property in Bahia with active and passive remote sensing

Marcelo de Carvalho Alves - Federal University of Lavras, Department of Agricultural Engineering, email: *marcelo.alves@ufla.br*

Luciana Sanches - Federal University of Mato Grosso, Department of Sanitary and Environmental Engineering, email: *lsanches@hotmail.com*

Abstract

The remote characterization of rural properties makes it possible to evaluate the occupation history of a given region, as well as its morphometric characteristics that influence in agricultural practices such as mechanization. The objective of the project is to evaluate the potential of using digital image processing techniques to remotely characterize the morphology and the land use of a rural property in the municipality of Correntina, Bahia, Brazil. Passive and active remote sensing enable the characterization of morphometric variables and land use of a rural property, as well as its potential for agricultural mechanization. The polygon of the area will be obtained in the KML format used in Google Earth and converted to ESRI shapefile. The contour of the region of interest will enable us to obtain the Shuttle Radar Topography Mission (SRTM) digital elevation model inside the area with the altitude values in meters using the AppEEARS platform. The morphometric characteristics of the area will be obtained by the Fit 2nd Degree Polynomial method using the

RSAGA package (Brenning et al., 2018) and **SAGA GIS**[9] software. Land use in the region will be remotely assessed by the Google Earth historical imagery toolbar of Google Earth Pro software.

Keywords: Google Earth historical imagery toolbar, relief, RSAGA, SRTM.

8.9   Exercises

8.9.1   Cite the topics used in the preparation of a scientific project in the area of remote sensing.

8.9.2   Cite applications of remote sensing that can be evaluated in scientific research.

8.9.3   In preparing the scientific project in remote sensing, in which section will the project's data analysis be described?

   a.   Methodology.
   b.   Conclusions.
   c.   Bibliographical references.
   d.   Objectives.
   e.   Hypotheses.

8.10   Homework

8.10.1   Subject

Practice writing a scientific project abstract and keywords in the area of remote sensing and digital image processing.

8.10.2   Assignment

Develop the subject presented with a practical application of remote sensing and digital image processing including the topics Abstract and Keywords.

---

[9]https://sourceforge.net/projects/saga-gis/

8.11   Resources on the Internet

As a study guide, slides and illustrative videos are presented about the scientific applications of remote sensing for project design (Table 8.4).

Table 8.4 Slide shows and video presentations on scientific applications of remote sensing for project design.

Guide	Address for Access
1	Slides on project design[10]
2	Collecting and analyzing geospatial data from the AppEEARS NASA platform using polygons to carry out a project in the area of remote sensing[11]
3	Collection and analysis of geospatial data from the AppEEARS NASA platform using points to carry out a project in the area of remote sensing[12]
4	NASA's EOSDIS data archiving and distributing Earth science data from multiple missions to users[13]
5	Copernicus open access hub; free and open access to Sentinel-1, Sentinel-2, Sentinel-3, and Sentinel-5P user products[14]
6	Slides on remote sensing project design[15]

8.12   Research Suggestion

The development of scientific research on remote sensing is stimulated by the activity proposals that can be used or adapted by the student to assess the applicability of the subject matter covered in the chapter (Table 8.5).

Table 8.5 Practical and research activities used or adapted by students using scientific applications of remote sensing for project design.

Activity	Description
1	Example of a website for ready access to geospatial data infrastructure retrieval via the NASA AppEEARS platform[16].
2	Tutorials for performing analysis of remote sensing image processing directly from SAGA GIS[17].

---

[10] http://www.sergeo.deg.ufla.br/geo/AulaProjetos.pdf
[11] https://youtu.be/Gb9E4TkTdrc
[12] https://youtu.be/Gb9E4TkTdrc
[13] https://asf.alaska.edu/
[14] https://scihub.copernicus.eu/
[15] http://www.sergeo.deg.ufla.br/sr/Presentation/Aula7/presentation.html#/
[16] https://lpdaac.usgs.gov/tools/appeears/
[17] https://sagatutorials.wordpress.com/

9

Visual Interpretation and Enhancement of Remote Sensing Images

9.1 Learning Questions

The learning questions answered by reading the chapter are as follows:

- How are remote sensing images interpreted?
- What techniques can be used to interpret remotely sensed images?
- What are the elements of remote sensing image interpretation?
- Why is the interpretation of remotely sensed images considered a scientific tool?
- How are search methods, supplementary information, evidence convergence, and the multi-concept applied in interpreting a remote location?

9.2 Learning Outcomes

Using the learning outcomes from the chapter, you should be able to do the following:

- Define remote sensing image interpretation.
- Apply digital image processing techniques to interpret remote sensing images.
- Understand the elements in interpreting remote sensing images.
- Use the interpretation of remote sensing images as a scientific tool.
- Perform a computational practice using search methods, supplementary information, convergence of evidence and the multi-concept to interpret a remote location.

9.3 Introduction

Image interpretation is defined as the inspection of images to identify objects and evaluate their meaning. Imagery for interpretation can be acquired by a variety of sensors. Characteristic elements of image interpretation are associated with different remote sensing resolutions. Quantitative methods of extracting information from images in the optical, infrared, and microwave portions of the spectrum can be used in modeling for mapping objects and processes monitored by remote sensing.

A significant number of aspects can be scientifically addressed in image interpretation, such as (Jensen, 2007):

- Aerial and regional perspective;
- Three-dimensional depth perception;
- Acquisition of knowledge beyond human visual perception;
- Acquisition of historical images to detect changes.

In an image taken from space, there may be a larger geographical area than a human being can cover in a day. Earth observation from an aerial perspective enables observation of objects and patterns, facilitating understanding of interactions that would be difficult to understand through views of the Earth's surface (Jensen, 2007).

Depth perspective can be achieved by imaging the terrain from different perspectives. Height, depth, and volume are important features for diagnosing the geographical environment. With stereoscopic image analysis, the three-dimensional nature of the undulating terrain, slope and appearance of landforms are evaluated. Three-dimensional information can also be obtained through RADAR, LIDAR, and SONAR remote sensing data (Jensen, 2007).

With the sensitivity of human eyes to blue, green and red lights, a limited portion of the electromagnetic spectrum is observed from the environment. Sensors are developed to measure x-rays, ultraviolet, near-infrared, mid-infrared, thermal infrared, microwaves and radio waves in order to provide information about objects complementing what is observed by human eyes. The information obtained is documented and compared with recent records indicating changes in the terrain (Jensen, 2007).

The analysis of remote sensing data is performed by elements of image interpretation that range from fundamental to complex, according to the options determined by the analyst in surveying the environmental variables of interest (Jensen, 2007).

9.4   Elements of Image Interpretation

Fundamentals of image interpretation are routinely used in the visual analysis of an image. A well-trained image interpreter integrates the image interpretation elements without having to think about them individually. And an inexperienced interpreter evaluates an unknown object against each of these elements to identify its meaning in relation to other objects and processes in the image (Table 9.1) (Jensen, 2007).

Table 9.1 Elements of image interpretation.

Elements	Description
Location x, y	Rows and columns of the image.
Hue and color	Gray levels, color models.
Size	Length, width, small, large.
Shape	Linear, circular, radial, rectangular.
Texture	Smooth, intermediate, rough.
Pattern	Spatial arrangement of objects on the terrain.
Shadow	Caused by solar sidelight.
Height, depth, volume, slope, aspect	Geomorphological analysis of digital elevation model in geographic information systems.

Elements	Description
Site	Context, e.g., proximity to water, transportation, utilities.
Situation	Orientation of objects in relation to other objects.
Association	Relationship between phenomena.
Auxiliary information	Additional and complementary information on objects.
Convergence of evidence	Evidence is used to interpret objects.
Multi-concept	Use of research methods to interpret objects.

The elements of image interpretation in increasing order of complexity are location, hue and color, size, shape, texture, pattern, shadow, height and depth, volume, slope, aspect, site, situation, and association. Geographic location, color, and pixel tone constitute a fundamental block of primary or first-order elements. Secondary and tertiary elements are arrangements of tone and color. The more complex order elements, site, situation, and association, are used through search methods such as use of complementary information, convergence of evidence, and the multi-concept (Jensen, 2007) (Figure 9.1).

9.4.1   Location x, y

The x, y, z coordinates of objects are obtained by field measurements with traditional surveying techniques or global navigation satellite systems (GNSSs). Coordinates can also be obtained from a base map and then applied to the image to be rectified. Most aircraft and satellites used for remote sensing have a GNSS receiver that provides precise coordinates for each scan line or the exact location of the center of the aerial photograph. Relief displacement correction can be used on the photograph or image to generate an orthophoto or ortho-image with metric qualities of a chart (Jensen, 2007).

9.4.2   Tone and color

The reflectance curves of selected objects are the basis for understanding how materials appear in monochrome or color imaging. The variations in gray or digital numbers in an image are defined as tone. The human eye differentiates between approximately 40 to 50 shades of gray in a remotely sensed image. Additive color matching techniques are used to create color compositions from individual remotely sensed bands. In these compositions the hue (color) and saturation of the grayscale (intensity) is observed. Some analysts may have limitations in color perception. Isaac Newton (1642-1727) verified the possibility of scattering white light into a spectrum of colors (red, orange, yellow, green, blue, indigo, and violet) and recombining the colors into white light (Figure 9.2) (Jensen, 2007).

The additive synthesis of colors is based on what happens when light is mixed. White light consists of the colors of the visible spectrum. Black is the absence of these colors. Blue, green, and red are the primary colors. The additive combination of green and red lights is yellow light. The additive combination of blue and green lights gives cyan light. The additive combination of blue and red lights gives magenta light. Yellow, magenta, and cyan are called "complementary colors" considering the formation of white light after adding these colors (Figure 9.3) (Jensen, 2007).

Additive color synthesis is the principle of image formation on television and computer monitors. Each pixel on the monitor screen consists of three color sources, blue, green and red. The intensity of the color source in each pixel is modulated according to the amount of primary color in the

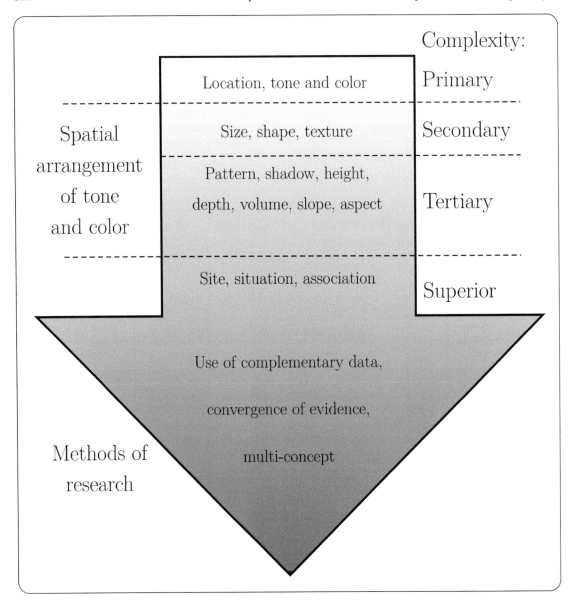

Figure 9.1 Elements of image interpretation with methods for developing accurate image interpretations.

transmitted scene that results in the color visual presentation of the object based on additive color synthesis. Subtractive color synthesis is based on the use of pigments or dyes and not on light. If all three subtractive dyes (yellow, magenta, and cyan) are used, all white light is subtracted and no color is perceived. A red object absorbs mostly blue and green incident light and reflects mostly red light towards the eyes or remote sensors (Table 9.2) (Jensen, 2007).

Table 9.2 Observed colors of an object seen under white light and absorbed light.

White Light Colors	Absorbed Light Colors
Blue	Green and red
Green	Blue and red
Red	Blue and green

White Light Colors	Absorbed Light Colors
Yellow (green and red)	Blue
Magenta (blue and red)	Green
Cyan (blue and green)	Red
Black	Blue, green, red
White	None
Gray	Equal parts blue, green and red

Digital remote sensing data is presented according to a red-green-blue (RGB) color coordinate system based on additive color theory and the three primary colors red, green, and blue. In additive color theory, a pixel with RGB values of 255,255,255 will display white. In the case of using 8-bit images in additive theory it is possible to present $2^{24} = 16777216$ color combinations. Under equal proportions of blue, green, and red, the pixel will present shades of gray in the direction of the gray line (Figure 9.4).

The high spectral resolution of a sensor allows acquisition of different color compositions of the monitored region. For a Landsat-5 image to be presented in a false-color composition, it is necessary to place band 4 in the near-infrared, band 3 in the red channel, band 2 in the green channel of the image processor. So healthy vegetation will occur in shades of red in the false-color composition (Figure 9.5).

9.4.3 Length, width, perimeter and area

The size of objects is one of the most important characteristics among the elements of image interpretation. The variables usually measured are length (m), width (m), perimeter (m), area (m^2), and volume (m^3). To measure objects in the image, it is necessary to know the scale of the photograph or the nominal spatial resolution of the sensor system used in digital imagery. Caution should be exercised when making accurate measurements of object length, perimeter and area in aerial imagery, since within the image field of view there may be points higher than others so that different parts of the image may have different scales. In this case it is necessary to perform an orthoimage to map the real location of all objects (Jensen, 2007).

9.4.4 Shape

Objects can present different shapes in nature, such as linear, curvilinear, circular, elliptical, radial, square, rectangular, triangular, hexagonal, star, elongated and amorphous (Jensen, 2007).

9.4.5 Texture

Texture of objects in the image is the arrangement and arrangement of repeating shades of gray or colors in an image. The spectral characteristics of objects can be similar but with different texture characteristics. Texture can be characterized by smooth (uniform, homogeneous), intermediate and rough (coarse, heterogeneous), mottled and stippled appearance. The texture can vary depending on the spatial resolution and the perception ability of the interpreter. A native forest and water in a dam can have coarse and smooth texture, respectively (Jensen, 2007).

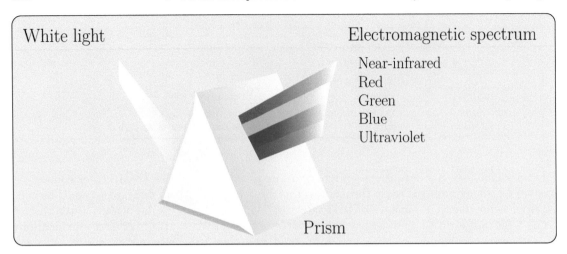

Figure 9.2 Scattering of white light into spectral components through a prism.

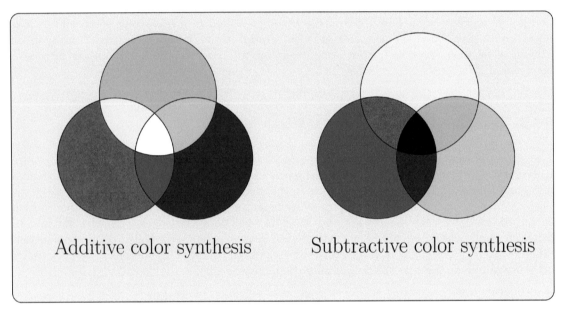

Figure 9.3 Additive and subtractive color synthesis to create white light and a black surface, respectively.

Texture is one of the most important features in image interpretation and classification. Texture analysis is successfully applied to forestry and vegetation studies using a variety of remote sensing data. The gray-level co-occurrence matrix (GLCM) is one of the most widely used methods for calculating second-order texture measures. In this method, spatial relationships between a reference pixel and another neighboring pixel are considered. The neighboring pixel can be in the east (0), northeast (45), north (90) or northwest (135) of the reference pixel. In texture analysis, we can determine the mean, variance, homogeneity, contrast, dissimilarity, entropy, second moment and correlation of a moving window in an image (Gonzalez, 2008; Haralick et al., 1973; Lu & Batistella, 2005; Zvoleff, 2020). These texture indices are used as input variables in principal component analysis and image classification (Lu & Batistella, 2005; Zakeri et al., 2017).

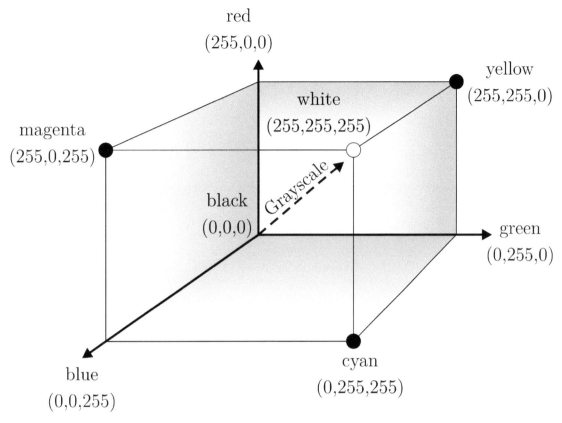

Figure 9.4 RGB coordinate system based on color addition theory.

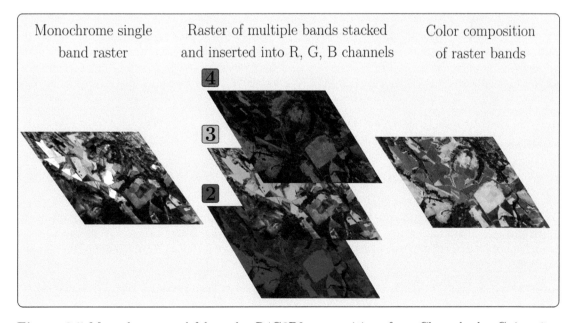

Figure 9.5 Monochrome and false-color R4G3B2 compositions from Chapada dos Guimarães, state of Mato Grosso, Brazil.

9.4.6   Pattern

Pattern is the spatial arrangement of objects in the image. The arrangement of objects in space can be random, systematic, circular, centripetal, oval, curvilinear, linear, radial, rectangular, hexagonal, pentagonal, and octagonal (Jensen, 2007).

9.4.7   Shadow

Remote sensing data can be collected 2 hours around noon to avoid extensive shading in the images. Shadows can obscure objects in the image, making detection and identification difficult. Shadows can be used to obtain information about the height of an object when stereoscopic imaging is not performed. In RADAR imaging, there is no information in the shadows, but in passive remote sensing, even if areas are shaded, there may be enough scattered light from neighboring areas to illuminate the terrain and get some information about the shaded area (Jensen, 2007).

9.4.8   Height and depth

The height or depth of an object can be obtained by stereoscopic parallax when the same object is observed from two different perspectives or by stereoscopic instruments as well as by active remote sensing techniques such as RADAR, LIDAR, and SONAR (Jensen, 2007).

9.4.9   Site, situation, and association

Site, situation, and association are important characteristics for identifying an object or process with remote sensing. Site refers to the context of an object in the landscape and can be described by physical and socio-economic characteristics such as elevation, slope, aspect, land value, and proximity to water. Situation refers to the organization and orientation of objects in relation to others in the scene. Association refers to related or associated features or activities. Site, situation, and association are usually used synergistically to reach a logical conclusion. It can be difficult to identify an object in an image when the object is never observed *in situ* and has not had site, situation, and association features evaluated (Jensen, 2007).

9.5   Research Methods

The complexity of environments cannot be fully monitored and understood with reductionism. With this, scientists have developed approaches for interpreting remote sensing data with use of complementary information, application of evidence convergence and the multi-concept in image analysis.

9.5.1 Use of complementary information

The main types of complementary information are a variety of maps for orientation, political boundary information, cadastral property data, geodetic control, agricultural, geological, hydrological, socio-economic, soils, topographic and bathymetric, transportation, wetland or flooded areas, among others (Table 9.3) (Jensen, 2007).

Table 9.3 Complementary information used in the interpretation of remote sensing data.

Complementary Information	Access to Information
General orientation	Image navigation systems, such as Google Earth[1]
Boundaries or districts	Boundaries of Brazilian municipalities 2017 at scale 1:250000
Cadastral	GDP per capita[2] of Brazil
Geodetic control	Brazilian geodetic control system[3] composed of altimetric, planimetric and gravimetric networks
Agriculture	Municipal agricultural production[4] on quantity produced, planted and harvested area, mean yield and value of agricultural production
Geology	Geology[5] of Brazil
Geomorphology	Geomorphology[6] of Brazil
Pedology	Pedology[7] of Brazil
Vegetation	Vegetation[8] of Brazil
Hydrology	Watersheds ottocoded level 1[9]
	Watersheds ottocoded level 2[10]
	Watersheds ottocoded level 3[11]
	Watersheds ottocoded level 4[12]
	Watersheds ottocoded level 5[13]
	Watersheds ottocoded level 6a[14]
	Watersheds ottocoded level 6b[15]
	Sanitation and supply
	Hydrography of Brazilian municipalities 2017 at scale 1:250000

---

[1]https://www.google.com.br/intl/pt-BR/earth/

[2]http://www.geoservicos.ibge.gov.br/geoserver/wms?service=WFS&version=1.0.0&request=GetFeature&typeName=CGEO:vw_pib_percapita&outputFormat=SHAPE-ZIP

[3]https://www.ibge.gov.br/geociencias/informacoes-sobre-posicionamento-geodesico/rede-geodesica/16327-banco-de-dados-geodesicos.html?=&t=o-que-e

[4]https://sidra.ibge.gov.br/pesquisa/pam/tabelas

[5]https://bdiaweb.ibge.gov.br/#/consulta/geologia

[6]https://bdiaweb.ibge.gov.br/#/consulta/geomorfologia

[7]https://bdiaweb.ibge.gov.br/#/consulta/pedologia

[8]https://bdiaweb.ibge.gov.br/#/consulta/vegetacao

[9]http://metadados.ana.gov.br/geonetwork/srv/en/resources.get?id=47&fname=NIVEL_1.7z&access=private

[10]http://metadados.ana.gov.br/geonetwork/srv/en/resources.get?id=47&fname=NIVEL_2.7z&access=private

[11]http://metadados.ana.gov.br/geonetwork/srv/en/resources.get?id=47&fname=NIVEL_3.7z&access=private

[12]http://metadados.ana.gov.br/geonetwork/srv/en/resources.get?id=47&fname=NIVEL_4.7z&access=private

[13]http://metadados.ana.gov.br/geonetwork/srv/en/resources.get?id=47&fname=NIVEL_5.7z&access=private

[14]http://metadados.ana.gov.br/geonetwork/srv/en/resources.get?id=47&fname=NIVEL6_A.7z&access=private

[15]http://metadados.ana.gov.br/geonetwork/srv/en/resources.get?id=47&fname=NIVEL6_B.7z&access=private

Complementary Information	Access to Information
Disasters	Flood vulnerability[16] in Brazil, 2014
	Fire outbreaks[17] in South America every two hours (KML file)
	INPE's burning database[18]
Socio-economic	Economic structure of Brazil in 2017
Altimetry	SRTM digital elevation model[19] of Brazil at 90-m spatial resolution
Transportation	Transportation infrastructure of Brazil in 2017
Weather and atmosphere	Weather forecast and climate studies[20] from INPE
	Global climate surfaces[21] Worldclim
Spatial data infrastructure	Forest-GIS Data[22] with multiple vector layers for use in Brazil
Image catalogs	INPE image catalog[23]
	INPE CDSR image catalog[24]
	EOS LandViewer[25]
	Earth Explorer USGS[26]
	Landsat Viewer USGS[27]
	ESA Sentinel-2[28]

9.5.2 Evidence convergence

An evaluation of the objects that are positioned around the object of interest can provide valuable information that makes it possible to identify the object. All available knowledge is important to interpret the image and converge evidence to identify the object under study (Jensen, 2007).

9.5.3 Multi-concept

Holism can be achieved with the multi-concept, referring to a useful and accurate scientific method of image interpretation by analyzing data considering multidisciplinary, multispectral, multiscale and multitemporal aspects. Scientific approaches enable interpretation of remote sensing data based on complementary information, evidence convergence and multi-concept in image analysis (Table 9.4) (Jensen, 2007).

---

[16] http://metadados.ana.gov.br/geonetwork/srv/en/resources.get?id=243&fname=Brasil_vulnerabilidade_inundacoes.zip&access=private

[17] http://firms.modaps.eosdis.nasa.gov/active_fire/viirs/kml/VNP14IMGTDL_NRT_South_America_24h.kml

[18] http://www.dpi.inpe.br/proarco/bdqueimadas/

[19] http://www.relevobr.cnpm.embrapa.br/download/

[20] https://www.cptec.inpe.br/

[21] http://www.worldclim.org/

[22] https://forest-gis.com/

[23] http://www.dgi.inpe.br/catalogo/

[24] http://www.dgi.inpe.br/CDSR/

[25] http://eos.com/landviewer

[26] http://earthexplorer.usgs.gov/

[27] http://landsatlook.usgs.gov/viewer.html

[28] http://cophub.copernicus.eu/dhus/

Table 9.4 Contribution of multi-disciplinary areas in the process of interpretation of remote sensing imagery.

Information	Some Courses and Knowledge Areas
Agriculture	Engineering, biology, ecology.
Biodiversity, habitat	Biology, ecology, biogeography, landscape ecology, marine science, soil science.
Data preparation and analysis and algorithms	Cartography, GIS, computer science, photogrammetry, digital image processing, statistics and geostatistics.
Geodetic control	Geodesy, topography, photogrammetry.
Soils and rocks	Engineering, geology, geomorphology, geography.
Disasters	Geology, hydrology, urban and physical geography.
Water resources	Hydrology, chemistry, geology, geography.
Surveying	Geodesy, topography, photogrammetry, digital image processing.
Transportation	Engineering, urban planning, urban geography.
Urban Studies	Urban geography, economics, politics, urban planning, transportation engineering, civil engineering, and landscape ecology.
Weather and atmosphere	Meteorology, climatology, physics, chemistry and atmospheric science.
Wetlands and flooded areas	Biology, ecology, biogeography.

9.6 Image Enhancement

The visual quality of images is improved by image enhancement or contrast procedures. The contrast of an image is a measure of the spread of gray levels in the image and some methods are linear, Gaussian, histogram equalization and square root.

Image enhancement algorithms are applied to remote sensing data to improve the visual appearance of images for human visual analysis. In point operations, the brightness value at each pixel in an image is independent of the characteristics of neighboring pixels. The value of each pixel is modified depending on the context of brightness values of neighboring pixels with local operations (Figure 9.6) (Jensen, 2007).

9.6.1 Contrast enhancement

In contrast enhancement or contrast stretching the original brightness values are expanded to the full dynamic range or full sensitivity of the output device. Satisfactory applications of linear contrast are seen in images with Gaussian or near-Gaussian histograms (Jensen, 2005):

$$BV_s = [\frac{(BV_e - min_k)}{(max_k - min_k)}]quant_k \tag{9.1}$$

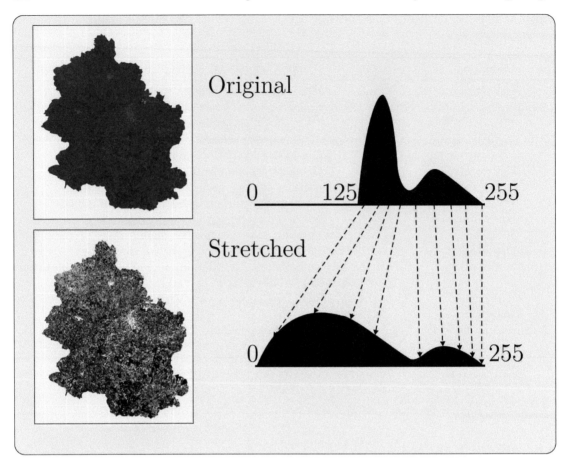

Figure 9.6 The original brightness values are expanded to the full dynamic range of the output device with contrast.

where BV_s is the determined output brightness value, BV_e, the original input brightness value, $quant_k$, the total number of possible brightness values analyzed, and min_k and max_k are the minimum and maximum brightness values, respectively.

For example, in an 8-bit image with the original minimum and maximum brightness values are 5 and 104, respectively, after enhancement these values will be 0 and 255, respectively.

9.6.2   Principal component analysis

Principal component analysis (PCA) has been applied to multispectral and hyperspectral remote sensing data in order to make the original data smaller and easier to interpret and represent the information contained in the original data. In PCA, in the eigenvalues there is important information to determine the percentage of total variance explained by principal components. Generally, in the first principal component, there is a higher percentage of the variance explained in relation to the total number of data used in the analysis (Jensen, 2005).

9.6.3 Tasseled cap

In the tasseled cap transformation, an orthogonal transformation of Landsat, TM sensor original data is proposed in order to create new variables concerning ground brightness (brightness) (B), green vegetation index (greenness) (G) and moisture (wetness) (W) (Crist, 1985; Crist & Kauth, 1986).

$$B = 0.2909TM1 + 0.2493TM2 + 0.4806TM3 + 0.5568TM4 + 0.4438TM5 + 0.1706TM7 \quad (9.2)$$

$$G = -0.2728TM1 - 0.2174TM2 - 0.5508TM3 + 0.7221TM4 + 0.0733TM5 - 0.1648TM7 \quad (9.3)$$

$$W = 0.1446TM1 + 0.1761TM2 + 0.3322TM3 + 0.3396TM4 - 0.6210TM5 - 0.4186TM7 \quad (9.4)$$

Currently the tasseled cap transformation is implemented on top-of-atmosphere reflectance data on Landsat-4 TM, Landsat-5 TM, Landsat-7 ETM+, Landsat-8 OLI, MODIS, QuickBird , Spot-5, and RapidEye satellites and sensors via the spectral bands (Table 9.5).

Table 9.5 Sensor systems, satellites, and their spectral bands used to calculate the tasseled cap transformation based on reflectance values at the top of the atmosphere.

Data Source	Spectral Band	Source
Landsat-4 TM	1,2,3,4,5,7	Crist (1985)
Landsat-5 TM	1,2,3,4,5,7	Crist (1985)
Landsat-7 ETM+	1,2,3,4,5,7	Huang et al. (2002)
Landsat-8 OLI	2,3,4,5,6,7	Baig et al. (2014)
MODIS	1,2,3,4,5,7	Lobser & Cohen (2007)
QuickBird	2,3,4,5	Yarbrough et al. (2005)
Spot-5	2,3,4,5	Ivits et al. (2008)
RapidEye	1,2,3,4,5	Schönert et al. (2014)

The tasseled cap transformation is an index that disaggregates the amount of soil brightness, vegetation and moisture content in each individual pixel with wide use by the scientific community (Jensen, 2005).

9.6.4 Topographic illumination correction and illumination map

Different methods can be used to consider corrections to images according to the illumination variation in the area as a function of terrain elevation. Topographic correction methods are covered in more detail in Riano et al. (2003). In the R package RStoolbox (Leutner et al., 2019), the topographical correction methods cosine ("cos"), mean cosine ("avgcos"), Minnaert ("minnaert"), C ("C"), and statistic ("stat") are implemented according to the variation of the relief, from the solar angle obtained in the metadata file of the images. The solar azimuth and zenith values are observed in the image metadata file or provided manually to perform calculations. In this case, the angles are converted to radians to apply topographic correction. With this methodology it is also possible to create a local terrain illumination map, used in different practical everyday applications.

9.6.5   Image fusion

Digital image processing techniques can be used to combine images of different spectral and spatial characteristics by fusion to synthesize a new image with enhanced spatial resolution compared to the original multispectral image. Some fusion methods can be performed such as by principal component analysis, intensity-hue-saturation space transformation, and the Brovey reweighting method (Leutner et al., 2019). In most cases, the sensor's panchromatic band is used as the higher spatial resolution data used in the enhancement of the coarser spatial resolution image.

9.7   Determination of Remote Sensing Big Data

Workflows for determining remote sensing big data at a site of interest can be established for processing images from different sensors and satellites, as an example from the Landsat-8 and Sentinel-2 missions.

9.7.1   Determination of remote sensing big data from Landsat-8 and SRTM imagery

Landsat-8 and SRTM data are used in this example, however, one may choose other freely distributed data at the student's discretion, such as Landsat-9 and ASTER GDEM or ALOS PALSAR altitude data.

Some characteristics of the Landsat-8 and SRTM sensor systems can be obtained in Chapter 3.

9.7.1.1   Obtaining images by web browsing

A practical solution to start remote sensing applications is to use the Landsat satellite for the evaluation of an object or process in the region chosen for a particular practical work. In this case, to obtain the information in radiance and thermal image, one can use the "Landsat Collection 1 Level-1" option and download the files instantly.

The Shuttle Radar Topography Mission (SRTM) digital elevation model, obtained by monitoring the surface with C-band radar with a wavelength of 5.6 cm, at spatial resolution of 1 arc second, can be used to retrieve altitude data of the area. These data are accessed in the tabs `Data Sets`, `Digital Elevation` and `SRTM 1 Arc-Second Global`.

9.7.1.2   Enabling R packages

Assuming the packages needed for analysis are already installed, the `library` function enables the R packages `raster` (Hijmans et al., 2020), `RStoolbox` (Leutner et al., 2019), `terra` (Hijmans, Bivand, et al., 2022), `sf` (Pebesma et al., 2022), `mapview` (Appelhans et al., 2020), `dplyr` (Wickham, François, et al., 2022), `ggplot2` (Wickham, Chang, et al., 2022), `stars` (Pebesma, Sumner, et al., 2021), `uavRst` (Reudenbach et al., 2022), and `RSAGA` (Brenning et al., 2018) in the R console.

```
library(raster)
library(RStoolbox)
library(terra)
library(sf)
library(mapview)
library(dplyr)
library(ggplot2)
library(stars)
library(uavRst)
library(RSAGA)
```

9.7.1.3 Importing digital elevation model of the area

The Shuttle Radar Topography Mission data at $\sim$ 30-m spatial resolution (1 Arc-Second) is used as a reference to further resample the Landsat-8 imagery data at the locality of interest (USGS, 2022).

The `raster` function is used to import the digital elevation model of the area already clipped and masked at the locality of interest and reprojected at 30-m spatial resolution, zone 23 South, WGS-84 reference ellipsoid.

```
srtmprj<-raster("C:/sr/c8/srtmprj.tif")
srtmprj
#class       : RasterLayer
#dimensions : 529, 860, 454940  (nrow, ncol, ncell)
#resolution : 30, 30  (x, y)
#extent     : 499835.6, 525635.6, 7651972, 7667842  (xmin, xmax, ymin, ymax)
#crs        : +proj=utm +zone=23 +south +datum=WGS84 +units=m +no_defs
#source     : srtmprj.tif
#names      : srtmprj
#values     : 771.8686, 1184.278  (min, max)
```

The `mapview` function is used to map the digital elevation model of the area.

```
mapview(srtmprj)
```

The `names` function is used to rename the layer as "altitude".

```
names(srtmprj)<-c("altitude")
```

With interactive mapping it is possible to perform spatial geovisualization of altitude data in the region surrounding the Funil dam, state of Minas Gerais, Brazil, from SRTM monitoring (Figure 9.7)

9.7.1.4 Importing Landsat-8 imagery data from metadata

The `readMeta` function is used to read metadata downloaded from the Earth Explorer website (USGS, 2021).

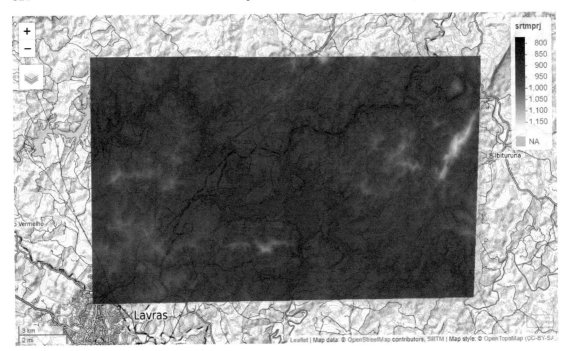

Figure 9.7 Geovisualization of altitude data in the region surrounding the Funil dam, state of Minas Gerais, Brazil, from SRTM monitoring of the region.

```
metaData <- readMeta("LC08_L1TP_218075_20210628_20210707_01_T1_MTL.txt")
```

The `stackMeta` function is used to stack image files stored in the same metadata directory.

```
lsat <- stackMeta("LC08_L1TP_218075_20210628_20210707_01_T1_MTL.txt")
lsat
#class       : RasterStack
#dimensions : 7771, 7671, 59611341, 10   (nrow, ncol, ncell, nlayers)
#resolution : 30, 30   (x, y)
#extent     : 422985, 653115, -2513415, -2280285   (xmin, xmax, ymin, ymax)
#crs        : +proj=utm +zone=23 +datum=WGS84 +units=m +no_defs
#names      : B1_dn, B2_dn, B3_dn, B4_dn, B5_dn, B6_dn, B7_dn, B9_dn, B10_dn, B11_dn
#min values :     0,     0,     0,     0,     0,     0,     0,     0,      0,      0
#max values : 65535, 65535, 65535, 65535, 65535, 65535, 65535, 65535,  65535,  65535
```

9.7.1.5   Reprojecting and resampling Landsat-8 imagery data

Landsat-8 imagery data is reprojected and resampled according to the digital elevation model of the SRTM mission area. The `projectRaster` function is used to perform the data transformation by setting the same coordinate reference system and resolution of the SRTM data in the analysis. The result is a `RasterBrick` class file.

```
lsatprj<- projectRaster(from = lsat,
                    to = srtmprj, crs = crs(srtmprj),
```

```
                            res= res(srtmprj))
lsatprj
#class      : RasterBrick
#dimensions : 529, 860, 454940, 10  (nrow, ncol, ncell, nlayers)
#resolution : 30, 30  (x, y)
#extent     : 499835.6, 525635.6, 7651972, 7667842  (xmin, xmax, ymin, ymax)
#crs        : +proj=utm +zone=23 +south +datum=WGS84 +units=m +no_defs
#source     : memory
#names      : B1_dn, B2_dn, B3_dn, B4_dn, B5_dn, B6_dn, B7_dn, B9_dn, B10_dn, B11_dn
#min values :  7661.043,  7194.099,  6242.465,  5730.900,  5333.544,  5046.435,
# 5049.757,  4991.062, 23422.994, 22112.100
#max values : 25047.055, 16958.410, 18198.040, 19730.633, 21464.667, 22280.547,
# 18087.425,  6200.025, 29531.718, 26623.650
```

9.7.1.6 Perform masking based on altitude data

Considering that the region studied is not a perfect rectangle, the data is masked in the altitude raster region with the mask function.

```
lsat<-mask(lsatprj, srtmprj)
```

9.7.1.7 Convert raster to stars and map

The st_as_stars function is used to convert the class of the raster files to stars.

```
lsat_stars <- st_as_stars(lsat)
```

The plot function is used for spatial and spectral visualization of the Landsat-8 bands.

```
plot(lsat_stars)
```

This provides a spatial and spectral geovisualization of Landsat-8 imagery in the region surrounding the Funil dam, Minas Gerais, Brazil, on June 28, 2021 (Figure 9.8).

9.7.1.8 Terrain illumination correction

Correction of Landsat-8 data for relief variation is performed with the topCor function and C method (Riano et al., 2003).

```
lsat_C <- topCor(lsat, dem = srtmprj, metaData = metaData, method = "C")
lsat_C
#class      : RasterBrick
#dimensions : 529, 860, 454940, 10  (nrow, ncol, ncell, nlayers)
#resolution : 30, 30  (x, y)
#extent     : 499835.6, 525635.6, 7651972, 7667842  (xmin, xmax, ymin, ymax)
#crs        : +proj=utm +zone=23 +south +datum=WGS84 +units=m +no_defs
```

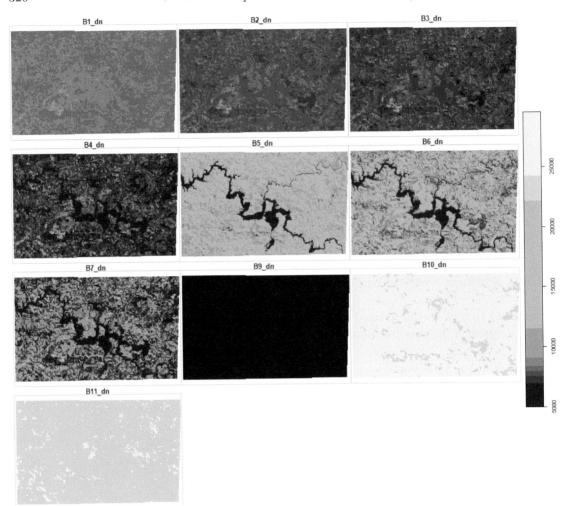

Figure 9.8 Spatial and spectral visualization of Landsat-8 imagery in the region surrounding the Funil dam, state of Minas Gerais, Brazil, on June 28, 2021 12:57:40 GMT, path 218, row 75.

```
#source      : r_tmp_2022-05-11_141633_5028_96265.grd
#names       : B1_dn,B2_dn,B3_dn,B4_dn,B5_dn,B6_dn,B7_dn,B9_dn,B10_dn,B11_dn
#min values  :  7702.158,  7214.950,  6319.177,  5648.323,  4766.403,  4227.340,
#4345.298,  4991.012, 23172.624, 21920.258
#max values  : 24934.290, 17003.788, 18074.355, 19323.301, 22090.662, 23964.669,
#18381.621,  6200.033, 29106.477, 26297.317
```

The lighting map is determined by setting the `method=illu` argument.

```
lsat_illu <- topCor(lsat, dem = srtmprj, metaData = metaData, method = "illu")
```

The results of terrain illumination mapping are visualized with the `mapview` function.

```
mapview(lsat_illu)
```

Using interactive mapping it is possible to perform the geovisualization of the illumination raster obtained from Landsat-8 imaging in the region surrounding the Funil dam and the SRTM digital elevation model (Figure 9.9).

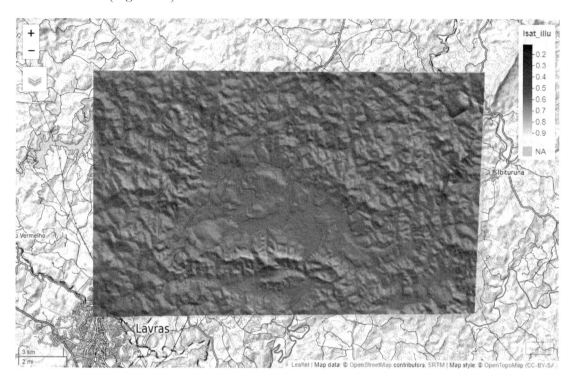

Figure 9.9 Geovisualization of illumination raster obtained from Landsat-8 imagery in the region surrounding the Funil dam, state of Minas Gerais, Brazil, on June 28, 2021 12:57:40 GMT, path 218, row 75 and SRTM digital elevation model.

9.7.1.9 Converting digital numbers to top-of-atmosphere reflectance and brightness temperature

A practical way to convert digital numbers into reflectance at the top of the atmosphere and brightness temperature is accomplished using the `radColor` function, with the `apref` method set. The `names` function enables us to see that the reflectance and thermal spectrum variables have been renamed with the names `_tre` and `bt`, respectively.

```
lsat_toa <- radCor(lsat_C, metaData = metaData, method = "apref")
#names(lsat_toa)
#[1]"B1_tre" "B2_tre" "B3_tre" "B4_tre" "B5_tre" "B6_tre" "B7_tre" "B9_tre"
#"B10_bt" "B11_bt"
```

Mapping the brightness temperature of the area at the time of Landsat-8 imagery, in Kelvin, is done with the `mapview` function.

```
mapview(lsat_toa$B10_bt)
```

In general, there were regions of water and dense vegetation with lower temperature when compared to urbanized areas and exposed soil from the geovisualization of the brightness temperature (Kelvin) of Landsat-8 imagery in the region surrounding the Funil dam, state of Minas Gerais, Brazil (Figure 9.10).

Figure 9.10 Geovisualization of brightness temperature (Kelvin) from Landsat-8 imagery in the region surrounding the Funil dam, state of Minas Gerais, Brazil, on June 28, 2021 12:57:40 GMT, path 218, row 75.

9.7.1.10   Converting digital numbers to reflectance

The atmospheric correction method `dos` is applied to relief-corrected Landsat-8 imagery data in order to determine the reflectance of the surface. The `radCor` function with the `method=dos` argument is used for this calculation.

```
lsat_sref <- radCor(lsat_C, metaData = metaData, method = "dos")
#names(lsat_sref)
#[1] "B1_sre" "B2_sre" "B3_sre" "B4_sre" "B5_sre" "B6_sre" "B7_sre" "B9_sre"
#"B10_bt" "B11_bt"
```

9.7.1.11   Mapping a color composition

The `viewRGB` function is used for mapping the results.

```
viewRGB(lsat_sref, r = 5, g = 4, b = 3)
```

Geovisualization of false-color composition R5G4B3 of Landsat-8 reflectance bands calculated by the `dos` method in the region surrounding the Funil dam, state of Minas Gerais, Brazil (Figure 9.11).

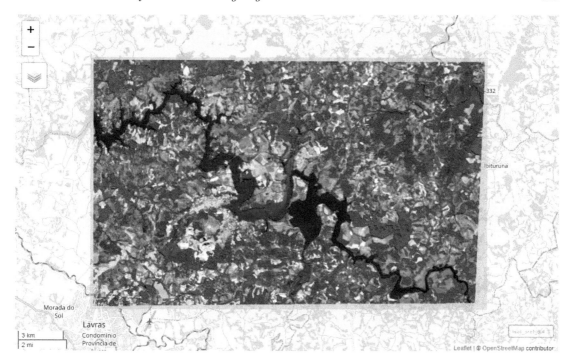

Figure 9.11 Visualization of false-color composition R5G4B3 of Landsat-8 reflectance bands calculated by the `dos` method in the region surrounding the Funil dam, state of Minas Gerais, Brazil, on 2021-06-28 12:57:40 GMT, path 218, row 75.

9.7.1.12 Perform a subset of reflectance bands and map

The reflectance bands are converted to class `stars` and mapped for viewing the results of surface reflectance determination by the `dos` method (Figure 9.12).

```
lsat_stars<-st_as_stars(lsat_sref[[1:8]])
plot(lsat_stars)
```

9.7.1.13 Determine spectral indices in the visible and infrared bands of the reflective spectrum

Landsat-8 OLI spectral bands and deterministic equation parameters were used to determine the vegetation indices, such as Corrected Transformed Vegetation Index (CTVI), Difference Vegetation Index (DVI), Enhanced Vegetation Index (EVI), Two-band Enhanced Vegetation Index (EVI2), Global Environmental Monitoring Index (GEMI), Green Normalized Difference Vegetation Index (GNDVI), Modified Normalized Difference Water Index (MNDWI), Modified Soil Adjusted Vegetation Index (MSAVI), Modified Soil Adjusted Vegetation Index 2 (MSAVI2), Normalized Burn Ratio Index (NBRI), Normalized Difference Vegetation Index (NDVI), Normalized Difference Water Index (NDWI), Normalized Difference Water Index 2 (NDWI2), Normalized Ratio Vegetation Index (NRVI), Ratio Vegetation Index (RVI), Soil Adjusted Total Vegetation Index (SATVI), Soil Adjusted Vegetation Index (SAVI), Specific Leaf Area Vegetation Index (SLAVI), Simple Ratio Vegetation Index (SR), Thiam's Transformed Vegetation Index (TTVI), Transformed Vegetation Index (TVI), and Weighted Difference Vegetation Index (WDVI) as shown in Table 9.6.

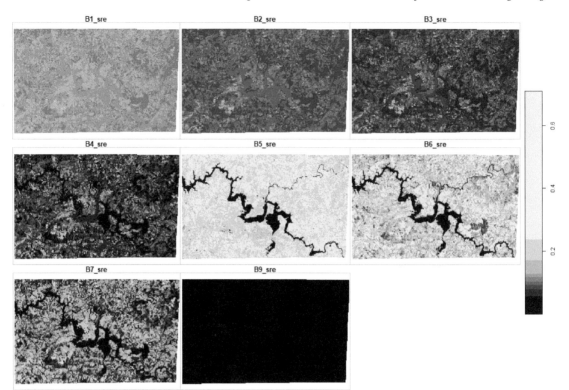

Figure 9.12 Visualization of Landsat-8 reflectance bands calculated by the dos method from Landsat-8 imagery in the region surrounding the Funil dam, state of Minas Gerais, Brazil, on June 28, 2021 12:57:40 GMT, path 218, row 75.

Some indices required additional parameters, such as the slope of the soil line and the soil brightness factor, specified by coefficients as shown in Table 9.7.

Table 9.6 Landsat-8 OLI derived spectral indices based on surface reflectance data.

Index	Source
CTVI - Corrected Transformed Vegetation Index	Perry & Lautenschlager (1984)
DVI - Difference Vegetation Index	Richardson & Wiegand (1977)
EVI - Enhanced Vegetation Index	Huete et al. (1999)
EVI2 - Two-band Enhanced Vegetation Index	Jiang et al. (2008)
GEMI - Global Environmental Monitoring Index	Pinty & Verstraete (1992)
GNDVI - Green Normalized Difference Vegetation Index	Gitelson et al. (1996)
MNDWI - Modified Normalized Difference Water Index	Xu (2006)
MSAVI - Modified Soil Adjusted Vegetation Index	Qi et al. (1994)
MSAVI2 - Modified Soil Adjusted Vegetation Index 2	Qi et al. (1994)
NBRI - Normalized Burn Ratio Index	García & Caselles (1991)

Index	Source
NDVI - Normalized Difference Vegetation Index	Rouse et al. (1974)
NDWI - Normalized Difference Water Index	McFeeters (1996)
NDWI2 - Normalized Difference Water Index 2	Gao (1996)
NRVI - Normalized Ratio Vegetation Index	Baret & Guyot (1991)
RVI - Ratio Vegetation Index	IDB (2022)
SATVI - Soil Adjusted Total Vegetation Index	Marsett et al. (2006)
SAVI - Soil Adjusted Vegetation Index	Huete (1988)
SLAVI - Specific Leaf Area Vegetation Index	Lymburner et al. (2000)
SR - Simple Ratio Vegetation Index	Birth & McVey (1968)
TTVI - Thiam's Transformed Vegetation Index	Thiam (1998)
TVI - Transformed Vegetation Index	Deering (1975)
WDVI - Weighted Difference Vegetation Index	Richardson & Wiegand (1977)

Table 9.7 Coefficients used to determine indices from spectral bands of the Landsat-8 OLI.

Coefficient	Description	Affected Indices
s	slope of the soil line	DVI, WDVI
Levi, C1, C2, G	parameters	EVI
L	soil brightness factor	SAVI, SATVI

RGB indices were also used to increase the spectral dimension of data used in the modeling, and improved the learning and prediction ability of the models in identifying coffee yield. The following RGB indices were calculated from the images: Visible Vegetation Index (VVI), Visible Atmospherically Resistant Index (VARI), Normalized Difference Turbidity Index (NDTI), Redness Index (RI), Soil Color Index (SCI), Brightness Index (BI), Spectra Slope Saturation Index (SI), Primary Colors Hue Index (HI), Triangular Greenness Index (TGI), Green Leaf Index (GLI), Normalized Green-Red Difference Index (NGRDI), Green-Red Vegetation Index (GRVI), Greenish Leaf Area Index (GLAI), Hue Index (HUE), Coloration Index (CI), Saturation Index (SAT), and Shape Index (SHP) as shown in Tables 9.8 and 9.9.

Table 9.8 Spectral indices calculation from Landsat-8 OLI red, green, and blue bands.

Index	Source
BI - Brightness Index	Richardson & Wiegand (1977), Mathieu et al. (1998)
SCI - Soil Color Index	Mathieu et al. (1998)
GLI - Green Leaf Index	Louhaichi et al. (2001)
HI - Primary Colors Hue Index	Escadafal (1994), Mathieu et al. (1998)
NDTI - Normalized Difference Turbidity Index	Lacaux et al. (2007)
NGRDI - Normalized Green Red Difference Index	Tucker (1979)
RI - Redness Index	Madeira et al. (1997)
SI - Spectral Slope Saturation Index	Escadafal (1994), Mathieu et al. (1998)

Index	Source
TGI - Triangular Greenness Index	Hunt Jr et al. (2011)
VARI - Visible Atmospherically Resistant Index	Gitelson et al. (2002)
VVI - Visible Vegetation Index	Ponti (2012), IDB (2022), Henrich et al. (2009)
GLAI - Green Leaf Area Index	Reudenbach et al. (2021)
GRVI - Green-Red Vegetation Index	Motohka et al. (2010)
CI - Coloration Index	Birth & McVey (1968), IDB (2022), Henrich et al. (2009)
HUE - Overall Hue Index	IDB (2022)
SAT - Overall Saturation Index	Escadafal (1994), IDB (2022), Henrich et al. (2009)
SHP - Shape Index	Boochs et al. (1990), IDB (2022), Henrich et al. (2009)

Table 9.9 Spectral indices calculation from Landsat-8 OLI and its equations.

Index	Equation
BI - Brightness Index	$\mathrm{sqrt}((R^2+G^2+B^2)/3$
SCI - Soil Color Index	$(R-G)/(R+G)$
GLI - Green Leaf Index	$(2G-R-B)/(2G+R+B)$
HI - Primary Colors Hue Index	$(2R-G-B)/(G-B)$
NDTI - Normalized Difference Turbidity Index	$(R-G)/(R+G)$
NGRDI - Normalized Green Red Difference Index	$(G-R)/(G+R)$
RI - Redness Index	$R^2/(BG^3)$
SI - Spectral Slope Saturation Index	$(R-B)/(R+B)$
TGI - Triangular Greenness Index	$-0.5[190(R670-R550)-120(R670 - R480)]$
VARI - Visible Atmospherically Resistant Index	$(G-R)/(G+R-B)$
VVI - Visible Vegetation Index	$(1-(R-30)/(R+30))(1-(G-50)/(G+50))(1-(B-1)/(B+1))$
GLAI - Green Leaf Area Index	$(25(G-R)/(G+R-B)+1.25)$
GRVI - Green-Red Vegetation Index	$(G-R)/(G+R)$
CI - Coloration Index	$(R-B)/R$
HUE - Overall Hue Index	$\mathrm{atan}(2(R-G-B)/30.5(G-B))$
SAT - Overall Saturation Index	$(\max(R,G,B)-\min(R,G,B))/\max(R,G,B)$
SHP - Shape Index	$2(R-G-B)/(G-B)$

The surface reflectance information of Landsat-8, in the area of interest, was stacked and renamed according to the spectral region in order to determine the spectral indices. All indices described in Table 9.8 were calculated in one go using C++, which was more efficient than calculating each index separately. In the EVI2 calculation there was an indeterminate problem in the algorithm used, so the EVI2 index was calculated separately and added to the database of vegetation indices.

A routine from the RStoolbox package is used to determine vegetation indices with the spectralIndices function. The scale factor can be set according to the file to deal with decimal place problems in the source variable. Using the names function it is possible to see the acronym of the variables derived from the surface reflectance data.

```
SI <- spectralIndices(lsat_sref, blue = "B2_sre", green= "B3_sre",
red = "B4_sre", nir = "B5_sre", swir2="B6_sre", swir3="B7_sre",
scaleFactor = 1,
coefs = list(L = 0.5, G = 2.5, L_evi = 1, C1 = 6, C2 = 7.5, s = 1))
names(SI)
#[1] "CTVI"    "DVI"     "EVI"     "EVI2"    "GEMI"    "GNDVI"   "MNDWI"   "MSAVI"
#"MSAVI2"  "NBRI"    "NDVI"    "NDWI"
#[13] "NDWI2"   "NRVI"    "RVI"     "SATVI"   "SAVI"    "SLAVI"   "SR"      "TTVI"
#"TVI"     "WDVI"
```

The plot function is used to map the results. The maxnl argument enables you to control the number of raster layers defined in the mapping, in this case 22 variables.

```
plot(SI, maxnl=22)
```

Thus, vegetation indices obtained from Landsat-8 surface reflectance imagery data are mapped in the region surrounding the Funil dam, Minas Gerais, Brazil (Figure 9.13)

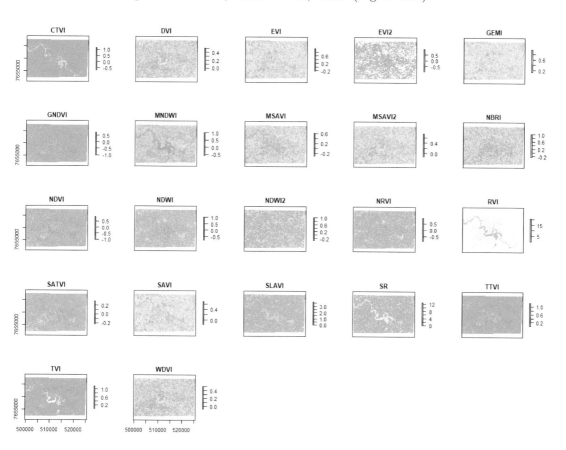

Figure 9.13 Vegetation indices obtained from Landsat-8 surface reflectance data in the region surrounding the Funil dam, state of Minas Gerais, Brazil, on June 28, 2021, 12:57:40 GMT, path 218, row 75.

9.7.1.14 Determining spectral indices in visible bands

The uavRst package is used to determine spectral indices of the blue, green and red bands obtained from Landsat-8 imagery. The function rgb_indices is used to determine the indices according to the surface reflectance bands.

```
rgbi <- rgb_indices(
red    = lsat_sref[[4]],
green = lsat_sref[[3]],
blue  = lsat_sref[[2]],
rgbi = c("VVI", "VARI", "NDTI", "RI", "SCI", "BI", "SI", "HI", "TGI", "GLI", "NGRDI",
         "GRVI", "GLAI", "HUE", "CI", "SAT", "SHP"))
#:::: Visible Vegetation Index    VVI
#:::: Visible Atmospherically Resistant Index   VARI
#:::: Normalized Difference Turbidity Index   NDTI
#:::: Redness Index   RI
#:::: Soil Colour Index   SCI
#:::: Brightness Index   BI
#:::: Spectra Slope Saturation Index   SI
#:::: Primary Colours Hue Index   HI
#:::: Triangular Greenness Index   TGI
#:::: Green Leaf Index   GLI
#:::: Normalized Green-Red Difference Index   NGRDI
#:::: Green-Red Vegetation Index   GRVI
#:::: Greenish Leaf Area Index   GLAI
#:::: Hue Index   HUE
#:::: Coloration Index   CI
#:::: Saturation Index   SAT
#:::: Shape Index   SHP
```

The results of 17 indices are mapped with the plot function (Figure 9.14).

```
plot(rgbi, maxnl=17)
```

9.7.1.15 Determining tasseled cap products

The tasseled cap transformation is used as a processing option to obtain three bands of brightness, greenness, and wetness (Baig et al., 2014).

```
lsat_tc <- tasseledCap(lsat_C[[c(1:5,7)]], sat = "Landsat8OLI")
lsat_tc
#class      : RasterBrick
#dimensions : 529, 860, 454940, 3   (nrow, ncol, ncell, nlayers)
#resolution : 30, 30   (x, y)
#extent     : 499835.6, 525635.6, 7651972, 7667842   (xmin, xmax, ymin, ymax)
#crs        : +proj=utm +zone=23 +south +datum=WGS84 +units=m +no_defs
#source     : memory
#names      : brightness,  greenness,    wetness
#min values :  14398.490,  -8534.226, -11222.679
#max values :  42662.967,  -1729.240,   1977.476
```

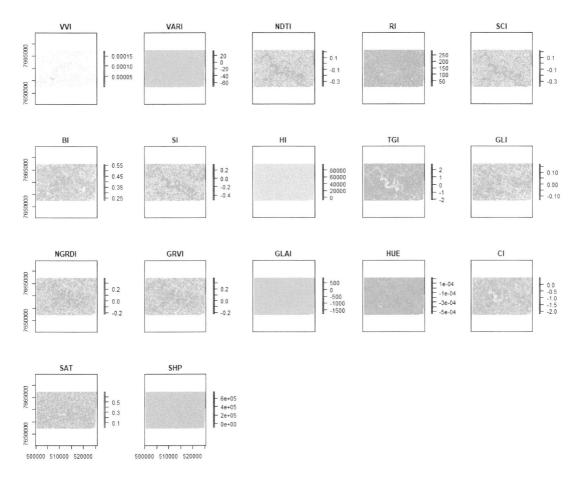

Figure 9.14 Mapping spectral indices from Landsat-8 surface reflectance bands with relief illumination correction, in the region surrounding the Funil dam, state of Minas Gerais, Brazil, on June 28, 2021, 12:57:40 GMT, path 218, row 75.

The results are mapped with an RGB composition of the brightness, greenness and wetness bands, respectively. The ggRGB function is used to map the results with linear stretch.

```
ggRGB(lsat_tc, r = 1, g = 2, b = 3, stretch = "lin") +
        ggtitle("R1G2B3")
```

The region with surface water was well defined in the color composition. Urban areas and exposed soil presented reddish tones, while the regions with dense vegetation presented greenish tones (Figure 9.15).

9.7.1.16 Determine morphometric and hydrologic variables of the terrain

The morphometric and hydrological terrain variables are determined in the area from the previously obtained SRTM data. More recent elevation models with greater detail in terms of spatial resolution can be used, as in the case of Alos PALSAR, if recommended based on the research conducted. The software **SAGA GIS**[29] with GUI interface can be obtained for free on the Internet (Conrad

---

[29]https://sourceforge.net/projects/saga-gis/

R1G2B3

Figure 9.15 RGB color composition mapping of brightness, greenness and wetness bands from tasseled cap transformation from Landsat-8 digital imagery data with relief illumination correction, in the region surrounding the Funil dam, state of Minas Gerais, Brazil, on 28 June 2021 12:57:40 GMT, path 218, row 75.

et al., 2015). The rsaga.env function is used to set up the installation location directory of SAGA GIS.

```
env <- rsaga.env('C:/SAGAGIS/saga-7.3.0_x64/saga-7.3.0_x64/')
#Verify specified path to SAGA command line program...
#Found SAGA command line program. Search for not specified SAGA modules path...
#Done
```

The writeRaster function is used to export the raster to a directory of interest in the SAGA format.

```
writeRaster(srtmprj,"C:/sr/RSAGA/srtmprj.sdat",format="SAGA",
            NAflag=-9999, overwrite=TRUE)
```

Considering that SRTM data may include conflicting data due to the occurrence of sinks in the studied region, the rsaga.sink.removal function is used as a sink smoothing approach in the digital elevation model.

```
rsaga.sink.removal(in.dem="C:/sr/RSAGA/srtmprj.sgrd",
                   out.dem="C:/sr/RSAGA/srtmfill.sgrd",
                   method=1, env = env)
```

The filled digital elevation model is used to determine the morphometric terrain attributes. The function `rsaga.slope.asp.curv` is used to calculate 12 morphometric variables from the altitude of the studied region, cell by cell, by the Zevenbergen & Thorne (1987) methodology (Table 9.10).

```
rsaga.slope.asp.curv(in.dem = "C:/sr/RSAGA/srtmfill.sgrd",
                     out.slope = "C:/sr/RSAGA/slope.sgrd",
                     out.aspect = "C:/sr/RSAGA/aspect.sgrd",
                     out.cgene = "C:/sr/RSAGA/cgene.sgrd",
                     out.cprof = "C:/sr/RSAGA/cprof.sgrd",
                     out.cplan = "C:/sr/RSAGA/cplan.sgrd",
                     out.ctang = "C:/sr/RSAGA/ctang.sgrd",
                     out.clong = "C:/sr/RSAGA/clong.sgrd",
                     out.ccros = "C:/sr/RSAGA/ccros.sgrd",
                     out.cmini = "C:/sr/RSAGA/cmini.sgrd",
                     out.cmaxi = "C:/sr/RSAGA/cmaxi.sgrd",
                     out.ctota = "C:/sr/RSAGA/ctota.sgrd",
                     out.croto = "C:/sr/RSAGA/croto.sgrd",
                     method = "poly2zevenbergen",
                     unit.slope = "degrees",
                     unit.aspect = "degrees",
                     env = env)
```

Table 9.10 Morphometric variables obtained from the SRTM digital elevation model.

Abbreviation	Terrain Variable Description	Unit
slope	slope	degree
aspect	aspect	degree
cgene	general curvature	1/m
cprof	profile curvature	1/m
cplan	plan curvature	1/m
ctang	tangential curvature	1/m
clong	longitudinal curvature	1/m
ccros	cross-sectional curvature	1/m
cmini	minimal curvature	1/m
cmaxi	maximal curvature	1/m
ctota	total curvature	1/m
croto	flow line curvature	1/m

The topographic wetness index is also determined to obtain information about the spatial variation of moisture in the studied region in relation to the relief. The SAGA Wetness Index (SWI) is similar to the Topographic Wetness Index (TWI), but is based on a modified catchment area calculation (out.mod.carea), which does not treat the flow as a thin film as is done in the calculation of catchment areas in conventional algorithms. SWI tends to assign a more realistic and higher potential soil moisture than TWI to cells located in valleys with a small vertical distance from a channel (Böhner et al., 2002; Böhner & Selige, 2006). The `rsaga.wetness.index` function is used to calculate the SWI based on the filled SRTM data.

```
rsaga.wetness.index(in.dem = "C:/sr/RSAGA/srtmfill.sgrd",
out.wetness.index = "C:/sr/RSAGA/swi.sgrd")
```

Calculating the size of the local catchment area (contribution area), accumulated material, and flow path length can be accomplished using top-down processing algorithms from the highest to the lowest cell. The `rsaga.topdown.processing` function is used to determine the contribution area by the multiple flow direction (mfd) method (Freeman, 1991).

```
rsaga.topdown.processing("C:/sr/RSAGA/srtmfill.sgrd",
                         out.carea = "C:/sr/RSAGA/carea.sgrd",
                         method = "mfd", env = env)
```

Some calculations can be performed cell by cell with RSAGA functions to perform operations on grids. Calculating the logarithm of the catchment area produces a layer that conveys much more information than the contribution area alone, and may in some cases determine greater spatial correlation with some variables of interest.

```
rsaga.grid.calculus(in.grids = "C:/sr/RSAGA/carea.sgrd",
                    out.grid = "C:/sr/RSAGA/log10_carea.sgrd",
                    formula = ~ log(a), env = env)
```

9.7.1.17　Import and stack results in raster format

The morphometric and hydrological terrain variables are imported into R with the `raster` function. The definition of the coordinate reference system (`crs`) is performed later with the argument "+proj=utm +zone=23 +south +datum=WGS84 +units=m +no_defs".

```
dem_fill <- raster("C:/sr/RSAGA/srtmfill.sdat")
crs(dem_fill) <- "+proj=utm +zone=23 +south +datum=WGS84 +units=m +no_defs"
slope <- raster("C:/sr/RSAGA/slope.sdat")
crs(slope) <- "+proj=utm +zone=23 +south +datum=WGS84 +units=m +no_defs"
aspect<-raster("C:/sr/RSAGA/aspect.sdat")
crs(aspect) <- "+proj=utm +zone=23 +south +datum=WGS84 +units=m +no_defs"
cgene <- raster("C:/sr/RSAGA/cgene.sdat")
crs(cgene) <- "+proj=utm +zone=23 +south +datum=WGS84 +units=m +no_defs"
cprof <- raster("C:/sr/RSAGA/cprof.sdat")
crs(cprof) <- "+proj=utm +zone=23 +south +datum=WGS84 +units=m +no_defs"
cplan <- raster("C:/sr/RSAGA/cplan.sdat")
crs(cplan) <- "+proj=utm +zone=23 +south +datum=WGS84 +units=m +no_defs"
ctang <- raster("C:/sr/RSAGA/ctang.sdat")
crs(ctang) <- "+proj=utm +zone=23 +south +datum=WGS84 +units=m +no_defs"
clong <- raster("C:/sr/RSAGA/clong.sdat")
crs(clong) <- "+proj=utm +zone=23 +south +datum=WGS84 +units=m +no_defs"
ccros <- raster("C:/sr/RSAGA/ccros.sdat")
crs(ccros) <- "+proj=utm +zone=23 +south +datum=WGS84 +units=m +no_defs"
cmini <- raster("C:/sr/RSAGA/cmini.sdat")
crs(cmini) <- "+proj=utm +zone=23 +south +datum=WGS84 +units=m +no_defs"
cmaxi <- raster("C:/sr/RSAGA/cmaxi.sdat")
crs(cmaxi) <- "+proj=utm +zone=23 +south +datum=WGS84 +units=m +no_defs"
ctota <- raster("C:/sr/RSAGA/ctota.sdat")
crs(ctota) <- "+proj=utm +zone=23 +south +datum=WGS84 +units=m +no_defs"
croto <- raster("C:/sr/RSAGA/croto.sdat")
crs(croto) <- "+proj=utm +zone=23 +south +datum=WGS84 +units=m +no_defs"
```

```
swi <- raster("C:/sr/RSAGA/swi.sdat")
crs(swi) <- "+proj=utm +zone=23 +south +datum=WGS84 +units=m +no_defs"
carea <- raster("C:/sr/RSAGA/carea.sdat")
crs(carea) <- "+proj=utm +zone=23 +south +datum=WGS84 +units=m +no_defs"
logcarea <- raster("C:/sr/RSAGA/log10_carea.sdat")
crs(logcarea) <- "+proj=utm +zone=23 +south +datum=WGS84 +units=m +no_defs"
```

The stack function is used to stack the raster surfaces resulting from the morphometric and hydrological terrain modeling into a single file.

```
terrain<-stack(dem_fill,slope,aspect,cgene,cprof,cplan,
ctang,clong,ccros,cmini,cmaxi,ctota,croto,swi,carea,logcarea)
```

9.7.1.18 Mapping morphometric and hydrological variables

The results of 16 obtained indices are mapped with the plot function.

```
plot(terrain, maxnl=16)
```

Therefore, the mapping of morphometric and hydrological variables of the terrain is performed from digital elevation model, in the region surrounding the Funil dam, state of Minas Gerais, Brazil (Figure 9.16).

9.7.1.19 Stack all variables

The stack function is used to stack all 69 variables and the names function is used to check the sequence and name of each stacked variable.

```
rsbd <- stack(lsat_sref, lsat_illu, SI, rgbi, lsat_tc, terrain)
names(rsbd)
#[1] "B1_sre" "B2_sre" "B3_sre"     "B4_sre"     "B5_sre"  "B6_sre"  "B7_sre"  "B9_sre"
#[9] "B10_bt" "B11_bt" "illu"       "CTVI"       "DVI"     "EVI"     "EVI2"    "GEMI"
#[17] "GNDVI" "MNDWI"  "MSAVI"      "MSAVI2"     "NBRI"    "NDVI"    "NDWI"    "NDWI2"
#[25] "NRVI"  "RVI"    "SATVI"      "SAVI"       "SLAVI"   "SR"      "TTVI"    "TVI"
#[33] "WDVI"  "VVI"    "VARI"       "NDTI"       "RI"      "SCI"     "BI"      "SI"
#[41] "HI"    "TGI"    "GLI"        "NGRDI"      "GRVI"    "GLAI"    "HUE"     "CI"
#[49] "SAT"   "SHP"    "brightness" "greenness"  "wetness" "srtmfill" "slope"  "aspect"
#[57] "cgene" "cprof"  "cplan"      "ctang"      "clong"   "ccros"   "cmini"   "cmaxi"
#[65] "ctota" "croto"  "swi"        "carea"      "log10_carea"
```

9.7.1.20 Exporting the resulting raster surfaces

The results are exported using the terra package. The rast function is used to convert the RasterStack class files into SpatRaster.

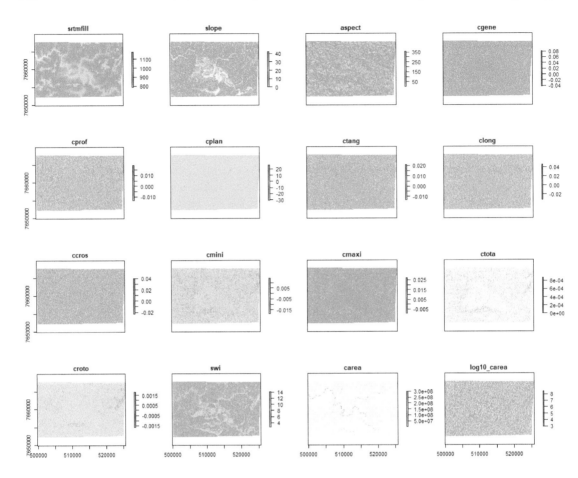

Figure 9.16 Mapping of morphometric and hydrological terrain variables from digital elevation models in the region surrounding the Funil dam, state of Minas Gerais, Brazil.

```
rsbdr <- rast(rsbd)
```

The writeRaster function is used to export the SpatRaster files into a directory of interest.

```
terra::writeRaster(rsbdr, "C:/sr/RSAGA/rsbdr.tif", filetype = "GTiff", overwrite = TRUE)
```

9.7.2   Determination of remote sensing big data from Sentinel-2 imagery

Similar to what was done previously for Landsat-8 imagery, Sentinel-2 imagery data can also be used to determine a workflow for determining remote sensing big data at a site of interest.

The characteristics of the spectral bands of the Sentinel-2 multispectral sensor (MSI) (A and B) can be obtained in more detail in Chapter 3.

9.7.2.1 Obtaining images by browsing the Internet

Obtaining remote sensing data directly on Internet platforms can be easier and more practical, requiring registration on the different websites available, such as

- EarthExplorer[30]
- Copernicus[31]

In the present study, the data was obtained from the Copernicus website.

R software is used as an example, however other digital image processing languages can be used to accomplish this task at the student's discretion. The images used refer to Level 2A. In the Level 2A product, lower atmosphere reflectance (BOA) images derived from the associated Level 1C products are obtained. Each Level-2A product is composed of tiles with 100 x 100 km^2 cartographic geometry, in UTM projection, WGS-84 datum.

Level-2A products have been systematically generated in the ground segment over Europe since March 2018, and production was extended to global in December 2018. If it is of interest to the user to perform atmospheric correction and reflectance calculation from the primary source of information, the Level 1C product can also be used.

9.7.2.2 Enable R packages

The packages needed for Sentinel-2 preprocessing, data analysis, and image mapping are enabled for analysis with the `library` function.

```
library(mapview)
library(rgdal)
library(gdalUtils)
library(raster)
library(sf)
library(ggplot2)
library(RStoolbox)
library(gridExtra)
```

9.7.2.3 Import digital elevation model of the area

The Shuttle Radar Topography Mission data at $\sim$ 30-m (1 Arc-Second) spatial resolution are used as a reference to later resample the Sentinel-2 imagery data at the locality of interest (USGS, 2022).

The `raster` function is used to import the digital elevation model of the area already cropped and masked at the locality of interest and reprojected at 30-m spatial resolution, zone 23 South, WGS-84 reference ellipsoid.

```
srtmprj<-raster("C:/sr/c8/srtmprj.tif")
srtmprj
#class      : RasterLayer
```

---

[30]https://earthexplorer.usgs.gov/
[31]https://scihub.copernicus.eu/dhus/#/home

```
#dimensions : 529, 860, 454940   (nrow, ncol, ncell)
#resolution : 30, 30   (x, y)
#extent      : 499835.6, 525635.6, 7651972, 7667842   (xmin, xmax, ymin, ymax)
#crs         : +proj=utm +zone=23 +south +datum=WGS84 +units=m +no_defs
#source      : srtmprj.tif
#names       : srtmprj
#values      : 771.8686, 1184.278   (min, max)
```

9.7.2.3.1 Modify spatial resolution of raster

The digital elevation model of the area is converted to a spatial resolution of 10 m. This is necessary because the geometry of this data will be used as a reference in the production of Sentinel-2 imagery data in the same geographical region studied. The `disaggregate` function is used to increase the spatial resolution of the data to 10 m. In this case, the brightness values in the new `RasterLayer` are the same as in the original larger cells.

```
dem <- disaggregate(srtmprj, fact=3)
dem
#class       : RasterLayer
#dimensions : 1587, 2580, 4094460   (nrow, ncol, ncell)
#resolution : 10, 10   (x, y)
#extent      : 499835.6, 525635.6, 7651972, 7667842   (xmin, xmax, ymin, ymax)
#crs         : +proj=utm +zone=23 +south +datum=WGS84 +units=m +no_defs
#source      : memory
#names       : srtmprj
#values      : 771.8686, 1184.278   (min, max)
```

9.7.2.4 Transform extension of Sentinel-2 imagery data

After obtaining the Sentinel-2 imagery data on June 25, 2021, an R wrapper of the `gdal_translate` function, part of the Geospatial Data Abstraction Library (GDAL), is used in transforming the `.jp2` extension to `.tif`. This procedure is performed on bands B02, B03, B04, B05, B06, B07, B08, B08AB, B9, and B12.

```
gdal_translate("T23KNS_20210625T131249_B02_10m.tif")
gdal_translate("T23KNS_20210625T131249_B03_10m.tif")
gdal_translate("T23KNS_20210625T131249_B04_10m.tif")
gdal_translate("T23KNS_20210625T131249_B08_10m.tif")
gdal_translate("T23KNS_20210625T131249_B05_20m.tif")
gdal_translate("T23KNS_20210625T131249_B06_20m.tif")
gdal_translate("T23KNS_20210625T131249_B07_20m.tif")
gdal_translate("T23KNS_20210625T131249_B8A_20m.tif")
gdal_translate("T23KNS_20210625T131249_B11_20m.tif")
gdal_translate("T23KNS_20210625T131249_B12_20m.tif")
gdal_translate("T23KNS_20210625T131249_B09_60m.tif")
```

9.7.2.5 Import Sentinel-2 imagery data

Once you have the files in geotiff format, the `raster` function is used to import each of the Sentinel-2 imagery bands into R.

```
b2 <- raster("T23KNS_20210625T131249_B02_10m.tif")
b3 <- raster("T23KNS_20210625T131249_B03_10m.tif")
b4 <- raster("T23KNS_20210625T131249_B04_10m.tif")
b8 <- raster("T23KNS_20210625T131249_B08_10m.tif")
b5 <- raster("T23KNS_20210625T131249_B05_20m.tif")
b6 <- raster("T23KNS_20210625T131249_B06_20m.tif")
b7 <- raster("T23KNS_20210625T131249_B07_20m.tif")
b8A <- raster("T23KNS_20210625T131249_B8A_20m.tif")
b11 <- raster("T23KNS_20210625T131249_B11_20m.tif")
b12 <- raster("T23KNS_20210625T131249_B12_20m.tif")
b9 <- raster("T23KNS_20210625T131249_B09_60m.tif")
```

After importing the raster files into R, the coordinate system is assigned to each file by a `+proj` argument, set to WGS-84 datum, Southern Hemisphere. This action is required only for bands without 10-m spatial resolution in the original file.

```
crs(b5) <-
"+proj=utm +zone=23 +south +datum=WGS84 +units=m +no_defs +ellps=WGS84 +towgs84=0,0,0"
crs(b6) <-
"+proj=utm +zone=23 +south +datum=WGS84 +units=m +no_defs +ellps=WGS84 +towgs84=0,0,0"
crs(b7) <-
"+proj=utm +zone=23 +south +datum=WGS84 +units=m +no_defs +ellps=WGS84 +towgs84=0,0,0"
crs(b8A) <-
"+proj=utm +zone=23 +south +datum=WGS84 +units=m +no_defs +ellps=WGS84 +towgs84=0,0,0"
crs(b11) <-
"+proj=utm +zone=23 +south +datum=WGS84 +units=m +no_defs +ellps=WGS84 +towgs84=0,0,0"
crs(b12) <-
"+proj=utm +zone=23 +south +datum=WGS84 +units=m +no_defs +ellps=WGS84 +towgs84=0,0,0"
crs(b9) <-
"+proj=utm +zone=23 +south +datum=WGS84 +units=m +no_defs +ellps=WGS84 +towgs84=0,0,0"
```

9.7.2.6 Reprojecting and resampling Sentinel-2 imagery data

Sentinel-2 imagery data are reprojected and resampled according to the SRTM digital elevation model of the area. The `projectRaster` function is used to perform the data transformation by setting the same coordinate reference system and resolution as the SRTM data in the analysis. The result is a `RasterBrick` class file.

```
b2 <-  projectRaster(from = b2, to = dem, crs = crs(dem), res= res(dem))
b3 <-  projectRaster(from = b3, to = dem, crs = crs(dem), res= res(dem))
b4 <-  projectRaster(from = b4, to = dem, crs = crs(dem), res= res(dem))
b5 <-  projectRaster(from = b5, to = dem, crs = crs(dem), res= res(dem))
b6 <-  projectRaster(from = b6, to = dem, crs = crs(dem), res= res(dem))
b7 <-  projectRaster(from = b7, to = dem, crs = crs(dem), res= res(dem))
b8 <-  projectRaster(from = b8, to = dem, crs = crs(dem), res= res(dem))
```

```
b8A <-  projectRaster(from = b8A, to = dem, crs = crs(dem), res= res(dem))
b9 <-  projectRaster(from = b9, to = dem, crs = crs(dem), res= res(dem))
b11 <-  projectRaster(from = b11, to = dem, crs = crs(dem), res= res(dem))
b12 <-  projectRaster(from = b12, to = dem, crs = crs(dem), res= res(dem))
```

9.7.2.7   Cropping and masking raster

The `mask` function is used to mask values around the border that defines the region of interest.

```
b2s <- mask(b2,dem)
b3s <- mask(b3,dem)
b4s <- mask(b4,dem)
b5s <- mask(b5,dem)
b6s <- mask(b6,dem)
b7s <- mask(b7,dem)
b8s <- mask(b8,dem)
b8As <- mask(b8A,dem)
b9s <- mask(b9,dem)
b11s <- mask(b11,dem)
b12s <- mask(b12,dem)
```

The results are stacked and divided by 10,000 to obtain the surface reflectance values from Sentinel-2 multispectral imagery in the region studied. The `stack` function is used to stack the obtained results.

```
bs <- stack(b2s,b3s,b4s,b5s,b6s,b7s,b8s,b8As,b9s,b11s,b12s)
bsr <- bs/10000
```

9.7.2.8   Map RGB compositions

The region of interest is mapped with some RGB compositions. The `ggRGB` function is used to define natural color (R4G3B2) and false-color RGB compositions with red edge band variations in the red channel (R5G3B2, R6G3B2, and R8aG3B2) from Sentinel-2 imagery in the region surrounding the Funil dam, state of Minas Gerais, Brazil. The `grid.arrange` function is used to define the order and layout of the comparison mapping.

```
m0 <- ggRGB(bsr, r = 3, g = 2, b = 1, stretch="lin") + ggtitle("R4G3B2")
m1 <- ggRGB(bsr, r = 4, g = 2, b = 1, stretch="lin") + ggtitle("R5G3B2")
m2 <- ggRGB(bsr, r = 5, g = 2, b = 1, stretch="lin") + ggtitle("R6G3B2")
m3 <- ggRGB(bsr, r = 8, g = 2, b = 1, stretch="lin") + ggtitle("R8aG3B2")
grid.arrange(m0, m1, m2, m3, ncol=2)
```

The targets in the Sentinel-2 scene can be observed in different tones from the color compositions performed (Figure 9.17).

The `drawExtent` function is used to define a region of interest for mapping in the neighborhood of the town of the Ijaci municipality. This function is applied to a plot performed with the `plotRGB` function with a drawing performed interactively on the mapped composition.

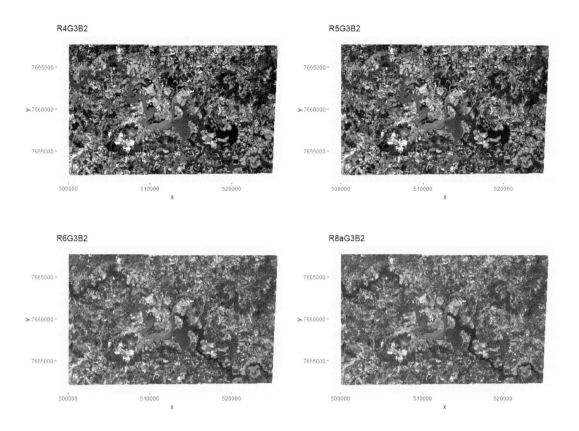

Figure 9.17 Visualization of natural color (R4G3B2) and false-color RGB compositions with red edge band variations in the red channel (R5G3B2, R6G3B2 and R8aG3B2) from Sentinel-2 imagery in the region surrounding the Funil dam, state of Minas Gerais, Brazil, on June 25, 2021.

```
plotRGB(bs, 5,2,1, stretch="lin")
e <- drawExtent()
# or e <- extent(505000, 516000, 7655000, 7664000)
```

The area in the new region of interest is mapped into the same RGB compositions as before. The ext argument is used to map the region defined with the drawExtent function.

```
m0 <- ggRGB(bsr, r = 3, g = 2, b = 1, stretch="lin", ext=e) + ggtitle("R4G3B2")
m1 <- ggRGB(bsr, r = 4, g = 2, b = 1, stretch="lin", ext=e) + ggtitle("R5G3B2")
m2 <- ggRGB(bsr, r = 5, g = 2, b = 1, stretch="lin", ext=e) + ggtitle("R6G3B2")
m3 <- ggRGB(bsr, r = 8, g = 2, b = 1, stretch="lin", ext=e) + ggtitle("R8aG3B2")
grid.arrange(m0, m1, m2, m3, ncol=2)
```

With this it is possible to see details of open-pit limestone mining exploration to the south of the image and, to the north, the town of Ijaci, near the Funil dam, state of Minas Gerais, Brazil (Figure 9.18).

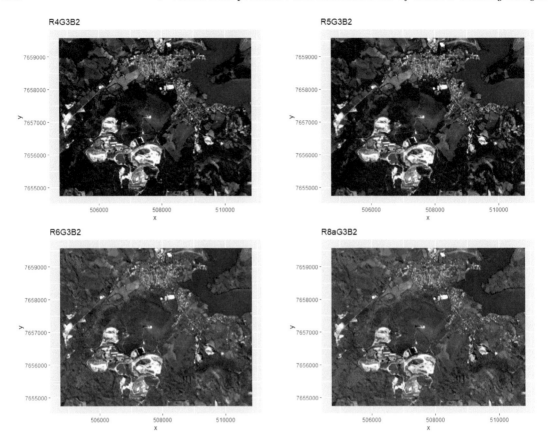

Figure 9.18 Visualization of a region of interest in natural color (R4G3B2) and false-color RGB compositions with red edge band variations in the red channel (R5G3B2, R6G3B2 and R8aG3B2) from Sentinel-2 imagery in the region surrounding the Funil dam, state of Minas Gerais, Brazil, on June 25, 2021.

9.7.2.9   Determining spectral indices

Different spectral indices can be determined from Sentinel-2 multispectral imaging. The spectralIndices function is used to determine 29 spectral indices from the performed imagery.

```
SI <- spectralIndices(bsr, blue = "T23KNS_20210625T131249_B02_10m",
green= "T23KNS_20210625T131249_B03_10m", red = "T23KNS_20210625T131249_B04_10m",
redEdge1="T23KNS_20210625T131249_B05_20m",redEdge2="T23KNS_20210625T131249_B06_20m",
redEdge3="T23KNS_20210625T131249_B07_20m",  nir = "T23KNS_20210625T131249_B08_10m",
swir2="T23KNS_20210625T131249_B11_20m", swir3="T23KNS_20210625T131249_B12_20m",
scaleFactor = 1,
coefs = list(L = 0.5, G = 2.5, L_evi = 1, C1 = 6, C2 = 7.5, s = 1))
```

9.7.2.10   Map spectral indices

Spectral indices are mapped onto a subset of the area defined earlier. The plot function is used for mapping, with the argument maxnl=29 (Figure 9.19).

```
plot(SI, maxnl=29, ext=e)
```

Some indices like MTCI and REIP were very homogeneous in the mapping and EVI2 determined some missing values as a result. In some situations it may be interesting to perform subsets of some indices of major interest or to calculate an index of interest with changing parameters to get more satisfactory results.

Figure 9.19 Spectral indices mapping from Sentinel-2 imagery in the region surrounding the Funil dam, state of Minas Gerais, Brazil, on June 25, 2021.

9.8 Application Gallery

Statistical learning is a technique in geoprocessing that uses statistical models to identify patterns in data and estimate dependent variables from these patterns. In statistical learning, statistical and machine learning methods are combined in supervised and unsupervised learning. Both are widely applied in various situations such as in landslide modeling, remote sensing, and geoprocessing (Lovelace et al., 2019; Muenchow et al., 2012).

In the case of using supervised techniques, there is a training data set, which can be a binary response, such as landslide occurrence, categorical, land use, integer, species richness count, or numerical, such as soil acidity measured in pH. With supervised techniques, the ratio of known responses to a sample of observations are modeled for predictions. Machine learning has been used on large amounts of data and few assumptions have been required in the data analysis. The predictive performance of the model can be evaluated by cross validation and a generalized linear model (Lovelace et al., 2019; Zuur et al., 2009).

Color and false-color compositions of digital images are presented in order to explore elements of primary order image interpretation and tertiary order vegetation indices of complexity.

A very high spatial resolution remote sensing image was obtained by WorldView-2 imaging of irrigated coffee plantations in the municipality of Carmo do Rio Claro, state of Minas Gerais, Brazil. In the false-color compositions, R7B5G3 on December 21, 2012 and R7B5G3 on April 30, 2013, variations of red tones in vegetation were determined when comparing the two months (December and April) of imaging, as well as variation of shape and tones of water near the center of the image (Figure 9.20).

The relationship between the spatial variability of soil physical-chemical attributes and the leaf area index of coffee plants obtained from a QuickBird satellite image was evaluated in an experiment conducted on the Cafua farm, municipality of Ijaci, state of Minas Gerais. The cultivar Catuaí Vermelho IAC 99 was sampled in an area of approximately 6.5 ha of coffee plantation (*Coffea arabica* L.). Transects in the area were demarcated with distances of 25 x 25 m and 50 x 50 m, totaling 67 sampling points where characteristics and crop vegetation index were performed based on multispectral imagery. The use of remote sensing and digital image processing allowed detection of spatial variation of vegetation in the crop, potentially influenced by soil physicochemical characteristics (Figure 9.21) (Alves et al., 2007).

Using a DJI Phantom 4 Advanced drone, experimental plots of coffee cultivars on the Federal University of Lavras campus were monitored by natural color composition (RGB) and green leaf indices over time (Figure 9.22).

The imaging potential with Sentinel-1 RADAR data of irrigated coffee plantations in Presidente Olegário, Minas Gerais, was evaluated by comparing the texture variation of the RADAR image and the IKONOS image without cloud in the same area in January of 2016. RADAR is a satisfactory option for monitoring coffee plantations under high cloud conditions when the intensity relationships of combinations of RADAR polarizations with *in situ* measurements in the same area are established (Figure 9.23).

WorldView-2 imaging was used to detect damage caused by thread caterpillar (*Agrotis ipsilon*) in maize (*Zea mays* L.). After atmospheric correction, the pest organism signals were evaluated by different band compositions, and by the soil-adjusted vegetation indices, leaf area index, fraction of absorbed photosynthetically active radiation, surface albedo, absorbed solar radiation flux, and the first principal component analysis of WorldView-2 multispectral bands. With this analysis approach it is possible to detect spatial variation of pest organisms in the state of Mato Grosso agroecosystem with very high spatial resolution multispectral imaging (Figure 9.24) (Adapted from Alves (2012)).

Spectral signatures of targets on WorldView-2 satellite images at 50-cm spatial resolution in June 2011 were selected for analysis of the agricultural crops maize and crotalaria. The images were submitted to atmospheric correction and conversion of digital pixel numbers into reflectance. For spectral signature extraction, 24-point profiles were selected for each crop studied, including 12 points in healthy locations and 12 points in locations with nematode damage. In the spectral profiles in the areas with maize and crotalaria damage there was lower reflectance when compared to the healthy areas. This occurred due to degradation of root structure, causing indirect damage to leaves caused by *Pratylenchus* nematodes in both crops (Figure 9.25) (Ferreira Sobrinho & Alves, 2013).

0 225 450 900 m

■ Red: Band_7
■ Green: Band_5
■ Blue: Band_3

21/12/2012

0 225 450 900 m

■ Red: Band_7
■ Green: Band_5
■ Blue: Band_3

30/04/2013

Figure 9.20 WorldView-2 imagery of irrigated coffee crops in Carmo do Rio Claro, Minas Gerais, in false-color compositions R7B5G3 (December 21, 2012) and R7B5G3 (April 30, 2013).

Figure 9.21 QuickBird imagery of coffee trees in the municipality of Ijaci, state of Minas Gerais, Brazil, representing panchromatic band (top), R4G3B2 false-color composition fused to panchromatic band (left), and NDVI (right) on May 27, 2003.

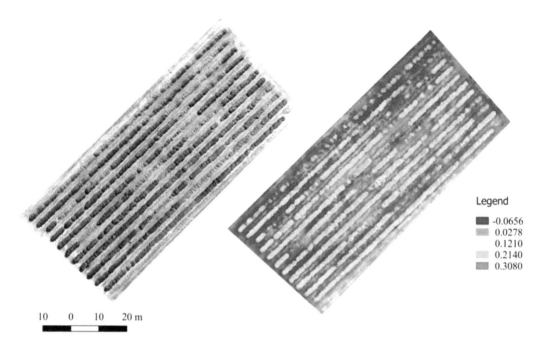

Figure 9.22 Natural color RGB composition and green leaf index (GLI) of coffee crops obtained with a DJI Phantom drone on the Federal University of Lavras campus, Brazil, in 2019.

High spatial resolution images have been used for monitoring urban areas in order to facilitate the planimetric and altimetric survey on university campuses, as well as the detailed planning of new building projects during the expansion of laboratories, classrooms, experimental and open-air sports fields (Figure 9.26).

The use of natural color and false-color compositions of wetlands facilitates monitoring of plant species that tolerate flooding in wetland regions, as well as contributing to the understanding of the times of year subject to flooding and their variation between seasons, and inter-annual variations. Monitoring of the Xingu Indigenous Park using images from the AWiFS sensor of the IRS-P6 satellite on June 11, 2010 was performed by determining soil-adjusted vegetation indices, leaf area index, fraction of absorbed photosynthetically active radiation, albedo, and solar absorbed radiation (W m^{-2}) obtained from images after radiometric and geometric correction of the images. Based on the visual analysis of the images, the satisfactory implementation of the AWiFS sensor in the monitoring of water resources and vegetation in the Xingu valley, state of Mato Grosso, Brazil was verified. Based on the vegetation indices, deforestation of areas near the river was observed according to the estimated values of the indices determined by the AWiFS spectral bands (Figures 9.27 and 9.28) (Silva et al., 2011).

The Pantanal is the largest flooded area of sedimentary plains on Earth with characteristic and well-defined seasons, with dry and flood seasons. Remote sensing allows us to improve the analysis of information such as water, soil and vegetation, by spatial and temporal monitoring of the Pantanal in the state of Mato Grosso with Landsat-5 TM using RGB compositions in bands 1 to 7: R3G2B1, R4G3B2, R5G4B3, R6G5B4, R7G4B3 R7B5G3. In the August 2009 image, it was observed that the river level remained in its bed, not reaching the ground vegetation. In November 2009, a reduction of the water flow detected in the plain was observed, with little flooding. In contrast, in April 2010, a flooded plain was observed, overflowing, causing flooding in vegetated areas. In the R5G4B3 composition, good visual differentiation of the water among the

IKONOS   LANDSAT-8

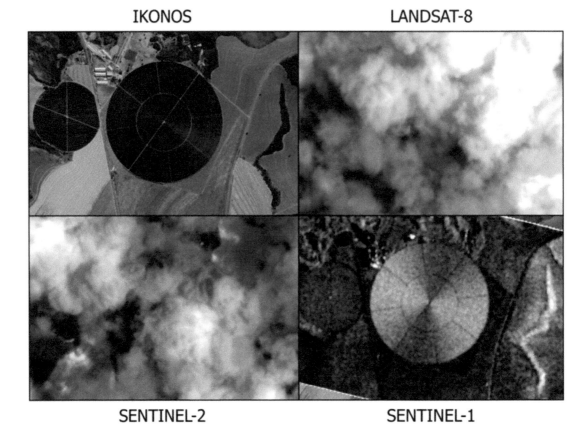

SENTINEL-2   SENTINEL-1

Figure 9.23 Coffee crop monitoring with Sentinel-1, Sentinel-2, and Landsat-8 OLI satellites in municipality of Presidente Olegário, state of Minas Gerais, Brazil, January 2016.

other objects is observed in all evaluated periods. In composition R7G4B3, it is possible to clearly differentiate vegetation, soil and water, being the best composition for visual differentiation of natural resources (Figures 9.29 and 9.30) (Rosa et al., 2011).

The vegetation indices, SAVI, LAI and FPAR, were analyzed as support in the identification of the Pantanal flooding dynamics on August 29, 2009 (a), November 1, 2009 (b), October 4, 2010 (c), showing low vegetation index values (Figure 9.31).

Target mapping can also be performed with Sentinel-1 RADAR data. In this case, Sentinel-1 B Ground Range Detected (GRD) data, mode IW, high resolution (H), Level-1, are used for mapping the region around the Funil dam in Minas Gerais, Brazil, on June 28, 2021. The image can be obtained from the **Copernicus Open Access Hub**[32]. The Sentinel Applications Platform (**SNAP Desktop 8.0**[33]) software from the European Space Agency (ESA) is used to process the digital data in BEAM-DIMAP format file. The data used consist of two different amplitude and intensity polarizations of vertical transmission and vertical reception (VV) and vertical transmission and horizontal reception (VH). With this, it is possible to explore the difference in backscattering of the RADAR echo between water and ground surfaces. A subset of the image is taken around the dam for image processing only in the region of interest, thus requiring less computational processing. The data were calibrated to sigma nought (Sigma0), followed by single product speckle filtering, Lee filter, size X, Y, 5. A geometric map projection transformation to correct the

---

[32]https://scihub.copernicus.eu/dhus/
[33]https://step.esa.int/main/download/snap-download/

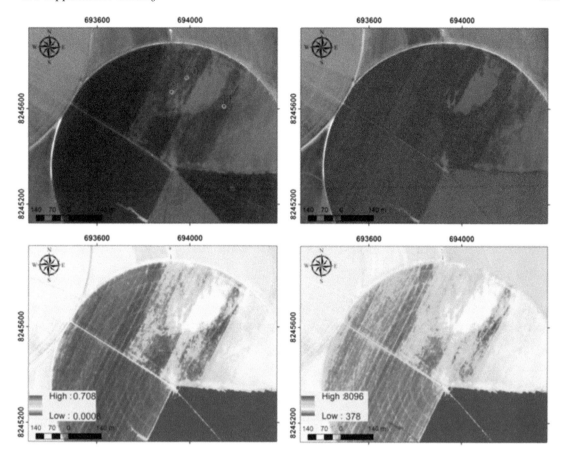

Figure 9.24 R5G3B2 and R8G5B3(top) WorldView-2 color compositions, SAVI and principal component of maize (*Zeamays* L.) (bottom), cultivar AG1051, on September 16, 2010 with damage caused by *Agrotisipsilon*.

data with respect to terrain was applied to the Sigma0_VH and Sigma0_VV bands with the `range-doppler terrain correction` function. The resulting Sigma0_VH and Sigma0_VV bands were converted to decibels (dB) to facilitate manipulation of the data on a logarithmic scale (Figures 9.32 and 9.33).

Color compositions can also be made with the different RADAR polarization bands from RGB color channels available in SNAP. In this case, Sigma0_VV_db was placed in the red channel, Sigma0_VH_db in the green channel, and Sigma0_VVV_db in the blue channel (Figure 9.34).

Other predefined color compositions can be realized, as in the case of the Dual Pol Ratio Sigma0 VV+VH, where Sigma0_VV is placed on the red channel, Sigma0_VH, on the green channel and the Sigma0_VV/Sigma0_VH ratio on the blue channel (Figure 9.35).

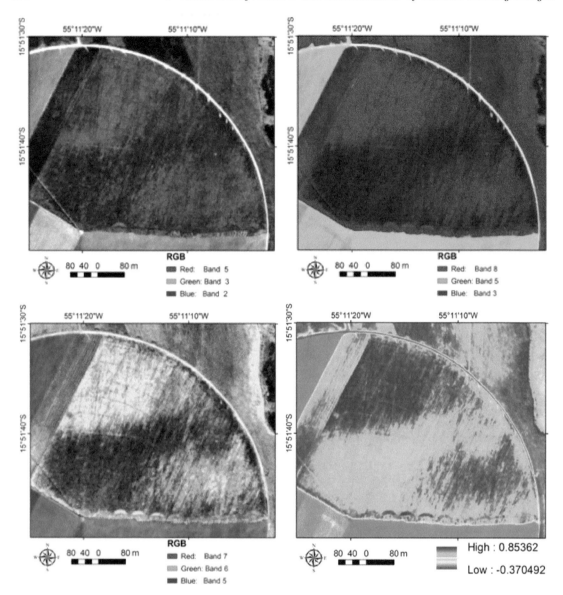

Figure 9.25 R5G3B2, R8G5B3 (top), R7G6B5 WorldView-2 color compositions and NDVI (bottom) from crotalaria crop in an irrigated area on December 06, 2010, in the municipality of Jaciara, state of Mato Grosso, Brazil.

9.9   Computational Practice

The graphical representation of vectors and images for visual interpretation can be performed by several functions in R (Table 9.11).

Figure 9.26 WorldView-2 imagery in natural color composition R5G3B2 from May 29, 2010 of Federal University of Mato Grosso campus, municipality of Cuiabá, state of Mato Grosso, Brazil.

Table 9.11 Some functions used for vector and raster representation in R.

Function	Description
plot	Plot vectors or individual bands in color palettes and digital gray levels.
plotRGB	Plot color and false-color RGB compositions.
ggR	Plot single layers.
ggRGB	Plot color and false-color RGB compositions.

9.9.1 Evaluating available colors

The colors and length functions can be used to evaluate color options for mapping in R and color statements. In this case, 60 different colors are presented.

```
cl <- colors()
length(cl); cl[1:60]
#[1] 657
#[1] "white"          "aliceblue"      "antiquewhite"    "antiquewhite1"
#[5] "antiquewhite2"  "antiquewhite3"  "antiquewhite4"   "aquamarine"
#[9] "aquamarine1"    "aquamarine2"    "aquamarine3"     "aquamarine4"
#[13] "azure"          "azure1"         "azure2"          "azure3"
```

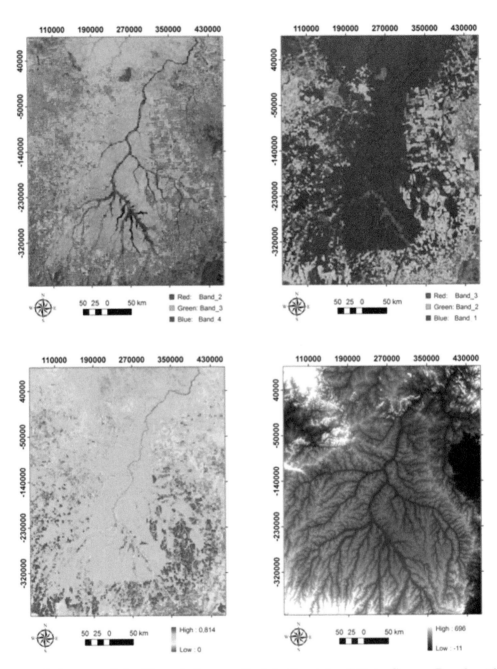

Figure 9.27 Imagery of the Xingu Indigenous Park in the state of Mato Grosso, Brazil, with the AWIFS sensor, satellite IRS-P6, on June 11, 2010, in false-color composition 3R2G1B, 2R3G4B (top), soil-adjusted vegetation index and SRTM digital elevation model of the area (2001) (bottom).

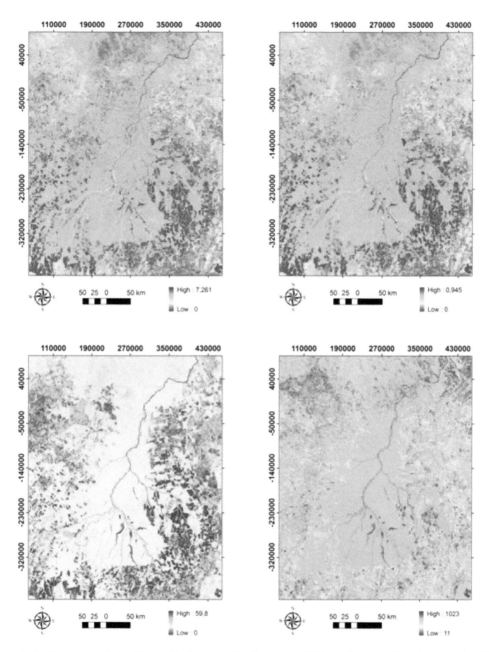

Figure 9.28 Imagery of the Xingu Indigenous Park, state of Mato Grosso, Brazil, with the AWIFS sensor, satellite IRS-P6, on June 11, 2010, to determine the leaf area index, absorbed fraction of photosynthetically active radiation (top), albedo, and absorbed solar radiation (bottom).

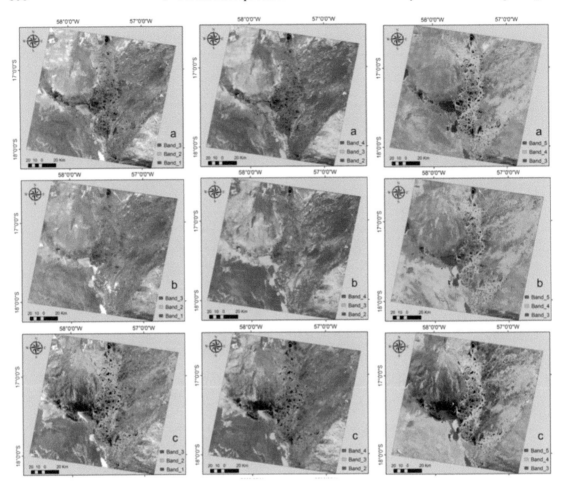

Figure 9.29 Natural color and false-color compositions of flooding dynamics in the Pantanal biome, state of Mato Grosso, Brazil, on August 29, 2009 (a), November 1, 2009 (b), October 4, 2010 (c).

```
#[17] "azure4"         "beige"         "bisque"         "bisque1"
#[21] "bisque2"        "bisque3"       "bisque4"        "black"
#[25] "blanchedalmond" "blue"          "blue1"          "blue2"
#[29] "blue3"          "blue4"         "blueviolet"     "brown"
#[33] "brown1"         "brown2"        "brown3"         "brown4"
#[37] "burlywood"      "burlywood1"    "burlywood2"     "burlywood3"
#[41] "burlywood4"     "cadetblue"     "cadetblue1"     "cadetblue2"
#[45] "cadetblue3"     "cadetblue4"    "chartreuse"     "chartreuse1"
#[49] "chartreuse2"    "chartreuse3"   "chartreuse4"    "chocolate"
#[53] "chocolate1"     "chocolate2"    "chocolate3"     "chocolate4"
#[57] "coral"          "coral1"        "coral2"         "coral3"
```

The names of specific colors and tones can be visualized graphically for a better understanding of the multiple geovisualization possibilities that can be experienced with the use of the demo function (Figure 9.36).

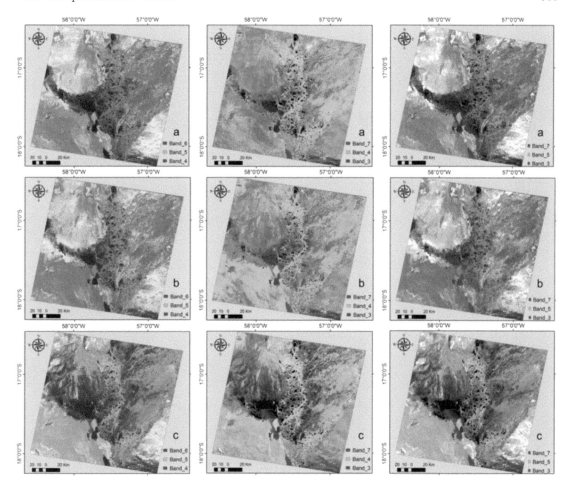

Figure 9.30 False-color compositions of the flooding dynamics in the Pantanal biome, state of Mato Grosso, Brazil, on August 29, 2009 (a), November 1, 2009 (b), and October 4, 2010 (c).

```
demo("colors")
```

Different color palettes can be used and applied to both individual images and color compositions of remotely sensed imaging bands.

In the following, computational practices are performed to explore the multi-concept of remote sensing in the analysis of different targets by different methodologies in order to improve the existing knowledge in a given remotely defined geographical region.

9.9.2 Installing and enabling packages

The `install` function installs the R packages `raster` (Hijmans et al., 2020), `RStoolbox` (Leutner et al., 2019), `rgdal` (Bivand et al., 2021), `ggplot2` (Wickham, Chang, et al., 2022), and `glcm` (Zvoleff, 2020). Packages already installed should be enabled and do not need to be installed again.

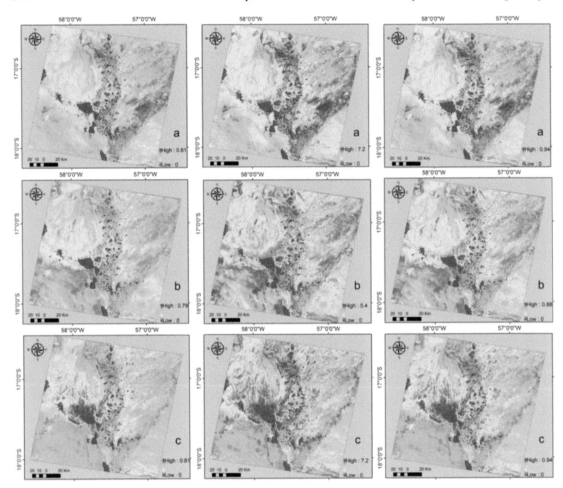

Figure 9.31 Vegetation indices, SAVI (a), LAI (b), and FPAR (c) used in the dynamics analysis of flooding in Pantanal biome, state of Mato Grosso, Brazil, on August 29, 2009 (a), November 1, 2009 (b), October 4, 2010 (c).

```
install.packages("raster")
install.packages("RStoolbox")
install.packages("rgdal")
install.packages("ggplot2")
install.packages("glcm")
```

The library function is used to enable the R packages raster, RStoolbox, rgdal, ggplot2, and glcm.

```
library(raster)
library(RStoolbox)
library(rgdal)
library(ggplot2)
library(glcm)
```

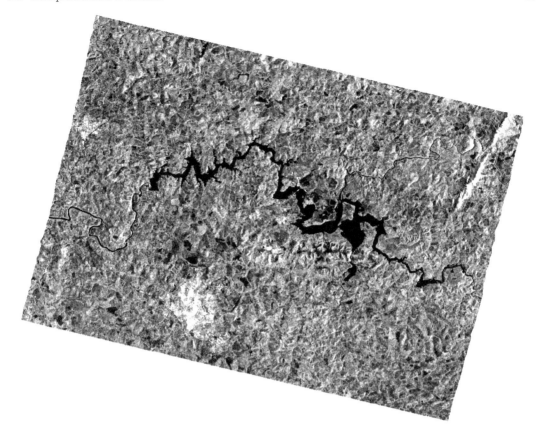

Figure 9.32 Sentinel-1 B, Level-1, IW, GRDH, 1SDV RADAR band mapping in VV polarization after radiometric correction processing, filtering, geometric correction and enhancement
manipulation in the region surrounding the Funil dam, state of Minas Gerais, Brazil, on June 28,
2021.

9.9.3   Monochrome image representation

In the computational practice of the previous chapter, we detailed how to obtain an area file,
referring to a digital elevation model, in the AppEEARS platform and perform the processing of
information about the altitude variation in the area. In this practice, the digital elevation model
is mapped with different types of colors and image enhancement methods in order to demonstrate
how to represent monochromatic images by different types of maps with single color and multiple
color tone variation.

9.9.3.1   Getting data

The raster file should be downloaded from the AppEEARS platform (AppEEARS Team, 2020). The
digital elevation model of the area of interest (SRTM ellipsoidal altitude) (NASA, 2013), performed
in computational practice, can be obtained via **download**[34].

The file must be unzipped into a directory on the computer where the file address is known. To set
the address of the file in the R console, for the purpose of importing the file into R, note the use
of "/" for the location of the file in the source directory. On this computer, the directory is located at

---

[34]http://www.sergeo.deg.ufla.br/sr/downloads/srtmTM.zip

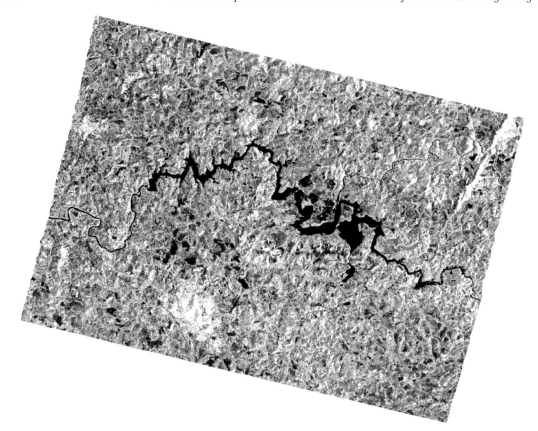

Figure 9.33 Sentinel-1 B, Level-1, IW, GRDH, 1SDV RADAR band mapping in VH polarization after radiometric correction processing, filtering, geometric correction and enhancement manipulation in the region surrounding the Funil dam, state of Minas Gerais, Brazil, on June 28, 2021.

"C:/sr/c6/AppeearsTerraMorena/SRTMGL1_NC.003_SRTMGL1_DEM_doy2000042_aid0001.tif". Note that the file extension used is `.tif`.

The SRTM file obtained from the rural property in the municipality of Correntina, state of Bahia, Brazil, is imported into R with the `raster` function, named "`srtm`", and stored in the computer memory.

```
srtm <- raster(
  "C:/sr/c6/AppeearsTerraMorena/
  SRTMGL1_NC.003_SRTMGL1_DEM_doy2000042_aid0001.tif")
```

9.9.3.2   Viewing the file header

The raster file header is viewed by typing the name of the imported file into the R command console.

```
srtm
#class      : RasterLayer
#dimensions: 325, 403, 130975  (nrow, ncol, ncell)
```

Figure 9.34 RGB color composite of Sentinel-1 B, Level-1, IW, GRDH, 1SDV RADAR bands, in VH and VV polarizations, after radiometric correction processing, filtering, geometric correction and enhancement manipulation in the region surrounding the Funil dam, state of Minas Gerais, Brazil, on June 28, 2021.

```
#resolution: 0.0002777778, 0.0002777778  (x, y)
#extent    : -45.29819, -45.18625, -13.28125, -13.19097  (xmin, xmax, ymin, ymax)
#crs       : +proj=longlat +datum=WGS84 +no_defs +ellps=WGS84 +towgs84=0,0,0
#source : C:/sr/c6/AppeearsTerraMorena/SRTMGL1_NC.003_SRTMGL1_DEM_doy2000042_aid0001.tif
#names     : SRTMGL1_NC.003_SRTMGL1_DEM_doy2000042_aid0001
#values    : -32768, 32767  (min, max)
```

This shows the numerical size of the file with 325 rows, 403 columns and 130975 pixels. The map projection system, as requested in the platform, is WGS-84 in geographic projection. Therefore, the spatial resolution of the file is 0.0002777778°. The magnitude of the values in the file is determined by the given type. Values between -32768 and 32767 are displayed, because integer type data is stored in the raster, with possible altitude values between -32767 and 32767.

9.9.3.3   Renaming the raster file attribute name

The raster file, originally with the attribute name:

"SRTMGL1_NC.003_SRTMGL1_DEM_doy2000042_aid0001",

Figure 9.35 RGB Dual Pol Ratio Sigma0 VV+VH color composite of Sentinel-1 B, Level-1, IW, GRDH, and 1SDV RADAR bands after radiometric correction processing, filtering, geometric correction and enhancement manipulation in the region surrounding the Funil dam, state of Minas Gerais, Brazil, on June 28, 2021.

is renamed to "altitude", using the `names` function.

```
names(srtm)<-c("altitude")
```

9.9.3.4   Determining summary statistics

The `summary` function provides the summary statistics about the digital elevation model.

```
summary(srtm)
#        altitude
#Min.          673
#1st Qu.       713
#Median        741
#3rd Qu.       765
#Max.          774
#NA's            0
```

Thus, the minimum and maximum altitude values of the area are 673 and 774 m, respectively. The first, second and third quartiles of the area's altitude are set at 713, 741 and 765 m, respectively.

Figure 9.36 Name demonstration of some colors and tones that can be used in graphical representations and mapping in R.

9.9.3.5 Determining boxplot and histogram

Graphical visualization of the results obtained using the `summary` function is accomplished with the `boxplot` function.

```
boxplot(srtm)
```

The histogram performed with the `hist` function checks the frequency of occurrence of the altitude values on the farm (Figure 9.37).

```
hist(srtm)
```

A higher frequency of altitude values was observed in the area above 760 m.

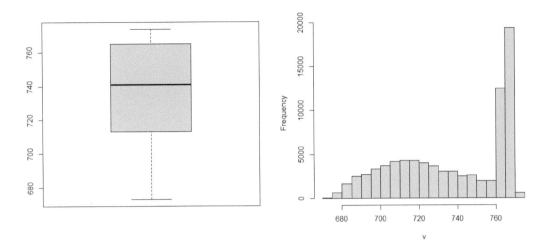

Figure 9.37 Boxplot used to assess altitude variation based on quartile intervals (left) and histogram of altitude variation (v) (right) in a monitored rural area in the municipality of Correntina, state of Bahia, Brazil.

9.9.3.6 Mapping with the `plot` function

The `plot` function is used to perform the mapping of the raster with the `topo.colors` and `gray.colors` color palette. The coordinate system used in the map is displayed using the `axes=TRUE` argument (Figure 9.38).

```
plot(srtm, axes=TRUE, col=topo.colors(20))
plot(srtm, axes=TRUE, col=gray.colors(20))
```

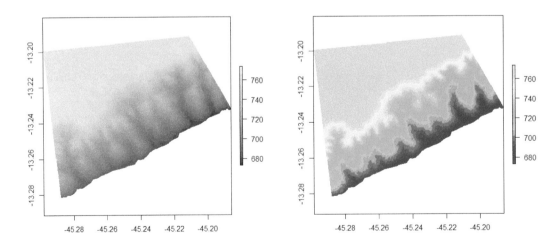

Figure 9.38 Use of the plot function to perform the false-color representation in the monochromatic color palette with shades of gray and with several colors to represent the relief variation in a monitored rural area in the municipality of Correntina, state of Bahia, Brazil.

The mapping allows visualization of the geospatial location of the altitude values in the area, with the highest altitude values occurring in the north of the property, with magnitude above 760 m. An intermediate region is generally located in the center of the area, with values around 720 m, and lower altitude to the south of the area, with values around 680 m.

9.9.3.7 Mapping with the `ggR` function

The altitude data is mapped with the `ggR` function from the R package `RStoolbox`, to evaluate the use of different types of color mapping and image enhancement.

The raster is false-color mapped with the `ggR` function, using the pixel fill option with the `geom_raster=TRUE` argument and `terrain.colors` color palette. Other color palette options can also be used, such as `rainbow`, `heat.colors`, `topo.colors`, `cm.colors` and `grey.colors`.

```
ggR(srtm, geom_raster = TRUE)+
    scale_fill_gradientn(colours = terrain.colors(100), name = "Altitude (m)")
```

The raster is false-color mapped with the same function as before to illustrate the use of different colors in representing the variation of the relief, but using the pixel fill option with the color palettes `terrain.colors`, `rainbow` (top), `heat.colors`, `topo.colors` (middle), `cm.colors` and `grey.colors` (bottom) (Figure 9.39).

The shading variation of the colors used allows observation of the variation in altitude gradient in the area. This type of map shows the recharge areas of groundwater where water runoff occurs in the lower parts of the relief, from the central portion towards the south of the mapped property. This type of mapping contributes to the decision-making of the owner, with the purpose of establishing soil and water conservation measures on the rural property.

To further exploit the aesthetic characteristics of the map, the argument `geom_raster` can be set to FALSE in order to enlarge the visualization of the mapped area without the legend. In addition, image enhancement techniques can be used to visualize details not seen in the false-color and legend mapping.

9.9.4 Evaluate the use of image enhancement and transparency

Various types of image enhancement can be used to alter image contrast, such as linear (`lin`), histogram equalization (`hist`), square root (`sqrt`), and logarithm (`log`). The types of enhancement evaluated in the altitude raster are no contrast, linear, and histogram equalization. Transparency realization is also performed using the parameter `alpha = 0.3` (Figure 9.40).

```
ggR(srtm, stretch = "none", geom_raster = F)
ggR(srtm, stretch = "none", alpha=0.3, geom_raster = F)
ggR(srtm, stretch = "lin", geom_raster = F)
ggR(srtm, stretch = "hist", geom_raster = F)
```

Using linear contrast, areas of higher and lower altitude are sharper in the image. With the contrast histogram, the highest part is highlighted with texture information from the image, probably due to vegetation or irregular objects present in the place.

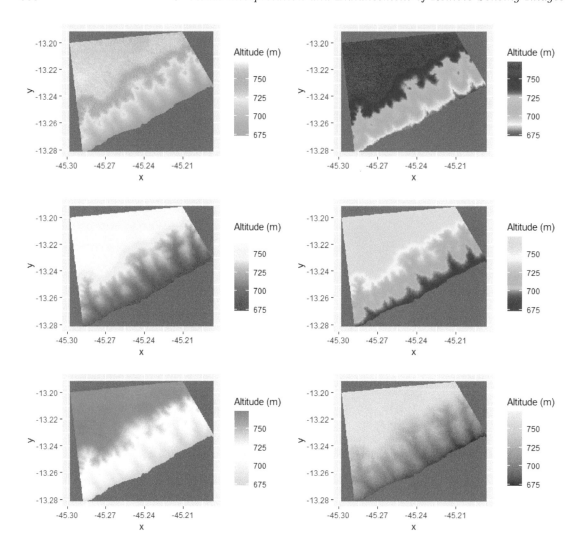

Figure 9.39 False-color representation of relief variation in the color palettes terrain.colors, rainbow (top), heat.colors, topo.colors (middle), cm.colors and grey.colors (bottom), in municipality of Correntina, state of Bahia, Brazil.

Transparency is a type of feature used in mapping with raster data layers that uses visual information from more than one object in the mapping in order to get multiple information from the region in a single map.

The terrain function can be used to determine the slope (slope) and the exposure of the slopes in the area (aspect). Based on these two new variables obtained from the relief, the hillShade function is used to create a relief shading variable for a shaded relief map representation.

```
terr <- terrain(srtm, c("slope", "aspect"))
hill <- hillShade(terr[["slope"]], terr[["aspect"]])
```

The combination of color variables and transparency allows us to obtain visual information of the variation of the relief in the area with visualization of the texture of the mapped area and to explore the multi-concept in remote sensing (Figure 9.41).

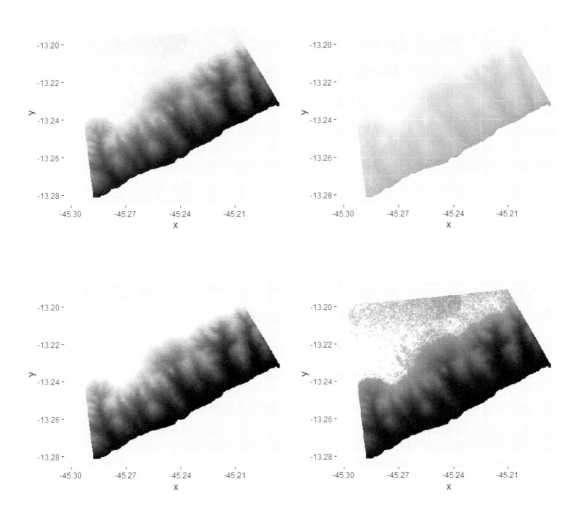

Figure 9.40 Use of the ggR function to perform false-color representation of the relief variation in digital gray levels without enhancement (top-left), layer transparency (top-right), enhancement with linear contrast (bottom-left), enhancement with histogram contrast (bottom-right), in a monitored rural area in the municipality of Correntina, state of Bahia, Brazil.

```
ggR(hill) +
   ggR(srtm, geom_raster = TRUE, ggLayer = TRUE, alpha = 0.3) +
   scale_fill_gradientn(colours = rev(terrain.colors(100)), name = "elevation")
```

9.9.5   Perform image enhancement by tasseled cap

A stacked raster image obtained in the state of Minas Gerais, near the municipality of Ijaci, is used as an example to evaluate the digital numbers referring to the radiance values registered by the Landsat-8 OLI/TIRS sensor. The scene information obtained is as follows: ID, LC08_L1TP_218075_20210628_20210707_01_T1; date acquired, June 28, 2021; path (orbit),

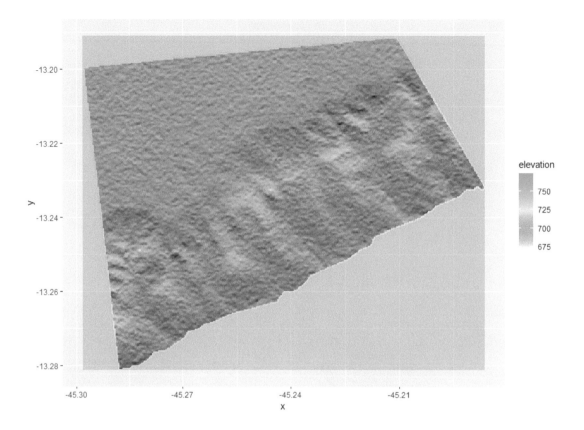

Figure 9.41 Terrain shading map overlayed with altitude layer under transparency and color gradient as an application of the multi-use concept in remote sensing in a monitored rural area in the municipality of Correntina, state of Bahia, Brazil.

218; line (point), 75. The image with the stacked bands and the metadata file can be obtained for **download**[35].

After obtaining the image from the Internet and unpacking the files into a known directory, the geotiff files are imported into R using the stack function. The names function is used to rename the files for each stacked image.

```
lsat<-stack("C:/sr/c8/lsat.tif")
names(lsat)<-c("B1_dn",  "B2_dn",  "B3_dn",  "B4_dn",  "B5_dn",
               "B6_dn",  "B7_dn", "B9_dn" , "B10_dn", "B11_dn")
```

9.9.6   Evaluating image metadata

The image metadata described earlier can be checked in R using the readMeta function. The values in the metadata file can be accessed through the summary function or by the name assigned to the metadata file itself. With this, it is possible to evaluate the image metadata to obtain the transformation parameters of the digital numbers of the bands, in case it is of interest to manually perform the conversion of the digital numbers of the image into reflectance and temperature.

---

[35]http://www.sergeo.deg.ufla.br/sr/downloads/lsat8.zip

```
metaData <- readMeta("C:/sr/c8/LC08_L1TP_218075_20210628_20210707_01_T1_MTL.txt")
summary(metaData)
```

#Scene: LC82180752021179LGN01
#Satellite: LANDSAT8
#Sensor: OLI_TIRS
#Date: 2021-06-28
#Path/Row: 218/75
#Projection: +proj=utm +zone=23 +units=m +datum=WGS84 +ellps=WGS84 +towgs84=0,0,0

#Data:
 #   FILES QUANTITY CATEGORY
#B1_dn   LC08_L1TP_218075_20210628_20210707_01_T1_B1.TIF   dn   image
#B2_dn   LC08_L1TP_218075_20210628_20210707_01_T1_B2.TIF   dn   image
#B3_dn   LC08_L1TP_218075_20210628_20210707_01_T1_B3.TIF   dn   image
#B4_dn   LC08_L1TP_218075_20210628_20210707_01_T1_B4.TIF   dn   image
#B5_dn   LC08_L1TP_218075_20210628_20210707_01_T1_B5.TIF   dn   image
#B6_dn   LC08_L1TP_218075_20210628_20210707_01_T1_B6.TIF   dn   image
#B7_dn   LC08_L1TP_218075_20210628_20210707_01_T1_B7.TIF   dn   image
#B9_dn   LC08_L1TP_218075_20210628_20210707_01_T1_B9.TIF   dn   image
#B10_dn LC08_L1TP_218075_20210628_20210707_01_T1_B10.TIF   dn   image
#B11_dn LC08_L1TP_218075_20210628_20210707_01_T1_B11.TIF   dn   image
#B8_dn   LC08_L1TP_218075_20210628_20210707_01_T1_B8.TIF   dn   pan
#QA_dn LC08_L1TP_218075_20210628_20210707_01_T1_BQA.TIF   dn   qa

#Available calibration parameters (gain and offset):
 #   dn -> radiance (toa)
 #   dn -> reflectance (toa)
 #   dn -> brightness temperature (toa)

Then, by typing `metaData` in the R console it is possible to get more details about the metadata file such as the values of gain, offset and the constants K1 and K2 used in the calibration of the image from mathematical models. In this case the main results from the metadata file are summarized as follows.

```
metaData
```
#$ACQUISITION_DATE
#[1] "2021-06-28 12:57:40 GMT"

#$SOLAR_PARAMETERS
 # azimuth elevation distance
#35.780623 35.853747 1.016589

#$CALRAD
 #   offset   gain
#B1_dn -60.74665 0.01214900
#B2_dn -62.20531 0.01244100
#B3_dn -57.32166 0.01146400
#B4_dn -48.33686 0.00966740
#B5_dn -29.57975 0.00591590
#B6_dn   -7.35621 0.00147120
#B7_dn   -2.47944 0.00049589

```
#B8_dn   -54.70402 0.01094100
#B9_dn   -11.56044 0.00231210
#B10_dn    0.10000 0.00033420
#B11_dn    0.10000 0.00033420


#$CALREF
#        offset  gain
#B1_dn    -0.1 2e-05
#B2_dn    -0.1 2e-05
#B3_dn    -0.1 2e-05
#B4_dn    -0.1 2e-05
#B5_dn    -0.1 2e-05
#B6_dn    -0.1 2e-05
#B7_dn    -0.1 2e-05
#B8_dn    -0.1 2e-05
#B9_dn    -0.1 2e-05


#$CALBT
#               K1         K2
#B10_dn 774.8853 1321.079
#B11_dn 480.8883 1201.144
```

Using the `radCor` function, the image metadata is accessed to determine the reflectance at the top of the atmosphere and brightness temperature of bands 10 and 11 in Kelvin, as follows.

9.9.7   Converting digital numbers to reflectance at the top of the atmosphere and brightness temperature

The digital numbers observed in the preprocessed image referring to the solar spectrum (bands 1,2,3,4,5,6,7,9 of the reflective spectrum) are converted to reflectance at the top of the atmosphere (TOA). Thermal bands number 10 and 11 are converted to brightness temperature. The `radCor` function and the `method="apref"` parameter are used to achieve this purpose.

```
lsat_toa <- radCor(lsat, metaData = metaData, method = "apref")
```

9.9.8   Determine tasseled cap

The TOA reflectance data from the region around the Funil dam, in bands 2 to 7 are used in determining the tasseled cap transformation. This gives a resulting `RasterBrick` according to Baig et al. (2014). The `tasseledCap` function is used by configuring the bands and the satellite used.

```
lsat_tc <- tasseledCap(lsat_toa[[c(2:7)]], sat = "Landsat8OLI")
lsat_tc
```

The brightness, greenness and wetness results can be mapped individually and into an R1G2B3 color composite, using the `plot` and `plotRGB` or `ggR` and `ggRGB` functions (Figures 9.42 and 9.43).

```
plot(lsat_tc)
plotRGB(lsat_tc, r = 1, g = 2, b = 3, axes=T, stretch = "lin", main = "R1G2B3")
```

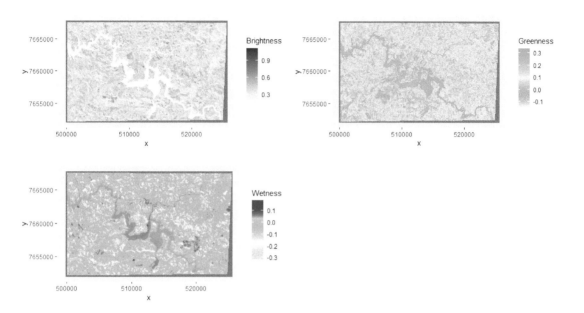

Figure 9.42 Brightness, greenness and wetness mapping as a result of tasseled cap transformation determined from Landsat-8 imagery of the Funil dam, state of Minas Gerais, Brazil, on June 28, 2021.

It can be seen that since in this case the color composition is performed on the data with TOA reflectance results, targets with vegetation showed bluish rather than greenish tones, as in the example used in previous topics to generate remote sensing big data, including results from the tasseled cap transformation.

9.9.9   Perform image fusion to improve spatial resolution

Band 8 with spectral data at 15-m spatial resolution, cropped and masked in the Funil dam region, is available for **download**[36].

The `raster` function is used to import band 8- and 15-m spatial resolution in digital numbers from the Landsat-8 monitoring of the Funil dam.

```
b8<-raster("C:/sr/c8/b8.tif")
```

Image fusion (pan sharpen) in `RStoolbox` can be performed by different methods such as principal components (`pca`), intensity-hue-saturation space transformation (`ihs`) and Brovey (`brovey`). In this case, the highest spatial resolution image (band 8) is used to enhance the spatial resolution of other bands. In this example, the `pca`, `ihs` and `brovey` methods are used comparatively to enhance the spatial resolution of Landsat-8 spectral bands corrected for terrain illumination. The `pca`

---

[36]http://www.sergeo.deg.ufla.br/sr/downloads/b8.zip

Figure 9.43 Mapping of color composition red = brightness, green = greenness and blue = wetness of tasseled cap transformation determined from Landsat-8 imagery of the Funil dam, state of Minas Gerais, on June 28, 2021.

method is the only method that applied fusion to all bands, however, for comparison purposes, only natural color compositions are used to compare the results obtained.

```
lsatPCA <- panSharpen(lsat, b8, r = 4, g = 3, b = 2, method = "pca")
lsatIHS <- panSharpen(lsat, b8, r = 4, g = 3, b = 2, method = "ihs")
lsatBrovey <- panSharpen(lsat, b8, r = 4, g = 3, b = 2, method = "brovey")
```

An extension was defined in a central region in the image to evaluate the fusion methods against an original Landsat-8 color composition (Figure 9.44).

```
e<-extent(505000, 516000, 7655000, 7664000)
```

The results are mapped using the ggRGB function.

```
ggRGB(lsat, r = 3, g = 2, b = 1, stretch="lin", ext=e) + ggtitle("Original")
ggRGB(lsatPCA, r = 3, g = 2, b = 1, stretch="lin", ext=e) + ggtitle("Pansharpened (PCA)")
ggRGB(lsatIHS, r = 3, g = 2, b = 1, stretch="lin", ext=e) + ggtitle("Pansharpened (IHS)")
ggRGB(lsatBrovey, r = 3, g = 2, b = 1, stretch="lin", ext=e) +
      ggtitle("Pansharpened (Brovey)")
```

Although the pca method came closest to the color tone of the original image, overall, the best apparent spatial resolution enhancement results are obtained with the brovey method, where bridge details, subdivisions, and the occupation of the dam edges with buildings can be seen in Figure 9.45.

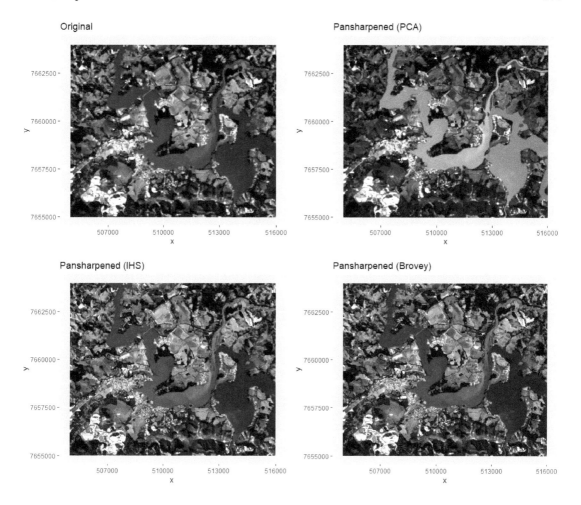

Figure 9.44 Original color composition mapping compared to PCA, IHS, and Brovey fusion methods determined from Landsat-8 imaging of the Funil dam, state of Minas Gerais, on June 28, 2021.

9.9.10 Evaluating color compositions, false-color compositions and different types of image enhancement

A radiometric correction of the Landsat-8 image by the `sdos` method is performed as a practice of color, false-color and image enhancement. In this case, the `estimateHaze` function is used to estimate the presence of fog in bands 1, 2, 3, 4, 5, 6, 7, and 9, at the proportion of dark pixels of 1% (0.01).

```
hazeDN  <- estimateHaze(lsat, hazeBands = 1:8, darkProp = 0.01, plot = TRUE)
```

Then, the simple dark object removal method of the image with haze correction is used with the `sdos` method in order to convert digital numbers of the images into surface reflectance by means of the `radCor` function, using the results of the previous function to remove the haze and fog in the bands.

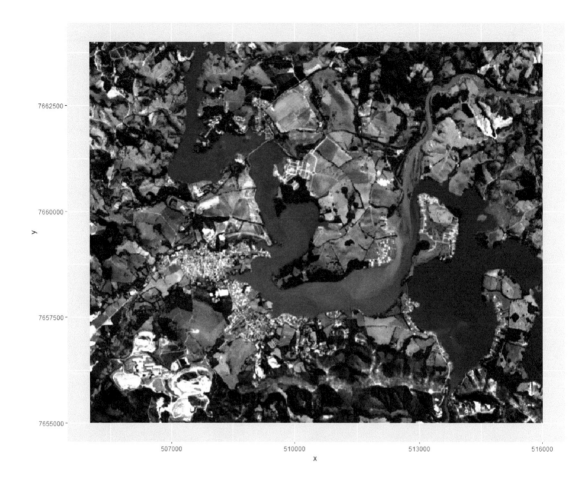

Figure 9.45 Color composition of Landsat-8 image after fusion by the Brovey method determined from Landsat-8 imagery of the Funil dam, state of Minas Gerais, on June 28, 2021.

```
lsat_sdos <- radCor(lsat, metaData = metaData, method = "sdos",
                    hazeValues = hazeDN, hazeBands = 1:8)
```

The bands used are renamed according to the name of the spectral region used, as follows.

```
names(lsat_sdos)<-c("costal","blue","green","red","nir","swir2",
                    "swir3","swir1","tir1","tir2")
```

Different types of natural and false-color compositions are evaluated with linearly enhanced images in a region near the Funil dam defined by the same extent as in the previous example with the parameter ext=e, in order to explore the mapping of the area in natural color (R4G3B2), agricultural studies (R6G5B2), vegetation analysis (R6G5B4), infrared vegetation (R5G4B3), land/water ratio (R5G6B4), urban area false-color (R7G6B4), shortwave infrared (R7G5B4), and atmospheric penetration (R7G6B5) (Figures 9.46 and 9.47).

```
plotRGB(lsat_sdos, r = 4, g = 3, b = 2, axes=T, stretch = "lin", main = "R4G3B2", ext=e)
plotRGB(lsat_sdos, r = 6, g = 5, b = 2, axes=T, stretch = "lin", main = "R6G5B2", ext=e)
plotRGB(lsat_sdos, r = 6, g = 5, b = 4, axes=T, stretch = "lin", main = "R6G5B4", ext=e)
plotRGB(lsat_sdos, r = 5, g = 4, b = 3, axes=T, stretch = "lin", main = "R5G4B3", ext=e)
plotRGB(lsat_sdos, r = 5, g = 6, b = 4, axes=T, stretch = "lin", main = "R5G6B4", ext=e)
plotRGB(lsat_sdos, r = 7, g = 6, b = 4, axes=T, stretch = "lin", main = "R7G6B4", ext=e)
plotRGB(lsat_sdos, r = 7, g = 5, b = 4, axes=T, stretch = "lin", main = "R7G5B4", ext=e)
plotRGB(lsat_sdos, r = 7, g = 6, b = 5, axes=T, stretch = "lin", main = "R7G6B5", ext=e)
```

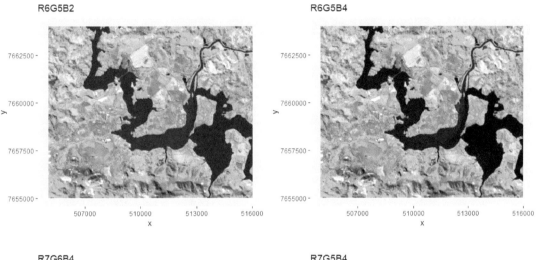

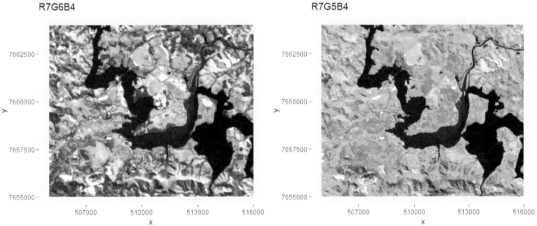

Figure 9.46 RGB 652, 654, 764, and 754 color compositions of surface reflectance bands (sdos) from Landsat-8 imagery of the Funil dam, state of Minas Gerais, on June 28, 2021.

Using the composition R7G6B5, it is observed that the watercourse is demarcated without the presence of sediments in the water, which are observed in the compositions R4G3B2 and R5G4B3, due to the high absorption of energy by the water in the infrared bands.

Different types of enhancement can be used in order to exploit reflectance data transformation functions of the Landsat-8 image. Contrasts of the linear (`lin`), histogram (`hist`), square root (`sqrt`), and logarithm (`log`) types are compared with the application of no contrast to the R4G3B2

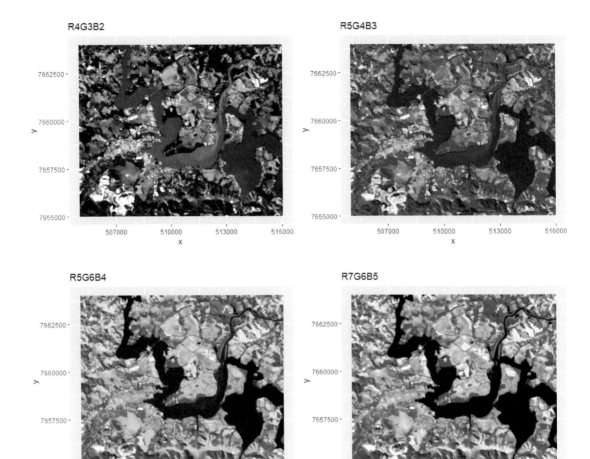

Figure 9.47 RGB 432, 543, 564, and 765 color compositions of surface reflectance bands (sdos) from Landsat-8 imaging of the Funil dam, state of Minas Gerais, on June 28, 2021.

color composition of the sdos corrected reflectance data in a defined subset around the Funil dam, state of Minas Gerais, Brazil (Figure 9.48).

```
ggRGB(lsat_sdos, r = 4, g = 3, b = 2, stretch = "lin", ext=e) + ggtitle("lin")
ggRGB(lsat_sdos, r = 4, g = 3, b = 2, stretch = "hist", ext=e) + ggtitle("hist")
ggRGB(lsat_sdos, r = 4, g = 3, b = 2, stretch = "sqrt", ext=e) + ggtitle("sqrt")
ggRGB(lsat_sdos, r = 4, g = 3, b = 2, stretch = "log", ext=e) + ggtitle("log")
ggRGB(lsat_sdos, r = 4, g = 3, b = 2, stretch = "none", ext=e) + ggtitle("none")
```

With this, it can be observed that the lin and hist enhancements determined higher contrast to discriminate the targets in the subset of the color composition when compared to no contrast. However, the lin method better preserved the hue of the objects when compared to the hist method. Thus, even when performing atmospheric image correction, performing contrast transformations is useful for improving the geovisualization of objects in the scene in scientific remote sensing studies.

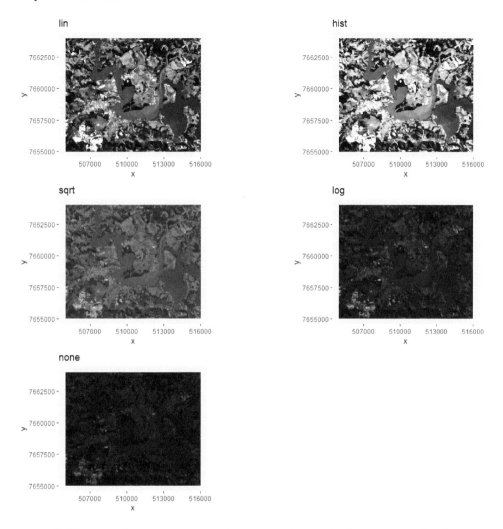

Figure 9.48 RGB 432 color composition submitted to linear (lin), histogram (hist), square root (sqrt), and logarithm (log) contrasts compared to no contrasts applied to the surface reflectance bands (sdos) from Landsat-8 imagery of the Funil dam, state of Minas Gerais, on June 28, 2021.

9.9.11   Performing image texture and principal component statistics

Image texture analysis can be used to determine big data from Landsat-8 bands in order to determine a moving window of rows and columns to calculate mean, variance, homogeneity, contrast, dissimilarity, entropy, second moment and correlation values. The image texture measurements can be applied to all Landsat bands and then stacked into a single file. In the end, principal component analysis is used to determine the top 10 components with the greatest explanation of variability across the scene. The results can be mapped into simple raster files or color compositions of principal components.

The `glcm` function is used to perform texture analysis on Landsat-8 OLI/TIRS image bands.

```
# costal
glcm1 <- glcm(lsat_sdos$costal,
                    window = c(3, 3),
```

```r
                    shift=list(c(0,1), c(1,1), c(1,0), c(1,-1)),
                    statistics = c("mean",
                                    "variance",
                                    "homogeneity",
                                    "contrast",
                                    "entropy",
                                    "dissimilarity",
                                    "second_moment",
                                    "correlation"))
# blue
glcm2 <- glcm(lsat_sdos$blue,
                    window = c(3, 3),
                    shift=list(c(0,1), c(1,1), c(1,0), c(1,-1)),
                    statistics = c("mean",
                                    "variance",
                                    "homogeneity",
                                    "contrast",
                                    "entropy",
                                    "dissimilarity",
                                    "second_moment",
                                    "correlation"))
# green
glcm3 <- glcm(lsat_sdos$green,
                    window = c(3, 3),
                    shift=list(c(0,1), c(1,1), c(1,0), c(1,-1)),
                    statistics = c("mean",
                                    "variance",
                                    "homogeneity",
                                    "contrast",
                                    "entropy",
                                    "dissimilarity",
                                    "second_moment",
                                    "correlation"))
# red
glcm4 <- glcm(lsat_sdos$red,
                    window = c(3, 3),
                    shift=list(c(0,1), c(1,1), c(1,0), c(1,-1)),
                    statistics = c("mean",
                                    "variance",
                                    "homogeneity",
                                    "contrast",
                                    "entropy",
                                    "dissimilarity",
                                    "second_moment",
                                    "correlation"))
# nir
glcm5 <- glcm(lsat_sdos$nir,
                    window = c(3, 3),
                    shift=list(c(0,1), c(1,1), c(1,0), c(1,-1)),
                    statistics = c("mean",
                                    "variance",
                                    "homogeneity",
```

```
                                          "contrast",
                                          "entropy",
                                          "dissimilarity",
                                          "second_moment",
                                          "correlation"))
# swir2
glcm6 <- glcm(lsat_sdos$swir2,
                  window = c(3, 3),
                  shift=list(c(0,1), c(1,1), c(1,0), c(1,-1)),
                  statistics = c("mean",
                                          "variance",
                                          "homogeneity",
                                          "contrast",
                                          "entropy",
                                          "dissimilarity",
                                          "second_moment",
                                          "correlation"))
# swir3
glcm7 <- glcm(lsat_sdos$swir3,
                  window = c(3, 3),
                  shift=list(c(0,1), c(1,1), c(1,0), c(1,-1)),
                  statistics = c("mean",
                                          "variance",
                                          "homogeneity",
                                          "contrast",
                                          "entropy",
                                          "dissimilarity",
                                          "second_moment",
                                          "correlation"))
# swir1
glcm8 <- glcm(lsat_sdos$swir1,
                  window = c(3, 3),
                  shift=list(c(0,1), c(1,1), c(1,0), c(1,-1)),
                  statistics = c("mean",
                                          "variance",
                                          "homogeneity",
                                          "contrast",
                                          "entropy",
                                          "dissimilarity",
                                          "second_moment",
                                          "correlation"))
# tir1
glcm9 <- glcm(lsat_sdos$tir1,
                  window = c(3, 3),
                  shift=list(c(0,1), c(1,1), c(1,0), c(1,-1)),
                  statistics = c("mean",
                                          "variance",
                                          "homogeneity",
                                          "contrast",
                                          "entropy",
                                          "dissimilarity",
                                          "second_moment",
```

```
                                  "correlation"))
# tir2
glcm10 <- glcm(lsat_sdos$tir2,
                 window = c(3, 3),
                 shift=list(c(0,1), c(1,1), c(1,0), c(1,-1)),
                 statistics = c("mean",
                                "variance",
                                "homogeneity",
                                "contrast",
                                "entropy",
                                "dissimilarity",
                                "second_moment",
                                "correlation"))
```

Images with texture measurements are stacked into a single file with the `stack` function.

```
r<-stack(glcm1, glcm2, glcm3, glcm4, glcm5, glcm6, glcm7, glcm8, glcm9, glcm10)
```

The stacked data is scaled with the `scale` function to perform principal component analysis. Values `NA` are set to 0 using the `is.na` function and the `rasterPCA` function is used to perform principal component analysis.

```
r1<-scale(r)
r1[is.na(r1)] <- 0
rpc <- rasterPCA(r1, nComp=10)
```

The importance of each component is observed with the scree plot performed with the `screeplot` function (Figure 9.49).

```
screeplot(rpc$model, main="", ylim=c(0, 30))
```

The first component with the greatest explanation of the variability of the data, as well as the color composition with the first three components determine patterns of objects occurring in the Landsat-8 scene, from analysis of big data obtained from remotely sensed Imagery bands of the Funil dam (Figure 9.50).

```
plot(rpc$map[[1]])
plotRGB(rpc$map, r = 2, g = 1, b = 3, axes=T, stretch = "lin", main = "R2G1B3")
```

9.9.12   Terrain illumination correction and local illumination map determination

The illumination correction of the Landsat-8 image can be performed using information about the altitude of the studied geographical region. An illumination map can also be created as a function of the relief variation. The SRTM digital elevation model with the altitude data can be obtained from **download**[37].

---

[37] http://www.sergeo.deg.ufla.br/sr/downloads/srtmprj.zip

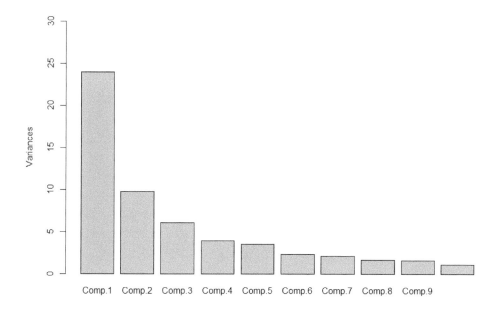

Figure 9.49 Scree plot of principal components according to the importance of explanation of each component.

After downloading the digital elevation model into a directory, the altitude data is imported into R with the `raster` function.

```
srtmprj<-raster("C:/sr/c8/srtmprj.tif")
```

The correction of the relief illumination of the Landsat-8 image used in previous examples can be accomplished by the `cos`, `avgcos`, `minnaert`, `C`, and `stat` methods. In this example, for illustration, the `C` correction method is used to correct the image radiance data according to the topographic variation of the terrain.

```
lsat_C <- topCor(lsat, dem = srtmprj, metaData = metaData, method = "C")
```

The same `topColor` function can be used to determine the illumination map of the area. For this, the `method` parameter is set with the `illu` argument.

```
lsat_ilu <- topCor(lsat, dem = srtmprj, metaData = metaData, method = "illu")
```

The altitude and terrain illumination map can be mapped with the `plot` or `ggR` function (Figure 9.51).

```
plot(srtmprj)
plot(lsat_ilu)
```

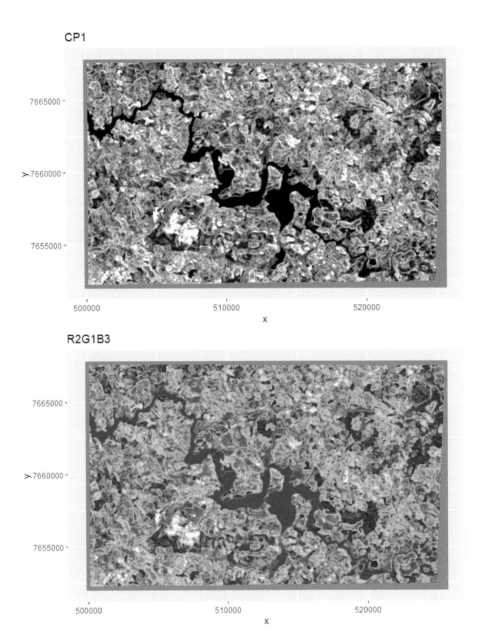

Figure 9.50 Mapping of the first principal component (CP1) and color composition R2G1B3 of the first three principal components with the greatest explanation of the variability of the Landsat-8 imagery data from the Funil dam, state of Minas Gerais, on June 28, 2021.

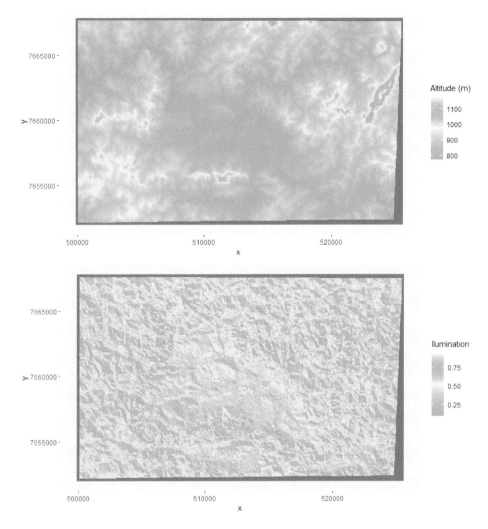

Figure 9.51 Mapping altitude and illumination determined from Landsat-8 imagery and SRTM altitude data of the Funil dam, state of Minas Gerais, on June 28, 2021.

9.10　Exercises

9.10.1　In additive color theory, a pixel with RGB digital values of 255,255,255 will show white color. In the case of using 3 images of 8 bits in the additive theory, how many different digital numbers in the RGB coordinate system are represented?

9.10.2　A linear contrast is applied to a Landsat-5 image with 8 bits of radiometric resolution. The minimum and maximum brightness values are 4 and 105, respectively. Determine the output brightness values for the original minimum and maximum brightness values.

9.10.3　Define "image interpretation".

9.10.4　List the aspects that make image interpretation a scientific tool.

9.10.5　Explain how research methods are applied to image interpretation of higher orders of complexity.

9.10.6　Define color and false-color compositions used in the practical work justifying the choice.

9.10.7　Cite four graphical representation commands used in processing remotely sensed digital images in R.

9.10.8　Justify the use of a false-color composition to detect vegetation in municipalities in southern Minas Gerais state.

9.11　Homework

9.11.1　Subject

Determination of remote sensing variables and mapping of RGB color compositions from MODIS imagery.

9.11.2　Assignment

Develop the subject presented with a practical application of remote sensing and digital image processing including the topics Introduction and Objective. Then present the development of the task.

9.12 Resources on the Internet

As a study guide, slides and illustrative videos are presented about the subject covered in the chapter (Table 9.12).

Table 9.12 Slide show and video presentation on scientific applications of visual interpretation and enhancement of digital remote sensing imagery.

Guide	Address for Access
1	Landsat-8: band by band[38]
2	Lecture on remote sensing and digital image interpretation[39]
3	Slides on elements of image interpretation in coffee growing[40]
4	Slides about visual interpretation and enhancement of digital remote sensing imagery[41]

9.13 Research Suggestion

The development of scientific research on remote sensing for visual interpretation and enhancement of digital remote sensing imagery is stimulated through activity proposals that can be used or adapted by the student to assess the applicability of the subject matter covered in the chapter (Table 9.13).

Table 9.13 Practical and research activities used or adapted by students using remote sensing for visual interpretation and enhancement of digital remote sensing imagery.

Activity	Description
1	Perform natural and false-color RGB compositions on a Landsat8 OLI image in a given studied area or using the imagery used by the teacher in the computational practice.
2	Perform false-color mapping and image enhancement in a given studied area or using the digital elevation model used by the teacher in the computational practice.

---

[38]https://youtu.be/A6WzAc1FTeA
[39]https://youtu.be/HW6ZFbXYwuQ
[40]http://www.sergeo.deg.ufla.br/palestras/necaf2019/index.html
[41]http://www.sergeo.deg.ufla.br/sr/Presentation/Aula8/presentation.html#/

10

Unsupervised Classification of Remote Sensing Images

10.1 Learning Questions

The learning questions answered by reading the chapter are as follows:

- What is the definition of unsupervised classification of remote sensing imagery?
- How are attribute space and distance measurements defined considering different dimensions in space?
- What are the steps used in an unsupervised classification analysis?
- Which algorithms are used in unsupervised classification?
- How are pixel-by-pixel unsupervised classifications performed?
- How are images analyzed by area segments in remote sensing imagery?

10.2 Learning Outcomes

Using the learning outcomes from the chapter, you should be able to do the following:

- Define unsupervised classification of remote sensing imagery.
- Define attribute space and perform distance measurements considering different dimensions in space.
- Understand the steps used in an unsupervised classification analysis.
- Know which algorithms are used in unsupervised classification.
- Understand how to perform unsupervised classification pixel by pixel.
- Analyze images by area segments in remote sensing imagery.

10.3 Introduction

Earth remote sensing data can be used to extract thematic information at local, regional and global scales after pattern recognition by statistical and computational intelligence techniques. The steps to obtain thematic information from remote sensing data are (Jensen, 2005):

- Selecting the nature of the problem <- Specify the geographic region; define classes of interest; evaluate whether the classification should be discrete or continuous; define whether the classification should be pixel-by-pixel or object-oriented;

- Obtain remote sensing data of satisfactory quality and field reference data <- Spatial, spectral, temporal and radiometric resolutions; obtain field data based on knowledge of the area studied;
- Process the remote sensing data to extract thematic information <- Assess for geometric, radiometric corrections and select appropriate classification logic;
- Perform classification accuracy evaluation <- Define the method, determine the number of evaluation samples, define the sampling criteria, analyze error matrix;
- Approve the classification <- Accept or reject the hypothesis based on accuracy information.

Digital image classification is defined simply as the process of assigning classes to pixels. By comparing pixels of an object with other pixels of the same object, similarity groups are associated with the remote sensing information of interest. In this case, it is assumed that pixels of the same object show greater spectral similarity than in another class. In digital image classification, each pixel of the image is associated with a label referring to a real object, such as vegetation, water, and soil. Digital numeric values are identified in terms of a type of land surface cover imaged, such as vegetation, water, and soil. The classified remote sensing imagery can be considered a thematic digital map (Figure 10.1) (Campbell & Wynne, 2011).

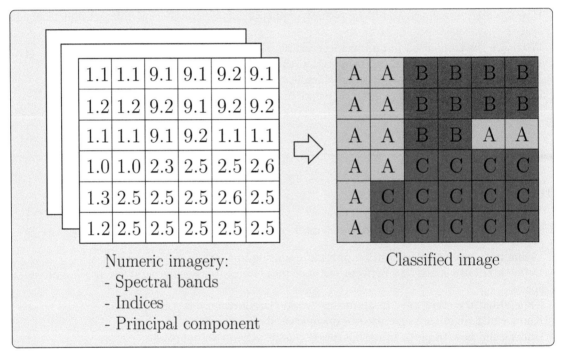

Figure 10.1 Numerical image and classified image after applying a classification algorithm to generate a thematic map with classes A, B, and C.

10.4   Unsupervised Classification

Unsupervised classification, also called "clustering", is an efficient method of separating multispectral data and remote sensing indices based on features in the attribute space of the images in order to extract terrain information. In unsupervised classification, a minimal number of input values are required by the analyst when compared to supervised classification. In unsupervised classification, no prior knowledge about land use and land cover types is required (Campbell & Wynne, 2011;

Jensen, 2005). Numerical operations are performed to define natural groupings of spectral features of pixels. The clustering process results in a classified map with n spectral classes. Image pixels are grouped (clustered) by the computer based on similar spectral features according to some statistical criterion (Kassambara, 2017; Kassambara, 2018). Based on the result obtained, the defined classes are renamed by the analyst by means of experience and complementary information from the area, viewing images by different color compositions, image enhancement techniques, indices and variables derived from remote sensor spectral bands.

Some clusters may be meaningless because they represent a mixture of object classes. Hundreds of different algorithms can be evaluated in unsupervised classification in an attempt to get a better analysis result. Another option is to change the number of classes in the classification algorithm in an attempt to generalize the difficult-to-separate classes and get some satisfactory result (Campbell & Wynne, 2011; Jensen, 2005).

The advantages of unsupervised classification when compared to supervised classification are (Campbell & Wynne, 2011):

- No need for prior knowledge of the region;
- Human error is minimized;
- Single classes are recognized as distinct units.

The disadvantages of unsupervised classification when compared to supervised classification are (Campbell & Wynne, 2011):

- The classifier may recognize homogeneous spectral classes that do not match the analyst's categories of interest;
- The analyst has little control over existing classes and specific identity;
- The classes may change over time according to the spectral variation of the monitored objects and with this the classifier algorithm may generate different classification results of the same target.

10.5   Distance Measures in Attribute Space

The basic elements in unsupervised classification can be represented in one-dimensional, two-dimensional and multidimensional dimensions using diagrams or attribute space. The one-dimensional dimension can be obtained by means of a frequency distribution diagram of the variable of interest. In the one-dimensional attribute space, the pixel similarity criterion can be evaluated as a function of the x and y coordinate axes of a band or a remote sensing index, such as a digital terrain elevation model. In the two-dimensional dimension, the brightness intensity of two bands is used to evaluate the relationship between objects in the scene in attribute space. In the multidimensional dimension, the relationship between objects in the scene is evaluated based on the attribute space of multiple spectral bands (Figure 10.2) (Campbell & Wynne, 2011).

With the classification of observations into groups, some methods are employed to calculate the distance or dissimilarity between each pair of observations. The result of this calculation is known as the "dissimilarity" or "distance matrix" (Kassambara, 2017). Several methods can define the distances in attribute space. One of the simplest methods to define the similarity of two elements (a, b) is the Euclidean distance, based on the Pythagorean theorem (Campbell & Wynne, 2011):

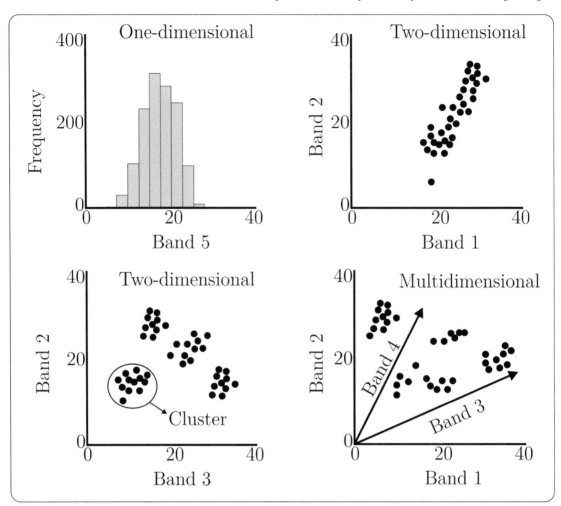

Figure 10.2 One-dimensional attribute space, two-dimensional without clear cluster definition, two-dimensional with cluster definition, and multidimensional with spectral bands.

$$ED_{ab} = \sqrt{\sum_{i=1}^{n} (a_i - b_i)^2} \tag{10.1}$$

where ED_{ab} is the Euclidean distance between two pixels a, b, and i, one of n spectral bands.

Another classic method used in distance measurement is the Manhattan (Kassambara, 2017):

$$MD_{ab} = \sum_{i=1}^{n} |(a_i - b_i)| \tag{10.2}$$

where MD_{ab} is the Manhattan distance, and a, b, are two vectors of length n.

Other measures of dissimilarity exist, such as distances based on Pearson correlations, Spearman, Eisen cosine, and Kendall (Kassambara, 2017).

Unsupervised classification is processed interactively by seeking the optimal allocation of pixels to categories according to constraints specified by the analyst. In a computer program for unsupervised classification, an algorithm determines the calculation of distances between pixels in the attribute space and a procedure is used to find, test and review classes according to parameters set by the analyst. The analyst must specify the number of clusters to be generated by the classifier to restrict the diversity of values within classes and to have a specified minimum degree of class distinction from neighboring clusters. Specific classification procedures may define distinct distances as a refinement alternative in certain situations. Variations in the details of how each classification program is developed can achieve the same purposes, but with improved computational efficiency, depending on the algorithm used (Campbell & Wynne, 2011).

10.6 Sequence for Unsupervised Classification

A typical sequence for unsupervised classification starts with the analyst specifying the minimum and maximum number of categories to be generated by the classification algorithm. These values can be based on the analyst's knowledge of the scene or on settings made by the user so that the final classification displays a certain number of classes. The classification starts with a set of randomly selected pixels as cluster centers to ensure that the analyst does not influence the classification and that the selected pixels are representative of the values obtained across the scene. The classification algorithm then finds distances between pixels and determines initial cluster center estimates considering the constraints specified by the analyst. A class can be represented by a single point, known as the "class centroid", defined as the center of the pixel cluster for a given class. At this point, the classes consist only of arbitrarily selected pixels chosen as initial estimates of the class centroids. In the next step, all remaining pixels in the scene are assigned to the nearest class centroid. The entire scene is classified, but this classification forms only an estimate of the final result. As a result, the classes formed by this initial attempt are unlikely to match the ideal set of classes and may not meet the constraints specified by the analyst. To begin the next step, the algorithm finds new centroids for each class. The entire scene is re-ranked, with each pixel assigned to the nearest centroid. New centroids are calculated again; if the new centroids differ from those found in the previous step, the process is repeated until no significant change is detected in the centroid locations meeting all the constraints required by the analyst. During the entire process, the analyst has no interaction with the classification, so the classification is performed objectively within the constraints provided by the analyst. Furthermore, with the unsupervised approach, natural image structures are identified in the sense of finding uniform groupings of pixels that form distinct classes without the influence of data identities or distributions. The whole process, however, cannot be considered completely objective, as the analyst makes decisions regarding the data to be examined, the algorithm to be used, the number of classes to be determined, and possibly the uniformity and distinctiveness of classes. Each of these decisions influences the type and accuracy of the final product, and is not considered a result isolated from the context in which it is produced. Many different procedures for unsupervised classification are available. Despite the diversity of algorithms, most are based on the general strategy described above (Campbell & Wynne, 2011).

In summary, a typical unsupervised classification sequence is subdivided into the following steps:

- Specification of the minimum and the maximum number of categories by the analyst to be generated by the classification algorithm;

- The algorithm randomly selects cluster centers to ensure that the analyst does not influence the classification and that the selected pixels are representative of the values found in the entire scene;
- The algorithm determines distances between pixels and initial estimates of cluster centers considering the constraints specified by the analyst;
- The algorithm assigns all remaining pixels in the scene to the class of the nearest centroid;
- The process is repeated iteratively until no significant change is detected in the centroid locations and the constraints required by the analyst are met.

10.7   Unsupervised Classification Algorithms

Clustering partitioning is a method used to classify observations from a dataset into several groups based on similarity criteria. In the algorithms, it is necessary for the analyst to specify the number of clusters to be generated. Some methods for partitioning images by clustering are (Hartigan & Wong, 1979; Kassambara, 2017; Kaufman & Rousseuw, 2009; Lloyd, 1982; MacQueen, 1967):

- Clustering k-means <- Each cluster is represented by the center or average of data in the cluster. The k-means method is sensitive to conflicting data;
- k-medoids clustering or partitioning around medoids (PAM) <- Each cluster is represented by one of the objects within the cluster. In PAM there is more sensitivity to conflicting data than in k-means;
- Clustering Algorithm for Large Applications (CLARA) <- This method is an extension of PAM for large databases.

The basic idea of the k-means algorithm is to define clusters so that the total variance within the cluster is minimized. There are several k-means algorithms available. The standard algorithm is the Hartigan & Wong (1979) algorithm, which defines the total variation within the cluster as the sum of the square of the Euclidean distance between the data and the corresponding centroid. The K-medoids algorithm (PAM) is a robust alternative to k-means for partitioning a dataset into observation clusters. In the k-medoids method, each cluster is represented by a selected object within the group. The selected objects are called "medoids" and correspond to the points located in the center within the cluster. Instead of finding medoids for the entire dataset, in the CLARA algorithm, a small sample of the data with fixed size is considered each time for applying the PAM algorithm to generate an optimal set of medoids for the sample. The quality of the resulting medoids is measured by the average dissimilarity between all objects in the entire dataset and the medoid of each cluster. In CLARA, the sampling and clustering processes are repeated a pre-specified number of times to minimize sampling bias. The final clustering results correspond to a set of medoids with minimal computational memory cost. A satisfactory approach to determine the best number of clusters to classify an image can be performed by the silhouette method (Kassambara, 2017).

The unsupervised k-means algorithm is applied to altitude data from a rural property, in the state of Bahia, Brazil. In this case, a comparison of the unsupervised classification by the k-means clustering method, implemented with the Hartigan-Wong algorithm (Hartigan & Wong, 1979), was performed in order to evaluate the difference of altitude mapping with 4, 5, and 6 classes (Figure 10.3).

It is observed that the number of each class defined by the k-means method was not continuous, making it necessary to evaluate the altitude threshold defined for each class so as not to generate deception about the mapped result.

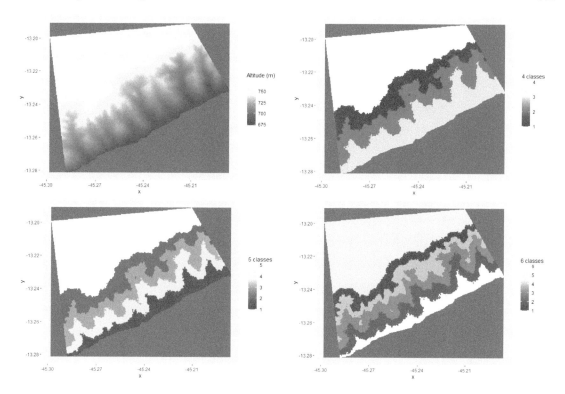

Figure 10.3 Unsupervised altitude classification by the k-means clustering method, Hartigan-Wong algorithm, with 4, 5, and 6 classes, in a rural property, state of Bahia, Brazil.

10.8   Unsupervised Segmentation

Image segmentation considered a fundamental area in the field of computer vision has been widely employed to solve image processing and pattern recognition problems. Segmentation is usually performed to identify differences between objects in an image (Figure 10.4).

As a result, the image is divided into different sets composed of homogeneous regions with common features. Segmentation can be performed using a simple and fast approach based on the concept of superpixels. A superpixel can be defined as a small group of pixels with homogeneous color. This concept has been used in various computer vision techniques such as image segmentation and pattern recognition. Compared to the traditional pixel, the superpixel representation reduces the number of image primitives and thus improves the representation efficiency and simplifies vision tasks for object recognition. The regions extracted by superpixel segmentation form a compact representation of an image compared to a grid of original pixels. To achieve more accurate results and shorter execution time, image segmentation uses an enhanced superpixel variant called "simple linear iterative cluster superpixel" (SLIC), which makes superpixel segmentation applicable in real time. The cluster affinity propagation (AP) method can be jointly used in image segmentation with superpixels. The AP algorithm is originally used to analyze complex data sets called "affinity propagation" and presented satisfactory results when compared to other clustering methods. The AP algorithm can be applied to solve non-symmetric similarity problems more effectively than k-means (Zhou, 2015).

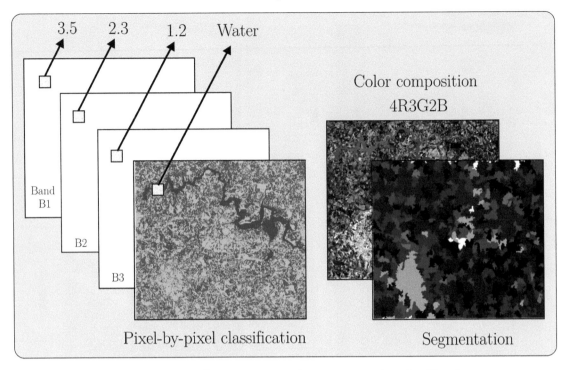

Figure 10.4 Pixel-by-pixel classification compared to segmentation classification.

Another R package used in unsupervised segmentation is `supercells` (Nowosad et al., 2022). In `supercells` the concept of superpixels is used for a variety of spatial data, either for a single variable in a raster layer or for many variables as in the case of an RGB raster color composite. Spatial patterns in categorical rasters can also be used in the analysis. The development of `supercells` is based on the SLIC algorithm (Achanta et al., 2011), re-adapted to work with arbitrary dissimilarity measures (Nowosad & Stepinski, 2021).

SLIC starts with regularly located cluster centers spaced across the S interval. Each cell is assigned to the nearest cluster center, and the distance D is calculated between the cluster centers and the cells in the $2S$ by $2S$ region (Nowosad & Stepinski, 2021):

$$D = \sqrt{(\frac{d_c}{m})^2 + (\frac{d_s}{S})^2} \tag{10.3}$$

where d_c is the color (spectral) distance, m, the compactness parameter, d_s, the spatial (Euclidean) distance, and S, the interval between initial cluster centers.

The (spectral) color distance is calculated between the values $I(x_i, y_i, s_p)$ and $I(x_j, y_j, s_p)$ for a spectral band s_p in the spectral band set B (Nowosad & Stepinski, 2021):

$$d_c = \sqrt{\sum_{p \in B} (I(x_i, y_i, s_p) - I(x_j, y_j, s_p))^2} \tag{10.4}$$

The Euclidean distance between cells represents spatial proximity (Nowosad & Stepinski, 2021):

$$d_s = \sqrt{(x_j - x_i)^2 + (y_j - y_i)^2} \tag{10.5}$$

Color distance controls the homogeneity of superpixels, while spatial distance is related to spatial contiguity. Superpixels are created by assigning each cell to the cluster center with the smallest distance. Subsequently, new cluster centers (centroids) are updated for the new superpixels, and their color values are the average of all the cells belonging to the superpixel. The SLIC algorithm runs iteratively until it reaches the expected number of iterations (Nowosad & Stepinski, 2021).

Nowosad & Stepinski (2021) proposed an extension of SLIC that allows using any distance measure to calculate the color distance and d_c can be replaced by any distance/dissimilarity measure. Therefore, a raster time series can be compared with dynamic time warping, while distances between sets of categorical variables can be calculated using the Jenson-Shannon distance:

$$d_c = H(\frac{A+B}{2}) - \frac{1}{2}[H(A) + H(B)] \tag{10.6}$$

where A and B are normalized sets of values that characterize the compared cells, and H(A) and H(B) indicate Shannon entropy values for these sets (Nowosad & Stepinski, 2021):

$$H(A) = -\sum_{p\in A} A_p log_2 A_p \tag{10.7}$$

where A_p is the *pth* value of the compared cell.

Any number of variables in raster layers and Euclidean, Manhattan, Jensen-Shannon, and dynamic time wrapping distances can be used with this methodology.

As an example, the superpixel technique is used to classify the relief variation around the Funil dam, state of Minas Gerais, Brazil. It should be noted that at the time the digital elevation model of the area was obtained by the Shuttle Radar Topographic Mission, the dam had not yet been dammed.

The R packages `supercells`, `terra` (Hijmans, Bivand, et al., 2022), `sf` (Pebesma et al., 2022), `ggplot2` (Wickham, Chang, et al., 2022), and `gridExtra` (Auguie & Antonov, 2017) are required for analysis. The packages are enabled with the `library` function.

```
library(supercells)
library(terra)
library(sf)
library(ggplot2)
library(gridExtra)
```

The raster layer of interest in the classification is imported into R with the `rast` function.

```
srtmprj<-rast("C:/sr/c8/srtmprj.tif")
```

You can see the `SpatRaster` file class, with a spatial resolution of 30 m.

```
srtmprj
#class       : SpatRaster
#dimensions  : 529, 860, 1  (nrow, ncol, nlyr)
#resolution  : 30, 30  (x, y)
#extent      : 499835.6, 525635.6, 7651972, 7667842  (xmin, xmax, ymin, ymax)
```

```
#coord. ref. : WGS 84 / UTM zone 23S (EPSG:32723)
#source      : srtmprj.tif
#name        :  srtmprj
#min value   : 771.8686
#max value   : 1184.278
```

The altitude visualization is performed with the `plot` function by setting the grayscale color palette in the `col` argument.

```
plot(srtmprj, col=grey.colors(100, start=0, end=1))
```

Thereby, it is possible to observe the relief inside the Funil dam, before the construction of the dam. Highlighted in dark tones are cells with brightness values that characterize lower altitude, where there is water runoff in the watershed and greater storage capacity and extension in the central region, in places where the watercourse passes longitudinally throughout the image (Figure 10.5).

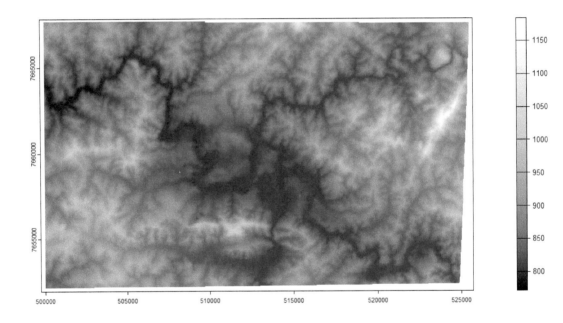

Figure 10.5 Mapping altitude variation (m) in the region of the Funil dam, state of Minas Gerais, Brazil.

A first way to recognize patterns in the image is to locally reclassify the raster pixel by pixel. Thus, a matrix of values with altitude class intervals is created with the `matrix` function defining four altitude classes every 100 m of level change from sea level in a `matrix array class` file of 3 columns and 5 rows.

```
rcl = matrix(c(771, 871, 1, 871, 971, 2, 971, 1071, 3, 1071, 1171, 4, 1171, 1185, 5),
             ncol = 3, byrow = TRUE)
rcl
#      [,1] [,2] [,3]
```

```
#[1,]   771   871    1
#[2,]   871   971    2
#[3,]   971 1071    3
#[4,] 1071 1171    4
#[5,] 1171 1185    5
```

The classify function is used to reclassify the altitude data from the region around the Funil dam according to the previously defined matrix.

```
srtm_recl = classify(srtmprj, rcl = rcl)
```

The plot function is used to map the results with a grayscale palette.

```
plot(srtm_recl, col=grey.colors(10))
```

The highest altitude values are defined in ascending order according to increasing class number (Figure 10.6).

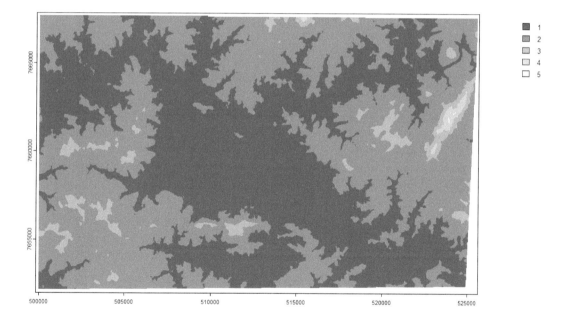

Figure 10.6 Reclassification of altitude into 5 classes of variation in the region of the Funil dam, state of Minas Gerais, Brazil.

However, it may often be necessary to separate a large amount of data based on similarity criteria between adjacent pixels. In this case, the logical reasoning used in this pixel grouping criterion is that objects tend to be similar in their closest neighborhood.

In a first segmentation approach, the supercells function is used with the number of supercells k=50 and compression factor 1 to classify the raster with altitude brightness values.

```
vol_srtm50 <- supercells(srtmprj, k = 50, compactness = 1)
```

The results obtained from the attribute table resulted in multipolygon vector geometries with attributes of supercells, x, y coordinates, and cell altitude value in a `sf` data model with 52 features and 4 fields.

```
vol_srtm50
#Simple feature collection with 52 features and 4 fields
#Geometry type: MULTIPOLYGON
#Dimension:     XY
#Bounding box:  xmin: 499985.6 ymin: 7652182 xmax: 525485.6 ymax: 7667692
#Projected CRS: WGS 84 / UTM zone 23S
#First 10 features:
#    supercells        x        y srtmprj                      geometry
#1            1 500870.6 7666867 915.1043 MULTIPOLYGON (((499985.6 76...
#2            2 502820.6 7666417 889.2291 MULTIPOLYGON (((501545.6 76...
#3            3 502880.6 7664107 846.3587 MULTIPOLYGON (((502535.6 76...
#4            4 501920.6 7663447 809.2935 MULTIPOLYGON (((504875.6 76...
#5            5 502730.6 7661587 875.2774 MULTIPOLYGON (((502235.6 76...
#6            6 502460.6 7658707 912.7219 MULTIPOLYGON (((505025.6 76...
#7            7 500750.6 7658497 875.9202 MULTIPOLYGON (((500495.6 76...
#8            8 502160.6 7655857 962.4358 MULTIPOLYGON (((501785.6 76...
#9            9 501530.6 7653277 878.2094 MULTIPOLYGON (((502175.6 76...
#10          10 504020.6 7660417 962.6539 MULTIPOLYGON (((506045.6 76...
```

The results can be mapped according to the attribute table for each geometry obtained after segmentation. The ggplot, geom_sf, aes, and `scale_fill_distiller` functions are used to map the segmented altitude into regions with `k=50`.

```
ggplot() + geom_sf(data = vol_srtm50[,4], aes(fill = srtmprj)) +
    scale_fill_distiller(palette = "Greys")
```

Thus, it is possible to visualize the recognized altitude segments from a similarity criterion established to generate superpixels. In addition, the lower altitude areas in the region are better highlighted after segmentation due to the simplification of the original data (Figure 10.7).

The k values can be varied according to the analyst's experience in obtaining more reliable results according to the objective of the analysis. In this example, k is evaluated with values 4, 5, 10, and 500 in a perspective of comparative analysis of result detail as a function of the size of supercell areas. The function `supercells` is used with compactness factor 1 for all values of k.

```
vol_srtm4 <- supercells(srtmprj, k = 4, compactness = 1)
vol_srtm5 <- supercells(srtmprj, k = 5, compactness = 1)
vol_srtm10 <- supercells(srtmprj, k = 10, compactness = 1)
vol_srtm500 <- supercells(srtmprj, k = 500, compactness = 1)
```

The results are mapped with functions from the `ggplot2` package, and the `grid.arrange` function from the `gridExtra` package is used to comparatively group the maps.

Thus, it is possible to observe a higher sensitivity of the method to define distinct geometric patterns with lower k values. Under higher k values, the final geometric result of the segments

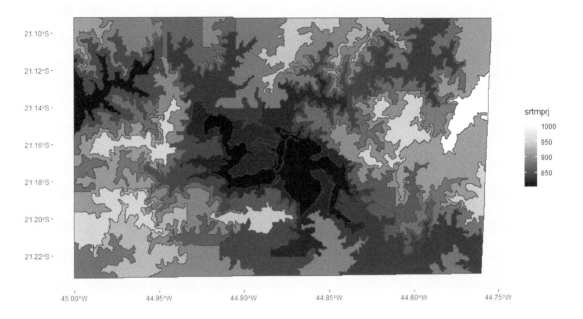

Figure 10.7 Supercells segmentation (k = 50) used for attribute class recognition in a simple raster of altitude in the region of the Funil dam, state of Minas Gerais, Brazil.

shows less visual difference, although it increases the number of features and demands more storage of vector features with attributes (Figure 10.8).

The `object.size` function is used to compare the storage of the vector files resulting from the superpixel analysis, and it can be seen that there is a tendency for the storage demand to increase with increasing `k`, except between values of `k` 5 and 10 which showed close values, but with less storage under `k = 10`.

10.9 Unsupervised Classification with Cloud Processing

Using Earth Engine and R, it is possible to run algorithms on georeferenced images and vectors stored in Google's infrastructure. A library of functions can be applied to the data for display and analysis. Earth Engine's public data catalog contains a large amount of publicly available imagery and vector datasets. Using the `ee$Clusterer` function, it is possible to perform unsupervised classification in Earth Engine. These algorithms are currently based on algorithms from Weka software, a working platform with a collection of machine learning and data preprocessing algorithms (Frank et al., 2016; Witten et al., 2016).

Clusters are used in the same way as classifiers in Earth Engine. The general workflow for a clustering is:

- Assemble elements with numeric properties on which clusters can be found;
- Instantiate a clusterer and set parameters if necessary;
- Train the clusterer using input data;

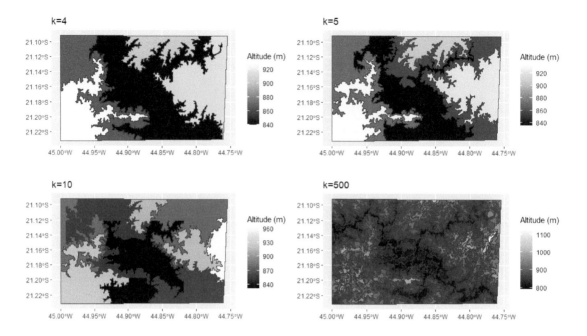

Figure 10.8 Supercell segmentation with k-values 4, 5, 10, and 500 used for attribute class recognition in a simple raster of altitude in the region of the Funil dam, state of Minas Gerais, Brazil.

- Apply to the clusterer a collection of data, such as a collection of images or indices obtained with spectral bands;
- Label clusters.

It should be noted that:

- The same inputs should always produce the same outputs, but reordering the inputs can change the results;
- Training can produce Out of Memory error;
- It may take a long time to finish and may produce a large number of clusters;
- The output clusters and their IDs depend on the algorithm and the inputs.

An example is performed to visualize features classified into agroecosystems, ecosystems, and urbanized regions of the state of Mato Grosso from an annual collection of Landsat-7 data. The rgee package (Aybar et al., 2022) is enabled with the library function and the Earth Engine is initialized with the ee_Initialize function.

```
library(rgee)
ee_Initialize()
```

The 1-year imagery compositions are created from all Landsat-7 images between 1999 and 2014, excluding images taken with negative Sun elevation in the metadata. Compositions are created using the ee.Algorithms.Landsat.simpleComposite() method under default settings. The reflectance with range 0 to 1 in bands B1, B2, B3, B4, B5, and B7 is scaled to 8 bits (0 to 255). The temperature in band B6_VCID_2 is converted to Kelvin-100. The ee$Image function is used to import into R a 2001 Landsat-7 collection as input data for unsupervised classification.

```
input <- ee$Image("LANDSAT/LE7_TOA_1YEAR/2001")
```

A region in the center of Mato Grosso state is defined to generate a sample with input data for the classification algorithm. The `ee$Geometry$Rectangle` function is used to create the rectangle of interest.

```
region <- ee$Geometry$Rectangle(-59.47, -14.73, -53.76, -10.84)
```

The sampling region for the classification is mapped with the `Map$setCenter` and `Map$addLayer` functions.

```
Map$setCenter(-56.57, -12.89, 7)
Map$addLayer(eeObject = ee$Image()$paint(region, 0, 2), name = "region")
```

With this it is possible to observe that to the north of the quadrant is located the city of Sinop, to the south, outside the quadrant, is the Manso dam near Cuiabá, and to the west, the Campo Novo dos Parecis, Brasnorte and Sapezal, agricultural frontier regions (Figure 10.9).

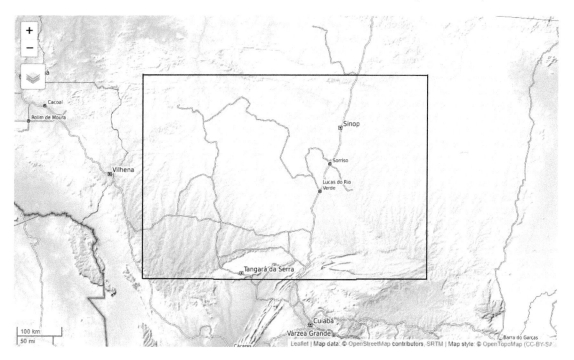

Figure 10.9 Geographic region defined for unsupervised classification of environments from a 2001 annual Landsat-7 collection, state of Mato Grosso, Brazil.

The training data is set with the `input$sample` function, in the region of interest, with the parameters `scale` and `numPixels` equal to 30 and 5000, respectively.

```
training <- input$sample(region = region, scale = 30, numPixels = 5000)
```

Clustering is instantiated and trained with the ee$Clusterer$wekaKMeans()$train() function.

```
clusterer <- ee$Clusterer$wekaKMeans(15)$train(training)
```

The input data is clustered using the input data and the trained clusterer.

```
result <- input$cluster(clusterer)
```

The results are mapped with random colors with the map$centerObject and Map$addLayer functions.

```
Map$centerObject(region)
Map$addLayer(eeObject = result$randomVisualizer(), name = "clusters")
```

Therefore, it is possible to observe the diversity of targets in the region, characterizing agroecosystems in yellow and greenish tones (includes exposed soil and some urbanized areas), water in light pink tones and native vegetation with dark pink, beige and brown. Given the complexity of targets and the extent of the analyzed region, clustering can be challenging when it is desired to obtain reliable results in scientific applications (Figure 10.10).

Figure 10.10 Unsupervised classification of environments from a 2001 annual Landsat-7 collection based on top-of-atmosphere reflectance data in state of Mato Grosso, Brazil.

10.10 Computational Practice

The unsupervised classification can be performed on both single and multiple remote sensing bands. In this computational practice, the use of unsupervised classification algorithms applied to the study of relief, and subsequently to big data from remote sensing obtained from the Funil dam in state of Minas Gerais, Brazil, are explored.

10.10.1 Installing R packages

The R packages used in the classification can be installed and enabled to perform the computational practice. The `install.packages` function installs the R packages RStoolbox (Leutner et al., 2019), raster (Hijmans et al., 2020), ggplot2 (Wickham, Chang, et al., 2022), randomForest (Breiman et al., 2018), cluster (Maechler et al., 2022), SuperpixelImageSegmentation (Mouselimis, 2022; Zhou, 2015), and terra (Hijmans, Bivand, et al., 2022). Packages already installed should not be re-installed to avoid upgrade problems, but need to be enabled for analysis.

```
install.packages("RStoolbox")
install.packages("raster")
install.packages("ggplot2")
install.packages("randomForest")
install.packages("cluster")
install.packages("SuperpixelImageSegmentation")
install.packages("terra")
```

10.10.2 Enabling R packages

The `library` function enables the R packages RStoolbox, raster, ggplot2, randomForest, cluster, SuperpixelImageSegmentation, and terra.

```
library(RStoolbox)
library(raster)
library(ggplot2)
library(randomForest)
library(cluster)
library(SuperpixelImageSegmentation)
library(terra)
```

10.10.3 Applying unsupervised classification on a raster layer

10.10.3.1 Obtaining data

The digital elevation model of the area of interest (NASA, 2013), realized in computational practice, can be obtained for **download**[1].

The file must be unzipped into a directory on the computer knowing the address of the file. To set the address of the file in the R console for the purpose of importing the file into R, note the use of "/" for the location of the file in the source directory. On this computer, the directory is located at "G:/sr/c6/AppeearsTerraMorena/ SRT-MGL1_NC.003_SRTMGL1_DEM_doy2000042_aid0001.tif". Note that the file extension used is .tif.

The SRTM file obtained from the rural property located in Bahia is imported into R with the raster function, named "srtm", and stored in the computer memory under that name.

```
srtm <- raster(
  "C:/sr/c6/AppeearsTerraMorena/SRTMGL1_NC.003_SRTMGL1_DEM_doy2000042_aid0001.tif")
```

10.10.3.2 Unsupervised Classification

Unsupervised classification is performed by k-means method, Hartigan-Wong algorithm, with 5 classes. The function unsuperClass is used to perform the classification with the parameters nSamples and nStarts equal to 100 and 5, respectively.

```
# Set number of method initialization values
set.seed(100)
# Perform unsupervised classification
unC <- unsuperClass(srtm, nSamples = 100, nClasses = 5, nStarts = 5,
                    algorithm = "Hartigan-Wong")
```

10.10.3.3 Evaluating the intervals defined by the unsupervised classification

The altitude ranges defined by the classification are evaluated.

```
unC$model
#K-means clustering with 5 clusters of sizes 12, 20, 18, 42, 8
#Cluster means:
#       [,1]
#1 741.5000
#2 705.8500
#3 722.3889
#4 766.7619
#5 690.8750
#Clustering vector:
# [1] 3 4 2 4 3 5 2 4 3 1 2 3 4 4 1 4 3 4 1 2 4 2 2 1 4 4 3 3 4 3 2 2 4 5 2 2 4
```

---

[1]http://www.sergeo.deg.ufla.br/sr/downloads/srtmTM.zip

```
# [38] 3 2 4 4 5 5 3 2 1 2 3 4 1 4 4 4 4 4 4 4 1 3 4 1 5 2 4 1 4 2 1 4 2 4 4 4 3
# [75] 1 3 3 5 2 4 3 2 3 3 4 4 5 4 4 5 2 4 4 4 2 4 4 4 4 1
#Within cluster sum of squares by cluster:
#[1] 507.0000 242.5500 368.2778 203.6190 260.8750
# (between_SS / total_SS =  98.0 %)
#Available components:
#[1] "cluster"      "centers"      "totss"        "withinss"     "tot.withinss"
#[6] "betweenss"    "size"         "iter"         "ifault"
```

Using the evaluation of modeling results performed, it is observed that classes 1, 2, 3, 4, and 5 are defined according to the average altitude thresholds of 741.5000, 705.8500, 722.3889, 766.7619 and 690.8750 m, respectively. Therefore, the defined classes are not continuous, and there may be problems interpreting the mapping if they are not replaced with the altitude thresholds defined for each class.

10.10.3.4 Replacing class identifiers with the clustering altitude threshold

The raster values are replaced with the actual values for each altitude threshold defined by the unsupervised clustering.

```
alt<-unC$map
alt[alt == 1] <- 741.5000
alt[alt == 2] <- 705.8500
alt[alt == 3] <- 722.3889
alt[alt == 4] <- 766.7619
alt[alt == 5] <- 690.8750
```

10.10.3.5 Mapping the unsupervised classification

The result of the classification coded in classes 1, 2, 3, 4, and 5, is mapped using the ggR function.

```
ggR(unC$map, geom_raster = TRUE) +
   scale_fill_gradientn(colours = terrain.colors(100), name = "id class")
```

The classification result with the average altitude ranges of 741.5000, 705.8500, 722.3889, 766.7619 and 690.8750 m, is mapped using the ggR function.

```
ggR(alt, geom_raster = TRUE) +
   scale_fill_gradientn(colours = terrain.colors(100), name = "Alt class")
```

With this, a map is made with the continuous altitude classes and with altitude values corresponding to the pixel cluster classes defined by the k-means method (Figure 10.11).

With the classified altitude mapping, the use of classification enables simplification of the detailing of information from the original map into 5 altitude classes. If it is necessary to differentiate the management of the property according to altitude classes, the number of pixels within each class can be obtained and the area in which it will be necessary to provide strategies and tactics

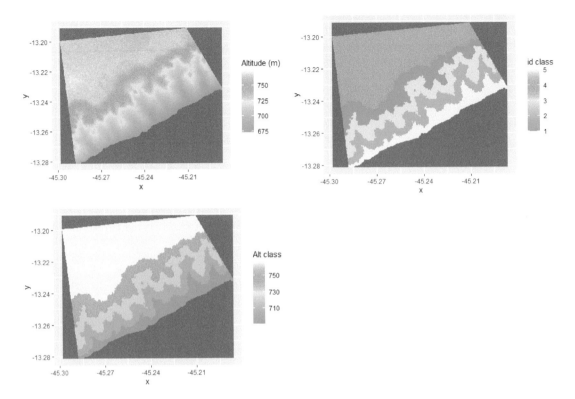

Figure 10.11 Unsupervised classification of altitude (top-left) by the k-means method, Hartigan-Wong algorithm with 5 altitude classes identified by the class number (top-right) or by the threshold of each altitude class defined by clustering (bottom-left), in a rural property, state of Bahia, Brazil.

for intervention in the environment considering the entire property with homogeneous regions of management within each class can be determined.

Considering the size of the altitude pixel with a spatial resolution of 30 m, it is possible to estimate the area of each altitude class of the classified and recoded image with actual altitude ranges defined by the k-means method (Table 10.1). For more accurate area determinations it may be necessary to include the curvature of the Earth in the calculations or to consider transforming the data geometry to a flat map projection, but the method used here can be well applied for small areas, provided the image pixel size is known.

Table 10.1 Estimated area of altitude classes defined by unsupervised k-means classification in a rural property, state of Bahia, Brazil.

Altitude Threshold Class (m)	Area (ha)
690.875	857.43
705.850	1143.27
722.3889	1210.32
741.500	1083.60
766.7619	3123.54

```
r <-alt
app<-30*30
am<-table(r[]) * app
aha<-am/10000
aha
```

Thus, it is possible to verify that the altitude class defined in the highest part of the terrain is observed in the largest mapped area, in the amount of 3123.54 ha.

The geodetic area calculation can be performed with the expanse function of the terra package. Using the terra package it is possible to perform operations with vectors and rasters in the same package and sometimes with the same function name, as in the case of area calculation. The raster r is transformed into the class SpatRaster with the rast function, and the object r1 is created.

```
r1 <-rast(r)
r1
#class        : SpatRaster
#dimensions   : 325, 403, 1   (nrow, ncol, nlyr)
#resolution   : 0.0002777778, 0.0002777778  (x, y)
#extent       : -45.29819, -45.18625, -13.28125, -13.19097   (xmin, xmax, ymin, ymax)
#coord. ref. : +proj=longlat +datum=WGS84 +no_defs
#source(s)    : memory
#name         :     class
#min value    : 690.8750
#max value    : 766.7619
```

The expanse function is used to calculate the geodetic area in ha. The byValue=TRUE argument is used to calculate the area of each altitude threshold defined by the clustering.

```
expanse(r1, unit="ha", transform=FALSE, byValue=TRUE)
#      layer     value       area
#[1,]      1 690.8750   881.3844
#[2,]      1 705.8500 1175.2302
#[3,]      1 722.3889 1244.1929
#[4,]      1 741.5000 1113.9535
#[5,]      1 766.7619 3211.2665
```

You can see that the area values are higher than those defined in Table 10.1, since the pixel value is not fixed at 30m, and the variation of the curvature of the Earth is considered in this new area calculation. In the case of using remote sensing data with coordinates in a plane projection system, the argument transform = TRUE can be used to transform the coordinates into lon/lat and increase the accuracy of results.

10.10.4   Unsupervised classification on multiple images

Unsupervised classification can be used to extract thematic information from the area and calculate the area of objects with a similar pattern detected in the scene. The k-means random forest classification is used in a perspective to classify big remote sensing data acquired from the Funil dam, state of Minas Gerais, based on the knowledge acquired in previous classes.

Spectral indices were calculated and the images stacked with raster data from Landsat-8 OLI/TIRS (June 28, 2021), Sentinel-1 (June 25, 2021) and Sentinel-2 (June 28, 2021) imaging, respectively, obtained in the region of the Funil dam in Minas Gerais. After unpacking the file into a directory of interest, the `stack` and `names` functions are used to import and rename the spectral variables used in the classification.

```
bigdata <- stack("C:/sr/c10/bdsub.tif")
names(bigdata) <- c("costal","blue","green","red","nir","swir2","swir3",
"swir1","tir1","tir2","brightness","greenness","wetness","CTVI.1",
"DVI.1","EVI.1","EVI2","GEMI.1","GNDVI.1","MNDWI.1","MSAVI.1",
"MSAVI2.1","NBRI.1","NDVI.1","NDWI.1","NDWI2.1","NRVI.1","RVI.1",
"SATVI.1","SAVI.1","S1B_IW_GRDH_1SDV_20210628T082946_Cal_Spk_TC.3",
"S1B_IW_GRDH_1SDV_20210628T082946_Cal_Spk_TC.4",
"T23KNS_20210625T131249_B02_10m", "T23KNS_20210625T131249_B03_10m",
"T23KNS_20210625T131249_B04_10m", "T23KNS_20210625T131249_B05_20m",
"T23KNS_20210625T131249_B06_20m", "T23KNS_20210625T131249_B07_20m",
"T23KNS_20210625T131249_B08_10m", "T23KNS_20210625T131249_B8A_20m",
"T23KNS_20210625T131249_B09_60m", "T23KNS_20210625T131249_B11_20m",
"T23KNS_20210625T131249_B12_20m", "CLG", "CLRE","CTVI.2","DVI.2",
"EVI.2","GEMI.2","GNDVI.2","MCARI", "MNDWI.2","MSAVI.2","MSAVI2.2",
"NBRI.2","NDREI1","NDREI2","NDVI.2", "NDWI.2","NDWI2.2","NRVI.2",
"RVI.2","SATVI.2","SAVI.2","SLAVI","SR","WDVI")
```

The `getValues` function is used to extract values from the raster images used in the classification, and the `which(!is.na())` and `na.omit` functions are used so that missing data (`NA`) is not considered in the analysis.

```
v <- getValues(bigdata)
i <- which(!is.na(v))
v <- na.omit(v)
```

A sample data set `vx` is obtained using 500 samples with the use of the `sample(nrow())` function. Then the `randomForest` function is used to create 1000 random trees used for unsupervised classification by the k-means method.

```
vx<-v[sample(nrow(v), 500),]
rf <- randomForest(vx)
rf_prox <- randomForest(vx,ntree = 1000, proximity = TRUE)$proximity
```

The classification is performed considering a comparative total number of 3, 4, 5, and 6 classes in order to visually determine the pattern recognition results of the classifier. The `kmeans` function is used and the number of classes parameter is varied, with the other parameters remaining identical for the purpose of comparing the results of the classifier. Finally, the `randomForest` function is used to perform the final model fitting and the `predict` function to predict the results using the raster stacked with the remote sensing big data.

```
# Classification k-means random forest 3 classes
E_rf3 <- kmeans(rf_prox, 3, iter.max = 100, nstart = 5)
rf3 <- randomForest(vx,as.factor(E_rf3$cluster),ntree = 500)
rf_raster3<- predict(bigdata,rf3)
```

```
# Classification k-means random forest 4 classes
E_rf4 <- kmeans(rf_prox, 4, iter.max = 100, nstart = 5)
rf4 <- randomForest(vx,as.factor(E_rf4$cluster),ntree = 500)
rf_raster4<- predict(bigdata,rf4)
# Classification k-means random forest 5 classes
E_rf5 <- kmeans(rf_prox, 5, iter.max = 100, nstart = 5)
rf5 <- randomForest(vx,as.factor(E_rf5$cluster),ntree = 500)
rf_raster5<- predict(bigdata,rf5)
# Classification k-means random forest 6 classes
E_rf6 <- kmeans(rf_prox, 6, iter.max = 100, nstart = 5)
rf6 <- randomForest(vx,as.factor(E_rf6$cluster),ntree = 500)
rf_raster6<- predict(bigdata,rf6)
```

The results of each algorithm can be mapped comparatively using the `plot` function (Figure 10.12).

```
plot(rf_raster3)
plot(rf_raster4)
plot(rf_raster5)
plot(rf_raster6)
```

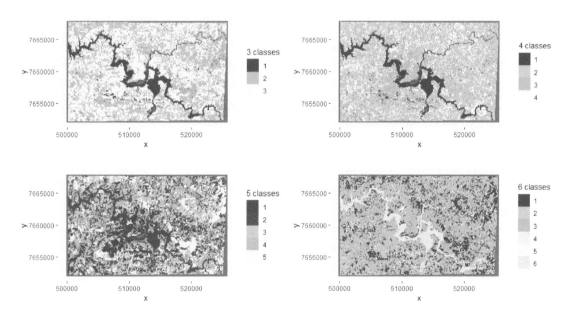

Figure 10.12 Unsupervised classification by the k-means method, random forest algorithm with 3, 4, 5, and 6 classes of patterns recognized by clustering (bottom-left), in the region of the Funil dam, state of Minas Gerais, Brazil.

As shown in the mapping results, there was a mixture of targets among the evaluated classification methods, which made it difficult, a priori, to determine the optimal number of classes to be used to exactly separate the targets in the image.

The most important variables used in the classification can be evaluated with the `importance` functions to get the numerical result, or with the `varImpPlot` function to get the graphical result, based on the Gini index criteria.

```
importance(rf3)
importance(rf4)
importance(rf5)
importance(rf6)
```

The graphical result with the ranking of the first 20 most important variables used in the ranking is configured using the parameter n.var=20 (Figure 10.13).

```
par(mfrow=c(2,2))
varImpPlot(rf3, n.var=20, main="3 classes")
varImpPlot(rf4, n.var=20, main="4 classes")
varImpPlot(rf5, n.var=20, main="5 classes")
varImpPlot(rf6, n.var=20, main="6 classes")
```

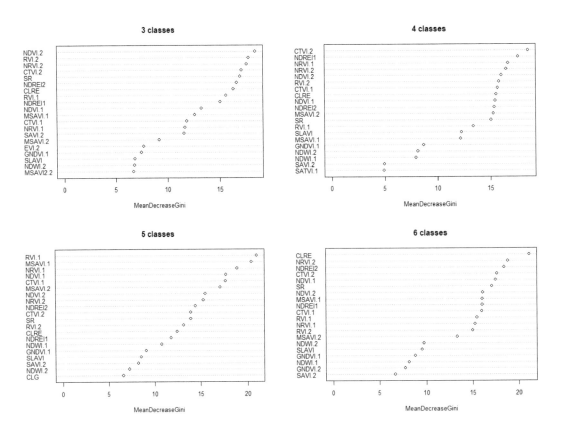

Figure 10.13 Ranking of the 20 main variables considered by the random forest algorithm in the unsupervised k-means classification with 3,4,5, and 6 classes, in the region of the Funil dam, state of Minas Gerais, Brazil.

With this, we observed that the combination of biophysical and terrain variables can be useful in pattern recognition of remote sensing images by unsupervised classification, random forest algorithm, k-means clustering method. However, we should evaluate the number of classes that will be considered as reference in mapping.

Models fitted with 3, 4, 5, and 6 classes by the unsupervised classification are exported for further use in spatial prediction using the saveRDS function.

```
saveRDS(rf3, "C:/sr/c9/rfbdsub3.RDS")
saveRDS(rf4, "C:/sr/c9/rfbdsub4.RDS")
saveRDS(rf5, "C:/sr/c9/rfbdsub5.RDS")
saveRDS(rf6, "C:/sr/c9/rfbdsub6.RDS")
```

10.10.5 Unsupervised image segmentation

An R7G6B5 Landsat-8 OLI color composition is used as an example of unsupervised classification with the superpixels and clustering methods.

A file in the `.jpeg` extension is exported from R from a color composition and is performed from the previous example data with the use of the `plotRGB` function (Figure 10.14).

```
jpeg(file= "C:/sr/c9/lsatR7G6B5.jpeg")
plotRGB(bigdata, r=7, g=6, b=5, axes=F, stretch="lin")
dev.off()
```

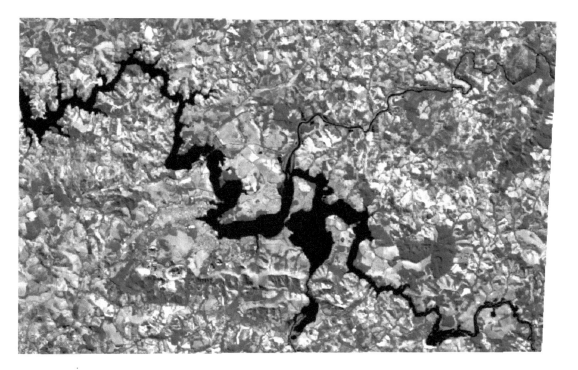

Figure 10.14 R7G6B5 color composite used for unsupervised segmentation of Funil dam images, state of Minas Gerais, on June 28, 2021.

The image is imported back into R using the `OpenImageR` package (Mouselimis et al., 2022) and the `readImage` function.

```
im <- OpenImageR::readImage("C:/sr/c9/lsatR7G6B5.jpeg")
```

Segmentation based on SLIC superpixels and affinity propagation clustering is performed with the unsupervised classification parameter setting as described below.

```
init <- Image_Segmentation$new()
spx <- init$spixel_segmentation(input_image = im,
                                superpixel = 600,
                                AP_data = TRUE,
                                use_median = TRUE,
                                sim_wL = 3,
                                sim_wA = 10,
                                sim_wB = 10,
                                sim_color_radius = 10,
                                verbose = TRUE)
```

Affinity propagation completed after 131 iterations, determining the choice of 6 clusters based on superpixels and affinity propagation.

The segmentation results are mapped with the imageShow function (Figure 10.15).

```
OpenImageR::imageShow(spx$AP_image_data)
```

Figure 10.15 R7G6B5 color composite segmentation used in the unsupervised segmentation of Funil dam images, state of Minas Gerais, on June 28, 2021.

10.11 Exercises

10.11.1 Briefly define digital image classification.

10.11.2 What are the advantages and disadvantages of unsupervised classification of digital images?

10.11.3 Cite three methods of defining distances in attribute space for unsupervised classification of digital images.

10.11.4 Cite three algorithms for unsupervised classification of digital images.

10.11.5 What is the basic difference between pixel-by-pixel and object-based classification?

10.11.6 Determine the Euclidean distance of pixels.

Pixel values are presented to determine the Euclidean distance between vertices A and B in bands 1 to 4 of Landsat-8 image (Table 10.2).

Table 10.2 Values of pixels A and B in multiple bands of Landsat-8.

Pixel	Band 1	Band 2	Band 3	Band 4
A	34	28	22	6
B	26	16	52	29

10.11.7 Classifying pixel data A, B, and C

Given that the interest of a remote sensing analyst is to classify pixel data A, B, and C, determine the Euclidean distance between A, B; B, C and A, C and propose a criterion for separating the pixels into only two classes (Table 10.3).

Table 10.3 Values of pixels A, B, and C in multiple bands of Landsat-8.

Pixel	Band 1	Band 2	Band 3	Band 4
A	5	10	15	15
B	25	30	35	38
c	18	25	23	20

10.12   Homework

10.12.1   Subject

Unsupervised segmentation analysis applied to multispectral imaging from CBERS-04A satellite monitoring urban and rural environments.

10.12.2   Assignment

Develop the subject presented with a practical application of remote sensing and digital image processing including the topics Introduction and Objective. Then present the development of the task.

10.13   Resources on the Internet

As a study guide, slides and illustrative videos are presented about the subject covered in the chapter (Table 10.4).

Table 10.4 Slide show and video presentation on scientific applications of unsupervised classification of remote sensing imagery.

Guide	Address for Access
1	How does unsupervised machine learning with k-means work?[2]
2	Introduction to the k-means algorithm[3]
3	Slides about unsupervised classification of digital images[4]

10.14   Research Suggestion

The development of scientific research on remote sensing for unsupervised classification of remote sensing imagery is stimulated through activity proposals that can be used or adapted by the student to assess the applicability of the subject matter covered in the chapter (Table 10.5).

---

[2] https://youtu.be/xjpzDx_nywc
[3] https://youtu.be/WqMnQuC19Rg
[4] http://www.sergeo.deg.ufla.br/sr/Presentation/Aula9/presentation.html#/

Table 10.5 Practical and research activities used or adapted by students using remote sensing for unsupervised classification of remote sensing imagery.

Activity	Description
1	Perform unsupervised classification of a Landsat-8 OLI image in a given area.
2	Perform unsupervised classification of a digital elevation model of a given area.

11

Supervised Classification of Remote Sensing Images

11.1 Learning Questions

The learning questions answered through reading the chapter are as follows:

- What is the difference between supervised and unsupervised classification?
- How are training samples for classification identified?
- How is supervised classification of remotely sensed images performed?
- How are training samples for supervised classification obtained?
- How are supervised classification algorithms used?

11.2 Learning Outcomes

Using the learning outcomes from the chapter, you should be able to do the following:

- Understand the difference between supervised and unsupervised classification.
- Identify training samples for supervised classification.
- Perform supervised classification of remotely sensed images.
- Obtain training samples to perform supervised classification.
- Use a supervised classification algorithm.

11.3 Introduction

Digital image classification is the process of assigning classes to pixels to determine similarity groups associated with the information of interest in remote sensing. The purpose of classification is to generate a thematic digital map with satisfactory accuracy for a given application. Useful thematic information can be obtained by supervised classification algorithms. The analyst must specify the geographical regions of interest (ROI) in which the classification hypotheses will be tested. The classes of interest must be carefully defined in a classification scheme to generate continuous or discrete products according to the appropriate logic, either pixel-by-pixel or object-based. Field reference data should be obtained at the same time as the remote sensing data is obtained. Additional training data may be required to obtain the final classified map. After the classification accuracy analysis, if the results are acceptable, the final map can be distributed for use by the community of interest (Jensen, 2005).

A good option for visual inspection of ROI samples or area reconnaissance is to define the contour coordinates using points or polygons with attributes, according to the following procedures:

- Obtain regions of interest on site visit and precisely define the target with geodetic coordinates;
- Define a region of interest and evaluate the area with data available on the Internet;
- Obtain regions of interest from another project and perform the update by editing the original database;
- Use the result of a reliable classification as training to perform another classification with a larger number of training samples.

The ROI can be evaluated and compared based on very high resolution remote sensing imagery available on the Internet, as in the case of the data obtained from **Geoportal do Café**[1]. This data is used in this chapter as a reference for the location of coffee plantations after checking and editing the geometry of the database with a negative buffer of 20 m in the polygons of coffee plantations and coding of the attribute class, in this case number 1. It is worth mentioning that the reliability of results depends on the reliability and number of samples used in the training of the classification algorithm, resulting in different mapping results according to the quality of these data.

As an example of manipulating vector data defined by geometries around targets of interest in the landscape, an example is performed for automatic mapping of coffee crops from training supervised classification algorithms. The `library` function is used to enable packages needed to manipulate the training samples in R.

```
library(raster)
library(sf)
library(mapview)
```

Some polygons extracted from the Geoportal do Café data are obtained in the region around the Funil dam, state of Minas Gerais. The `st_read` function is used to import the polygons where there were coffee crops in the 2018 harvest. The `st_crs` function is used to assign a reference coordinate system to the polygons from the `EPSG = 4326` code.

```
cafesub <- st_read('C:/geo/c8/cafesub.shp')
st_crs(cafesub) <- 4326
cafesub
#Simple feature collection with 3 features and 2 fields
#Geometry type: MULTIPOLYGON
#Dimension:     XY
#Bounding box:  xmin: -44.99985 ymin: -21.2314 xmax: -44.75518 ymax: -21.09206
#Geodetic CRS:  WGS 84
#    AREA_ha   area                        geometry
#1 123010.2 427783 MULTIPOLYGON (((-44.80944 -...
#2 190657.6 427783 MULTIPOLYGON (((-44.99985 -...
#3 180190.7 427783 MULTIPOLYGON (((-44.99985 -...
```

The data consists of a simple feature collection with 3 features and 2 fields, geometry `MULTIPOLYGON` and dimension `XY`. The reference geodetic datum is `WGS-84`. The geometries are reduced to polygon features with the `st_cast` function.

---

[1]https://portaldocafedeminas.emater.mg.gov.br/

```
pl <- st_cast(cafesub, "POLYGON")
pl
#Simple feature collection with 463 features and 2 fields
#Geometry type: POLYGON
#Dimension:     XY
#Bounding box:  xmin: -44.99985 ymin: -21.2314 xmax: -44.75518 ymax: -21.09206
#Geodetic CRS:  WGS 84
#First 10 features:
#     AREA_ha   area                          geometry
#1    123010.2 427783 POLYGON ((-44.80944 -21.149...
#1.1  123010.2 427783 POLYGON ((-44.8029 -21.1541...
#1.2  123010.2 427783 POLYGON ((-44.76045 -21.194...
#2    190657.6 427783 POLYGON ((-44.99985 -21.094...
#2.1  190657.6 427783 POLYGON ((-44.99985 -21.097...
#2.2  190657.6 427783 POLYGON ((-44.99985 -21.103...
#2.3  190657.6 427783 POLYGON ((-44.99985 -21.105...
#2.4  190657.6 427783 POLYGON ((-44.99985 -21.108...
#2.5  190657.6 427783 POLYGON ((-44.99985 -21.109...
#2.6  190657.6 427783 POLYGON ((-44.99775 -21.107...
```

Thereby, 463 features of polygons of coffee crops in the evaluated geographic region are obtained. An interactive map of the crop location is made with the `mapview` function.

```
mapview(pl)
```

The distribution of crops occurred mainly in the north and west of the region, leaving a gap without coffee crops to the south of the Hydroelectric Power Plant of Funil reservoir (Figure 11.1).

The data with polygons of coffee crops are exported for further use with the `st_write` function.

```
st_write(pl, dsn = "C:/sr/c10/plcafe1.shp")
```

11.4   Supervised Classification

In supervised classification, the identity of land use targets is known a priori. Target recognition can be done by a combination of *in situ* data collection, image interpretation, maps of the region studied, and analyst experience. The identity of targets in regions of interest is used to train the classification algorithm. Parameters and statistical indices are calculated and a class is associated with each pixel.

In addition to the previously used packages, the `dplyr` package is enabled to manipulate polygon attribute data and assign distinct classes to each landscape target.

```
library(dplyr)
```

Figure 11.1 Evaluating the quality of training samples in the coffee growing class using interactive web mapping at Funil dam, state of Minas Gerais, Brazil.

Polygons with other targets observed in the area by color composition of Google Earth images are delineated in the same geographic region, and polygons of tree vegetation, grassland, bare ground, water, and urbanized areas with buildings are defined. The st_read function is used to import the polygons with coffee crops into R.

```
plcafe<-st_read("C:/sr/c10/plcafe1.shp")
```

The AREA_ha, area columns are removed from the attribute table (data.frame) using the select function.

```
plcafe <- dplyr::select(plcafe, -AREA_ha, -area)
```

The mutate function is used to create a column of class 1 assigned to the coffee polygons.

```
plcafe <- plcafe %>% mutate(class = 1)
```

The other targets of interest in the region are preprocessed similarly, except that there is an additional step of transforming the reference coordinate system from EPSG = 32723 (WGS-84, UTM, 23 S) to EPSG = 4326 (WGS-84). The assigned classes are water (class = 2), urbanized areas with buildings (class = 3), native tree vegetation (class = 4), bare soil (class = 5), and grassland (class = 6), for a total of six classes including coffee plantations (class = 1).

The vectors with attributes are imported with the `st_read` function.

```
agua <- st_read("C:/sr/c10/agua.shp")
urbana <- st_read("C:/sr/c10/Area_Urbana.shp")
vegetacao <- st_read("C:/sr/c10/vegetacao.shp")
solo <- st_read("C:/sr/c10/Solo_Exposto.shp")
pastagem <- st_read("C:/sr/c10/Pastagem.shp")
#Reading layer `Agua' from data source using driver `ESRI Shapefile'
#Simple feature collection with 54 features and 2 fields
#Geometry type: POLYGON
#Dimension:     XY
#Bounding box:  xmin: 500138.9 ymin: 7652742 xmax: 520797.1 ymax: 7665805
#Projected CRS: WGS 84 / UTM zone 23S
#Reading layer `Area_Urbana' from data source using driver `ESRI Shapefile'
#Simple feature collection with 53 features and 2 fields
#Geometry type: POLYGON
#Dimension:     XY
#Bounding box:  xmin: 500037.1 ymin: 7652217 xmax: 515070.8 ymax: 7662582
#Projected CRS: WGS 84 / UTM zone 23S
#Reading layer `Vegetacao' from data source using driver `ESRI Shapefile'
#Simple feature collection with 71 features and 2 fields
#Geometry type: POLYGON
#Dimension:     XY
#Bounding box:  xmin: 504434.6 ymin: 7652705 xmax: 525296.7 ymax: 7666209
#Projected CRS: WGS 84 / UTM zone 23S
#Reading layer `Solo_Exposto' from data source using driver `ESRI Shapefile'
#Simple feature collection with 60 features and 2 fields
#Geometry type: POLYGON
#Dimension:     XY
#Bounding box:  xmin: 500042 ymin: 7652689 xmax: 521619.2 ymax: 7662465
#Projected CRS: WGS 84 / UTM zone 23S
#Reading layer `Pastagem' from data source using driver `ESRI Shapefile'
#Simple feature collection with 51 features and 2 fields
#Geometry type: POLYGON
#Dimension:     XY
#Bounding box:  xmin: 510419.8 ymin: 7655361 xmax: 518056.9 ymax: 7663343
#Projected CRS: WGS 84 / UTM zone 23S
```

Note that the files consist of simple feature collection, with 54, 53, 71, 60, and 51 features in geometry of water polygons, urban area, tree vegetation, bare ground, and grassland, respectively. The `st_transform` function is used in the transformation between reference coordinate systems.

```
aguawgs <- st_transform(agua, crs=4326)
urbanawgs <- st_transform(urbana, crs=4326)
vegwgs <- st_transform(vegetacao, crs=4326)
solowgs <- st_transform(solo, crs=4326)
pastagemwgs <- st_transform(pastagem, crs=4326)
```

Unused columns in the attribute table are removed with the `select` function.

```
aguawgs <- dplyr::select(aguawgs,-id, -Classe)
urbanawgs <- dplyr::select(urbanawgs,-id, -Classe)
vegwgs <- dplyr::select(vegwgs,-id, -Classe)
solowgs <- dplyr::select(solowgs,-id, -Classe)
pastagemwgs <- dplyr::select(pastagemwgs,-id, -Classe)
```

The classes of interest are assigned to the polygons of each target with the `mutate` function.

```
aguawgs <- aguawgs %>% mutate(class = 2)
urbanawgs <- urbanawgs %>% mutate(class = 3)
vegwgs <- vegwgs %>% mutate(class = 4)
solowgs <- solowgs %>% mutate(class = 5)
pastagemwgs <- pastagemwgs %>% mutate(class = 6)
```

The `rbind` function is used to gather all polygon features of each class into a single file.

```
classid<-rbind(plcafe,aguawgs, urbanawgs, vegwgs, solowgs, pastagemwgs)
classid
#Simple feature collection with 752 features and 1 field
#Geometry type: POLYGON
#Dimension:     XY
#Bounding box:  xmin: -44.99985 ymin: -21.23163 xmax: -44.75518 ymax: -21.09206
#Geodetic CRS:  WGS 84
#First 10 features:
#    class                        geometry
#1       1 POLYGON ((-44.80944 -21.149...
#2       1 POLYGON ((-44.8029 -21.1541...
#3       1 POLYGON ((-44.76045 -21.194...
#4       1 POLYGON ((-44.99985 -21.094...
#5       1 POLYGON ((-44.99985 -21.097...
#6       1 POLYGON ((-44.99985 -21.103...
#7       1 POLYGON ((-44.99985 -21.105...
#8       1 POLYGON ((-44.99985 -21.108...
#9       1 POLYGON ((-44.99985 -21.109...
#10      1 POLYGON ((-44.99775 -21.107...
```

This yields a simple feature collection with 762 features and 1 field with the class of each file. The polygons are mapped with the `mapview` function.

```
mapview(classid, layer.name = 'classidsp')
```

The polygons were well distributed around almost the entire study region, except for a few sparse regions that can be filled in future studies for more critical modeling (Figure 11.2).

The file is exported for later use with the `st_write` function.

```
st_write(classid, dsn = "C:/sr/c10/classid1.shp")
```

Figure 11.2 Interactive mapping of regions of interest on coffee crop targets (1), water (2), urban landscape (3), forest (4), bare soil (5), and grassland (6) to sample pixels per training class to perform supervised classification at Funil dam, state of Minas Gerais, Brazil.

The advantages of supervised classification when compared to the unsupervised classification method are (Campbell & Wynne, 2011):

- The analyst can control the classes used for training in geographic regions of interest;
- Training data is known in the region;
- Spectral mixing between classes can be minimized by choosing distinct training data features;
- The analyst can detect classification errors by examining the training data and the results of the classifier algorithm.

The disadvantages of supervised classification are (Campbell & Wynne, 2011):

- A classification structure is imposed on the data by the analyst;
- The classes defined by the analyst may not be distinct in multidimensional space;
- Training data is chosen first on the basis of classes and then on the basis of spectral features;
- Training data may not be representative of the conditions observed in the entire image;
- The process of choosing training data can be time-consuming, expensive and tiring;
- Overlapping problems in choosing classes according to the spatial resolution of the image used;
- Recognition of specific classes may not be possible in the images if they are not included in the training data, due to lack of knowledge or because they occupy small areas in the image.

11.5 Steps for Supervised Classification

The steps for supervised classification are:

- Selection of the classes that will be mapped on the image;
- Selection and definition of training data;

- Modification of training data to meet classification quality requirements;
- Classification of the image;
- Evaluation of classification quality.

11.6   Key Characteristics of Training Areas

Training samples are used in some regions of the image in a machine learning process to train algorithms by computational intelligence to classify the entire image based on the given patterns.

Important characteristics considered when selecting training areas are:

- Number of pixels (preferably 100 pixels per class);
- Size (selecting smaller areas generally determines greater homogeneity);
- Shape (varied);
- Location (different locations on the image);
- Uniformity (look for homogeneity).

11.6.1   Exploratory analysis of training regions

Exploratory analysis can be performed with summary statistics, boxplots, histogram analysis, and barplots. As an example of application, samples are extracted from Landsat-8, Sentinel-1, Sentinel-2 imagery data and indices derived from these images to evaluate the spectral signature of targets according to the comparative magnitude variation of each variable for each target with the use of a barplot.

A multisensor remote sensing big data is used for identification of coffee crops and other environmental targets in the Funil dam area, state of Minas Gerais, Brazil. The Landsat-8 OLI/TIRS imagery data are from imagery performed on June 28, 2021, Sentinel-1 GRD and Sentinel-2 on June 25, 2021. The data are imported in R with the `stack` function and renamed with the `names` function.

```
bigdata<-stack("C:/sr/c10/bdsub.tif")
names(bigdata)<-c("costal","blue","green","red","nir","swir2",
"swir3","swir1","tir1","tir2","brightness","greenness","wetness",
"CTVI.1","DVI.1","EVI.1","EVI2","GEMI.1","GNDVI.1","MNDWI.1","MSAVI.1",
"MSAVI2.1","NBRI.1","NDVI.1","NDWI.1","NDWI2.1","NRVI.1","RVI.1",
"SATVI.1","SAVI.1","S1B_IW_GRDH_1SDV_20210628T082946_Cal_Spk_TC.3",
"S1B_IW_GRDH_1SDV_20210628T082946_Cal_Spk_TC.4",
"T23KNS_20210625T131249_B02_10m","T23KNS_20210625T131249_B03_10m",
 "T23KNS_20210625T131249_B04_10m","T23KNS_20210625T131249_B05_20m",
 "T23KNS_20210625T131249_B06_20m","T23KNS_20210625T131249_B07_20m",
 "T23KNS_20210625T131249_B08_10m","T23KNS_20210625T131249_B8A_20m",
 "T23KNS_20210625T131249_B09_60m","T23KNS_20210625T131249_B11_20m",
 "T23KNS_20210625T131249_B12_20m","CLG","CLRE","CTVI.2","DVI.2",
 "EVI.2","GEMI.2","GNDVI.2","MCARI","MNDWI.2","MSAVI.2","MSAVI2.2",
 "NBRI.2","NDREI1","NDREI2","NDVI.2","NDWI.2","NDWI2.2","NRVI.2",
"RVI.2","SATVI.2","SAVI.2","SLAVI"  , "SR" , "WDVI")
```

A `RasterStack` file is obtained at 10-m spatial resolution and 67 layers.

```
bigdata
#class       : RasterStack
#dimensions : 1587, 2580, 4094460, 67   (nrow, ncol, ncell, nlayers)
#resolution : 10, 10   (x, y)
#extent      : 499835.6, 525635.6, 7651972, 7667842   (xmin, xmax, ymin, ymax)
#crs         : +proj=utm +zone=23 +south +datum=WGS84 +units=m +no_defs
```

The polygon features are reprojected to a Cartesian plane coordinate system with the same transformation parameters as the raster layers, in order to be able to sample the raster from the vector data in the same coordinate system.

```
classidprj<-st_transform(classid, crs=32723)
```

The polygon features with the target classes of interest in the region are transformed into `SpatialPolygonsDataFrame` with the `as_Spatial` function.

```
classidsp <- as_Spatial(classidprj)
classidsp
#class       : SpatialPolygonsDataFrame
#features    : 752
#extent      : 500015.6, 525425.6, 7652217, 7667662   (xmin, xmax, ymin, ymax)
#crs         : +proj=utm +zone=23 +south +datum=WGS84 +units=m +no_defs
#variables   : 1
#names       : class
#min values  :     1
#max values  :     6
```

The polygons are converted into a raster layer to later sample the imagery data and evaluate pixel brightness results obtained within each class.

```
poligonos_raster <- rasterize(classidsp, bigdata, field = "class")
poligonos_raster
#class       : RasterLayer
#dimensions : 1587, 2580, 4094460   (nrow, ncol, ncell)
#resolution : 10, 10   (x, y)
#extent      : 499835.6, 525635.6, 7651972, 7667842   (xmin, xmax, ymin, ymax)
#crs         : +proj=utm +zone=23 +south +datum=WGS84 +units=m +no_defs
#source      : memory
#names       : layer
#values      : 1, 6   (min, max)
```

A color palette is proposed for mapping targets in the `RasterLayer` class. The `plot` function is used for mapping the raster layer (Figure 11.3).

```
plot(poligonos_raster, col=c("DarkOliveGreen", "blue", "grey", "ForestGreen",
                            "brown", "LightGreen"))
```

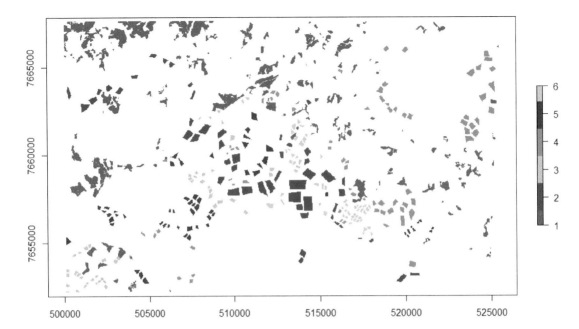

Figure 11.3 Raster polygon mapping of sample targets in coffee crops (1), water (2), urban landscape (3), forest (4), bare soil (5), and grassland (6) in the Funil dam region, state of Minas Gerais, Brazil.

A zonal spatial analysis is performed to obtain the average value of each big data variable for each raster class value. The zonal function is used with the fun=mean argument to obtain the mean values of the imagery variables.

```
cafe_zonal <- zonal(bigdata, poligonos_raster, fun="mean", na.rm=TRUE)
class(cafe_zonal)
#[1] "matrix" "array"
```

An object of class matrix array is obtained as a result of the analysis. The matrix transpose is performed for exploratory analysis graphs.

```
assinatura <- t(cafe_zonal)
```

A barplot is made for exploratory analysis of mean values of spectral variables from Landsat-8 OLI sampled at targets relative to coffee crops (1), water (2), urban landscape (3), forest (4), bare soil (5), and grassland (6) in the Funil dam region, state of Minas Gerais, Brazil. A subset of the matrix data values in rows 2 to 9 is taken for plotting. Colors and legends are created for the identification of targets and spectral regions considered in the imagery.

```
par(mfrow = c(1, 1),mar = c(3.5, 4.0, 0.5, 5), mgp = c(2.0, 0.5, 0.0))
colors <- c("skyblue","blue","green","red","brown","black","grey50","grey")
Target <- c('1','2','3','4','5','6')
bands <- c("costal","blue","green","red","nir","swir2","swir3","swir1")
Values <- matrix(c(assinatura[2:9,]), nrow = 8, ncol = 6, byrow = F)
barplot(Values, main = "", names.arg = Target, xlab = "Target",
```

```
            ylab = "Spectral target information", col = colors)
legend("topleft", bands, cex = 0.9, fill = colors, xpd=TRUE, inset=c(0.98,0))
```

The exploratory analysis shows that there are different effects on the spectral response of each target in relation to the Landsat-8 OLI spectral bands in the reflective spectrum region. It is observed that water presented the lowest spectral response followed by forest, coffee crops, grassland, urban landscape, and bare soil (Figure 11.4).

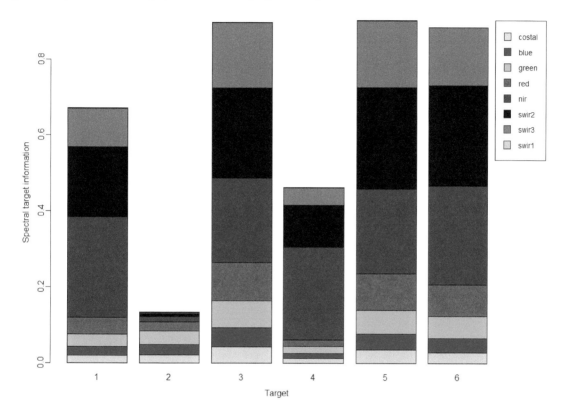

Figure 11.4 Using barplots as exploratory analysis of Landsat-8 spectral variables used in supervised classification of targets in coffee crops (1), water (2), urban landscape (3), forest (4), bare soil (5), and grassland (6) in the Funil dam region, state of Minas Gerais, Brazil.

The previous code is adapted to obtain Sentinel-2 imagery information. Minor modifications are made to the color palette, band name and data row in the spectral signature matrix.

```
par(mfrow = c(1, 1),mar = c(3.5, 4.0, 0.5, 5), mgp = c(2.0, 0.5, 0.0))
colors <- c("blue","green","red","maroon","darkred","brown","firebrick","tomato",
            "black", "grey50", "grey")
Target <- c('1','2','3','4','5','6')
bands <- c("blue","green","red","nir5","nirb6","nirb7","nirb8","nirb8a",
           "swirb9","swirb11","swirb12")
Values <- matrix(c(assinatura[34:44,]), nrow = 11, ncol = 6, byrow = F)
barplot(Values, main = "", names.arg = Target, xlab = "Target",
        ylab = "Spectral target information", col = colors)
legend("topright", bands, cex = 0.9, fill = colors, xpd=TRUE, inset=c(-0.10,0))
```

Regarding Sentinel-2 imagery data, there was higher energy absorption in the water targets followed by forest, coffee crops, bare soil, urban landscape and grassland (Figure 11.5). The difference between the Landsat-8 results is due in this case to the different spectral regions of bands obtained with Sentinel-2 imagery.

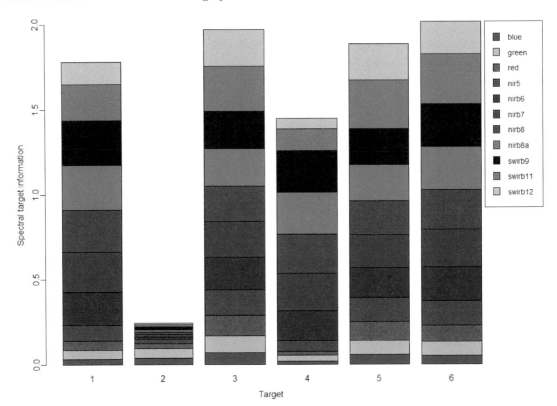

Figure 11.5 Using barplots as exploratory analysis of Sentinel-2 spectral variables used in supervised classification of targets in coffee crops (1), water (2), urban landscape (3), forest (4), bare soil (5), and grassland (6) in the Funil dam region, state of Minas Gerais, Brazil.

The same code is also adapted to evaluate the Sentinel-1 GRD data signature in vertical horizontal (s0VH) and vertical vertical (s0VV) polarizations.

```
par(mfrow = c(1, 1),mar = c(3.5, 4.0, 0.5, 1), mgp = c(2.0, 0.5, 0.0))
colors <- c("black","grey")
Target <- c('1','2','3','4','5','6')
bands <- c("s0VH","s0VV")
Values <- matrix(c(assinatura[32:33,]), nrow = 2, ncol = 6, byrow = F)
barplot(Values, main = "", names.arg = Target, xlab = "Target",
        ylab = "Spectral target information", col = colors)
legend("bottomleft", bands, cex = 0.9, fill = colors)
```

The Sentinel-1 backscatter in the VH and VV polarizations, calibrated and noise-corrected (sigma0), showed the most negative values in the water targets, followed by bare soil, grassland, coffee crops, urban landscape, and forest (Figure 11.6).

The spectral signature of variables can also be performed with a continuous two-dimensional plot of the variation of each band used in the analysis according to the reflexive, thermal infrared and

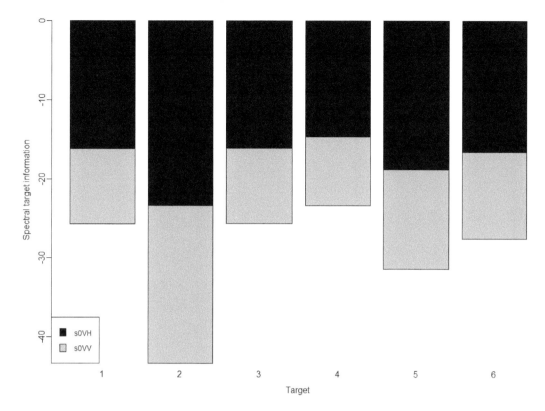

Figure 11.6 Using barplots as exploratory analysis of Sentinel-1 spectral variables used in supervised classification of targets in coffee crops (1), water (2), urban landscape (3), forest (4), bare soil (5), and grassland (6) in the Funil dam region, state of Minas Gerais, Brazil.

RADAR range spectra on the y axis and the wavelength on the x axis for each target analyzed with the Sentinel-1,2 and Landsat-8 satellite sensors.

A chunk of code is also developed to characterize the spectral signature of each target in the form of continuous lines according to the wavelength variation of the blue, green, red, nir, swir2, and swir3 bands (bands 3 to 8 of the big data).

```
par(mfrow = c(1, 1),mar = c(3.5, 4.0, 0.5, 1), mgp = c(2.0, 0.5, 0.0))
plot(0, ylim=c(0,0.4), xlim = c(3,8), type='n', xlab="Bands",
     ylab = "Surface reflectance")
lines(assinatura[,1], col="DarkOliveGreen", lwd=3)
lines(assinatura[,2], col="blue", lwd=3)
lines(assinatura[,3], col="grey", lwd=3)
lines(assinatura[,4], col="ForestGreen", lwd=3)
lines(assinatura[,5], col="brown", lwd=3)
lines(assinatura[,6], col="LightGreen", lwd=3)
legend("topleft", legend = c('1','2','3','4','5','6'),
       col=c("DarkOliveGreen", "blue", "grey", "ForestGreen",
             "brown", "LightGreen"), lty=1, lwd=3)
```

Thus, it is possible to see high absorption of water at all wavelengths. There was more separability of vegetation types in the red and swir2 bands, although they were visibly well separated throughout the spectrum shown in the graph. In general, forest reflected less than coffee crops and grassland.

Bare soil showed an increasing pattern in the visible and infrared with reduced reflectance only in band 8 (swir3). Urbanized area reflected more than bare soil in the visible region and less than bare soil in the shortwave infrared region (Figure 11.7).

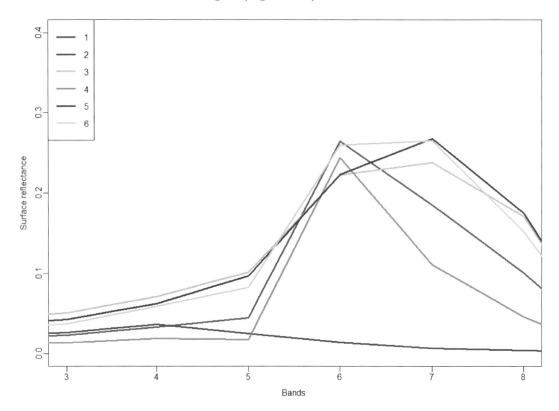

Figure 11.7 Spectral signature of blue (3), green (4), red (5), near-infrared (6), shortwave infrared 1 (7), and shortwave infrared 2 (8) bands of Landsat-8 OLI used in supervised classification of targets in coffee crops (1), water (2), urban landscape (3), forest (4), bare soil (5), and grassland (6) in the Funil dam region, state of Minas Gerais, Brazil.

The previous code is adapted to explore the effect of each target and its emissivity in the form of radiant temperature (K). The big data bands 10 and 11 are selected from the limits 10.1 and 10.9 on the x-axis of the graph.

```
par(mfrow = c(1, 1),mar = c(3.5, 4.0, 0.5, 1), mgp = c(2.0, 0.5, 0.0))
plot(0, ylim=c(280,300), xlim = c(10.1,10.9), type='n', xlab="Bands",
     ylab = "Temperature (K)")
lines(assinatura[,1], col="DarkOliveGreen", lwd=3)
lines(assinatura[,2], col="blue", lwd=3)
lines(assinatura[,3], col="grey", lwd=3)
lines(assinatura[,4], col="ForestGreen", lwd=3)
lines(assinatura[,5], col="brown", lwd=3)
lines(assinatura[,6], col="LightGreen", lwd=3)
legend("bottomleft", legend = c('1','2','3','4','5','6'),
       col=c("DarkOliveGreen", "blue", "grey", "ForestGreen",
             "brown", "LightGreen"), lty=1, lwd=3)
```

Considering the radiant temperature variation of targets, bare soil showed the highest temperature, followed by urban landscape, grassland, coffee crops, water and forest (Figure 11.8).

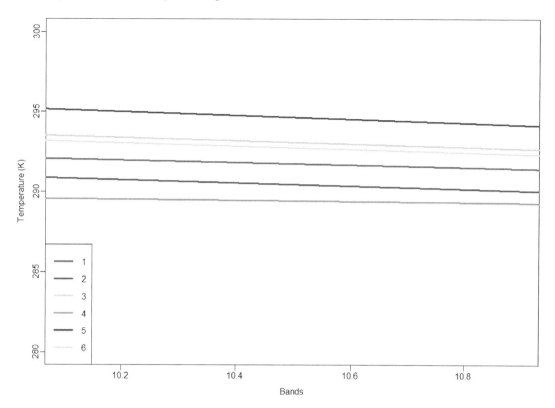

Figure 11.8 Spectral signature of thermal infrared spectral bands (10,11) from Landsat-8 TIRS used in supervised classification of targets in coffee crops (1), water (2), urban landscape (3), forest (4), bare soil (5), and grassland (6) in the Funil dam region, state of Minas Gerais, Brazil.

By adapting the code, it is possible to explore the variation of the targets according to Sentinel-2 imagery data.

```
par(mfrow = c(1, 1),mar = c(3.5, 4.0, 0.5, 1), mgp = c(2.0, 0.5, 0.0))
plot(0, ylim=c(0,0.4), xlim = c(34.4,43.6), type='n', xlab="Bands",
     ylab = "Surface reflectance")
lines(assinatura[,1], col="DarkOliveGreen", lwd=3)
lines(assinatura[,2], col="blue", lwd=3)
lines(assinatura[,3], col="grey", lwd=3)
lines(assinatura[,4], col="ForestGreen", lwd=3)
lines(assinatura[,5], col="brown", lwd=3)
lines(assinatura[,6], col="LightGreen", lwd=3)
legend("topleft", legend = c('1','2','3','4','5','6'),
       col=c("DarkOliveGreen", "blue", "grey", "ForestGreen",
             "brown", "LightGreen"), lty=1, lwd=3)
```

Water showed an absorption pattern along the entire spectrum. Urban landscape and soil reflected with progressive increase in wavelength and with very close values. The grassland vegetation showed a pattern similar to that of soil and urban area, but with higher absorption in the visible and higher reflectance in the infrared (Figure 11.9).

By adapting the code to capture the variation of bands 32 and 33 of the big data it is possible to explore the variation of radar backscatter polarizations in decibels.

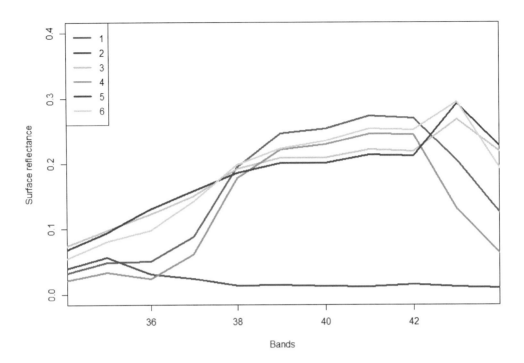

Figure 11.9 Spectral signature of blue (35), green (36), red (37), near-infrared-B5 (38), near-infrared-B6 (39), near-infrared-B7 (40), near-infrared-B8 (41), near-infrared-B8A (42), mid-infrared-B11 (43), and Sentinel-2 mid-infrared-B12 (44) used in supervised classification of the targets coffee crops (1), water (2), urban landscape (3), forest (4), bare soil (5), and grassland (6) in the region of the Funil dam, state of Minas Gerais, Brazil.

```
par(mfrow = c(1, 1),mar = c(3.5, 4.0, 0.5, 1), mgp = c(2.0, 0.5, 0.0))
plot(0, ylim=c(-30,-1), xlim = c(32.1,32.9), type='n', xlab="Polarizations",
     ylab = "Range (decibels)")
lines(assinatura[,1], col="DarkOliveGreen", lwd=3)
lines(assinatura[,2], col="blue", lwd=3)
lines(assinatura[,3], col="grey", lwd=3)
lines(assinatura[,4], col="ForestGreen", lwd=3)
lines(assinatura[,5], col="brown", lwd=3)
lines(assinatura[,6], col="LightGreen", lwd=3)
legend("topleft", legend = c('1','2','3','4','5','6'),
       col=c("DarkOliveGreen", "blue", "grey", "ForestGreen",
             "brown", "LightGreen"), lty=1, lwd=3)
```

The most negative backscatter values are observed for water, followed by bare soil, grassland, coffee crops, urban landscape and forest (Figure 11.10).

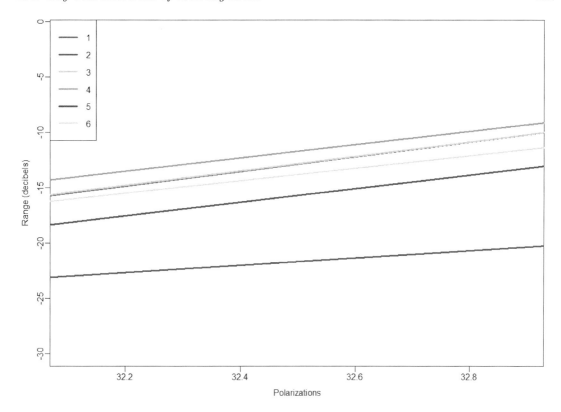

Figure 11.10 Spectral signature of Sentinel-1 GRD polarizations VH (32) and VV (33) in decibels used in supervised classification of the targets coffee crops (1), water (2), urban landscape (3), forest (4), bare soil (5), and grassland (6) in the Funil dam region, state of Minas Gerais, Brazil.

11.6.2   Machine learning

Machine learning is a branch of computer science that studies the design of algorithms that can learn. Typical machine learning tasks are concept learning, function learning or "predictive modeling", clustering, and predictive pattern finding. These tasks are learned from available data observed through experimentation or instruction, for example. Machine learning hopes that including experience in its tasks will improve the learning so that it becomes automatic, with self-adaptation.

11.6.3   Deep learning

Deep neural networks (deep learning) are based on a multi-feeder artificial neural network, trained with stochastic gradient descent using backpropagation. The network can contain many hidden layers consisting of neurons with activation functions. Advanced features such as adaptive learning rate, rate annealing, momentum training, dropout, L1 or L2 regularization, checkpoint, and grid search enable high predictive accuracy. Each computer node trains a copy of the global model parameters on its local multi-threaded data (asynchronously) and periodically contributes to the global model by averaging the model over the network.

11.6.4   Steps for selecting training samples

The steps for selecting training samples are:

- Seek additional information about the geographic region;
- Perform field studies;
- Evaluate the image to be classified;
- Identify training areas in the image;
- Evaluate and edit training data;
- Use the training data in classification.

11.7   Supervised classification algorithms

Some methods for supervised classification are available for image analysis as shown in Table 11.1. Nevertheless, the main focus of scientific remote sensing applications has been on naive Bayes, support vector machine, random forest and neural network classification algorithms.

Table 11.1 Supervised classification algorithms for digital images.

Algorithm	Description
Parallelepiped	A rectangle is formed around the training data set.
Minimum distance	The minimum distance algorithm is used to define spectral symmetry.
Spectral angle	The angle between training samples in the attribute space is used to determine the pixels of each class.
Maximum likelihood	The probability that each pixel belongs to a set of predefined classes is determined by assuming normal distribution for the pixel groupings.
Naive Bayes	Belongs to the family of probabilistic classifiers based on Bayes' theorem naive Bayes.
Support vector machine	A hyperplane defined with support vectors is used to separate the different classes.
Random forest	Multiple decision trees are built by decision tree algorithms.
Neural networks	An activation function is used in the summation of the input information, generating an output result.

Supervised classifications are performed with the random forest (`rf`), classification and regression trees (CART) (`rpart1SE`), and support vector machine (`svmLinear2`) algorithms. The R packages `RStoolbox` (Leutner et al., 2019), `lattice` (Sarkarand et al., 2021), `ggplot2` (Wickham, Chang, et al., 2022), and `gridExtra` (Auguie & Antonov, 2017) are needed for analysis, and enabled with the `library` function.

```
library(RStoolbox)
library(lattice)
library(ggplot2)
library(gridExtra)
```

The supervised classification is set up with the training data defined in the previous topics classidsp, the data being partitioned into 98% for training and 2% for validation of fitted models. The kfold = 10 method is used in the validation of the results being repeated k-times where each of the k-subsets are used as a test set and other k-1 subsets are used for training purposes. The superClass function is used to perform supervised classification with the rf, rpart1SE, and svmLinear2 algorithms.

```
SC1 <- superClass(bigdata, trainData = classidsp, responseCol = "class",
  model = "rf", kfold = 10, trainPartition = 0.98)
SC2 <- superClass(bigdata, trainData = classidsp, responseCol = "class",
  model = "rpart1SE", kfold = 10, trainPartition = 0.98)
SC3 <- superClass(bigdata, trainData = classidsp, responseCol = "class",
  model = "svmLinear2", kfold = 10, trainPartition = 0.98)
```

The results obtained are exported to a directory on the computer for later use. The saveRSTBX function is used to export the classification results for each evaluated machine learning algorithm.

```
saveRSTBX(SC1, filename="C:/sr/c10/new/SC1", overwrite=TRUE)
saveRSTBX(SC2, filename="C:/sr/c10/new/SC2", overwrite=TRUE)
saveRSTBX(SC3, filename="C:/sr/c10/new/SC3", overwrite=TRUE)
```

11.7.1   Naive Bayes method

The naive Bayes method belongs to the family of probabilistic classifiers based on Bayes' theorem. It assumes that a particular class is independent of the characteristics of other classes. It has high efficiency under supervised training and requires few samples to define parameters needed in the classification. It may perform better than random forest in highly complex situations.

11.7.2   Support vector machine

Support vector machines (SVM) are a set of supervised learning methods used for classification, regression, and outlier detection. A hyperplane defined with support vectors is used to separate the different classes. Kernel functions of different types can be used in model fitting and decision. Efficient in multi-dimensional spaces and not very efficient under low sample sizes.

11.7.3   Decision tree method

The decision tree method is a non-parametric classifier based on inductive learning, where the algorithm learns the rules to separate classes according to training samples. Decision rules are obtained by defining the best discriminant function, based on linear combinations of given attributes (multivariate trees).

In the case of the rpart1SE algorithm, a decision tree is used to represent the model's reasoning when performing class prediction as a function of the input spectral variables. The plot and text functions are used to determine the decision tree fitted by the rpart1SE model.

```
par(mfrow = c(1, 1),mar = c(3.5, 4.0, 1.5, 1), mgp = c(2.0, 0.5, 0.0))
plot(SC2$model$finalModel, uniform=TRUE)
text(SC2$model$finalModel, digits = 3)
```

Therefore, it can be seen that Sentinel-2 band 8A (red edge) was decisive at the beginning of the classification to discriminate water from other targets. Next, the Normalized Difference Water Index (NDWI) determined from Landsat-8 data is used to separate coffee crops and forest from urban landscape and bare soil. Subsequently, radiant temperature (band 10, Landsat-8 TIRS), B09 (water vapor), B12 (SWIR) (Sentinel-2), SATVI (Landsat-8 OLI), SAVI (Sentinel-2) and MSAVI (Landsat-8 OLI) are used to discriminate the remaining targets (Figure 11.11).

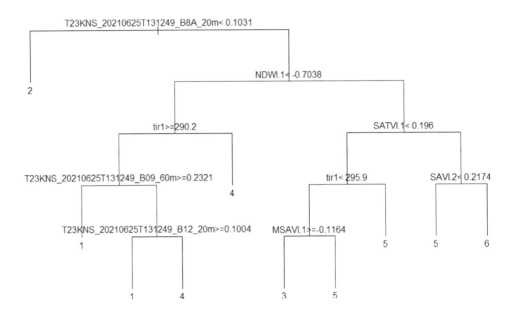

Figure 11.11 Decision tree used by the `rpart1SE` model in the supervised classification of the targets coffee crop (1), water (2), urban landscape (3), forest (4), bare soil (5), and grassland landscape (6) in the region of the Funil dam, state of Minas Gerais, Brazil.

11.7.4   Random forest method

Multiple decision trees are built by decision tree algorithms such as the Gini index and information gain. The use of a decision tree enables us to work with large databases and multidimensionality. However, with the use of this methodology there is little control over the model. With the increasing use of machine learning methods in all areas, the use of random forest is more recommended for classification than for regression. Each tree grows to the largest possible extent in the model. Prediction is done by aggregating predictions from n trees.

The Gini index enables evaluation of the importance of variables used in the random forest classification. The importance of variables for performing the random forest classification is obtained graphically with the function `plot(varImp())`. Numerical results about the importance of variables are obtained with the `varImp` function.

```
plot(varImp(object=SC1$model))
varImp(object=SC1$model)
```

In the case of the fitted random forest model, the variables obtained with Landsat-8 imagery MNDWI, tir1, NDWI, GNDVI, SATVI, and the variables obtained with Sentinel-2 imagery, B8A, B12, and B09 were the first 7 most important variables as a proposal to perform target separability in the Funil dam region (Figure 11.12).

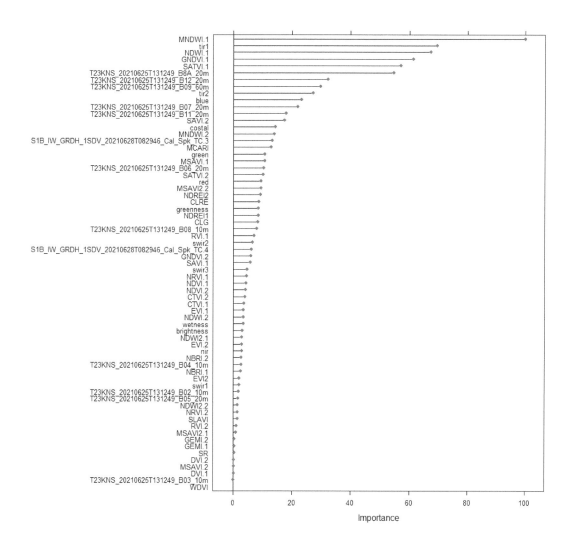

Figure 11.12 Importance of variables used by the random forest model in pixel-by-pixel supervised classification of targets in coffee crops (1), water (2), urban landscape (3), forest (4), bare soil (5), and grassland (6) in the Funil dam region, state of Minas Gerais, Brazil.

Comparative mapping of the targets coffee plantations (DarkOliveGreen), water (blue), urban landscape (grey), forest (ForestGreen), bare soil (brown), and grassland (LightGreen) is performed with the functions ggR, scale_fill_manual and grid.arrange.

```
cl<-c("DarkOliveGreen", "blue", "grey", "ForestGreen", "brown", "LightGreen")
m1<-ggR(SC1$map, geom_raster = TRUE)+
```

```
    scale_fill_manual(values = cl, breaks = 1:6,
                labels = c("1", "2", "3", "4", "5", "6"), name = "rf")
m2<- ggR(SC2$map, geom_raster = TRUE) +
    scale_fill_manual(values = cl, breaks = 1:6,
                labels = c("1", "2", "3", "4", "5", "6"), name = "rpart1SE")
m3<- ggR(SC3$map, geom_raster = TRUE) +
    scale_fill_manual(values = cl, breaks = 1:6,
                labels = c("1", "2", "3", "4", "5", "6"), name = "svmLinear2")
grid.arrange(m1, m2, m3, ncol=1)
```

The random forest (rf), CART (rpart1SE), and support vector machines with linear kernel (svmLinear2) algorithms are comparatively evaluated for spatial prediction of coffee crop (1), water (2), urban landscape (3), forest (4), bare soil (5), and grassland (6) classes in the Funil dam region, state of Minas Gerais, Brazil. In general, the mapping results are quite similar in terms of the spatial pattern of targets in the scene; however, the results of the rpart1SE algorithm determined higher occurrence of bare soil and lower occurrence of water when compared to rf and svmLinear2 (Figure 11.13). For a scientific analysis of the best results obtained, the accuracy analysis of these results is performed in the next chapter.

11.7.5   Neural network method

The neural network method is inspired by biological neurons and the parallel structure of the brain, with learning capabilities. The networks consist of a set of input elements connected to other processing elements simulating the synapse process. The processing of the neurons consists of applying an activation function on the sum of the input information, generating an output result.

11.7.6   Hybrid classification

Hybrid classification is the association of a classification algorithm with another, such as an unsupervised algorithm with a supervised algorithm in digital image processing. This methodological approach is recommended in classification situations where more detailed image stratification is required.

The method that incorporates the skill and knowledge of the interpreter and the speed of the machine to classify the images is also considered a type of hybrid classification. Interpreter interference can be accomplished through matrix editing (Moreira, 2011).

11.8   Supervised Segmentation

Supervised segmentation has been used with a hybrid object-based approach for the analysis and classification of high or very high spatial resolution Earth observing images. The analyst's experience in geographic information systems, digital image processing, and remote sensing should be considered due to the pre-processing of input data and the need for a hybrid approach with more than one computer program (external programs) to obtain the segmentation result. In

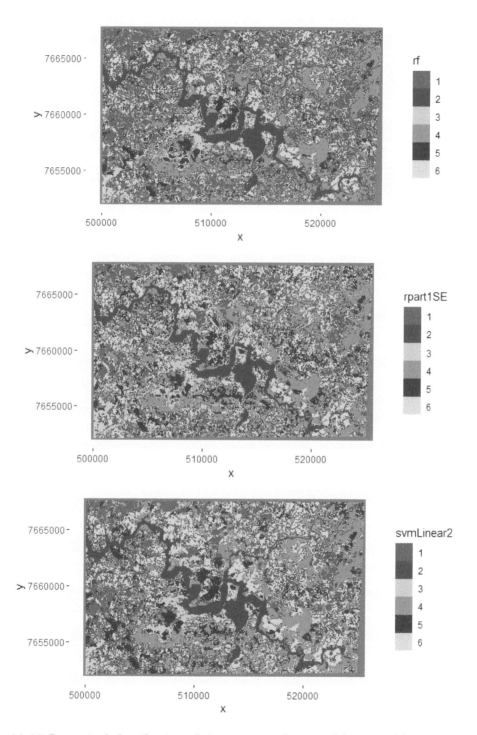

Figure 11.13 Supervised classification of the targets coffee crop (1), water (2), urban landscape (3), forest (4), bare soil (5), and grassland landscape (6) with the machine learning algorithms: rf, rpart1SE, and svmLinear2, in the region of the Funil dam, state of Minas Gerais, Brazil.

general, the image is divided into spectrally homogeneous regions by processes such as region growing, edge detection, of the combination of both. Clustering of regions is performed according to the similarity criteria of adjacent areas.

11.8.1   Object-based image analysis

Object-based image analysis (OBIA) is a technique (or set of techniques) for analyzing digital images that has been relatively recently developed in comparison with the classical pixel-based imaging approaches (Burnett & Blaschke, 2003). While object-based image analysis relies on spectral information of individual pixels, OBIA is based on information from sets of pixels called "objects". An object is a set of pixels with similar or relatively homogeneous spectral characteristics connected along the space. Within objects there are different shapes, sizes, scales and temporal properties.

In the R package `SegOptim` (Gonçalves, 2020), image segmentation and supervised classification are combined into a single workflow, making it easy to perform the two steps in sequence. External computer programs such as SAGA GIS are used to perform the segmentation step. In R, the other image processing and analysis tasks are performed. In R, the classification stage is performed, considering the large number of algorithms available for this purpose and packages like `randomForest` (Breiman et al., 2018), `e1071` (Meyer et al., 2021), `clusterCrit` (Desgraupes, 2018), and `caret` (Kuhn et al., 2020). Also in R, raster images can be processed in the packages `raster` (Hijmans et al., 2020) or `rgdal` (Bivand et al., 2021).

The R package `SegOptim` makes it possible to run different image segmentation algorithms, fill image segments with aggregate statistics with user-defined functions, run supervised object-based classification with various methods, evaluate classification performance for single or multi-class problems, optimize image segmentation parameters using genetic algorithms and other methods, compare different algorithms based on optimized solutions, run unsupervised classification with various methods, and compare the results with internal cluster storage criteria (Gonçalves, 2020).

The supervised classification algorithms in `SegOptim` are (Gonçalves, 2020):

- Flexible Discriminant Analysis (FDA);
- Generalized Boosted Model (GBM);
- K-Nearest Neighbor (KNN);
- Random Forest (RF);
- Support Vector Machines (SVM).

The unsupervised classification algorithms in `SegOptim` are (Gonçalves, 2020):

- Clustering LARge Applications (CLARA);
- Hard competitive learning;
- K-means;
- Neural gas.

It is important to know the terminology used throughout the data analysis process to perform object-based segmentation as shown in Table 11.2 (Gonçalves, 2020):

Table 11.2 Definitions for performing object-based segmentation.

Term	Definition
Image segmentation	Process of partitioning an image into multiple segments (sets of pixels); or decomposing an input image into smaller (non-overlapping) parts that are meaningful in relation to a specific task.
Image segments	Set of pixels with similar spectral characteristics.
Image objects	Image segments after being filled with spectral, spatial, and temporal data attributes.
Supervised classification	Process of inferring a classification function from labeled training data or user-supplied examples.
Single class	Supervised classification problem type with only one class with two mutually exclusive levels, such as presence or absence of species, burned and unburned, deforestation and non-deforestation.
Multi-class	Supervised classification problem type with multiple mutually exclusive classes, such as discrete land cover classes of vegetation, soil, water, and urban.
Features	Any spectral, spatial, temporal and terrain data used to perform image segmentation or to infer in the classification function as input or predictive variables.

In the R package `SegOptim`, there is a simplified workflow to create a supervised object-based classification of images according to the following sequential steps (Gonçalves, 2020):

1. Image segmentation (using external software, e.g., SAGA GIS);
2. Load training data into the segmented image (threshold rule);
3. Calculate segment statistics (e.g., mean, standard deviation) for feature classification;
4. Merge training statistics and segment statistics (from steps 2 to 3);
5. Training and data partitioning;
6. For each training set and partitions: (i) supervised object-based classification;(ii) performance evaluation for each subset;
7. Final calibration round with all data;
8. Accuracy evaluation, confusion matrix and trained classifiers;
9. From the results of step 8, apply the classifier to the entire scene.

Performing the above workflow to implement object-based supervised classification requires three basic data inputs (Gonçalves, 2020):

- Training data-> Typically, a single-layer raster dataset containing samples to train a classifier. The labels, classes or categories should be encoded as integers (0, 1) for single-class problems or, $1, 2, \ldots, n$, for multi-class situations in `raster` and `rgdal` format;
- Segmentation features-> This consists of a multi-layer raster dataset with features used only for the segmentation stage (e.g., spectral bands, spectral band indices, texture). The format of this data depends on the algorithm used to perform the segmentation, such as `.sgrid` files in SAGA GIS;
- Classification features-> This consists of a multi-layered raster dataset with features used for classification (e.g., spectral bands and indices, texture, elevation). The input formats should be those used in the `raster` and `rgdal` packages.

The result of pixel-by-pixel prediction of classes by the `svmLinear2` algorithm are used in the classification training of Landsat-8, Sentinel-1, and Sentinel-2 imagery data segments, with spectral indices, in the Funil dam region, state of Minas Gerais, Brazil. The random forest algorithm is used in the spatial prediction of segments of coffee crop (1), water (2), urban landscape (3), forest (4), bare soil (5), and grassland landscape (6) classes in the evaluated region (Figure 11.14).

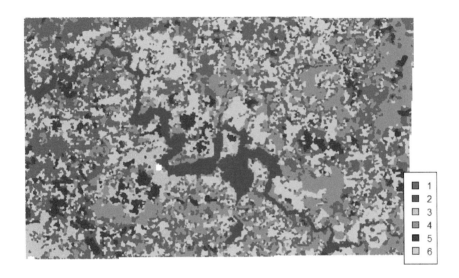

Figure 11.14 Supervised random forest segmentation of coffee crop (1), water (2), urban landscape (3), forest (4), bare soil (5), and grassland landscape (6) targets with training from pixel-by-pixel classification results with the **svmLinear2** algorithm in the region of the Funil dam, state of Minas Gerais, Brazil.

The importance of the variables considered in the random forest segmentation is also determined as a way to evaluate the reasoning used by the algorithm in predicting classes in the Funil dam, state of Minas Gerais (Figure 11.15).

The evaluation of classification and segmentation results can be assessed using color compositions performed over the entire evaluated area or in greater detail on specific regions of interest defined by subsets of the image. These color compositions can also be useful for identifying and selecting targets used for reference to obtain supervised classification samples. Infrared and agricultural color compositions from Landsat-8 and Sentinel-2 imagery are comparatively performed on the Funil dam at different spectral and spatial resolutions (Figure 11.16).

11.9   Supervised Classification with Cloud Processing

Supervised classification can be developed using a cloud processing routine. In this case the rgee package is enabled and the ee_Initialize function is used to initialize the Earth Engine.

```
library(rgee)
ee_Initialize()
```

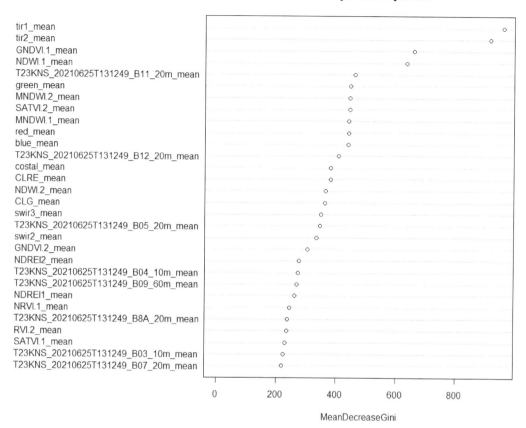

Figure 11.15 Importance of variables used in supervised random forest segmentation of targets coffee crop (1), water (2), urban landscape (3), forest (4), bare soil (5), and grassland landscape (6) trained from pixel-by-pixel classification results with the svmLinear2 algorithm in the region of the Funil dam, state of Minas Gerais, Brazil.

Landsat-8 imagery data in a cloud-free collection are used as input data for the classification. Tier 1 (T1) data are those that meet geometric and radiometric quality requirements. The ee$ImageCollection function is used to access data from the Landsat-8 collection.

```
l8 <- ee$ImageCollection("LANDSAT/LC08/C01/T1")
```

The ee$Algorithms$Landsat$simpleComposite function is used to obtain a top of atmosphere (TOA) collection with as few clouds as possible. The imagery dates are selected from January 1 to December 31, 2018 with the $filterDate function. The asFloat = TRUE argument determines that output bands are in TOA units.

```
image <- ee$Algorithms$Landsat$simpleComposite(collection =
    l8$filterDate("2018-01-01", "2018-12-31"), asFloat = TRUE)
```

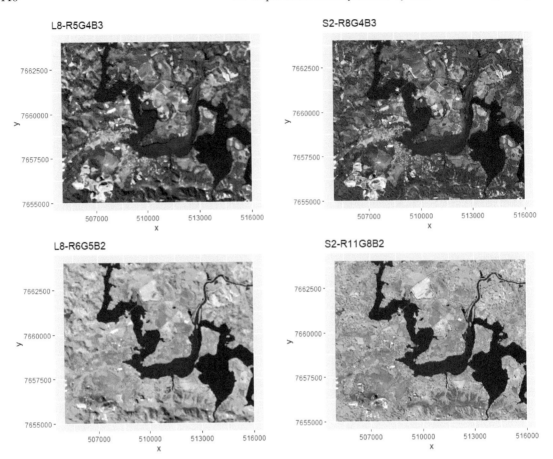

Figure 11.16 Landsat-8 (R5G4B3 and R6G5B2) and Sentinel-2 (R8G4B3 and R11G8B2) color compositions in subset performed at Funil dam, state of Minas Gerais, Brazil.

Bands 2 to 11 are used in this example and selected from an atomic `c()` vector.

```
bands <- c("B2", "B3", "B4", "B5", "B6", "B7", "B10", "B11")
```

The training polygons defined in previous topics are converted into a `ee.featurecollection` object for use in Earth Engine.

```
polygons <- sf_as_ee(classid, check_ring_dir = TRUE)
```

Some metadata of the polygons can be observed with the `ee_print` function, for example, the 752 target features used.

```
ee_print(polygons, max_display = 4)
#------------ Earth Engine FeatureCollection --
#FeatureCollection Metadata:
# - Class                    : ee$FeatureCollection
# - Number of Features       : 752
# - Number of Properties     : 0
#Feature Metadata:
```

```
# - Number of Properties      : 1
#Geometry Metadata (f_index = 0):
# - CRS                       : WGS 84 (EPSG:4326)
# - proj4string               : +proj=longlat +datum=WGS84 +no_defs
# - Geotransform              : 1 0 0 0 1 0
# - Geodesic                  : TRUE
# - Geo Type                  : POLYGON
# ----------------------------------------
```

Pixel values are obtained within each polygon with the `$sampleRegions` function. The scale of 30 m is used to define the size of pixels considered in the analysis with the `scale` argument.

```
training <- image$sampleRegions(collection = polygons,
    properties = list("class"), scale = 30)
```

A support vector machine (SVM) classifier is set up with custom parameters from the `ee$Classifier$libsvm` function. The arguments `gamma` and `cost` are set to 0.5 and 10, respectively. Other classification algorithms can be chosen at the analyst's discretion, such as for CART classification (smileCart), random forest (smileRandomForest), and naive Bayes (smileNaiveBayes).

```
classifier <- ee$Classifier$libsvm(kernelType = "RBF", gamma = 0.5, cost = 10)
```

Training of the classifier is performed with the `$train` function.

```
trained <- classifier$train(training, "class", bands)
```

The Landsat-8 image collection is classified with the `$classify` function.

```
classified <- image$classify(trained)
```

A color palette for classes 1 to 6 is defined with the `list` function.

```
geoviz_image = list(bands = c("B4", "B3", "B2"), max = 0.5, gamma = 2)
geoviz_class <- list(min = 1, max = 6, palette =
    c("#556b2f", "#0000FF", "#808080", "#228B22", "#964B00", "#90ee90"))
```

The result of the SVM classification is performed with the functions `Map$setCenter` and `Map$addLayer`. In this case, a Landsat-8 color composition, the training polygons and the classified image are mapped.

```
Map$setCenter(-44.87022, -21.15752, 11)
Map$addLayer(eeObject = image, visParams = geoviz_image, name = "L8 image") +
Map$addLayer(eeObject = classified, visParams = geoviz_class,
            name = "SVM", legend = TRUE) +
Map$addLayer(eeObject = polygons, name = "Training polygons")
```

However, in the figure only the result of the classification map is presented by selecting the layer display order in the interactive view. Note that the classification results extrapolate the region of interest in view of the cloud data processing (Figure 11.17).

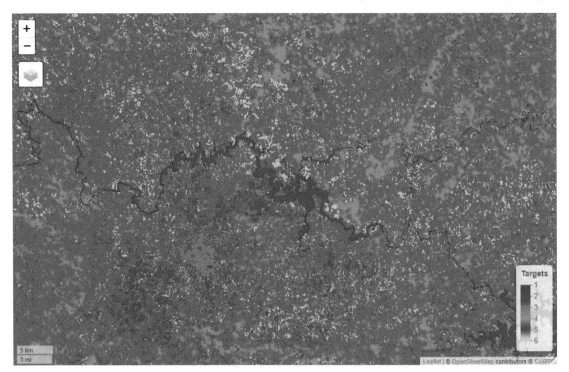

Figure 11.17 Supervised support vector machine classification on cloudless Landat-8 imaging data obtained from Earth Engine, referring to the year 2018 at Funil dam, state of Minas Gerais, Brazil.

11.10   Computational Practice

11.10.1   Installing and enabling packages

Several R packages perform supervised assessment, for example, the RStoolbox (Leutner et al., 2019), caret (Kuhn et al., 2020), randomForest (Breiman et al., 2018), SegOptim (Gonçalves, 2020) and RSAGA (Brenning et al., 2018). Packages like the xROI (Seyednasrollah et al., 2021) can be used to obtain training samples and mapview (Appelhans et al., 2020) to perform interactive mapping over the Internet. Other packages like raster (Hijmans et al., 2020), sf (Pebesma et al., 2022), sp (Pebesma, Bivand, et al., 2021), rgdal (Bivand et al., 2021), and terra (Hijmans, Bivand, et al., 2022) are also used in geoprocessing tasks required in preprocessing and geospatial analysis techniques.

The install. packages installs the R packages RStoolbox, raster, caret, randomForest, e1071 (Meyer et al., 2021), rgdal, xROI, mapview, sf, dplyr (Wickham, François, et al., 2022), SegOptim, RSAGA, and terra. Previously installed packages should not be reinstalled to avoid upgrade problems, but only enabled for analysis.

```
install.packages("RStoolbox")
install.packages("raster")
install.packages("caret")
install.packages("randomForest")
```

```
install.packages("xROI")
install.packages("e1071")
install.packages("rgdal")
install.packages("mapview")
install.packages("sf")
install.packages("dplyr")
install.packages("SegOptim")
install.packages("RSAGA")
install.packages("terra")
```

The `library` function enables the `RStoolbox`, `raster`, `caret`, `randomForest`, `xROI`, `e1071`, `rgdal`, `mapview`, `sf`, `dplyr`, `SegOptim`, `RSAGA`, and `terra` packages.

```
library(RStoolbox)
library(raster)
library(caret)
library(randomForest)
library(xROI)
library(e1071)
library(rgdal)
library(mapview)
library(sf)
library(dplyr)
library(SegOptim)
library(RSAGA)
library(terra)
```

11.10.2 Performing supervised classification of a raster layer

11.10.2.1 Getting data

It is necessary to download the `raster` file from the AppEEARS platform (AppEEARS Team, 2020). The digital elevation model of the area of interest (SRTM ellipsoidal altitude) (NASA, 2013), realized in computational practice, can be obtained to **download**[2].

The file must be unzipped into a directory on the computer where the file address is known. To set the address of the file in the R console, for the purpose of importing the file into R, note the use of "/" for the location of the file in the source directory. On this computer, the directory is located at "C:/.../SRTMGL1_NC.003_SRTMGL1_DEM_doy2000042_aid0001.tif". Note that the file extension used is `.tif`.

The SRTM file obtained from the rural property, in the state of Bahia, is imported into R with the `raster` function, named "srtm", and stored in the computer memory under that name.

```
srtm <- raster(
"C:/sr/c6/AppeearsTerraMorena/SRTMGL1_NC.003_SRTMGL1_DEM_doy2000042_aid0001.tif")
```

---

[2]http://www.sergeo.deg.ufla.br/sr/downloads/srtmTM.zip

11.10.2.2   Mapping the image to obtain training samples

The SRTM image is mapped in order to obtain training samples to express the relief variation, with four variation classes.

```
plot(srtm, axes=TRUE)
```

11.10.2.3   Creating training polygons

Geospatial polygons are created to collect pixel samples. This process should be interactive, drawing polygons on the image after performing each command, with three repetitions for each altitude class to be mapped, using functions from the xROI package (Seyednasrollah et al., 2021). The polygon is defined from vertices created by left-clicking to create a polygon vertex. At the end of editing, the polygon is closed by accessing the finish button on the plot screen where each polygon is created. In this case, four altitude classes are created (Figure 11.18).

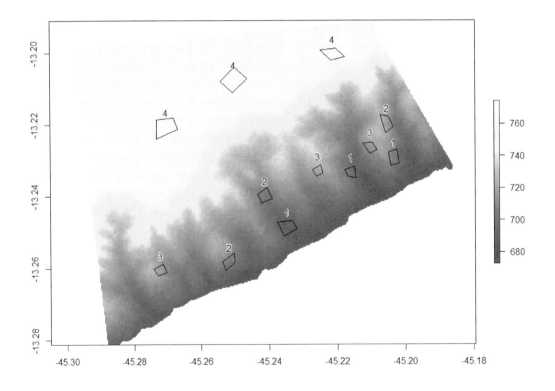

Figure 11.18 Procedure used to obtain regions of interest to sample pixels per training class for supervised classification in rural property, state of Bahia, Brazil.

11.10.2.4   Exporting training regions

Training regions are exported to a directory of interest on the computer using the `writeOGR` function. The address must be adapted according to the computer being used. In this case, the address is `C:/sr/c9/p1.shp`.

```
writeOGR(obj=p1, dsn="C:/sr/c9/p1.shp", layer="p1", driver="ESRI Shapefile")
```

11.10.2.5   Importing training regions

Geographical regions of interest for training are imported to perform classification. If you are unable to create your own training sample, the file used in compressed format can be obtained for **download**[3].

```
p1<-readOGR(dsn="C:/sr/c9/p1.shp", layer="p1")
```

11.10.2.6   Interactive visualization on the Internet

The interactive visualization of the analyzed region on the Internet is performed with the `mapview` function (Figure 11.19).

```
mapview(p1)
```

Figure 11.19 Interactive visualization of training samples associated with Internet mapping bases.

---

[3]http://www.sergeo.deg.ufla.br/sr/downloads/p1.zip

11.10.2.7 Exploratory analysis

The average altitude of each training region is obtained by zonal statistics. Thus, the average altitude within each of the four classes sampled from the digital elevation model is averaged using the `rasterize` and `zonal` functions.

```
# Convert samples from vector to raster
poligonos_raster <- rasterize(p1,
srtm, field = "ID")

# Zonal statistics of the average altitude within each class
srtm_zonal <- zonal(srtm,
poligonos_raster, fun="mean", na.rm=TRUE)
srtm_zonal
```

11.10.2.8 Performing supervised classification

To avoid problems with the column name where the training class codes are stored, especially in updated versions of `RStoolbox`, the column name `ID` is renamed to `class` using the `names` function.

```
names(p1) <- c("class")
```

The supervised classification is performed with the random forest (`rf`) classification algorithm, based on the training areas, by means of the `superClass` function. The random forest classification is tuned by considering 60% of data for training and 40% for model validation, by setting the `trainPartition` parameter to 0.6.

```
SC <- superClass(srtm, trainData = p1, responseCol = "class",
model = "rf", tuneLength = 1, trainPartition = 0.6)
```

11.10.2.9 Mapping the classification

The result of the classification can be mapped with the `plot` function.

```
plot(SC$map)
```

In this case, the mapped area is shown in the Figure 11.20.

11.10.2.10 Calculate area

More precise area determinations can be obtained by using cartographic projections of equal area. Another option may be to perform a geodetic area calculation, considering the curvature of the Earth, according to the needs of the project and the size of the mapped region. In the present study, the area of each altitude class is determined considering the raster spatial resolution of 30 m (Table 11.3).

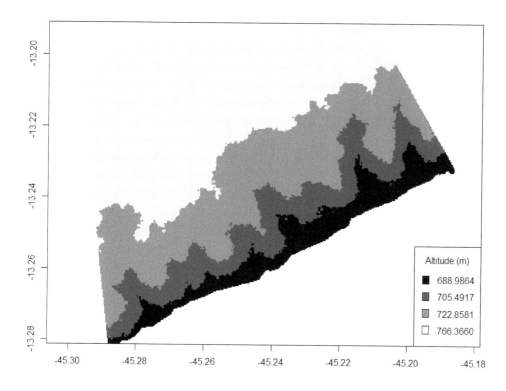

Figure 11.20 Supervised random forest classification with four altitude classes in a rural property, state of Bahia, Brazil.

```
r <-SC$map
app<-30*30
am<-table(r[]) * app
aha<-am/10000
aha
```

Table 11.3 Estimated area of altitude classes defined by supervised random forest classification on rural property in Bahia, Brazil.

Mean Altitude (m)	Area (ha)
688.9864	741.51
705.4917	1101.78
722.8581	2124.54
766.3660	3450.33

Most of the property is found to be in altitude class 4, with an area of 3450.33 ha.

The geodetic area calculation is also performed with the expanse function of the terra package. The raster layer SC$map is transformed into the class SpatRaster with the rast function, and the object r1 is created.

```
r1 <-rast(SC$map)
r1
#class       : SpatRaster
#dimensions  : 325, 403, 1  (nrow, ncol, nlyr)
#resolution  : 0.0002777778, 0.0002777778  (x, y)
#extent      : -45.29819, -45.18625, -13.28125, -13.19097  (xmin, xmax, ymin, ymax)
#coord. ref. : +proj=longlat +datum=WGS84 +no_defs
#source      : SC.grd
#categories  : value
#name        : ID
#min value   :  1
#max value   :  4
```

The expanse function is used to calculate the geodetic area in ha. The byValue=TRUE argument is used to calculate the area of each class.

```
expanse(r1, unit="ha", transform=FALSE, byValue=TRUE)
#      layer value        area
#[1,]      1     1   762.2255
#[2,]      1     2  1132.5763
#[3,]      1     3  2184.0127
#[4,]      1     4  3547.2129
```

You can see that the geodetic area values are higher than those defined in Table 11.3.

11.10.2.11   Export the classification result

The writeRaster function allows you to export the classified altitude raster to file.

```
writeRaster(SC$map, filename="G:/sr/c9/srtmrf.tif", overwrite=TRUE)
```

11.10.2.12   Export the fitted model with the classification result

The saveRSTBX function exports the classification model with fit and parameter information.

```
saveRSTBX(SC, filename="C:/sr/c9/SC", overwrite=TRUE)
```

11.11   Exercises

11.11.1   Explain supervised classification of digital imagery.

11.11.2   What are the advantages and disadvantages of supervised classification of digital imagery?

11.11.3   Cite three algorithms for supervised classification of digital images.

11.11.4   Cite three application areas of supervised classification and the type of image used.

11.11.5   What are the important features for obtaining reliable training samples?

11.12   Homework

11.12.1   Subject

Supervised classification analysis applied to multispectral imaging from CBERS-04A satellite for environmental monitoring.

11.12.2   Assignment

Develop the subject presented with a practical application of remote sensing and digital image processing including the topics Introduction and Objective. Then present the development of the task.

11.13   Resources on the Internet

As a study guide, slides and illustrative videos are presented about the subject covered in the chapter (Table 11.4).

Table 11.4 Slide presentation and illustrative video on supervised classification of remote sensing imagery.

Guide	Address for Access
1	3D simulation of a neural network for character recognition[4]
2	Random forest simulation[5]
3	Machine learning illustration[6]
4	Deep learning illustration[7]
5	Support vector machine classifier[8]
6	Naive Bayes classifier[9]
7	Slides on supervised classification of digital images[10]

11.14   Research Suggestion

The development of scientific research on supervised classification of remote sensing imagery is stimulated through activity proposals that can be used or adapted by the student to assess the applicability of the subject matter covered in the chapter (Table 11.5).

Table 11.5 Practical and research activities used or adapted by students using remote sensing for supervised classification of remote sensing imagery.

Activity	Description
1	Perform supervised classification of remote sensing multispectral imagery in a given area.
2	Perform supervised classification of remote sensing single raster layer of a given area.

---

[4] https://youtu.be/3JQ3hYko51Y
[5] https://youtu.be/XmnenS9d3cA
[6] https://youtu.be/f_uwKZIAeM0
[7] https://youtu.be/6M5VXKLf4D4
[8] https://youtu.be/Y6RRHw9uN9o
[9] https://youtu.be/CPqOCI0ahss
[10] http://www.sergeo.deg.ufla.br/sr/Presentation/Aula10/presentation.html#/

12

Uncertainty and Accuracy Analysis in Remote Sensing and Digital Image Processing

12.1 Learning Questions

The learning questions answered through reading the chapter are as follows:

- How can we determine the classification accuracy of remote sensing data?
- Which metrics are used to evaluate classified thematic maps?
- How many data are required to evaluate a classification considering a predetermined error value and the required classification accuracy?
- What is the importance of evaluating the quality of information contained in thematic mapping?

12.2 Learning Outcomes

Using the learning outcomes from the chapter, you should be able to do the following:

- Determine the classification accuracy of remote sensing data.
- Know which metrics are used to evaluate classified thematic maps.
- Understand how to calculate the number of data required to evaluate a classification according to a predetermined error value and required classification accuracy.
- Understand the importance of the quality of the information contained in thematic mapping by remote sensing.

12.3 Introduction

Information obtained by remote sensing is important in environmental models at local, regional and global scales, used in the form of thematic maps or statistics of sampling areas by quadrants. Thematic information must be accurate for decision making. Unfortunately, thematic information contains errors. Remote sensing scientists must recognize the sources of error and minimize the error as much as possible, and inform the user of the confidence gained from the thematic information generated. Thematic maps should undergo accuracy evaluation before use in scientific projects or policy decisions (Jensen, 2005).

12.4   Sources of Errors in Remote Sensing Information

The sources of error in thematic products obtained by remote sensing varied according to sensor limitation, analysis method, and target complexity, from the data and image acquisition process by passive and active remote sensing systems, through preprocessing and modeling steps, to the final product (Figure 12.1). In the data acquisition stage, errors can occur according to the sensor system used, platform motion, field geodetic control data, and geographic extent of the scene in which the image is acquired. In pre-processing, errors may occur due to geometric and radiometric corrections and conversions performed on the data. During information extraction, errors may occur due to the classification system adopted, qualitative and quantitative analysis performed, and data generalization. During data conversion, there may be errors in converting raster to vector and vector to raster. On error determination, there may be errors in sampling design, definition of the number of samples per class, evaluation of local sampling accuracy, spatial autocorrelation analysis, discrete multivariate statistics, and standard reports. In the final product there may be spatial error and thematic error. In the decision making and implementation of thematic classification, it may not be possible to apply the necessary solutions due to resolution incompatible with the possibility of action, leading to errors by generalization or excessive detailing of the mapping performed.

12.5   Determining Accuracy in Thematic Maps

12.5.1   Steps to perform accuracy analysis

The steps to perform accuracy analysis of thematic information from remote sensing data are: Determine the nature of the thematic information to be evaluated; define methods for evaluating thematic accuracy; determine the total number of observations needed in the analysis; define sampling scheme; obtain reference information on the ground; create the error matrix, and accept or reject the hypothesis according to the results of acceptance of the accuracy magnitude (Figure 12.2) (Jensen, 2005).

12.6   Target Reference Pixels

Field reference information can be obtained prior to classification, but most test information is obtained after classification by random sampling, which enables the collection of a larger number of unbiased observations per category (class).

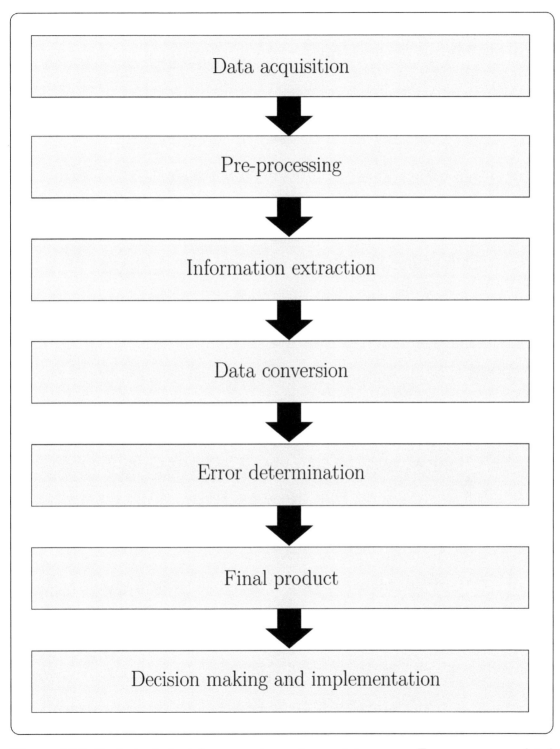

Figure 12.1 Products derived from remote sensing contain errors. Errors are accumulated throughout the entire process from obtaining data to implementing the decision. Methodologies for evaluating errors define the type and number of errors in the final product.

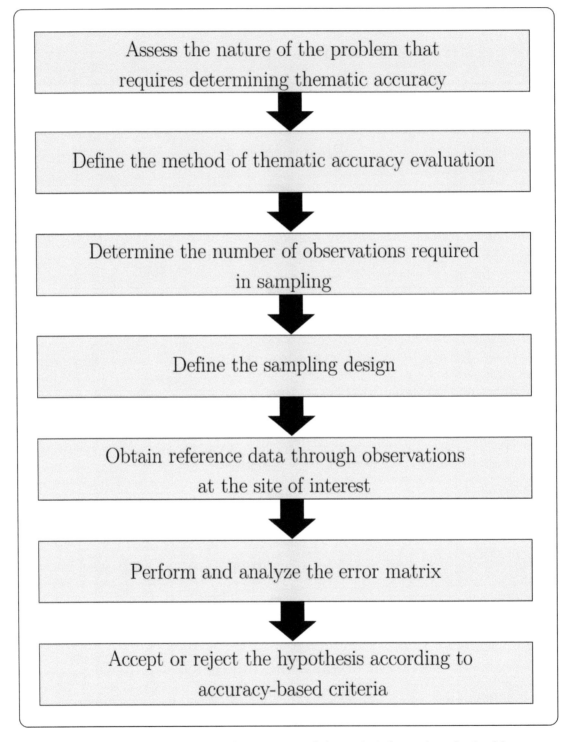

Figure 12.2 Steps used to evaluate the accuracy of thematic information obtained by remote sensing.

12.6.1 Sample Size

The sample size (N) for determining the accuracy of a land use classification map can be determined by binomial probability theory:

$$N = \frac{Z^2(p)(q)}{E^2} \tag{12.1}$$

where p, is the expected map accuracy as a whole in percent, $q = 100 - p$, E, the tolerable error, and $Z = 2$, the standard deviation parameter of the normal distribution curve for the 95% probability level.

12.6.2 Sampling design

There are sampling design schemes used to obtain field references to evaluate the accuracy of thematic maps obtained by remote sensing. The possible sampling schemes used are (Figure 12.3) (Jensen, 2005):

- Random;
- Systematic;
- Stratified random;
- Non-aligned stratified systematic;
- Clustered.

12.7 Unsupervised Classification Accuracy Analysis

It should be noted that there is no single, universally acceptable measure of accuracy, but rather a variety of indices, each with different sensitivity, for evaluating the error obtained by applying a model to solve a geographic problem. The determination of the silhouette index is a method to interpret and validate the consistency of model clustering of a remote sensing database. The silhouette index can be used to select the best number of clusters in data modeling and evaluate the performance of each clustering result. The silhouette value is a measure of how similar an object is to its own cluster compared to other clusters. The silhouette index ranges from -1 to 1 where a high value indicates satisfactory fit of an object with respect to its cluster. The index processing is performed by a stratified random sampling approach to minimize the slow calculation process due to the high number of observations. The silhouette index can be calculated with any distance metric, such as Euclidean distance or Manhattan distance (Amorim & Hennig, 2015; Kaufman & Rousseeuw, 2009; Rousseeuw, 1987).

A remote sensing big data set used in previous chapters is evaluated in relation to the silhouette index. The packages needed for analysis are `vegan` (Oksanen et al., 2022), `fpc` (Hennig, 2020), `raster` (Hijmans et al., 2020), and `cluster` (Maechler et al., 2022). The packages are enabled with the `library` function.

```
library(vegan)
library(fpc)
```

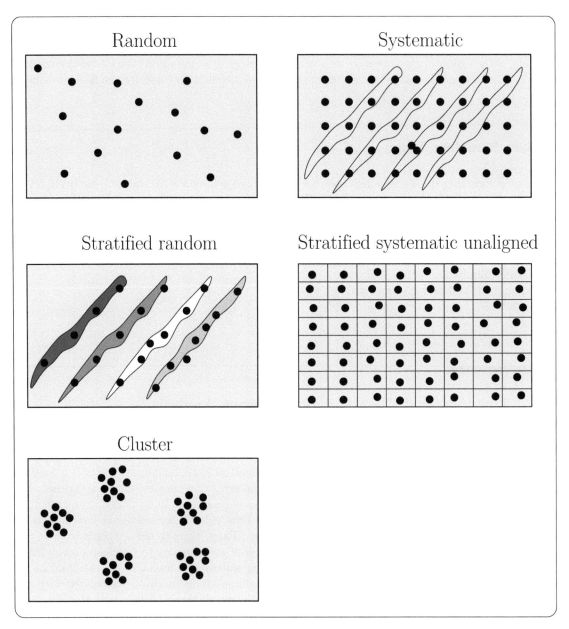

Figure 12.3 Random, systematic, stratified random, non-aligned stratified systematic, and clustered sampling schemes.

```
library(raster)
library(cluster)
```

Imagery data on raster layers are imported into R with the `stack` function and the layers are renamed with the `names` function.

```
bigdata <- stack("C:/sr/c10/bdsub.tif")
names(bigdata) <- c("costal","blue","green","red","nir","swir2","swir3",
"swir1","tir1","tir2","brightness","greenness","wetness","CTVI.1",
"DVI.1","EVI.1","EVI2","GEMI.1","GNDVI.1","MNDWI.1","MSAVI.1",
"MSAVI2.1","NBRI.1","NDVI.1","NDWI.1","NDWI2.1","NRVI.1","RVI.1",
"SATVI.1","SAVI.1","S1B_IW_GRDH_1SDV_20210628T082946_Cal_Spk_TC.3",
"S1B_IW_GRDH_1SDV_20210628T082946_Cal_Spk_TC.4",
"T23KNS_20210625T131249_B02_10m", "T23KNS_20210625T131249_B03_10m",
"T23KNS_20210625T131249_B04_10m", "T23KNS_20210625T131249_B05_20m",
"T23KNS_20210625T131249_B06_20m", "T23KNS_20210625T131249_B07_20m",
"T23KNS_20210625T131249_B08_10m", "T23KNS_20210625T131249_B8A_20m",
"T23KNS_20210625T131249_B09_60m", "T23KNS_20210625T131249_B11_20m",
"T23KNS_20210625T131249_B12_20m", "CLG", "CLRE","CTVI.2","DVI.2",
"EVI.2","GEMI.2","GNDVI.2","MCARI", "MNDWI.2","MSAVI.2","MSAVI2.2",
"NBRI.2","NDREI1","NDREI2","NDVI.2", "NDWI.2","NDWI2.2","NRVI.2",
"RVI.2","SATVI.2","SAVI.2","SLAVI","SR","WDVI")
```

The data is resampled to get samples without missing data with the `getValues`, `which`, `na.omit` and `sample(nrow())` functions.

```
v <- getValues(bigdata)
i <- which(!is.na(v))
v <- na.omit(v)
vx<-v[sample(nrow(v), 500),]
```

The result of the samples is evaluated against the silhouette index. The function `pamk` is used to evaluate the optimal number of clusters estimated by the optimal mean silhouette. The function `cat` displays the optimal number of clusters in the R console.

```
pamk.best <- pamk(vx)
cat("number of clusters estimated by optimum average silhouette width:",
    pamk.best$nc, "\n")
#number of clusters estimated by optimum average silhouette width: 3
```

Thus, it can be seen that the optimal number of clusters for the unsupervised classification is 3.

With the use of the functions `plot` and `pam` it is possible to represent the components that explain the most point variability in the analysis from the `cluster` package (Maechler et al., 2022).

```
plot(pam(vx, pamk.best$nc))
```

The first two components explain 85.56% of the results (Figure 12.4).

The largest silhouette width is observed with 3 clusters (0.67) (Figure 12.5).

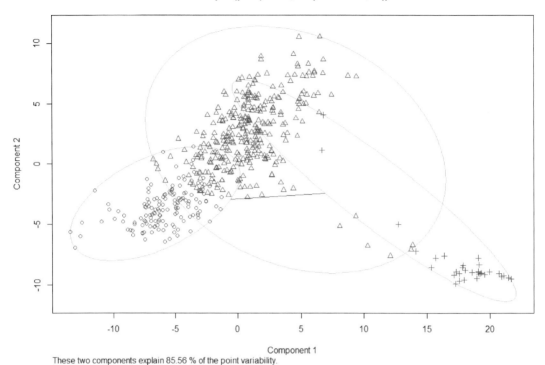

clusplot(pam(x = vx, k = pamk.best$nc))

These two components explain 85.56 % of the point variability.

Figure 12.4 Analysis of cluster formation that explains the largest data variability for unsupervised classification from remote sensing big data.

The Calinski criterion (Calinski & Harabasz, 1974) is another method used to determine the optimal number of clusters in unsupervised classification. The `cascadeKM` and `as.numeric` functions are used to obtain the optimal number of clusters for the unsupervised classification.

```
fit <- cascadeKM(scale(vx, center = TRUE,  scale = TRUE), 1, 10, iter = 1000)
calinski.best <- as.numeric(which.max(fit$results[2,]))
cat("Calinski criterion optimal number of clusters:", calinski.best, "\n")
#Calinski criterion optimal number of clusters: 3
```

Thereby, it can be seen that the optimal number of clusters is 3 according to Calinski's criterion. The results are represented graphically with the function `plot`.

```
plot(fit, sortg = TRUE, grpmts.plot = TRUE)
```

In the graphical result it is possible to check the number of clusters in each partition between 0 and 500 and the optimal number of clusters in graphical format. Based on the graphical analysis it can be seen that using 4 clusters is the second best clustering result obtained with this analysis (Figure 12.6).

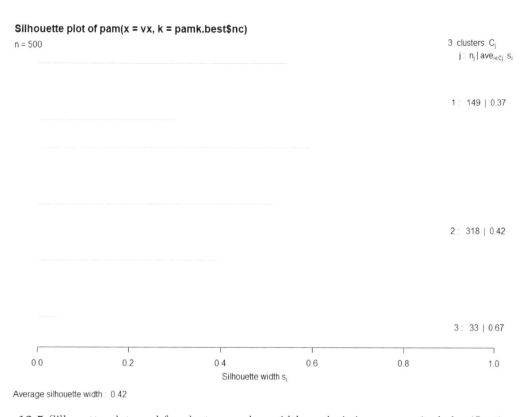

Figure 12.5 Silhouette plot used for cluster number width analysis in unsupervised classification from remote sensing big data.

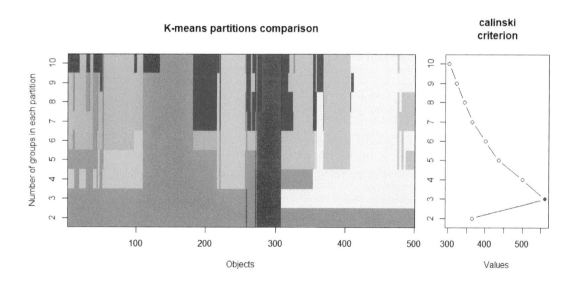

Figure 12.6 Calinski's criterion used to define the optimal number of classes in unsupervised classification from remote sensing big data.

12.8   Supervised Classification Accuracy Analysis

12.8.1   Determination of accuracy by confusion matrix

After obtaining the field reference at random locations, the reference information is compared pixel by pixel with the information obtained from the classified map. Hits and misses are summarized in the cells of the error or confusion matrix. The error matrix information can be evaluated by simple summary statistics or multivariate statistical analysis techniques (Table 12.1) (Jensen, 2005).

Table 12.1 Characteristics of a typical error matrix with k classes and N test reference samples from terrain.

		Observed				
	Class	1	2	3	k	Line Total
	1	$x_{1,1}$	$x_{1,2}$	$x_{1,3}$	$x_{1,k}$	x_{1+}
	2	$x_{2,1}$	$x_{2,2}$	$x_{2,3}$	$x_{2,k}$	x_{2+}
Predicted	3	$x_{3,1}$	$x_{3,2}$	$x_{3,3}$	$x_{3,k}$	x_{3+}
	k	$x_{k,1}$	$x_{k,2}$	$x_{k,3}$	$x_{k,k}$	x_{k+}
	Column total	x_{+1}	x_{+2}	x_{+3}	x_{+k}	N

The overall accuracy (OA) of a classified map is determined by dividing the total correct pixels (sum of the main diagonal) by the total number of pixels in the error matrix (N) (Jensen, 2005):

$$OA = \frac{\sum_{i=1}^{k} x_{ii}}{N} \tag{12.2}$$

The total number of correct pixels in a category divided by the total number of pixels of the same category in the reference data indicates the probability that a pixel has been correctly classified and is the measure of the omission error and the produced accuracy (PA) (Jensen, 2005):

$$PA = \frac{x_{ii}}{x_{+i}} \tag{12.3}$$

The total number of correct pixels in a category divided by the total number of pixels of the same category in the classified data indicates the probability that a pixel has been correctly classified and is the measure of the commission error and user accuracy (UA) (Jensen, 2005):

$$UA = \frac{x_{ii}}{x_{i+}} \tag{12.4}$$

The Kappa index ($\hat{K}$) of accuracy is another measure of accuracy between remotely sensed classification-derived data and reference data, determined by (Jensen, 2005):

$$\hat{K} = \frac{N \sum_{i=1}^{k} x_{ii} - \sum_{i=1}^{k} (x_{i+} x_{+i})}{N^2 \sum_{i=1}^{k} (x_{i+} x_{+i})} \tag{12.5}$$

The conditional accuracy coefficient, (K), can be used to calculate the match between reference and remote sensing data (Jensen, 2005):

$$K = \frac{N(x_{ii}) - (x_{i+}x_{+i})}{N(x_{i+})(x_{i+}x_{+i})} \tag{12.6}$$

where x_{ii} is the number of observations correctly classified for a particular category (summarized on the diagonal of the matrix), x_{i+} and x_{+i}, the marginal totals of the row $i+$ and column $+i$ associated with the category, and N, the total number of observations in the entire error matrix.

12.8.2   Determining accuracy by cross validation

Cross validation is one of the most widely used data resampling methods for estimating the true prediction error of models and adjusting model parameters (Berrar, 2019; Wong, 2015). Cross validation is a technique for evaluating the generalization ability of a model from a data set, where the goal of modeling is to predict and evaluate the model's performance for a new data set. The central concept of cross validation techniques is to partition the data set into subsets, and then use these subsets to estimate the model parameters from the training data. The remaining subsets are used for validation or testing to validate the model. Several ways of performing data partitioning can be used, such as holdout, k-fold, and leave-one-out (Kohavi, 1995).

In the holdout method, the total data set is divided into two subsets, one for training and parameter estimation and another for testing and validation. The data set can be separated into equal amounts or not. A very common ratio is to consider 2/3 of the data for training and the remaining 1/3 for testing (Kohavi, 1995). In the k-fold method, the total data set is divided into k subsets of the same size and from there, one subset is used for testing and the remaining k-1 for estimating the model parameters. The process is performed k times alternating the test subset. At the end of the k iterations the classification accuracy is calculated with respect to the errors found (Kohavi, 1995).

The leave-one-out method is a specific case of k-fold, with k equal to the total number of data (N). Error calculations are performed to fully evaluate the variation of the model with respect to the data used. Considering the high computational cost of this method, it is recommended to limit the use of the method to situations where few data are available (Kohavi, 1995).

12.8.3   Machine learning nomenclature for determining the confusion matrix

Another nomenclature used for the confusion matrix in machine learning approaches is exemplified by a table with the same logic as the previous example, but with nomenclature in terms of binary results, where the goal is to classify a geographic object in relation to others. As an example, imagine a situation where the aim is to classify the spatial object water, positive (P), relative to the spatial object non-water, negative (N), defined by other objects in the image. Pixels with the water spatial object predicted into the water class by the classifier algorithm are called "true positive" (TP). The remaining pixels without water (non-water) spatial objects predicted with class other are called "true negative" (TN). Geographic objects water predicted as non-water are called "false positive" (FP) and geographic objects water predicted as non-water are called "false negative" (FN). The results of FP and FN are called "type I error" and "type II error", respectively (Table 12.2) (Kassambara, 2017).

Table 12.2 Binary confusion matrix with positive condition (P) and negative condition (N) used to classify the spatial object, water, relative to another spatial object, non-water (other).

		Observed		
	Class	Water (P)	Other (N)	Line total (L)
Predicted	Water (P)	TP	FP	$\sum P_L$
	Other (N)	FN	TN	$\sum N_L$
	Column total (C)	$\sum P_C$	$\sum N_C$	Overall total (T)

The accuracy (ACC) is determined on the basis of the sum of the diagonal correct score divided by the overall total:

$$ACC = \frac{TP + TN}{T} \tag{12.7}$$

where T is the total of the entire matrix (total population).

The sensitivity or true positive rate (TPR) is determined by the ratio of true positives (TP) to the sum of the column total ($\sum P_C$):

$$TPR = \frac{TP}{\sum P_C} = \frac{TP}{TP + FN} = 1 - FNR \tag{12.8}$$

where FNR is a false negative rate.

The specificity or true negative rate (TNR) is determined by the ratio of true negatives (TN) to the column total ($\sum N_C$):

$$TNR = \frac{TN}{\sum N_C} = \frac{TN}{FP + TN} = 1 - FPR \tag{12.9}$$

where FPR is a false positive rate.

The balanced accuracy (BA) is determined by the mean between sensitivity and specificity:

$$BA = \frac{TPR + TNR}{2} \tag{12.10}$$

The accuracy or positive predictive value (PPV) is determined by the ratio of the true positive values (TP) to the row total ($\sum P_L$):

$$PPV = \frac{TP}{\sum P_L} = \frac{TP}{TP + FP} = 1 - FDR \tag{12.11}$$

where FDR is a false discovery rate.

The negative predictive value (NPV) is determined by the ratio of the true negative values (TN) to the row total ($\sum N_L$):

$$NPV = \frac{TN}{\sum N_L} = \frac{TN}{FN + TN} = 1 - FOR \qquad (12.12)$$

where FOR is a false omission rate.

The loss rate or false negative rate (FNR) is determined by the ratio of false negatives (FN) to the column total ($\sum P_C$):

$$FNR = \frac{FN}{\sum P_C} = \frac{FN}{TP + FN} = 1 - TPR \qquad (12.13)$$

where TPR is a true positive rate.

The drop rate or false positive rate (FPR) is determined by the ratio of false positives (FP) to the column total ($\sum N_C$):

$$FPR = \frac{FP}{\sum N_C} = \frac{FP}{FP + TN} = 1 - TNR \qquad (12.14)$$

where TNR is a true negative rate.

The false discovery rate (FDR) is determined by the ratio of false positives (FP) to the row total ($\sum P_L$):

$$FDR = \frac{FP}{\sum P_L} = \frac{FP}{TP + FP} = 1 - PPV \qquad (12.15)$$

where PPV is a positive predictive value.

The false omission rate (FOR) is determined by the ratio of false negatives (FN) to the row total ($\sum P_L$):

$$FOR = \frac{FN}{\sum N_L} = \frac{FN}{FN + TN} = 1 - NPV \qquad (12.16)$$

where NPV is a negative predictive value.

The prevalence (P) is determined by the column total ($\sum P_C$) in relation to the overall total (T):

$$P = \frac{\sum P_C}{T} \qquad (12.17)$$

The prevalence threshold (PT) is determined by:

$$PT = \frac{\sqrt{TPR(-TNR + 1)} + TNR - 1}{(TPR + TNR - 1)} \qquad (12.18)$$

The Matthews correlation coefficient (MCC) is defined by:

$$MCC = \frac{(TP \; TN) - (FP \; FN)}{\sqrt{(TP + FP)(TP + FN)(TN + FP)(TN + FN)}} \qquad (12.19)$$

As an example of accuracy analysis, the supervised classification results from the previous chapter used to classify the coffee crops (1), water (2), urban landscape (3), forest (4), exposed soil (5), and grassland landscape (6) targets in the Funil dam region are evaluated. The quality of results obtained using each algorithm is evaluated with a confusion matrix. In the training phase of the algorithms, the data was partitioned 98% for training and 2% for validation.

The R packages RStoolbox (Leutner et al., 2019) and caret (Kuhn et al., 2020) are enabled with the library function.

```
library(RStoolbox)
library(caret)
```

The readRSTBX function is used to import the classification results into R.

```
SC1 <- readRSTBX("C:/sr/c10/new/SC1")
SC2 <- readRSTBX("C:/sr/c10/new/SC2")
SC3 <- readRSTBX("C:/sr/c10/new/SC3")
```

The list function is used to create a list of the models used. The resamples function from the caret package is used to re-sample the list of models. The bwplot function is used to represent the accuracy analysis and kappa index in graphical form.

```
# Create model list
model_list <- list(rf = SC1$model, rpart1SE = SC2$model, svmLinear2 = SC3$model)
# Resample model list
resamples <- caret::resamples(model_list)
# Display metrics in boxplots
bwplot(resamples)
```

In the model fitting phase, the highest accuracy and kappa values were found for the rf algorithm, followed by svmLinear2 and rpart1SE. However, all algorithms used presented satisfactory performance to classify the targets, and it is important to evaluate other features of each model to perform the classification for scientific use of thematic results (Figure 12.7).

More details about model validation can be obtained with the validation function.

```
SC1$validation # rf
#$performance
#Confusion Matrix and Statistics
#          Reference
#Prediction  1    2    3    4    5    6
#      1  881    0    0   18    6  144
#      2    0  770    0    0    0    0
#      3   33    0  396    0    0    8
#      4   29    0    0  432    0    0
#      5   30    0  130    0  528  106
#      6   32    0    5    0   14   91
#Overall Statistics
#               Accuracy : 0.8481
#                 95% CI : (0.836, 0.8596)
#     No Information Rate : 0.2751
```

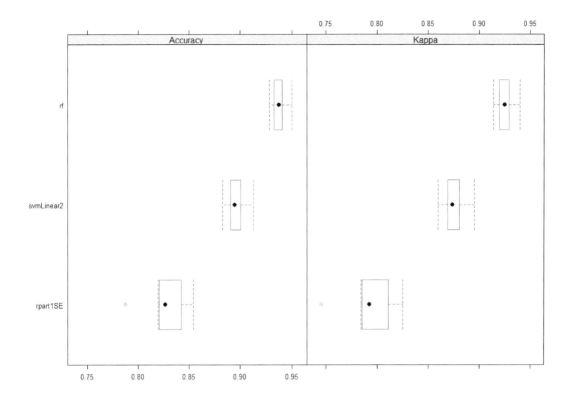

Figure 12.7 Accuracy analysis and kappa index in model fitting after supervised classification of remote sensing big data to compare `rf`, `svmLinear2`, and `rpart1SE` algorithms in predicting the targets coffee crops, water, urban landscape, forest, bare soil, and grassland landscape in the Funil dam region, state of Minas Gerais, Brazil.

```
#      P-Value [Acc > NIR] : < 2.2e-16
#                   Kappa : 0.8118
# Mcnemar's Test P-Value : NA
#Statistics by Class:
#                    Class: 1 Class: 2 Class: 3 Class: 4 Class: 5 Class: 6
#Sensitivity           0.8766   1.0000   0.7458   0.9600   0.9635   0.26074
#Specificity           0.9366   1.0000   0.9869   0.9909   0.9143   0.98456
#Pos Pred Value        0.8398   1.0000   0.9062   0.9371   0.6650   0.64085
#Neg Pred Value        0.9524   1.0000   0.9580   0.9944   0.9930   0.92652
#Prevalence            0.2751   0.2108   0.1454   0.1232   0.1500   0.09554
#Detection Rate        0.2412   0.2108   0.1084   0.1183   0.1445   0.02491
#Detection Prevalence  0.2872   0.2108   0.1196   0.1262   0.2174   0.03887
#Balanced Accuracy     0.9066   1.0000   0.8663   0.9755   0.9389   0.62265

SC2$validation # rpart1SE
#$performance
#Confusion Matrix and Statistics
#          Reference
#Prediction    1    2    3    4    5    6
#          1 438    0    0  271    0    0
```

```
#        2   0 729   0   0   0   0
#        3 154   0 313   0   0   0
#        4  68   0   0 446   0   0
#        5 311   0   0   0 200   0
#        6  34   0   0   0   2 157
#Overall Statistics
#              Accuracy : 0.731
#                95% CI : (0.7151, 0.7465)
#    No Information Rate : 0.3218
#    P-Value [Acc > NIR] : < 2.2e-16
#                 Kappa : 0.6663
# Mcnemar's Test P-Value : NA
#Statistics by Class:
#               Class: 1 Class: 2 Class: 3 Class: 4 Class: 5 Class: 6
#Sensitivity          0.4358   1.0000   1.0000   0.6220   0.99010  1.00000
#Specificity          0.8720   1.0000   0.9452   0.9717   0.89353  0.98786
#Pos Pred Value       0.6178   1.0000   0.6702   0.8677   0.39139  0.81347
#Neg Pred Value       0.7651   1.0000   1.0000   0.8961   0.99923  1.00000
#Prevalence           0.3218   0.2334   0.1002   0.2296   0.06468  0.05027
#Detection Rate       0.1402   0.2334   0.1002   0.1428   0.06404  0.05027
#Detection Prevalence 0.2270   0.2334   0.1495   0.1646   0.16362  0.06180
#Balanced Accuracy    0.6539   1.0000   0.9726   0.7969   0.94181  0.99393


SC3$validation # svmLinear2
#$performance
#Confusion Matrix and Statistics
#         Reference
#Prediction   1   2   3   4   5   6
#        1 942   0   0  30  16   1
#        2   0 109   0   0   0   0
#        3   0   0 251   0   0   0
#        4   5   0   0 740   0   0
#        5  32   0   2   0 737   0
#        6  26   0   0   0   0 381
#Overall Statistics
#              Accuracy : 0.9658
#                95% CI : (0.959, 0.9717)
#    No Information Rate : 0.3072
#    P-Value [Acc > NIR] : < 2.2e-16
#                 Kappa : 0.956
# Mcnemar's Test P-Value : NA
#Statistics by Class:
#               Class: 1 Class: 2 Class: 3 Class: 4 Class: 5 Class: 6
#Sensitivity          0.9373  1.00000  0.99209   0.9610   0.9788   0.9974
#Specificity          0.9793  1.00000  1.00000   0.9980   0.9865   0.9910
#Pos Pred Value       0.9525  1.00000  1.00000   0.9933   0.9559   0.9361
#Neg Pred Value       0.9724  1.00000  0.99934   0.9881   0.9936   0.9997
#Prevalence           0.3072  0.03331  0.07732   0.2353   0.2301   0.1167
#Detection Rate       0.2879  0.03331  0.07671   0.2262   0.2252   0.1164
#Detection Prevalence 0.3023  0.03331  0.07671   0.2277   0.2356   0.1244
#Balanced Accuracy    0.9583  1.00000  0.99605   0.9795   0.9826   0.9942
```

Note that although the random forest model did better in the training phase than the support vector machine, in the validation phase the svmLinear2 algorithm performed better based on the statistical results of the confusion matrix.

12.9 Supervised Segmentation Accuracy Analysis

For accuracy analysis of object-based supervised segmentation, the methods used are almost the same as those used in pixel-by-pixel classification. Considering the R package SegOptim, the available methods are cross validation k-fold 10 (10FCV), k-fold 5 (5FCV), holdout (HOCV), and out-of-bag (OOB) (Gonçalves, 2020).

12.10 Confusion Matrix in Cloud Processing

Supervised classification accuracy analysis can be developed using a cloud processing routine. The rgee and sf packages are enabled and the ee_Initialize function is used to initialize the Earth Engine.

```
library(sf)
library(rgee)
ee_Initialize()
```

Landsat-8 imagery data in a cloudless collection is used as input data for the classification with function ee$ImageCollection.

```
l8 <- ee$ImageCollection("LANDSAT/LC08/C01/T1")
```

The ee$Algorithms$Landsat$simpleComposite function is used to obtain a top of atmosphere (TOA) collection with minimal clouds from January 1 to December 31, 2018.

```
image <- ee$Algorithms$Landsat$simpleComposite(collection =
    l8$filterDate("2018-01-01", "2018-12-31"), asFloat = TRUE)
```

Bands 2 to 11 are selected from an atomic c() vector.

```
bands <- c("B2", "B3", "B4", "B5", "B6", "B7", "B10", "B11")
```

The training polygons used in the previous chapter are imported into R with the st_read function.

The sf_as_ee function is used to convert the sf object into ee.featurecollection for use in Earth Engine.

```
polygons <- sf_as_ee(classid, check_ring_dir = TRUE)
```

The pixel values are obtained within each polygon with the `sampleRegions` function.

```
training <- image$sampleRegions(collection = polygons,
                                properties = list("class"), scale = 30)
```

Classifier configuration is done with the `Classifier` function and training with the `train` function. The classifiers support vector machine (libsvm), CART classification (smileCart), and random forest (smileRandomForest) are configured for supervised classification.

```
trained <- ee$Classifier$libsvm(kernelType = "RBF", gamma = 0.5, cost = 10)$
         train(training, "class", bands) # SVM
trained1 <- ee$Classifier$smileCart()$train(training, "class", bands) # CART
trained2 <- ee$Classifier$smileRandomForest(10)$train(training, "class",
                                                 bands) # RF
```

The confusion matrix is determined with the `confusionMatrix` function. Then, the total accuracy and kappa index are determined from the confusion matrix, which can be obtained with the `getInfo` function.

```
trained$confusionMatrix()$getInfo() # SVM
#[[1]]
#[1] 0 0 0 0 0 0 0
#[[2]]
#[1]     0 20384     0    35   366   205   124
#[[3]]
#[1]    0   28 8414    0    1    7   22
#[[4]]
#[1]    0  364    1 1253    0  316   13
#[[5]]
#[1]    0  680    0    0 4474    0    0
#[[6]]
#[1]    0  809    3  168  105 2114   82
#[[7]]
#[1]   0 866   0    2    0   17 982
trained1$confusionMatrix()$getInfo() # CART
#[[1]]
#[1] 0 0 0 0 0 0 0
#[[2]]
#[1]     0 21114     0     0     0     0     0
#[[3]]
#[1]    0    0 8472    0    0    0    0
#[[4]]
#[1]    0    9    0 1938    0    0    0
#[[5]]
#[1]    0    0    0    0 5154    0    0
#[[6]]
#[1]    0    0    0    0    0 3281    0
#[[7]]
```

```
#[1]     0    0    0    0    0    0 1867
trained2$confusionMatrix()$getInfo() # RF
#[[1]]
#[1] 0 0 0 0 0 0 0
#[[2]]
#[1]     0 21075    0    4   14   12    9
#[[3]]
#[1]   0    3 8468    0    0    0    1
#[[4]]
#[1]   0   58    0 1876    0   11    2
#[[5]]
#[1]   0  118    0    0 5036    0    0
#[[6]]
#[1]   0   47    2   33   15 3179    5
#[[7]]
#[1]   0   52    0    1    0   10 1804
```

The total accuracy and kappa index are determined from each confusion matrix obtained associated with the use of the `confusionMatrix`, `accuracy`, `kappa`, `getInfo`, and `cat` functions.

```
trainAccuracy <- trained$confusionMatrix() # SVM
cat('Overall accuracy: ', trainAccuracy$accuracy()$getInfo())
# Overall accuracy:  0.8992709
trainKappa <- trained$confusionMatrix()
cat('Kappa: ', trainAccuracy$kappa()$getInfo())
# Kappa:  0.8468517
trainAccuracy1 <- trained1$confusionMatrix() # CART
cat('Overall accuracy: ', trainAccuracy1$accuracy()$getInfo())
# Overall accuracy:  0.9997849
trainKappa1 <- trained1$confusionMatrix()
cat('Kappa: ', trainAccuracy1$kappa()$getInfo())
# Kappa:  0.8468517
trainAccuracy2 <- trained2$confusionMatrix() # RF
cat('Overall accuracy: ', trainAccuracy2$accuracy()$getInfo())
# Overall accuracy:  0.9905103
trainKappa2 <- trained2$confusionMatrix()
cat('Kappa: ', trainAccuracy2$kappa()$getInfo())
# Kappa:  0.9859701
```

Based on the information obtained from the confusion matrix, the lowest training error is obtained for the CART and RF algorithms. The highest error is obtained for the SVM algorithm.

Both training results are used in classifying the Landsat-8 image collection. Classifications are performed with the `image` and `classify` functions.

```
classified <- image$classify(trained) # SVM
classified1 <- image$classify(trained1) # CART
classified2 <- image$classify(trained2) # RF
```

A color palette for classes 1 to 6 is defined with the `list` function for all mapping situations and for the color composition that is used for visual analysis of the classification results of each training algorithm. The colors "DarkOliveGreen", "blue", "grey", "ForestGreen", "brown", and "LightGreen" are converted to the hexadecimal system for use in mapping results.

The result of SVM, CART, and RF classification is performed with the Map, setCenter, and addLayer functions. Landsat-8 color compositions are also performed.

```
Map$setCenter(-44.87022, -21.15752, 11)
Map$addLayer(eeObject = image, visParams = geoviz_image, name = "L8 natural") +
Map$addLayer(eeObject = image, visParams = geoviz_image1, name = "L8 false") +
Map$addLayer(eeObject = classified, visParams = geoviz_class,
             name = "SVM", legend = TRUE) +
Map$addLayer(eeObject = classified1, visParams = geoviz_class,
             name = "CART", legend = TRUE) +
Map$addLayer(eeObject = classified2, visParams = geoviz_class,
             name = "RF", legend = TRUE)
```

Since results of the SVM classification have already been presented in the previous chapter, only the best results from training with the CART and RF algorithms are presented.

It can be seen that there is a well-defined division of water, bare soil, urban areas, and dense vegetation targets in some regions. Coffee crops occur in large numbers in a shade that has determined some mixing among other green vegetation classes. The grasslands appear well fragmented around the entire image (Figure 12.8).

Figure 12.8 CART classification mapping from remote sensing big data used in the prediction of targets coffee crops, water, urban landscape, forest, bare soil, and grassland landscape in the region of the Funil dam, state of Minas Gerais, Brazil.

In the random forest classification, there is a clear difference in the grassland class occurring in less fragmented regions, especially in the north of the area, when compared to the CART classification. However, the targets of interest were also well defined in the classification and it is necessary to evaluate specific regions or validate the classification results to define which result to use for scientific applications (Figure 12.9).

Figure 12.9 Mapping random forest classification from remote sensing big data used in the prediction of targets coffee crops, water, urban landscape, forest, bare soil, and grassland landscape in the region of the Funil dam, state of Minas Gerais, Brazil.

The natural color and false color infrared compositions are also mapped to provide geovisualization results.

In the natural color composition, it is possible to verify the absence of clouds in the image and the complexity of targets that can be mapped in the region, such as urban areas, mining area, exposed soil and the spectral mixture that occurs from the water with the other targets of the landscape in view of the occurrence of sediments, microorganisms and algae in the water (Figure 12.10).

In the infrared color composition, the water is much clearer in the image, and it is also possible to detect urbanized regions, mining in light tones, and vegetation in reddish tones. Tree vegetation is represented in darker red tones on the image (Figure 12.11).

A greater generalization of classes may be necessary for applications with a great mixture in the classification due to the use of 3 vegetation classes with similar spectral characteristics. The images can also be corrected and transformed in surface reflectance and even use other remote sensing data of higher spatial resolution and already classified images from other sensors as source of information for training with larger number of samples.

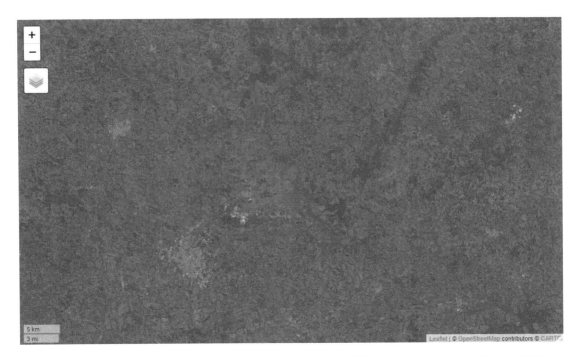

Figure 12.10 Natural color RGB composition mapping of Landsat-8 imagery taken in 2018 in the Funil dam region, state of Minas Gerais, Brazil.

Figure 12.11 Infrared false color RGB composition mapping of Landsat-8 imagery taken in 2018 in the Funil dam region, state of Minas Gerais, Brazil.

12.11 Computational Practice

12.11.1 Evaluating the unsupervised classification of a digital elevation model

The classification of a digital elevation model into 4 classes by the supervised classification method performed in the previous chapter is evaluated in terms of accuracy by a confusion matrix. The result of the classification performed in the previous chapter can be obtained by re-analyzing the routine presented in that situation or it can be obtained in compressed format for **download**[1]. The file, after being obtained from the Internet, should be unzipped into a known directory on your computer for use afterwards.

12.11.2 Installing and enabling packages

To evaluate the classification accuracy, the `install.packages` function installs the R packages `RStoolbox` (Leutner et al., 2019), `raster` (Hijmans et al., 2020), `vegan`, and `caret`. Packages already installed should not be reinstalled to avoid upgrade problems, but only enabled for analysis.

```
install.packages("RStoolbox")
install.packages("raster")
install.packages("vegan")
install.packages("caret")
```

The `library` function enables the R packages `RStoolbox`, `raster`, `vegan`, and `caret` to run the computational practice.

```
library(RStoolbox)
library(raster)
library(vegan)
library(caret)
```

12.11.2.1 Evaluating the accuracy of the classification model

The random forest classification model used in the previous chapter to classify the digital elevation model into four categorical classes is used to illustrate the accuracy analysis of the supervised method. The classified model with the obtained results and fit parameters is imported from the computer directory with the `readRSTBX` function.

```
SC <- readRSTBX("C:/sr/c9/SC")
```

Information about the model fit, after training the classifier algorithm, is obtained by means of the confusion matrix and 5-fold cross validation, exploring the results of `SC$modelFit`.

---

[1] http://www.sergeo.deg.ufla.br/sr/downloads/SC.zip

```
SC$modelFit
#[[1]]
#  TrainAccuracy TrainKappa method
#1     0.9951605   0.993165      rf
#[[2]]
#Cross-Validated (5 fold) Confusion Matrix
#(entries are average cell counts across resamples)
#           Reference
#Prediction    1     2     3     4
#         1  69.0   0.0   0.0   0.0
#         2   0.0  55.8   0.8   0.0
#         3   0.0   0.6  42.0   0.0
#         4   0.0   0.0   0.0 121.0
# Accuracy (average) : 0.9952
```

Thus, it is observed that the accuracy of the model is evaluated by 5-fold cross validation, obtaining an average accuracy of 0.9952. Only in class 2, there was an average of 0.6 pixels mistakenly predicted as belonging to class 3.

The model validation information is obtained with the code SC$validation. In model validation, based on 40% of the data used in model training, accuracy, balanced accuracy, and kappa equal to 100% were observed, based on the determination of the confusion matrix used as validation information.

```
SC$validation
#$performance
#Confusion Matrix and Statistics
#           Reference
#Prediction   1    2    3    4
#         1  96    0    0    0
#         2   0  141    0    0
#         3   0    0   82    0
#         4   0    0    0  365
#Overall Statistics
#               Accuracy : 1
#                 95% CI : (0.9946, 1)
#    No Information Rate : 0.5336
#    P-Value [Acc > NIR] : < 2.2e-16
#                  Kappa : 1
# Mcnemar's Test P-Value : NA
#Statistics by Class:
#                      Class: 1 Class: 2 Class: 3 Class: 4
#Sensitivity            1.0000   1.0000   1.0000   1.0000
#Specificity            1.0000   1.0000   1.0000   1.0000
#Pos Pred Value         1.0000   1.0000   1.0000   1.0000
#Neg Pred Value         1.0000   1.0000   1.0000   1.0000
#Prevalence             0.1404   0.2061   0.1199   0.5336
#Detection Rate         0.1404   0.2061   0.1199   0.5336
#Detection Prevalence   0.1404   0.2061   0.1199   0.5336
#Balanced Accuracy      1.0000   1.0000   1.0000   1.0000
```

12.11.3 Number of optimal classes in unsupervised classification

An example to determine the number of optimal classes in unsupervised classification is performed with stacked raster data from Landsat-8 OLI/TIRS (June 28, 2021) and Sentinel-1,2 imagery obtained at the Funil dam, state of Minas Gerais, between June 25, 2021 and June 28, 2021, respectively. The data used in the practice can be adapted and used with previous images made available by the teacher. The `stack` and `names` functions are used to import and rename the spectral variables used in the classification.

```
bdsub<-stack("C:/sr/c10/bdsub.tif")
names(bdsub)<-c("costal","blue","green","red","nir","swir2","swir3",
"swir1","tir1","tir2","brightness","greenness","wetness","CTVI.1",
"DVI.1","EVI.1","EVI2","GEMI.1","GNDVI.1","MNDWI.1","MSAVI.1",
"MSAVI2.1","NBRI.1","NDVI.1","NDWI.1","NDWI2.1","NRVI.1","RVI.1",
"SATVI.1","SAVI.1","S1B_IW_GRDH_1SDV_20210628T082946_Cal_Spk_TC.3",
"S1B_IW_GRDH_1SDV_20210628T082946_Cal_Spk_TC.4",
"T23KNS_20210625T131249_B02_10m", "T23KNS_20210625T131249_B03_10m",
"T23KNS_20210625T131249_B04_10m","T23KNS_20210625T131249_B05_20m",
"T23KNS_20210625T131249_B06_20m","T23KNS_20210625T131249_B07_20m",
"T23KNS_20210625T131249_B08_10m","T23KNS_20210625T131249_B8A_20m",
"T23KNS_20210625T131249_B09_60m","T23KNS_20210625T131249_B11_20m",
"T23KNS_20210625T131249_B12_20m","CLG", "CLRE","CTVI.2","DVI.2",
"EVI.2","GEMI.2","GNDVI.2","MCARI","MNDWI.2","MSAVI.2","MSAVI2.2",
"NBRI.2","NDREI1","NDREI2","NDVI.2", "NDWI.2","NDWI2.2","NRVI.2",
"RVI.2","SATVI.2","SAVI.2","SLAVI","SR","WDVI")
```

The `getValues` function is used to extract values from the raster images used in the classification, and the `which(!is.na())` and `na.omit` functions are used so that missing data (`NA`) is not considered in the analysis.

```
v <- getValues(bdsub)
i <- which(!is.na(v))
v <- na.omit(v)
```

A sample data set `vx` is obtained using 500 samples with the function `sample(nrow())`.

```
vx<-v[sample(nrow(v), 500),]
```

Using the `cascadeKM` function enables evaluation of the optimal number of clusters for supervised classification based on the Calinski criteria.

```
fit <- cascadeKM(scale(vx, center = TRUE,  scale = TRUE), 1, 10, iter = 1000)
```

The results are presented in graphs with the `plot` function (Figure 12.12).

```
plot(fit, sortg = TRUE, grpmts.plot = TRUE)
```

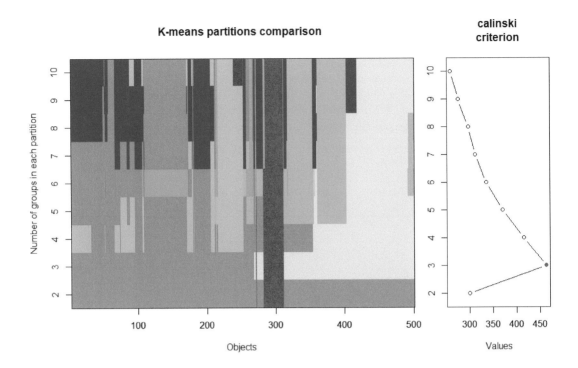

Figure 12.12 Optimal number of unsupervised classification classes based on the Calinski criterion.

A code chunk can be used to evaluate the best results in numerical format.

```
calinski.best <- as.numeric(which.max(fit$results[2,]))
cat("Calinski criterion optimal number of clusters:",
    calinski.best, "\n")
#Calinski criterion optimal number of clusters: 3
```

Therefore, based on this method, 3 and 4 clusters are defined as ideal for use in unsupervised classification. It should be noted that other methods can be used to define the best number of clusters, and it is necessary that the analyst perform tests and observe the mapping results with different classes in order to define the best result in each application.

12.11.4 Evaluating the confusion matrix of supervised classification

The results of supervised classification models from the previous chapter are compared in terms of the confusion matrix. The readRSTBX function is used to import the results of classification by random forest (rf), support vector machine (svmLinear2), and CART (rpart1SE) methods.

```
SC1 <- readRSTBX("C:/sr/c10/SC1")
SC2 <- readRSTBX("C:/sr/c10/SC2")
SC3 <- readRSTBX("C:/sr/c10/SC3")
```

A list of model results is created with the `list` function.

```
model_list <- list(rf = SC1$model, rpart1SE = SC2$model, svmLinear2 = SC3$model)
```

The results are resampled with the `resamples` function of the `caret` package. Then, the `bwplot` function is used to compare accuracy and kappa metrics of each fit (Figure 12.13).

```
resamples <- caret::resamples(model_list) # Resample
bwplot(resamples) #bwplot
```

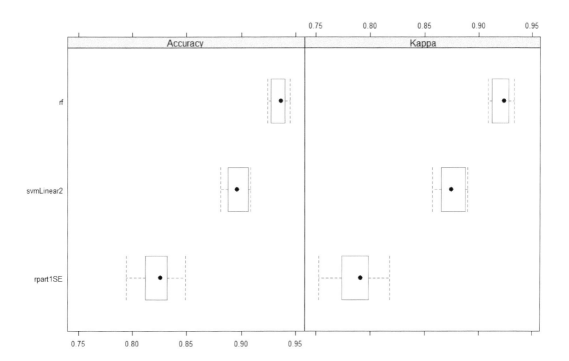

Figure 12.13 Accuracy and kappa metrics used in the comparative evaluation of the fit of machine learning algorithms used in supervised classification in the Funil dam region, state of Minas Gerais, in June 2021.

Both results presented metrics with high accuracy and kappa values; however, the `rf` method was superior to `svmLinear2` and `rpart1SE`, according to the training samples, after `10-fold` cross validation. The confusion matrix results are also evaluated in order to assess which algorithm performed better in classifying coffee crops based on the fit result of each algorithm.

Detailed confusion matrix results for the `RF` method can be obtained by exploring the attribute results recorded in `modelFit`.

```
SC1$modelFit
#[[1]]
#  TrainAccuracy TrainKappa method
#1      0.934981  0.9219623     rf
#[[2]]
#Cross-Validated (10 fold) Confusion Matrix
```

```
#(entries are average cell counts across resamples)
#          Reference
#Prediction    1     2     3     4     5     6
#          1 101.3   0.1   1.5   4.3   0.1   1.7
#          2   0.0 102.2   0.0   0.0   0.0   0.0
#          3   1.9   0.0  95.1   0.0   5.3   1.3
#          4   7.7   0.0   0.0  99.3   0.0   0.0
#          5   3.5   0.1   2.8   0.0  95.1   1.5
#          6   5.1   0.0   3.6   0.0   0.6  98.1
# Accuracy (average) : 0.935
```

The detailed results of the confusion matrix by the svmLinear2 method can be obtained by exploring the attribute results recorded in modelFit.

```
SC3$modelFit
#[[1]]
#  TrainAccuracy TrainKappa      method
#1    0.8957647  0.8749218 svmLinear2
#[[2]]
#Cross-Validated (10 fold) Confusion Matrix
#(entries are average cell counts across resamples)
#          Reference
#Prediction    1     2     3     4     5     6
#          1  97.5   0.0   2.2   3.7   1.1   0.8
#          2   0.0 102.4   0.0   0.0   0.0   0.0
#          3   1.9   0.0  88.3   0.0  10.4   1.5
#          4   6.7   0.0   0.0  99.9   0.0   0.1
#          5   7.6   0.0   9.7   0.0  86.7   8.7
#          6   5.8   0.0   2.8   0.0   2.9  91.5
# Accuracy (average) : 0.8958
```

The detailed results of the confusion matrix by the rpart1SE algorithm can be obtained by exploring the attribute results recorded in modelFit.

```
SC2$modelFit
#[[1]]
#  TrainAccuracy TrainKappa    method
#1    0.8215699   0.785741 rpart1SE
#[[2]]
#Cross-Validated (10 fold) Confusion Matrix
#(entries are average cell counts across resamples)
#          Reference
#Prediction    1     2     3     4     5     6
#          1  92.1   0.0   2.1  25.0   0.6   0.6
#          2   0.0 102.3   0.0   0.1   0.0   0.0
#          3   1.9   0.1  75.1   0.0   8.9   1.5
#          4   8.3   0.0   0.0  78.5   0.0   0.0
#          5   9.0   0.0   9.8   0.0  82.9  12.0
#          6   8.2   0.0  16.0   0.0   8.7  88.5
# Accuracy (average) : 0.8216
```

We observed that the svmLinear2 algorithm better separated the coffee classes (1) in relation to forest (4) when compared to the rf and rpart1SE algorithms. However, there was a lot of mixing of coffee with exposed soil, probably due to the fact that it considered the tillage paths as coffee, affecting the interpretation and classification of the results.

12.12 Exercises

12.12.1 What are the sources of errors in information obtained by remote sensing?

12.12.2 What are the steps to determine classification accuracy?

12.12.3 Determine the number of points required to evaluate a classification with expected accuracy of 85% and tolerable error of 5% based on binomial probability theory.

12.12.4 Determine the number of points required to evaluate a classification with expected accuracy of 85% and tolerable error of 10% based on binomial probability theory.

12.12.5 Cite five types of sampling plans used in remote sensing map accuracy analysis.

12.12.6 What are the commands used to determine the silhouette index and confusion matrix in practice in R?

12.12.7 Evaluate the overall accuracy of a supervised classification according to the confusion matrix data of vegetation, soil, water, and urban targets (Table 12.3).

Table 12.3 Confusion matrix of the observed and predicted vegetation, soil, water, and urban targets by the naive Bayes classifier.

	Class	Vegetation	Soil	Water	Urban	Line total
		Observed				
	Vegetation	98	5	0	1	104
	Soil	0	34	36	4	74
Predicted	water	1	0	70	0	71
	Urban	0	26	0	129	155
	Column total	99	65	106	134	404

12.12.8 **In a classification analysis of remote sensing data in which the class `water` (1) and `non-water` (0) are evaluated in terms of prediction of the classifier algorithm, determine the confusion matrix, accuracy, sensitivity and specificity of the classification, based on the following data:**

Observed pixel values with water and non-water: 1, 1, 0, 1, 0, 0, 1, 0, 0, 0.

Predicted pixel values with water and non-water: 1, 0, 0, 1, 0, 0, 1, 1, 0.

12.13   Homework

12.13.1   Subject

Accuracy analysis of supervised classification applied to multispectral imagery from CBERS-04A satellite for environmental monitoring.

12.13.2   Assignment

Develop the subject presented with a practical application of remote sensing and digital image processing including the topics Introduction and Objective. Then present the development of the task.

12.14   Resources on the Internet

As a study guide, slides and illustrative videos are presented about the subject covered in the chapter (Table 12.4).

Table 12.4 Slide show and video presentation on uncertainty and accuracy analysis in remote sensing image processing.

Guide	Address for Access
1	Video on determining accuracy in R^2
2	Slides on accuracy analysis of thematic information derived from remote sensing imagery classification[3]

---

[2]https://youtu.be/Fcanny-v-7c
[3]http://www.sergeo.deg.ufla.br/sr/Presentation/Aula11/presentation.html#/

12.15 Research Suggestion

The development of scientific research on accuracy analysis of thematic information derived from remote sensing image classification is stimulated through activity proposals that can be used or adapted by the student to assess the applicability of the subject matter covered in the chapter (Table 12.5).

Table 12.5 Description of practical activities that can be used or adapted by students with suggested research in remote sensing.

Activity	Description
1	Evaluate the accuracy of unsupervised and supervised classification and define which is the best method to map geographic objects. Choose the best image processing results to elaborate the abstract according to the obtained results.
2	Perform comparative accuracy analysis of supervised classification on fusion and non-fusion images with the same training samples. Evaluate the best results.
3	Perform comparative accuracy analysis of supervised classification on images with many and few training samples. Evaluate the best results.

13

Scientific Applications of Remote Sensing and Digital Image Processing to Enhance Articles

13.1 Learning Questions

The learning questions answered by reading the chapter are as follows:

- How can the science of remote sensing be applied in preparing articles?
- What is the relationship between remote sensing applications and science practice?
- How are geographic problems with remote sensing science solved objectively?

13.2 Learning Outcomes

Using the learning outcomes from the chapter, you should be able to do the following:

- Use scientific applications of remote sensing in article writing.
- Identify scientific hypotheses related to remote sensing in scientific articles.
- Write an example of scientific paper on remote sensing with R.
- Understand an example of scientific dissemination of remote sensing with R.

13.3 Introduction

Scientific articles are written communications, published in specialized journals, with the objective of disseminating to the scientific community the results, even if partial, of research in a specific area. According to the Brazilian Association of Technical Standards (ABNT - Associação Brasileira de Normas Técnicas, 2003), a scientific article can be defined as part of a publication with declared authorship, which presents and discusses ideas, methods, techniques, processes and results in various areas of knowledge.

The scientific article can be:

- Original <- works resulting from scientific research presenting original data of findings with respect to experimental or observational aspects of medical, biochemical and social characteristics and includes descriptive analysis and/or inferences of own data;

- Review <- critical synthesis of available knowledge on a given topic, through analysis and interpretation of pertinent bibliography, that discusses the limits and methodological reaches, allowing us to indicate perspectives of continuity of studies in that line of research, i.e., works that have the objective of summarizing, analyzing, evaluating or synthesizing already published research works, bibliographic reviews, among others.

13.4   Popular Knowledge and Scientific Knowledge

Common or popular knowledge is called common sense and represents a type of knowledge with some degree of veracity and the nature of the object known. Scientific knowledge can be similar to common sense; however, there are differences in the way, form, method and instruments used to know the object (Marconi & Lakatos, 2021).

Scientific knowledge differs from popular, philosophical and religious knowledge in different contexts. Scientific knowledge is real, because it deals with occurrences or facts. It constitutes knowledge contingent on propositions that can be evaluated by experience and reason, as in philosophical knowledge. It is systematic, logically ordered by a system of oriented and connected ideas and theories. It can be verified and validated so that hypotheses can be refuted. It is approximately exact by proposing the development of techniques that can reformulate the existing body of theory (Marconi & Lakatos, 2021) (Figure 13.1).

Popular	Scientific
○ Valuative ○ Reflective ○ Unsystematic ○ Verifiable ○ Fallible ○ Inexact	○ Real (factual) ○ Contingent ○ Systematic ○ Verifiable ○ Fallible ○ Approximately exact
Philosophical	Religious
○ Valuative ○ Rational ○ Systematic ○ Not verifiable ○ Infallible ○ Exact	○ Valuative ○ Inspiracional ○ Systematic ○ Not verifiable ○ Infallible ○ Exact

Figure 13.1 Characteristics of four types of knowledge.

13.5 The Concept of Science

Science is a systematization of knowledge and a set of propositions about the behavior of phenomena to be studied using verifiable and systematized methods. Sciences have an objective, function, material and formal objects. Several branches of study and specific sciences have emerged and can be classified in order of complexity according to content, object, statement and methodology employed. A basic classification can be used to separate types of sciences into formal and factual with subdivisions into specific branches with further distinctions of object and method of investigation (Marconi & Lakatos, 2021). Remote sensing and digital image processing can be applied in formal and factual sciences in different contexts, be it in everyday situations, in historical facts that have already occurred, or in the development, extension, and improvement of existing technology itself (Figure 13.2).

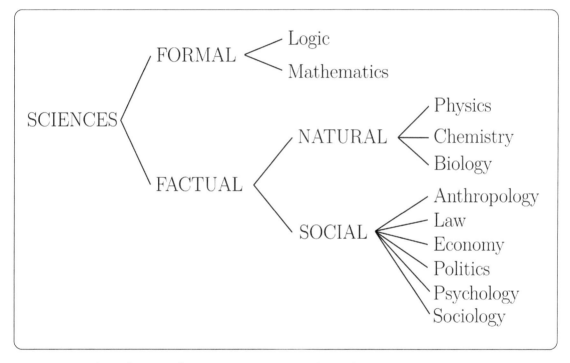

Figure 13.2 Classification of science into subareas of knowledge.

13.6 Scientific Methods

Scientific methods are used in science as a set of systematic and rational activities used to produce knowledge and aid in decision making. The scientific method can be considered in the form of a theory of investigation subdivided into several steps from the discovery of the problem to the proof of the solution or correction of hypotheses, theories and procedures in case the incorrect solution is obtained (Marconi & Lakatos, 2021) (Figure 13.3).

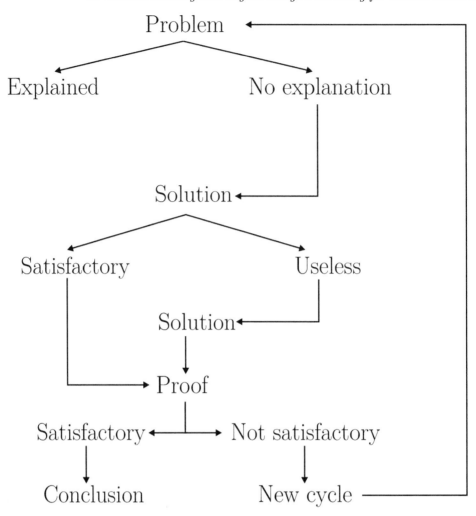

Figure 13.3 Stages of the theory of investigation by the scientific method.

13.7　Deductive and Inductive Methods

Deductive and inductive arguments have different purposes, the deductive being intended to explain the content of premises, and the inductive being intended to broaden the scope of knowledge. Deductive arguments can be correct or not, while inductive arguments admit different degrees of strength depending on the ability of premises to support the conclusion (Marconi & Lakatos, 2021). Therefore, deductive and inductive arguments can be distinct in basic characteristics (Salmon, 1978) (Figure 13.4).

Deductive	Inductive
1. If all the premises are true, the conclusion must be true.	1. If all the premises are true the conclusion is probably true.
2. All the information or factual content of the conclusion was already implicit in the premises.	2. The conclusion contains information that was not implicit in the premises.

Figure 13.4 Basic characteristics of deductive and inductive arguments.

13.8 Variables in the Universe of Science

Variables in the context of science must be translated into measurable concepts. The universe of science can be thought of as being in levels, the first level being where observations of real facts, phenomena, behaviors, and activities occur. At the second level there are valid and sustainable hypotheses through the enunciation of variables. At the third level theories emerge. Variables can be independent and dependent. The independent variable is the one that influences, determines, or affects another variable, being a determining factor to cause a certain result, effect, or outcome. The dependent variable consists of values to be explained or discovered and can be influenced, determined, or affected by the independent variable (Marconi & Lakatos, 2021) (Figure 13.5).

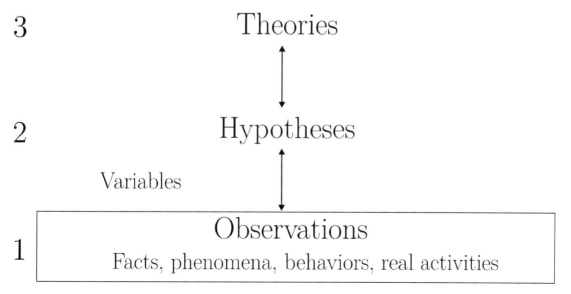

Figure 13.5 Universe of science in levels.

13.9   Implementation of Scientific Projects in Remote Sensing

In the implementation cycle of scientific projects in remote sensing, the development occurs as a continuous and recursive process in which modifications and improvements can be made according to adaptations needed to new scientific and technological advances. With the implementation of the projects, results are obtained in order to enable the elaboration of articles for scientific dissemination (Alves & Sanches, 2022).

13.10   Scientific Dissemination in Remote Sensing

In scientific dissemination, considerations are presented about scientific writing in the form of a scientific paper and scientific presentation in the format of a slide show (Alves & Sanches, 2022).

13.10.1   Scientific writing

Scientific writing, although an indispensable step in the scientific process, is often overlooked in undergraduate courses in favor of maximizing class time devoted to scientific concepts. However, the ability to effectively communicate research findings is crucial to success in science. Students and professional scientists are judged by the number of papers published and the number of citations those papers have received. Therefore, a solid foundation in scientific writing can better prepare undergraduate and graduate students for productive academic careers (Alves & Sanches, 2022; Turbek et al., 2016).

In writing a scientific paper, the structure of the manuscript should be similar to that of an hourglass, with an open and broad beginning, tapering off as it narrows down to the relevant literature that determined the relevance of the paper as unpublished, definition of the hypothesis, material and methods used. The knowledge gap that will be evaluated should be clear by this point. In the results phase, corresponding to the middle of the hourglass, the objectives are achieved by means of remote sensing and statistical techniques used to evaluate the acceptance of the hypothesis. In the discussion phase of the results obtained, the hourglass is again enlarged to interpret the results based on the existing literature in order to make clear that the knowledge gap detected previously is filled, culminating in conclusions and implication of the work (Alves & Sanches, 2022).

Therefore, in the Introduction one should start from broad ideas to specific questions, using a structure that resembles the image of a funnel or an inverted pyramid. The operation of the Discussion and Introduction sections should be opposite and mirrored. In the Discussion, the pyramid presents the conventional format, starting from specific questions (study findings) to more comprehensive elaborations (Alves & Sanches, 2022; Cáceres et al., 2011).

The immutable characteristics of good scientific writing that distinguish it from other literature are accuracy, clarity, and brevity. A vague text cannot be considered a scientific text, because it lacks clarity or is ambiguous. A prolix and unnecessarily discursive scientific manuscript was considered poor in terms of scientific writing. Therefore, a clear, precise and brief text can be read and understood by a larger number of readers (Alves & Sanches, 2022; Lindsay, 2011).

When writing the scientific article in the field of remote sensing, often the topics should be written with the verb in the past tense, because the text was written in the context of presenting the results of the work with relevant scientific conclusions about a given geographic problem. In summary, topics ranging from the title to the bibliographic references are contemplated in the preparation of a scientific article (Table 13.1).

Table 13.1 Aspects considered in the development of scientific paper topics in remote sensing.

Topic	Aspects Considered
Title	It should be succinct and try to contain, in a few words, what is intended to be accomplished with the work.
Authors	Include sequence of authors, advisor and affiliation according to the norms.
Abstract and keywords	Include index words for the abstract that are not part of the title.
Introduction	Get to the point: point out the problem, the demand, and show that you have not only been able to diagnose the problem, but that you are able to solve it. Get information about what has already been done in other work on a similar subject. At the end of the introduction, briefly present the objective and the hypothesis.
Methods	It is necessary to include as many details as possible, but without exaggerating. For example: Variable studied, date when the radiometric data was obtained, analysis performed on the data.
Results	Present the results obtained based on the data analysis.
Discussion	Discuss the results obtained based on the available literature.
Conclusion	Address what was obtained with the execution of the work within what was proposed in the objective.
References	Include the bibliographical references used. Prioritize citations of scientific articles in journals with an editorial board and renowned in the area.

13.10.2 Scientific dissemination

Formal scientific dissemination is accomplished through presentations in different types of media. The use of short video presentations has been used by researchers and in scientific journals. However, transforming a scientific publication into a short video with accessible language can be a complex mission for researchers with little affinity and availability of these resources (Alves & Sanches, 2022).

Dissemination of science means allowing other people to learn about the research conducted. Scientists working in academia (universities, research centers) and in research and development in large corporations and small companies need to disseminate research results to gain respect and credibility in society and boost careers. This can create a market for products and attract talented employees, as well as build a network of collaborations with other research groups. This can increase the chances of obtaining funding for projects and research with public and private investors (Alves & Sanches, 2022; WEBforSCIENCE, 2016).

Scientists should include information on contributor and investor accountability, and if possible, the positive impact of research on health and socio-economic progress of society. An effective communication strategy can increase the likelihood that it will attract the attention of decision makers and that science will be used to support decisions about strategic evidence-based policy priorities to meet the needs of the population (Alves & Sanches, 2022; WEBforSCIENCE, 2016).

Researchers can disseminate scientific work through articles, review papers, workshops, posters, and talks at conferences, seminars, reports. In addition, written and visual materials (video and infographics) can be used for flyers, brochures, press releases, websites, newsletters, blogs, and the entire broad spectrum of social media (Alves & Sanches, 2022; WEBforSCIENCE, 2016).

When preparing the presentation of the scientific article using slides, the following aspects on each topic proposed in the dissemination of the research conducted are considered (Alves & Sanches, 2022) (Table 13.2).

Table 13.2 Aspects considered in developing presentation topics for remote sensing scientific papers with slides.

Topic	Aspects Considered
Title	It should be succinct and try to contain, in a few words, what is intended to be accomplished with the work.
Authors	Include sequence of authors, advisor and affiliation according to the norms. The name of the authors must appear on the cover page, below the title of the paper.
Introduction	Get to the point: point out the problem, the demand, and show that you have not only been able to diagnose the problem, but that you are able to solve it. Get information about what has already been done in other work on a similar subject. The text should be presented briefly and in topics that facilitate the sequence of ideas.
Objectives	They should be written in a way that leaves no doubt as to what is to be achieved in the work.
Methods	It is necessary to include as many details as possible, but without exaggerating. Ex: Variable studied, date when the radiometric data was obtained, analysis performed on the data.
Results and discussion	Present the results obtained based on the data analysis. Images, graphs, tables should be legible and avoid too much text for participants to read the slides. The discussion can be held immediately after the presentation of each result.
Conclusions	Address what was obtained with the execution of the work within what was proposed in the objective. Open space for discussion and debate with the public.
References	Include the bibliographical references used.

13.10.3   The predatory journals

With today's technological development, one can publish a book or scientific article on a website with all the necessary characteristics to simulate the image and procedures of a major publisher. In predatory journals, classified as open access, the scientific quality of the publications is highly questionable. In these journals, peer review of low-quality academic manuscripts is requested from authors in order to collect payments for publication. The number of articles in these journals that have actually been read, cited, or have any significant research impact in the same area of knowledge may be low. Citation statistics over a five-year period in Google Scholar for 250 random articles published in predatory journals in 2014 averaged 2.6 citations per article, with 56% of the articles having no citations at all. Based on a comparative random sample of articles published in approximately 25000 peer-reviewed journals included in the Scopus index, an average of 18.1 article citations was observed over the same period, with only 9% of articles having no citations at all. Therefore, it was concluded that in articles published in predatory journals there was little scientific impact (Alves & Sanches, 2022; Björk et al., 2020).

With the subversion of the scientific publication process, not validated by peers, the basic foundation of communication in science can be discredited, ultimately turning it into mere opinion pieces disguised as scientific articles, without any validation of the published content. Therefore, choosing the journal in which to publish a paper can be a challenge full of pitfalls for the less and more experienced authors, and it is important to evaluate whether some knowledge about the credibility of the journal and the publisher has been made available, in addition to exercising the authors' critical sense in choosing a journal with credibility (Alves & Sanches, 2022; Penedo & Borges, 2017).

13.11 Practice for Writing an Article

In the practical activity, a scientific article abstract was made as an example of remote sensing applications.

13.11.1 Preparation of a scientific article abstract

The article abstract was prepared as follows:

Potential effects of spatio-temporal temperature variation for monitoring coffee leaf rust progress under CMIP6 climate change scenarios

Marcelo de Carvalho Alves - Federal University of Lavras, Department of Agricultural Engineering, email: *marcelo.alves@ufla.br*

Luciana Sanches - Federal University of Mato Grosso, Department of Sanitary and Environmental Engineering, email: *lsanches@hotmail.com*

Abstract

Plant diseases occur in all regions of the globe where there are susceptible hosts, aggressive and virulent pathogens, and a favorable environment. We aimed to evaluate potential effects of temperature variation on the monocyclic and polycyclic processes of coffee leaf rust in susceptible Arabica coffee cultivars cultivated in Minas Gerais state, Brazil. Historical monthly mean air temperature data, from 1970-2000, was downscaled and used as the temperature reference period and maximum and minimum temperature for four future scenarios, 2021-2040, 2041-2060, 2061-2080, and 2081-2100 (SSP126 scenario) from Coupled Model Intercomparison Project phase 6 (CMIP6) were used to characterize the future mean air temperature variation in the modeling of areas favorable to the progress of coffee leaf rust in Minas Gerais using spatial data techniques. A digital elevation model was considered for downscaling climate data. A non-linear regression model simulating the monocyclic process of coffee leaf rust was used to simulate the potential progress of the disease in susceptible cultivars under the different scenarios evaluated. In general, coffee leaf rust progress increased in susceptible cultivars located in areas with higher ground elevation, with emphasis in the south of the state, as well as in the main Arabica coffee producing regions. There was a reduction of areas favorable to rust in the north of the state due to temperature increase considering a climate change scenario; however, new areas in the south of the state became more favorable to the disease. Temperature increase between the periods from 2021 to 2040, 2041 to 2060, 2061 to 2081, and from 2081 to 2100, was 1.2, 0.6, 0.2, and 0.1°C, respectively.

Keywords: CNRM-ESM2-1 model, epidemiology, WorldClim, Shared Socioeconomic Pathways.

13.12   Exercises

13.12.1   List the topics used in writing a scientific paper in the remote sensing area.

13.13   Homework

13.13.1   Subject

Multisensor analysis for identification of coffee crops and other environmental targets in the region of Funil dam, state of Minas Gerais, Brazil.

13.13.2   Assignment

Develop the subject presented with a practical application of remote sensing and digital image processing, including the topics Introduction and Objective; Material and Methods; Results and Discussion; and Conclusions.

13.14   Resources on the Internet

As a study guide, you are asked to view slides and illustrative videos on the subject presented (Table 13.3).

Table 13.3 Perform slide reading and check out illustrative video and manuscript about article elaboration in remote sensing.

Guide	Address for Access
1	Norms for elaborating articles according to NBR 6022/ABNT/Brazil[1]
2	Video with results of scientific paper on remote sensing presented by professor[2]
3	Slides on article writing in remote sensing[3]

---

[1] https://posticsenasp.ufsc.br/files/2014/04/abntnbr6022.pdf
[2] https://youtu.be/UN3L-lG9trY
[3] http://www.sergeo.deg.ufla.br/sr/Presentation/Aula12/presentation.html#/

13.15   Research Suggestion

Activities are proposed to develop scientific research on remote sensing that can be used or adapted by the student to assess the applicability of geoinformation science (Table 13.4).

Table 13.4 Practices that can be used or adapted by students in remote sensing.

Activity	Description
1	Conduct a review of scientific papers on a topic of interest in remote sensing.
2	Prepare a scientific abstract based on original results or conduct a scientific literature review on a topic in remote sensing.
3	Prepare a scientific abstract based on scientific literature review on a topic in remote sensing.

References

Abatzoglou, J. T., Dobrowski, S. Z., Parks, S. A., & Hegewisch, K. C. (2018). TerraClimate, a high-resolution global dataset of monthly climate and climatic water balance from 1958–2015. *Scientific Data, 5*(1), 1–12. https://doi.org/10.1038/sdata.2017.191

ABNT - Associação Brasileira de Normas Técnicas. (2003). *NBR 6022 Informação e documentação - Artigo em publicação periódica científica impressa - Apresentação* (pp. 1–5). Associação Brasileira de Normas Técnicas.

Achanta, R., Shaji, A., Smith, K., Lucchi, A., Fua, P., & Susstrunk, S. (2011). SLIC Superpixels compared to state-of-the-art superpixel methods. *Journal of Latex Class Files, 6*(1), 1–16. https://doi.org/10.1109/TPAMI.2012.120

Adrien, P.-M., & Baumgardner, M. F. (1977). Landsat, computers, and development projects. *Science, 198*(4316), 466–470. https://doi.org/10.1126/science.198.4316.466

Alawadi, F. (2010). Detection of surface algal blooms using the newly developed algorithm surface algal bloom index (SABI). In C. R. Bostater, Jr., S. P. Mertikas, X. Neyt, & M. Velez-Reyes (Eds.), *SPIE Remote Sensing* (p. 782506). https://doi.org/10.1117/12.862096

Alves, M. C. (2012). *Signature of pest-organisms in Mato Grosso agroecosystems using WorldView-2 imagery.* White Paper, Intergraph Erdas.

Alves, M. C., Oliveira, L. T., & Silva, F. M. (2016). Levantamento topográfico com LiDAR. In M. C. Alves & F. M. Silva (Eds.), *Geomática para levantamento de ambientes: Base para aplicações em topografia, georreferenciamento e agricultura de precisão* (1st ed., pp. 393–458). Editora UFLA.

Alves, M. C., & Sanches, L. (2022). *Surveying with geomatics and R* (1st ed., p. 400). CRC Press.

Alves, M. C., & Silva, F. M. (2016a). Geomática aplicada em levantamentos: A profissão. In M. C. Alves & F. M. Silva (Eds.), *Geomática para levantamento de ambientes: Base para aplicações em topografia, georreferenciamento e agricultura de precisão* (1st ed., pp. 27–52). Editora UFLA.

Alves, M. C., & Silva, F. M. (2016b). Levantamento topográfico com GNSS. In M. C. Alves & F. M. Silva (Eds.), *Geomática para levantamento de ambientes: Base para aplicações em topografia, georreferenciamento e agricultura de precisão* (1st ed., pp. 281–315). Editora UFLA.

Alves, M. C., Silva, F. M., & Carvalho, L. G. (2016). Levantamento topográfico com RaDAR. In M. C. Alves & F. M. da Silva (Eds.), *Geomática para levantamento de ambientes: Base para aplicações em topografia, georreferenciamento e agricultura de precisão* (1st ed., pp. 581–606). Editora UFLA.

Alves, M. C., Silva, F. M., Pozza, E. A., Oliveira, M. S., Souza, J. C. S., & Souza, P. E. (2007). Variabilidade espacial e relação do índice de vegetação de imagem Quickbird com características físico-químicas do solo de lavoura cafeeira. *5 Simpósio de Pesquisa de Cafés do Brasil*, 1–5.

Amorim, R. C., & Hennig, C. (2015). Recovering the number of clusters in data sets with noise features using feature rescaling factors. *Information Sciences, 324*, 126–145. https://doi.org/10.1016/j.ins.2015.06.039

AppEEARS Team. (2020). *Application for extracting and exploring analysis ready samples (AppEEARS). Ver. 2.43 NASA EOSDIS land processes distributed active archive center (LP DAAC).* USGS/Earth resources observation; science (EROS) center.

Appelhans, T., Detsch, F., Woellauer, C. R. S., Forteva, S., Nauss, T., Pebesma, E., Russell, K., Sumner, M., Darley, J., Roudier, P., Schratz, P., Marburg, E. I., & Busetto, L. (2020). *mapview: Interactive Viewing of Spatial Data in R* (R package version 2.11.0.9002). https://github.com/r-spatial/mapview/

Arkin, P. A., Joyce, R., & Janowiak, J. E. (1994). The estimation of global monthly mean rainfall using infrared satellite data: The GOES precipitation index (GPI). *Remote Sensing Reviews, 11*(1-4), 107–124. https://doi.org/10.1080/02757259409532261

Arkin, P. A., & Meisner, B. N. (1987). The relationship between large-scale convective rainfall and cold cloud over the Western Hemisphere during 1982-84. *Monthly Weather Review, 115*(1), 51–74. https://doi.org/10.1175/1520-0493(1987)115%3C0051:TRBLSC%3E2.0.CO;2

Arvanitou, E.-M., Ampatzoglou, A., Chatzigeorgiou, A., & Carver, J. C. (2021). Software engineering practices for scientific software development: A systematic mapping study. *Journal of Systems and Software, 172*, 110848. https://doi.org/10.1016/j.jss.2020.110848

Auguie, B., & Antonov, A. (2017). *gridExtra: Miscellaneous Functions for "Grid" Graphics* (R package version 2.3). https://cran.r-project.org/web/packages/gridExtra/

Augusto Sarti, D. (2022). *InnoVaR: InnoVar a package to simulate MET* (R package version 0.1.0). https://danilosarti.github.io/InnoVaR/

Aybar, C., Qiusheng, W., Bautista, L., Yali, R., Barja, A., Ushey, K., Ooms, J., Appelhans, T., Allaire, J., Tang, Y., Roy, S., Adauto, M., Carrasco, G., Bengtsson, H., Hollister, J., Donchyts, G., & Appel, M. (2022). *rgee: R Bindings for Calling the 'Earth Engine' API* (R package version 1.1.4). https://cran.r-project.org/web/packages/rgee/

Baig, M. H. A., Zhang, L., Shuai, T., & Tong, Q. (2014). Derivation of a tasselled cap transformation based on Landsat 8 at-satellite reflectance. *Remote Sensing Letters, 5*(5), 423–431. https://doi.org/10.1080/2150704X.2014.915434

Balthasar, M. P. (2020). *S5Processor* (R package version 0.1.0). https://github.com/MBalthasar/S5Processor/

Baret, F., & Guyot, G. (1991). Potentials and limits of vegetation indices for LAI and APAR assessment. *Remote Sensing of Environment, 35*(2-3), 161–173.

Barrett, E. C., & Curtis, L. F. (1999). *Introduction to environmental remote sensing* (4th ed., p. 480). Taylor & Francis Ltd.

Barry, R. G., & Chorley, R. J. (2010). *Atmosphere, weather and climate* (9th ed., p. 533). Routledge.

Barsi, J. A., Lee, K., Kvaran, G., Markham, B. L., & Pedelty, J. A. (2014). The spectral response of the Landsat-8 operational land imager. *Remote Sensing, 6*(10), 10232–10251. https://doi.org/10.3390/rs61010232

Beaudette, D., Roudier, P., & Brown, A. (2021). *aqp: Algorithms for Quantitative Pedology* (R package version 1.42). https://cran.r-project.org/web/packages/aqp/

Beck, R., Xu, M., Zhan, S., Liu, H., Johansen, R., Tong, S., Yang, B., Shu, S., Wu, Q., Wang, S., Berling, K., Murray, A., Emery, E., Reif, M., Harwood, J., Young, J., Martin, M., Stillings, G., Stumpf, R., ... Huang, Y. (2017). Comparison of satellite reflectance algorithms for estimating phycocyanin values and cyanobacterial total biovolume in a temperate reservoir using coincident hyperspectral aircraft imagery and dense coincident surface observations. *Remote Sensing, 9*(6), 538. https://doi.org/10.3390/rs9060538

Beck, R., Zhan, S., Liu, H., Tong, S., Yang, B., Xu, M., Ye, Z., Huang, Y., Shu, S., Wu, Q., Wang, S., Berling, K., Murray, A., Emery, E., Reif, M., Harwood, J., Young, J., Nietch, C., Macke, D., ... Su, H. (2016). Comparison of satellite reflectance algorithms for estimating chlorophyll-a in a temperate reservoir using coincident hyperspectral aircraft imagery and dense coincident surface observations. *Remote Sensing of Environment, 178*, 15–30. https://doi.org/10.1016/j.rse.2016.03.002

Bengtsson, H. (2021). *R.utils: Various Programming Utilities* (R package version 2.10.1). https://cran.r-project.org/web/packages/R.utils/

Berrar, D. (2019). Cross-validation. *Encyclopedia of Bioinformatics and Computational Biology, 1*, 542–545.

Bevington, A. (2022). *planetR: Search, Activate and Download Satellite Imagery from the Planet API* (R package version 0.0.0.9000). https://github.com/bevingtona/planetR

Birth, G. S., & McVey, G. R. (1968). Measuring the color of growing turf with a reflectance spectrophotometer 1. *Agronomy Journal*, *60*(6), 640–643. https://doi.org/10.2134/agronj1968 .00021962006000060016x

Bivand, R., Keitt, T., Rowlingson, B., Pebesma, E., Sumner, M., Hijmans, R., Baston, D., Rouault, E., Warmerdam, F., Ooms, J., & Rundel, C. (2021). *rgdal: Bindings for the 'Geospatial' Data Abstraction Library* (R packdage version 1.5-19). https://r-forge.r-project.org/projects/rgdal/

Bivand, R., Nowosad, J., Lovelace, R., Monmonier, M., & Snow, G. (2020). *spData: Datasets for Spatial Analysis* (R package version 2.0.1). https://cran.r-project.org/web/packages/spData/

Björk, B.-C., Kanto-Karvonen, S., & Harviainen, J. T. (2020). How frequently are articles in predatory open access journals cited. *Publications*, *8*(2), 17. https://doi.org/10.3390/publicat ions8020017

Blumenfeld, J. (2020). *From TRMM to GPM: The evolution of NASA precipitation data*. https://earthdata.nasa.gov/learn/articles/tools-and-technology-articles/trmm-to-gpm

Böhner, J., & Antonić, O. (2009). Land-surface parameters specific to topo-climatology. In *Developments in soil science* (pp. 195–226). https://doi.org/10.1016/S0166-2481(08)00008-1

Böhner, J., Conrad, O., Gross, J., Ringeler, A., & Selige, T. (2002). *Soil regionalisation by means of terrain analysis and process parameterisation* (No. 7; pp. 213–222). European Soil Bureau.

Böhner, J., & Selige, T. (2006). Spatial prediction of soil attributes using terrain analysis and climate regionalisation. *Goettinger Geographische Abhandlungen*, *115*, 13–28.

Boochs, F., Kupfer, G., Dockter, K., & Kühbauch, W. (1990). Shape of the red edge as vitality indicator for plants. *Remote Sensing*, *11*(10), 1741–1753. https://doi.org/10.1080/0143116900 8955127

Bowers, D. G., & Binding, C. (2006). The optical properties of mineral suspended particles: A review and synthesis. *Estuarine, Coastal and Shelf Science*, *67*(1-2), 219–230. https://doi.org/10.1016/j.ecss.2005.11.010

Breiman, L., Cutler, A., Liaw, A., & Wiener, M. (2018). *randomForest: Breiman and Cutler's Random Forests for Classification and Regression* (R package version 4.6-14). https://cran.r-project.org/web/packages/randomForest/

Brenning, A., Bangs, D., Becker, M., Schratz, P., & Polakowski, F. (2018). *RSAGA: SAGA Geoprocessing and Terrain Analysis* (R package version 1.3.0). https://cran.r-project.org/web/packages/RSAGA/

Burnett, C., & Blaschke, T. (2003). A multi-scale segmentation/object relationship modelling methodology for landscape analysis. *Ecological Modelling*, *168*(3), 233–249. https://doi.org/10.1016/S0304-3800(03)00139-X

Butler, M. J. (1988). *The application of remote sensing technology to marine fisheries: An introductory manual* (No. 295; p. 165). Food & Agriculture Organization of the United States.

Cáceres, A. M., Gândara, J. P., & Puglisi, M. L. (2011). Scientific writing and the quality of papers: Towards a higher impact. *Jornal Da Sociedade Brasileira de Fonoaudiologia*, *23*(4), 401–406. https://doi.org/10.1590/S2179-64912011000400019

Calinski, T., & Harabasz, J. (1974). A dendrite method for cluster analysis. *Communications in Statistics - Theory and Methods*, *3*(1), 1–27. https://doi.org/10.1080/03610927408827101

Campbell, J. B., & Wynne, R. H. (2011). *Introduction to remote sensing* (5th ed., p. 667). The Guilford Press.

Canuto, M. A., Estrada-Belli, F., Garrison, T. G., Houston, S. D., Acuña, M. J., Kováč, M., Marken, D., Nondédéo, P., Auld-Thomas, L., Castanet, C., Chatelain, D., Chiriboga, C. R., Drápela, T., Lieskovský, T., Tokovinine, A., Velasquez, A., Fernández-Díaz, J. C., & Shrestha, R. (2018). Ancient lowland Maya complexity as revealed by airborne laser scanning of northern Guatemala. *Science*, *361*(6409), eaau0137. https://doi.org/10.1126/science.aau0137

Chandrasekar, K., Sesha Sai, M. V. R., Roy, P. S., & Dwevedi, R. S. (2010). Land Surface Water Index (LSWI) response to rainfall and NDVI using the MODIS Vegetation Index product. *International Journal of Remote Sensing*, *31*(15), 3987–4005. https://doi.org/10.1080/014311 60802575653

Chavez, P. S. J. (1989). Radiometric calibration of Landsat thematic mapper multispectral images. *Photogrammetric Engineering and Remote Sensing, 55*, 1285–1294.

Chavez, P. S. J. (1996). Image-based atmospheric corrections - revisited and improved. *Photogrammetric Engineering and Remote Sensing, 62*, 1025–1036.

Chemin, Y., Maunahan, A., Asilo, S., & Aunario, J. K. S. (2020). *water.R.* https://rdrr.io/rforge/RemoteSensing/src/R/water.R

Chen, J., Yuan Zhang, M., Wang, L., Shimazaki, H., & Tamura, M. (2005). A new index for mapping lichen-dominated biological soil crusts in desert areas. *Remote Sensing of Environment, 96*(2), 165–175. https://doi.org/10.1016/j.rse.2005.02.011

Chipman, J. W., Olmanson, L. G., & Gitelson, A. A. (2009). *Remote sensing methods for lake management: A guide for resource managers and decision-makers.* North American Lake Management Society; University of Minnesota; University of Nebraska.

Chuvieco, E. (2020). *Fundamentals of satellite remote sensing: An environmental approach* (3rd ed., p. 432). CRC Press.

Colwell, R. N. (1997). History and place of photographic interpretation. In *Manual of photographic interpretation.* American Society for Photogrammetry and Remote Sensing.

Congalton, R. G., & Green, K. (1998). *Assessing the accuracy of remotely sensed data: Principles and practices* (p. 137). Lewis Publishers.

Conrad, O., Bechtel, B., Bock, M., Dietrich, H., Fischer, E., Gerlitz, L., Wehberg, J., Wichmann, V., & Böhner, J. (2015). System for automated geoscientific analyses (SAGA) v. 2.1. 4. *Geoscientific Model Development, 8*(7), 1991–2007. https://doi.org/10.5194/gmd-8-1991-2015

Cook, G. D., Dixon, J. R., & Leopold, A. C. (1964). Transpiration: Its effects on plant leaf temperature. *Science, 144*(3618), 546–547. https://doi.org/10.1126/science.144.3618.546

Crist, E. P. (1985). A TM tasseled cap equivalent transformation for reflectance factor data. *Remote Sensing of Environment, 17*(3), 301–306. https://doi.org/10.1016/0034-4257(85)90102-6

Crist, E. P., & Kauth, R. J. (1986). The tasseled cap demystified. *Photogrammetric Engineering & Remote Sensing, 52*(1), 81–86.

Curran, P. J. (2020). *Principles of remote sensing* (p. 294). Hardback.

Decorps, J. P. (2021). *GADMTools: Easy Use of 'GADM' Maps* (R package version 3.9-1). https://cran.r-project.org/web/packages/GADMTools

Deering, D. W. (1975). Measuring 'forage production' of grazing units from Landsat MSS data. *Proceedings of the Tenth International Symposium of Remote Sensing of the Environment*, 1169–1198.

Demattê, J. A. M., Dotto, A. C., Paiva, A. F. S., Sato, M. V., Dalmolin, R. S. D., Araújo, M. S. B., Silva, E. B., Nanni, M. R., Caten, A. ten, Noronha, N. C., Lacerda, M. P. C., Araújo Filho, J. C., Rizzo, R., Bellinaso, H., Francelino, M. R., Schaefer, C. E. G. R., Vicente, L. E., Santos, U. J., Sá Barretto Sampaio, E. V., ... Couto, H. T. Z. (2019). The Brazilian Soil Spectral Library (BSSL): A general view, application and challenges. *Geoderma, 354*, 113793. https://doi.org/10.1016/j.geoderma.2019.05.043

Desachy, J., Begni, G., Boissin, B., & Perbos, J. (1985). Investigation of Landsat-4 thematic mapper line-to-line and band-to-band registration and relative detector calibration. *Photogrammetric Engineering and Remote Sensing, 51*(9), 1291–1298.

Desgraupes, B. (2018). *clusterCrit: Clustering Indices* (R package version 1.2.8). https://cran.r-project.org/web/packages/clusterCrit/

Devireddy, A. R., Zandalinas, S. I., Gómez-Cadenas, A., Blumwald, E., & Mittler, R. (2018). Coordinating the overall stomatal response of plants: Rapid leaf-to-leaf communication during light stress. *Science Signaling, 11*(518), eaam9514. https://doi.org/10.1126/scisignal.aam9514

Diek, S., Fornallaz, F., & Schaepman, M. E. (2017). Barest pixel composite for agricultural areas using Landsat time series. *Remote Sensing, 9*(12), 1245. https://doi.org/10.3390/rs9121245

Doxaran, D., Froidefond, J.-M., & Castaing, P. (2002). A reflectance band ratio used to estimate suspended matter concentrations in sediment-dominated coastal waters. *International Journal of Remote Sensing, 23*(23), 5079–5085. https://doi.org/10.1080/0143116021000009912

Dragulescu, A., & Arendt, C. (2020). *xlsx: Read, Write, Format Excel 2007 and Excel 97/2000/XP/2003 Files* (R package version 0.6.5). https://cran.r-project.org/web/packages/xlsx/

ESA. (2018). *Copernicus Sentinel-5P TROPOMI level 2 ultraviolet aerosol index products* (Version 01). European Space Agency. https://sentinels.copernicus.eu/web/sentinel/data-products

Escadafal, R. (1994). Soil spectral properties and their relationships with environmental parameters - examples from arid regions. In *Imaging spectrometry - a tool for environmental observations. Eurocourses: Remote sensing* (pp. 71–87). Springer.

Esch, T., Taubenböck, H., Roth, A., Heldens, W., Felbier, A., Thiel, M., Schmidt, M., Müller, A., & Dech, S. (2012). TanDEM-X mission-new perspectives for the inventory and monitoring of global settlement patterns. *Journal of Applied Remote Sensing, 6*(1), 061702–061701. https://doi.org/10.1117/1.JRS.6.061702

Falkenberg, N. R., Piccinni, G., Cothren, J. T., Leskovar, D. I., & Rush, C. M. (2007). Remote sensing of biotic and abiotic stress for irrigation management of cotton. *Agricultural Water Management, 87*(1), 23–31. https://doi.org/10.1016/j.agwat.2006.05.021

Fernández López, J., & Schliep, K. (2019). rWind: Download, edit and include wind data in ecological and evolutionary analysis. *Ecography, 42*(4), 804–810. https://doi.org/10.1111/ecog.03730

Fernández-López, J., Schliep, K., & Arjona, Y. (2021). *rWind: Download, Edit and Include Wind and Sea Currents Data in Ecological and Evolutionary Analysis* (R package version 1.1.7). https://cran.r-project.org/web/packages/rWind/

Ferreira Sobrinho, J. A., & Alves, M. C. (2013). Assinatura espectral de alvos agrícolas detectados em imagens do satélite WorldView-2. *XVI Simpósio Brasileiro de Sensoriamento Remoto*, 387–392.

Fick, S. E., & Hijmans, R. J. (2017). WorldClim 2: New 1-km spatial resolution climate surfaces for global land areas. *International Journal of Climatology, 37*(12), 4302–4315. https://doi.org/10.1002/joc.5086

Filippa, G., Cremonese, E., Migliavacca, M., Galvagno, M., Folker, M., Richardson, A. D., & Tomelleri, E. (2020). *phenopix: Process Digital Images of a Vegetation Cover* (R package version 2.4.2). https://cran.r-project.org/web/packages/phenopix/

Forkel, M., & Wutzler, T. (2015). *Greenbrown - land surface phenology and trend analysis* (R package version 2.2). https://greenbrown.r-forge.r-project.org/

Frank, E., Hall, M. A., Witten, I. H., & Kaufmann, M. (2016). *WEKA Workbench online appendix for 'Data mining: Practical machine learning tools and techniques'* (p. 128). Morgan Kaufmann.

Freeman, T. G. (1991). Calculating catchment area with divergent flow based on a regular grid. *Computers and Geosciences, 17*(3), 413–422. https://doi.org/10.1016/0098-3004(91)90048-I

Freitas, R. M. (2011). Virtual laboratory of remote sensing time series: Visualization of MODIS EVI2 data set over South America. *Journal of Computational Interdisciplinary Sciences, 2*(1). https://doi.org/10.6062/jcis.2011.02.01.0032

Frohn, R. C., & Autrey, B. C. (2009). Water quality assessment in the Ohio River using new indices for turbidity and chlorophyll-a with Landsat-7 Imagery. In *Draft internal report*. US Environmental Protection Agency.

FUNAI. (2022). *Geoserver*. http://geoserver.funai.gov.br/geoserver/web/

Funk, C. C., Peterson, P. J., Landsfeld, M. F., Pedreros, D. H., Verdin, J. P., Rowland, J. D., Romero, B. E., Husak, G. J., Michaelsen, J. C., & Verdin, A. P. (2014). *A quasi-global precipitation time series for drought monitoring* (p. 4). U.S. Geological Survey; USGS. https://doi.org/10.3133/ds832

Funk, C. C., Peterson, P. J., Landsfeld, M., Pedreros, D., Verdin, J., Shukla, S., Husak, G., Rowland, J., Harrison, L., & Hoell, A. (2015). The climate hazards infrared precipitation with stations-a new environmental record for monitoring extremes. *Scientific Data, 2*(1), 1–21. https://doi.org/10.1038/sdata.2015.66

Gao, B. (1996). NDWI A normalized difference water index for remote sensing of vegetation liquid water from space. *Remote Sensing of Environment*, *58*(3), 257–266. https://doi.org/10.1016/S0034-4257(96)00067-3

García, M. J. L., & Caselles, V. (1991). Mapping burns and natural reforestation using thematic Mapper data. *Geocarto International*, *6*(1), 31–37. https://doi.org/10.1080/10106049109354290

Gillespie, A., Abrams, M., & Yamaguchi, Y. (2005). Scientific results from ASTER. *Remote Sensing of Environment*, *99*(1–2), 1–220. https://doi.org/10.1016/j.rse.2005.05.014

Gitelson, A. A., Gritz, Y., & Merzlyak, M. N. (2003). Relationships between leaf chlorophyll content and spectral reflectance and algorithms for non-destructive chlorophyll assessment in higher plant leaves. *Journal of Plant Physiology*, *160*(3), 271–282. https://doi.org/10.1078/0176-1617-00887

Gitelson, A. A., Kaufman, Y. J., & Merzlyak, M. N. (1996). Use of a green channel in remote sensing of global vegetation from EOS-MODIS. *Remote Sensing of Environment*, *58*(3), 289–298. https://doi.org/10.1016/S0034-4257(96)00072-7

Gitelson, A. A., Kaufman, Y. J., Stark, R., & Rundquist, D. (2002). Novel algorithms for remote estimation of vegetation fraction. *Remote Sensing of Environment*, *80*(1), 76–87. https://doi.org/10.1016/S0034-4257(01)00289-9

Goetz, A. F. H., Vane, G., Solomon, J. E., & Rock, B. N. (1985). Imaging spectrometry for Earth remote sensing. *Science*, *228*(4704), 1147–1153. https://doi.org/10.1126/science.228.4704.1147

Gonçalves, J. (2020). *SegOptim: A R package for performing object-based image classification*. https://segoptim.bitbucket.io/docs/index.html

Gonzalez, R. C. (2008). *Digital image processing* (3rd ed., pp. pages 830–836.). Prentice Hall.

Google LLC. (2021). *Google Earth Engine*. https://earthengine.google.com/

Gorelick, N., Hancher, M., Dixon, M., Ilyushchenko, S., Thau, D., & Moore, R. (2017). Google Earth Engine: Planetary-scale geospatial analysis for everyone. *Remote Sensing of Environment*, *202*, 18–27. https://doi.org/10.1016/j.rse.2017.06.031

Goslee, S. C. (2011). Analyzing remote sensing data in R: The Landsat package. *Journal of Statistical Software*, *43*(4), 1–25. https://doi.org/10.18637/jss.v043.i04

Goward, S. N., & Zanoni, V. M. (2003). IKONOS fine spatial resolution land observation. *Remote Sensing of Environment*, *88*(1–2), 1–220.

Graves, S., Dorai-Raj, S., & Francois, R. (2020). *sos: Search Contributed R Packages, Sort by Package* (R package version 2.0-2). https://cran.r-project.org/web/packages/sos/

Greenberg, J. A. (2000). *Gdalutils* (R package version 2.0.3.2). https://github.com/cran/gdalUtils

Gu, Y., Brown, J. F., Verdin, J. P., & Wardlow, B. (2007). A five-year analysis of MODIS NDVI and NDWI for grassland drought assessment over the central Great Plains of the United States. *Geophysical Research Letters*, *34*(6), L06407. https://doi.org/10.1029/2006GL029127

Gupta, A., Rico-Medina, A., & Caño-Delgado, A. I. (2020). The physiology of plant responses to drought. *Science*, *368*(6488), 266–269. https://doi.org/10.1126/science.aaz7614

Guyot, G. (1990). Optical properties of vegetation canopies. In J. A. Steven, M. D.; Clark (Ed.), *Applications of remote sensing in agriculture* (pp. 19–43). Butterworth-Heinemann.

Haboudane, D. (2004). Hyperspectral vegetation indices and novel algorithms for predicting green LAI of crop canopies: Modeling and validation in the context of precision agriculture. *Remote Sensing of Environment*, *90*(3), 337–352. https://doi.org/10.1016/j.rse.2003.12.013

Hall, D. K., Riggs, G. A., Salomonson, V. V., DiGirolamo, N. E., & Bayr, K. J. (2002). MODIS snow-cover products. *Remote Sensing of Environment*, *83*(1-2), 181–194. https://doi.org/10.1016/S0034-4257(02)00095-0

Hammond, A. L. (1977a). Remote sensing (I): Landsat takes hold in South America. *Science*, *196*, 511–512.

Hammond, A. L. (1977b). Remote sensing (II): Brazil explores its Amazon wilderness. *Science*, *196*, 513–515.

Hansen, M. C., Potapov, P. V., Moore, R., Hancher, M., Turubanova, S. A., Tyukavina, A., Thau, D., Stehman, S. V., Goetz, S. J., Loveland, T. R., Kommareddy, A., Egorov, A., Chini, L., Justice, C. O., & Townshend, J. R. G. (2013). High-resolution global maps of 21st-century forest cover change. *Science, 342*(6160), 850–853. https://doi.org/10.1126/science.1244693

Haralick, R. M., Shanmugam, K., & Dinstein, I. (1973). Textural features for image classification. *IEEE Transactions on Systems, Man, and Cybernetics, SMC-3*(6), 610–621. https://doi.org/10.1109/TSMC.1973.4309314

Harris, I., Jones, P. D., Osborn, T. J., & Lister, D. H. (2014). Updated high-resolution grids of monthly climatic observations - the CRU TS3.10 dataset. *International Journal of Climatology, 34*(3), 623–642. https://doi.org/10.1002/joc.3711

Hartigan, J. A., & Wong, M. A. (1979). A K-means clustering algorithm. *Applied Statistics, 28*, 100–108.

Heng, T., Kempen, B., Heuvelink, G., & Malone, B. (2019). *gsif: Global Soil Information Facilities* (R package version 0.5-5). https://rdrr.io/rforge/GSIF

Hengl, T., Mendes de Jesus, J., Heuvelink, G. B. M., Ruiperez Gonzalez, M., Kilibarda, M., Blagotić, A., Shangguan, W., Wright, M. N., Geng, X., Bauer-Marschallinger, B., Guevara, M. A., Vargas, R., MacMillan, R. A., Batjes, N. H., Leenaars, J. G. B., Ribeiro, E., Wheeler, I., Mantel, S., & Kempen, B. (2017). SoilGrids250m: Global gridded soil information based on machine learning. *PLOS ONE, 12*(2), e0169748. https://doi.org/10.1371/journal.pone.0169748

Hennig, C. (2020). *fpc: Flexible Procedures for Clustering* (R package version 2.2-9). https://cran.r-project.org/web/packages/fpc/

Henrich, V., Götze, E., Jung, A., Sandow, C., Thürkow, D., & Gläßer, C. (2009). Development of an online indices database: Motivation, concept and implementation. *Proceedings of the 6th EARSeL Imaging Spectroscopy SIG Workshop Innovative Tool for Scientific and Commercial Environment Applications*, 16–18.

Hijmans, R. J., Bivand, R., Pebesma, E., & Sumner, M. D. (2022). *terra: Spatial Data Analysis* (R package version 1.6-7). https://rspatial.org/terra/

Hijmans, R. J., van Etten, J., Sumner, M., Cheng, J., Baston, D., Bevan, A., Bivand, R., Busetto, L., Canty, M., Fasoli, B., Forrest, D., Ghosh, A., Goliche, D., Gray, J., Greenberg, J. A., Hiemstra, P., Hingee, K., Ilich, A., Institute for Mathematics Applied Geosciences, … Wueest, R. (2023). *raster: Geographic Data Analysis and Modeling* (R package version 3.6-20). https://cran.r-project.org/web/packages/raster/

Hijmans, R. J., Ghosh, A., & Mandel, A. (2022). *geodata: Download Geographic Data* (R package version 0.4-11). https://cran.r-project.org/web/packages/geodata/

Hofierka, J., & Súri, M. (2002). The solar radiation model for open source GIS: Implementation and applications. *Open Source GIS - GRASS Users Conference*, 11–13.

Huang, C., Wylie, B., Yang, L., Homer, C., & Zylstra, G. (2002). Derivation of a tasselled cap transformation based on Landsat 7 at-satellite reflectance. *International Journal of Remote Sensing, 23*(8), 1741–1748. https://doi.org/10.1080/01431160110106113

Huete, A. R. (1988). A Soil-Adjusted Vegetation Index (SAVI). *Remote Sensing of Environment, 25*(3), 295–309. https://doi.org/10.1016/0034-4257(88)90106-X

Huete, A. R., Justice, C., & Van Leeuwen, W. (1999). *MODIS vegetation index (MOD 13): Algorithm theoretical basis document* (Version 3, p. 129). National Aeronautics; Space Administration.

Hunt Jr, E. R., Daughtry, C., Eitel, J. U., & Long, D. S. (2011). Remote sensing leaf chlorophyll content using a visible band index. *Agronomy Journal, 103*(4), 1090–1099. https://doi.org/10.2134/agronj2010.0395

IBGE. (2022). *Geociências: IBGE revê as altitudes de sete pontos culminantes.* https://agenciadenoticias.ibge.gov.br/agencia-sala-de-imprensa/2013-agencia-de-noticias/releases/15275-geociencias-ibge-reve-as-altitudes-de-sete-pontos-culminantes

IDB. (2022). *Index DataBase: A database for remote sensing indices.* https://www.indexdatabase.de/db/i.php

Idso, S. B., Jackson, R. D., & Reginato, R. J. (1977). Remote sensing of crop yields. *Science, 196*(4285), 19–25. https://doi.org/10.1126/science.196.4285.19

IEEE. (2004). IEEE Transactions on geoscience and remote sensing information for authors. *IEEE Transactions on Geoscience and Remote Sensing, 42*(12), c3–c3. https://doi.org/10.1109/TG RS.2004.841360

IEEE. (2005). IEEE Transactions on geoscience and remote sensing publication information. *IEEE Transactions on Geoscience and Remote Sensing, 43*(12), c2–c2. https://doi.org/10.1109/TG RS.2005.861471

INMET. (2020). *Mapas de temperatura da superfície do mar.* http://www.inmet.gov.br/portal/index.php?r=clima/temperaturaSuperficieMar

IUSS Working Group WRB. (2015). *World reference base for soil resources 2014 International soil classification system for naming soils and creating legends for soil maps* (p. 203). FAO.

Ivits, E., Lamb, A., Langar, F., Hemphill, S., & Koch, B. (2008). Orthogonal transformation of segmented SPOT5 images. *Photogrammetric Engineering & Remote Sensing, 74*(11), 1351–1364. https://doi.org/10.14358/PERS.74.11.1351

Jami, M., & Krehbiel, C. (2020). *Getting started with the AppEEARS API in R (point request).* https://lpdaac.usgs.gov/resources/e-learning/getting-started-appeears-api-r-point-request/

Jean, N., Burke, M., Xie, M., Davis, W. M., Lobell, D. B., & Ermon, S. (2016). Combining satellite imagery and machine learning to predict poverty. *Science, 353*(6301), 790–794. https://doi.org/10.1126/science.aaf7894

Jedlovec, G., & Meyer, P. J. (2020). *Interactive global geostationary weather satellite images.* https://weather.msfc.nasa.gov/GOES/

Jensen, J. R. (2005). *Introductory digital image processing: A remote sensing perspective* (3rd ed., p. 526). Pearson Prentice Hall.

Jensen, J. R. (2007). *Remote sensing of the environment: An Earth resource perspective* (2nd ed., p. 592). Pearson Prentice Hall.

Jensen, J. R., & Cowen, D. C. (1999). Remote sensing of urban/suburban infrastructure and socio-economic attributes. *Photogrammetric Engineering & Remote Sensing, 65*, 611–622. https://doi.org/10.1002/9780470979587.ch22

Jiang, Z., Huete, A., Didan, K., & Miura, T. (2008). Development of a two-band enhanced vegetation index without a blue band. *Remote Sensing of Environment, 112*(10), 3833–3845. https://doi.org/10.1016/j.rse.2008.06.006

Johannsen, C. J., Petersen, G. W., Carter, P. G., & Morgan, M. T. (2003). Remote sensing changing natural resource management. *Journal of Soil and Water Conservation, 58*(2), 42A–45A.

Johansen, R., Nowosad, J., Reif, M., Emery, E., & Army Corps of Engineers. (2020). *waterquality: Satellite Derived Water Quality Detection Algorithms* (R package version 0.2.6). https://cran.r-project.org/web/packages/waterquality/

Jong, S. M., Van Der Meer, F. D., & Clevers, J. G. P. W. (2004). Basics of remote sensing. In *Remote sensing image analysis: Including the spatial domain* (pp. 1–15). Kluwer Academic Publishers.

Justice, C. O., Vermote, E., Townshend, J. R. G., Defries, R., Roy, D. P., Hall, D. K., Salomonson, V. V., Privette, J. L., Riggs, G., Strahler, A., Lucht, W., Myneni, R. B., Knyazikhin, Y., Running, S. W., Nemani, R. R., Zhengming Wan, Huete, A. R., Leeuwen, W. van, Wolfe, R. E., . . . Barnsley, M. J. (1998). The Moderate Resolution Imaging Spectroradiometer (MODIS): Land remote sensing for global change research. *IEEE Transactions on Geoscience and Remote Sensing, 36*(4), 1228–1249. https://doi.org/10.1109/36.701075

Kalinowski, T., Ushey, K., Allaire, J., RStudio, Tang, Y., Eddelbuettel, D., Lewis, B., Keydana, S., Hafen, R., & Geelnard, M. (2022). *reticulate: Interface to 'Python'* (R package version 1.25). https://cran.r-project.org/web/packages/reticulate/

Karger, D. N., Conrad, O., Böhner, J., Kawohl, T., Kreft, H., Soria-Auza, R. W., Zimmermann, N. E., Linder, H. P., & Kessler, M. (2017). Climatologies at high resolution for the Earth's land surface areas. *Scientific Data, 4*(1), 170122. https://doi.org/10.1038/sdata.2017.122

Kassambara, A. (2017). *Practical guide to cluster analysis in R: Unsupervised machine learning.* STHDA.

Kassambara, A. (2018). *Machine learning essentials: Practical guide in R* (p. 210). Createspace Independent Publishing Platform.

Kaufman, L., & Rousseeuw, P. J. (2009). *Finding groups in data: An introduction to cluster analysis* (p. 342). Wiley-Interscience.

Kays, R., Crofoot, M. C., Jetz, W., & Wikelski, M. (2015). Terrestrial animal tracking as an eye on life and planet. *Science, 348*(6240), aaa2478–aaa2478. https://doi.org/10.1126/science.aaa2478

Kneubühler, M., Frank, T., Kellenberger, T., Pasche, N., Schmid, M., Lacoste, H., & Ouwehand, L. (2007). Mapping chlorophyll-a in Lake Kivu with remote sensing methods. *Envisat Symposium 2007, 1.*

Kohavi, R. (1995). A study of cross-validation and bootstrap for accuracy estimation and model selection. *IJCAI'95: Proceedings of the 14th International Joint Conference on Artificial Intelligence, 2,* 1137–1145.

Kong, D., Xiao, M., Zhang, Y., Gu, X., & Cui, J. (2021). *phenofit: Extract Remote Sensing Vegetation Phenology* (R package version 0.3.2). https://cran.r-project.org/web/packages/phenofit/

Kuehni, R. G. (2002). The early development of the Munsell system. *Color Research & Application, 27*(1), 20–27. https://doi.org/10.1002/col.10002

Kuhn, M., Wing, J., Weston, S., Williams, A., Keefer, C., Engelhardt, A., Cooper, T., Mayer, Z., Kenkel, B., Team, R. C., Benesty, M., Lescarbeau, R., Ziem, A., Scrucca, L., Tang, Y., Candan, C., & Hunt, T. (2020). *caret: Classification and Regression Training* (R package version 6.0-86). https://github.com/topepo/caret/

Kwok, R. (2018). Ecology's remote sensing revolution. *Nature, 556,* 137–138. https://www.nature.com/articles/d41586-018-03924-9

Laborte, A., Chemin, Y., & Hijmans, R. (2009). *RemoteSensing.* https://rdrr.io/rforge/RemoteSensing/man/RemoteSensing-package.html

Lacaux, J., Tourre, Y., Vignolles, C., Ndione, J., & Lafaye, M. (2007). Classification of ponds from high-spatial resolution remote sensing: Application to Rift valley fever epidemics in Senegal. *Remote Sensing of Environment, 106*(1), 66–74. https://doi.org/10.1016/j.rse.2006.07.012

Lange, M., & Doktor, D. (2017). *phenex: Auxiliary Functions for Phenological Data Analysis* (R package version 1.4-5). https://cran.r-project.org/web/packages/phenex/

Legleiter, C. J., Roberts, D. A., Marcus, W. A., & Fonstad, M. A. (2004). Passive optical remote sensing of river channel morphology and in-stream habitat: Physical basis and feasibility. *Remote Sensing of Environment, 93*(4), 493–510. https://doi.org/10.1016/j.rse.2004.07.019

Leutner, B. (2022). *Landsat 8 Esun Values.* http://bleutner.github.io/RStoolbox/r/2016/01/26/estimating-landsat-8-esun-values

Leutner, B., Horning, N., Schwalb-Willmann, J., & Hijmans, R. J. (2019). *RStoolbox: Tools for Remote Sensing Data Analysis* (R package version 0.2.6). https://cran.r-project.org/web/packages/RStoolbox/

Li, S., & Milliken, R. E. (2017). Water on the surface of the moon as seen by the moon mineralogy mapper: Distribution, abundance, and origins. *Science Advances, 3*(9), e1701471. https://doi.org/10.1126/sciadv.1701471

Liang, S. (2001). Narrowband to broadband conversions of land surface albedo I. *Remote Sensing of Environment, 76*(2), 213–238. https://doi.org/10.1016/S0034-4257(00)00205-4

Lindsay, D. (2011). *Scientific Writing = Thinking in Words* (p. 129). CSIRO Publishing.

Lloyd, S. (1982). Least squares quantization in PCM. *IEEE Transactions on Information Theory, 28*(2), 129–137. https://doi.org/10.1109/TIT.1982.1056489

Lobser, S. E., & Cohen, W. B. (2007). MODIS tasselled cap: Land cover characteristics expressed through transformed MODIS data. *International Journal of Remote Sensing, 28*(22), 5079–5101. https://doi.org/10.1080/01431160701253303

Louhaichi, M., Borman, M. M., & Johnson, D. E. (2001). Spatially located platform and aerial photography for documentation of grazing impacts on wheat. *Geocarto International, 16*(1), 65–70. https://doi.org/10.1080/10106040108542184

Lovelace, R., Nowosad, J., & Muenchow, J. (2019). *Geocomputation with R* (1st ed., p. 339). CRC Press.

Lu, D., & Batistella, M. (2005). Exploring TM image texture and its relationships with biomass estimation in Rondônia, Brazilian Amazon. *Acta Amazonica, 35*(2), 249–257. https://doi.org/10.1590/S0044-59672005000200015

Lymburner, L., Beggs, P. J., Jacobson, C. R., & Others. (2000). Estimation of canopy-average surface-specific leaf area using Landsat TM data. *Photogrammetric Engineering and Remote Sensing, 66*(2), 183–192.

Maciel, D. A., Novo, E. M. L. M., Barbosa, C. C. F., Martins, V. S., Flores Júnior, R., Oliveira, A. H., Carvalho, L. A., Sander, & Lobo, F. L. (2020). Evaluating the potential of CubeSats for remote sensing reflectance retrieval over inland waters. *International Journal of Remote Sensing, 41*(7), 2807–2817. https://doi.org/10.1080/2150704X.2019.1697003

Maciel, D. A., Silva, V. A., Alves, H. M. R., Volpato, M. M. L., Barbosa, J. P. R. A., Souza, V. C. O., Santos, M. O., Silveira, H. R. O., Dantas, M. F., Freitas, A. F., Carvalho, G. R., & Santos, J. O. (2020). Leaf water potential of coffee estimated by Landsat-8 images. *PLOS ONE, 15*(3), e0230013. https://doi.org/10.1371/journal.pone.0230013

MacQueen, J. (1967). Some methods for classification and analysis of multivariate observations. In J. Le Cam, L. M.; Neyman (Ed.), *Proceedings of the fifth berkeley symposium on mathematical statistics and probability* (pp. 281–297). University of California Press.

Madeira, J., Bedidi, A., Cervelle, B., Pouget, M., & Flay, N. (1997). Visible spectrometric indices of hematite (hm) and goethite (gt) content in lateritic soils: The application of a thematic mapper (TM) image for soil-mapping in Brasilia, Brazil. *International Journal of Remote Sensing, 18*(13), 2835–2852.

Maechler, M., Rousseeuw, P., Struyf, A., Hubert, M., Hornik, K., Studer, M., Roudier, P., Gonzalez, J., Kozlowski, K., Schubert, E., & Murphy, K. (2022). *cluster: "Finding Groups in Data"* (R package version 2.1.3). https://cran.r-project.org/web/packages/cluster/

Malavolta, E. (1980). *Elementos de Nutrição Mineral de Plantas* (p. 251). CERES.

Marconi, M. A., & Lakatos, E. M. (2021). *Fundamentos de metodologia científica* (9th ed., p. 354). Atlas.

Marin, D. B., Alves, M. C., Pozza, E. A., Gandia, R. M., Cortez, M. L. J., & Mattioli, M. C. (2019). Multispectral remote sensing in the identification and mapping of biotic and abiotic coffee tree variables. *Revista Ceres, 66*(2), 142–153. https://doi.org/10.1590/0034-737x201966020009

Marsett, R. C., Qi, J., Heilman, P., Biedenbender, S. H., Watson, C. M., Amer, S., Weltz, M., Goodrich, D., & Marsett, R. (2006). Remote sensing for grassland management in the arid Southwest. *Rangeland Ecology & Management, 59*(5), 530–540. https://doi.org/10.2111/05-201R.1

Masek, J. G., Vermote, E. F., Saleous, N. E., Wolfe, R., Hall, F. G., Huemmrich, K. F., Gao, F., Kutler, J., & Lim, T.-K. (2006). A Landsat surface reflectance dataset for North America, 1990-2000. *IEEE Geoscience and Remote Sensing Letters, 3*(1), 68–72. https://doi.org/10.1109/LGRS.2005.857030

Mather, R. S., Rizos, C., & Coleman, R. (1979). Remote sensing of surface ocean circulation with satellite altimetry. *Science, 205*(4401), 11–17. https://doi.org/10.1126/science.205.4401.11

Mathieu, R., Pouget, M., Cervelle, B., & Escadafal, R. (1998). Relationships between satellite-based radiometric indices simulated using laboratory reflectance data and typic soil color of an arid environment. *Remote Sensing of Environment, 66*(1), 17–28. https://doi.org/10.1016/S0034-4257(98)00030-3

Matias, F. I., Caraza-Harter, M. V., & Endelman, J. B. (2020). FIELDimageR: An R package to analyze orthomosaic images from agricultural field trials. *The Plant Phenome Journal, 3*(1). https://doi.org/10.1002/ppj2.20005

McFeeters, S. K. (1996). The use of the normalized difference water index (NDWI) in the delineation of open water features. *International Journal of Remote Sensing, 17*(7), 1425–1432. https://doi.org/10.1080/01431169608948714

Mesquita, C. M., Rezende, J. E., Carvalho, J. S., Fabri Júnior, M. A., Moraes, N. C., Dias, P. T., Carvalho, R. M., & Araújo, W. G. (2016). *Manual do café: Distúrbios fisiológicos, pragas e doenças do cafeeiro (Coffea arábica L.)* (p. 62). EMATER.

Meyer, D., Dimitriadou, E., Hornik, K., Weingessel, A., Leisch, F., Chang, C.-C., & Lin, C.-C. (2021). *e1071: Misc Functions of the Department of Statistics, Probability Theory Group (Formerly: E1071), TU Wien* (R package version 1.7-6). https://cran.r-project.org/web/packages/e1071/

Moeys, J., Shangguan, W., Petzold, R., Minasny, B., Rosca, B., Jelinski, N., Moeys, W. Z., Shangguan, W., Petzold, R., Minasny, B., Rosca, B., Jelinski, N., Zelazny, W., Souza, R. M. S., Safanelli, J. L., Caten, A. ten, Souza, R. M. S., Safanelli, J. L., & Caten, A. ten. (2018). *soiltexture: Functions for Soil Texture Plot, Classification and Transformation* (R package version 1.5.1). https://cran.r-project.org/web/packages/soiltexture/

Moran, M. S., Bryant, R., Holifield, C. D., & McElroy, S. (2003). Refined empirical line approach for retrieving surface reflectance from EO-1 ALI images. *IEEE Transactions on Geoscience and Remote Sensing, 41*(6), 1411–1414. https://doi.org/10.1109/TGRS.2003.813207

Moreira, M. A. (2011). *Fundamentos do sensoriamento remoto e metodologias de aplicação* (4th ed., p. 422). Editora UFV.

Motohka, T., Nasahara, K. N., Oguma, H., & Tsuchida, S. (2010). Applicability of green-red vegetation index for remote sensing of vegetation phenology. *Remote Sensing, 2*(10), 2369–2387. https://doi.org/10.3390/rs2102369

Mouselimis, L. (2022). *SuperpixelImageSegmentation: Superpixel Image Segmentation* (R package version 1.0.5). https://cran.r-project.org/web/packages/SuperpixelImageSegmentation/

Mouselimis, L., Machine, S., Buchner, J., Haghighat, M., Achanta, R., & Onyshchak, O. (2022). *OpenImageR: An Image Processing Toolkit* (R package version 1.2.5). https://cran.r-project.org/web/packages/OpenImageR/

Muenchow, J., Brenning, A., & Richter, M. (2012). Geomorphic process rates of landslides along a humidity gradient in the tropical Andes. *Geomorphology, 139-140*, 271–284. https://doi.org/10.1016/j.geomorph.2011.10.029

Nadeau, J. A. (2002). Control of stomatal distribution on the Arabidopsis leaf surface. *Science, 296*(5573), 1697–1700. https://doi.org/10.1126/science.1069596

NASA. (2013). *NASA Shuttle Radar Topography Mission Global 1 arc second NetCDF*. https://data.nasa.gov/w/5c2w-7b2v/default?cur=Shmh1SC7iKb

NASA. (2020). *Contaminated rio Doce water flows into the Atlantic*. https://earthobservatory.nasa.gov/images/87083/contaminated-rio-doce-water-flows-into-the-atlantic

Neuwirth, E. (2022). *RColorBrewer: ColorBrewer Palettes* (R package version 1.1-3). https://cran.r-project.org/web/packages/RColorBrewer/

Nowosad, J., Mettes, P., & Jekel, C. (2022). *supercells: Superpixels of Spatial Data* (R package version 0.9.1). https://cran.r-project.org/web/packages/supercells/

Nowosad, J., & Stepinski, T. (2021). *Generalizing the Simple Linear Iterative Clustering (SLIC) superpixels* (pp. 1–6). https://doi.org/10.25436/E2QP4R

Nychka, D., Furrer, R., Paige, J., Sain, S., Gerber, F., Iverson, M., & Research, U. C. for A. (2022). *fields: Tools for Spatial Data* (R package version 14.1). https://cran.r-project.org/web/packages/fields/

Oke, T. R. (2002). *Boundary layer climates* (2nd ed., p. 416). Routledge.

Oksanen, J., Simpson, G. L., Blanchet, G., Legendre, R. K. P., Minchin, P. R., O'Hara, R. B., Solymos, P., Stevens, M. H. H., Szoecs, E., Barbour, H. W. M., Bedward, M., Bolker, B., Borcard, D., Carvalho, G., Chirico, M., Caceres, M. D., Durand, S., Evangelista, H. B. A., FitzJohn, R., ... Weedon, J. (2022). *vegan: Community Ecology Package* (R package version 2.6-2). https://cran.r-project.org/web/packages/vegan/

Olmedo, G. F., Ortega-Farías, S., Fonseca-Luengo, D., Fuente-Sáiz, D. de la, Peñailillo, F. F., & Munafó, M. V. (2018). *water: Actual Evapotranspiration with Energy Balance Models* (R package version 0.8). http://midraed.github.io/water

Ooms, J. (2021). *magick: Advanced Graphics and Image-Processing in R* (R package version 2.7.3). http://www.github.com/16eagle/getSpatialData/

Ooms, J., & Lesiński, K. (2022). *gifski: Highest Quality GIF Encoder* (R package version 1.6.6-1). https://cran.r-project.org/web/packages/gifski/

Palmer, J. M. (1984). Effective bandwidths for Landsat-4 and Landsat-D' multispectral scanner and thematic mapper subsystems. *IEEE Transactions on Geoscience and Remote Sensing, GE-22*(3), 336–338. https://doi.org/10.1109/TGRS.1984.350630

Parkinson, C. L. (2003). Aqua: An Earth-observing satellite mission to examine water and other climate variables. *IEEE Transactions on Geoscience and Remote Sensing, 41*(2), 173–183. https://doi.org/10.1109/TGRS.2002.808319

Paul, C. K., & Mascarenhas, A. C. (1981). Remote sensing in development. *Science, 214*(4517), 139–145. https://doi.org/10.1126/science.214.4517.139

Pebesma, E., Bivand, R., Racine, E., Sumner, M., Cook, I., Keitt, T., Lovelac, R., Wickham, H., Ooms, J., Müller, K., Pedersen, T. L., & Baston, D. (2022). *sf: Simple Features for R* (R package version 1.0-9). https://cran.r-project.org/web/packages/sf/

Pebesma, E., Bivand, R., Rowlingson, B., Gomez-Rubio, V., Hijmans, R., Sumner, M., MacQueen, D., Lemon, J., Lindgren, F., ÓBrie, J., & ÓRourke, J. (2021). *sp: Classes and Methods for Spatial Data* (R package version 1.4-5). https://cran.r-project.org/web/packages/sp/

Pebesma, E., & Graeler, B. (2021). *gstat: Spatial and Spatio-Temporal Geostatistical Modelling, Prediction and Simulation* (R package version 2.0-9). https://cran.r-project.org/web/packages/gstat/

Pebesma, E., Nüst, D., & Bivand, R. (2012). The R software environment in reproducible geoscientific research. *Eos, Transactions American Geophysical Union, 93*(16), 163–163. https://doi.org/10.1029/2012EO160003

Pebesma, E., Sumner, M., Racine, E., Fantini, A., & Blodgett, D. (2021). *stars: Spatiotemporal Arrays, Raster and Vector Data Cubes* (R package version 0.5-3). https://cran.r-project.org/web/packages/stars/

Pecl, G. T., Araújo, M. B., Bell, J. D., Blanchard, J., Bonebrake, T. C., Chen, I.-C., Clark, T. D., Colwell, R. K., Danielsen, F., Evengård, B., Falconi, L., Ferrier, S., Frusher, S., Garcia, R. A., Griffis, R. B., Hobday, A. J., Janion-Scheepers, C., Jarzyna, M. A., Jennings, S., ... Williams, S. E. (2017). Biodiversity redistribution under climate change: Impacts on ecosystems and human well-being. *Science, 355*(6332), eaai9214. https://doi.org/10.1126/science.aai9214

Penedo, J., & Borges, N. (2017). The challenge of choosing where to publish: The predatory journals! *Revista Portuguesa de Cirurgia, II*(42), 5–6.

Peñuelas, J., Baret, F., & Filella, I. (1995). Semi-empirical indices to assess carotenoids/chlorophyll a ratio from leaf spectral reflectance. *Photosynthetica, 31*, 221–230.

Pereira, R. H. M., Goncalves, C. N., Araujo, P. H. F., Carvalho, G. D., Arruda, R. A., Nascimento, I., Costa, B. S. P., Cavedo, W. S., Andrade, P. R., Silva, A., Braga, C. K. V., Schmertmann, C., Samuel-Rosa, A., & Ferreira, D. (2021). *geobr: Download Official Spatial Data Sets of Brazil.* https://github.com/cran/geobr

Perry, C. R., & Lautenschlager, L. F. (1984). Functional equivalence of spectral vegetation indices. *Remote Sensing of Environment, 14*(1-3), 169–182. https://doi.org/10.1016/0034-4257(84)90013-0

Pezzopane, J. R. M., Pedro Júnior, M. J., Thomaziello, R. A., & Camargo, M. B. P. (2003). Coffee phenological stages evaluation scale. *Bragantia, 62*(3), 499–505. https://doi.org/10.1590/S0006-87052003000300015

Pinty, B., & Verstraete, M. M. (1992). GEMI: A non-linear index to monitor global vegetation from satellites. *Vegetatio, 101*(1), 15–20. https://doi.org/10.1007/BF00031911

Ponti, M. P. (2012). Segmentation of low-cost remote sensing images combining vegetation indices and mean shift. *IEEE Geoscience and Remote Sensing Letters, 10*(1), 67–70. https://doi.org/10.1109/LGRS.2012.2193113

Qi, J., Chehbouni, A., Huete, A. R., Kerr, Y. H., & Sorooshian, S. (1994). A modified soil adjusted vegetation index. *Remote Sensing of Environment, 48*(2), 119–126. https://doi.org/10.1016/0034-4257(94)90134-1

Ranghetti, L., Boschetti, M., Nutini, F., & Busetto, L. (2020). sen2r: An R toolbox for automatically downloading and preprocessing Sentinel-2 satellite data. *Computers & Geosciences, 139*, 104473. https://doi.org/10.1016/j.cageo.2020.104473

Ranghetti, L., & Busetto, L. (2021). *sen2r: Find, Download and Process Sentinel-2 Data* (R package version 1.5.0). https://cran.r-project.org/web/packages/sen2r/

Rast, M., Bezy, J. L., & Bruzzi, S. (1999). The ESA medium resolution imaging spectrometer MERIS a review of the instrument and its mission. *International Journal of Remote Sensing, 20*(9), 1681–1702. https://doi.org/10.1080/014311699212416

Reichardt, K., & Timm, L. C. (2004). *Solo, planta e atmosfera: Conceitos, processos e aplicações* (1st ed., p. 478). Editora Manole Ltda.

Resende, M., Curi, N., Rezende, S. B., & Corrêa, G. F. (2014). *Pedologia: Base para distinção de ambientes* (6th ed., p. 378). Universidade Federal de Lavras.

Reudenbach, C., Meyer, H., Detsch, F., Möller, F., Nauss, T., Opgenoorth, L., & Marburg, E. I. (2021). *uavRst: Unmanned Aerial Vehicle R Tools.* https://www.rdocumentation.org/packages/uavRst/versions/0.5-4/

Reudenbach, C., Meyer, H., Detsch, F., Möller, F., Nauss, T., Opgenoorth, L., & Marburg, E. I. (2022). *uavRst: Unmanned Aerial Vehicle R Tools* (R package version 0.5-4). https://github.com/gisma/uavRst/

Riano, D., Chuvieco, E., Salas, J., & Aguado, I. (2003). Assessment of different topographic corrections in Landsat-TM data for mapping vegetation types (2003). *IEEE Transactions on Geoscience and Remote Sensing, 41*(5), 1056–1061. https://doi.org/10.1109/TGRS.2003.811693

Ribeiro Jr, P. J., Diggle, P. J., Christensen, O., Schlather, M., Bivand, R., & Ripley, B. (2020). *geoR: Analysis of Geostatistical Data* (R package version 1.8-1). https://cran.r-project.org/web/packages/geoR/

Richardson, A. J., & Wiegand, C. L. (1977). Distinguishing vegetation from soil background information. *Photogrammetric Engineering and Remote Sensing, 43*(12), 1541–1552.

Rikimaru, A., Roy, P. S., & Miyatake, S. (2002). Tropical forest cover density mapping. *Tropical Ecology, 43*, 39–47.

Rosa, L., Alves, M. C., & Alves, L. S. (2011). Uso de composições de bandas do satélite LANDSAT 5 TM para caracterizar a dinâmica da variação de áreas alagadas no Pantanal Mato-grossense. *XV Simpósio Brasileiro de Sensoriamento Remoto*, 5292–5299.

Rouse, J. W., Hass, R. H., Schell, J. A., & Deering, D. W. (1974). Monitoring vegetation systems in the Great Plains with ERTS. *Earth Resources Technology Satellite Symposium*, 309–317.

Rousseeuw, P. J. (1987). Silhouettes: A graphical aid to the interpretation and validation of cluster analysis. *Journal of Computational and Applied Mathematics, 20*, 53–65. https://doi.org/10.1016/0377-0427(87)90125-7

Salmon, W. C. (1978). *Lógica* (4th ed., p. 74). Zahar.

Salomonson, V. V., Barker, J. L., & Knight, E. J. (1995). Spectral characteristics of the Earth Observing System (EOS) Moderate-Resolution Imaging Spectroradiometer (MODIS). In M. R. Descour, J. M. Mooney, D. L. Perry, & L. R. Illing (Eds.), *IAHS publication* (p. 142). https://doi.org/10.1117/12.210869

Santos, H. G., Carvalho Junior, W., Dart, R. O., Aglio, M. L. D., Sousa, J. S., Pares, J. G., Fontana, A., Martins, A. L. S., & Oliveira, A. P. (2011). *O novo mapa de solos do Brasil: Legenda atualizada* (p. 130). Embrapa Solos.

Santos, H. G., Jacomine, P. K. T., Anjos, L. H. C., Oliveira, V. A., Lumbreras, J. F., Coelho, M. R., Almeida, J. A., Araujo Filho, J. C., Oliveira, J. B., & Cunha, T. J. F. (2018). *Sistema Brasileiro de Classificação de Solos* (5th ed., p. 355). Empresa Brasileira de Pesquisa Agropecuária; Embrapa-Solos.

Sarkarand, D., Andrews, F., Wright, K., Klepeis, N., Larsson, J., & Murrell, P. (2021). *lattice: Trellis Graphics for R* (R package version 0.20-45). https://cran.r-project.org/web/packages/lattice/

Schiebe, F. R., Harrington, J. A., & Ritchie, J. C. (1992). Remote sensing of suspended sediments: The Lake Chicot, Arkansas project. *International Journal of Remote Sensing, 13*(8), 1487–1509. https://doi.org/10.1080/01431169208904204

Schmit, T. J., Lindstrom, S. S., Gerth, J. J., & Gunshor, M. M. (2018). Applications of the 16 spectral bands on the Advanced Baseline Imager (ABI). *Journal of Operational Meteorology, 06*(04), 33–46. https://doi.org/10.15191/nwajom.2018.0604

Schönert, M., Weichelt, H., Zillmann, E., & Jürgens, C. (2014). Derivation of tasseled cap coefficients for RapidEye data. In U. Michel & K. Schulz (Eds.), *International Society for Optics and Photonics* (p. 92450Q). https://doi.org/10.1117/12.2066842

Schowengerdt, R. A. (2006). *Remote sensing: Models and methods for image processing* (3rd ed., p. 560). Academic Press.

Schwalb-Willmann, J. (2022). *getSpatialData: Get different kinds of freely available spatial datasets* (R package version 0.1.2). http://www.github.com/16eagle/getSpatialData/

Science Direct. (2019). *Search for word.* https://www.sciencedirect.com/

Scofield, R. A. (2001). Comments on A quantitative assessment of the NESDIS auto-estimator. *Weather and Forecasting, 16*(2), 277–278. https://doi.org/10.1175/1520-0434(2001)016%3C0277:COAQAO%3E2.0.CO;2

Scofield, R. A. (1987). The NESDIS operational convective precipitation- estimation technique. *Monthly Weather Review, 115*(8), 1773–1793. https://doi.org/10.1175/1520-0493(1987)115%3C1773:TNOCPE%3E2.0.CO;2

Seager, S., & Bains, W. (2015). The search for signs of life on exoplanets at the interface of chemistry and planetary science. *Science Advances, 1*(2), e1500047. https://doi.org/10.1126/sciadv.1500047

Seyednasrollah, B. (2021). *Solrad: To calculate solar radiation and related variables based on location, time and topographical conditions.* https://zenodo.org/record/1249673

Seyednasrollah, B., Kumar, M., & Link, T. E. (2013). On the role of vegetation density on net snow cover radiation at the forest floor. *Journal of Geophysical Research: Atmospheres, 118*(15), 8359–8374. https://doi.org/10.1002/jgrd.50575

Seyednasrollah, B., Milliman, T., & Richardson, A. D. (2021). *xROI: Delineate Region of Interests (ROI's) and Extract Time-Series Data from Digital Repeat Photography Images* (R package version 0.9.20). https://cran.r-project.org/web/packages/xROI/

Shiratsuchi, L. S., Brandão, Z. N., Vicente, L. E., Victoria, D. C., Ducati, J. R., Oliveira, R. P., & Vilela, M. F. (2014). Sensoriamento remoto: Conceitos básicos e aplicações na agricultura de precisão. In A. C. C. Bernardi, J. M. Naime, Á. V. Resende, L. H. Bassoi, & R. Y. Inamasu (Eds.), *Sensoriamento remoto: Conceitos básicos e aplicações na agricultura de precisão* (pp. 58–73). Embrapa.

Silva, N. A. U. S., Alves, M. C., Sanches, L., & Salas, J. A. P. (2011). Monitoramento do parque indígena do Xingu em Mato Grosso por meio do sensor AWIFS do satélite IRS-P6. *XV Simpósio Brasileiro de Sensoriamento Remoto*, 1965–1973.

Siqueira, R. P. (2017). *brazilmaps: Brazilian Maps from Different Geographic Levels* (R package version 0.1.0). https://rdrr.io/cran/brazilmaps/

Sousa, K., Sparks, A. H., Ghosh, A., Peterson, P., Ashmall, W., Etten, J. van, & Solberg, S. Ø. (2022). *chirps: API Client for CHIRPS and CHIRTS* (R package version 0.1.4). https://cran.r-project.org/web/packages/chirps/

South, A. (2021). *rnaturalearth: World Map Data from Natural Earth* (R package version 0.1.0). https://cran.r-project.org/web/packages/rnaturalearth/

Spinu, V., Grolemund, G., Wickham, H., Vaughan, D., Lyttle, I., Costigan, I., Law, J., Mitarotonda, D., Larmarange, J., Boiser, J., Lee, C. H., & Google Inc. (2021). *lubridate: Make Dealing with Dates a Little Easier* (R package version 1.8.0). https://cran.r-project.org/web/packages/lubridate/

Taranik, J. V., & Settle, M. (1981). Space shuttle: A new era in terrestrial remote sensing. *Science, 214*(4521), 619–626. https://doi.org/10.1126/science.214.4521.619

Tennekes, M. (2021). *tmaptools: Thematic Map Tools* (R package version 3.1-1). https://cran.r-project.org/web/packages/tmaptools/

Tennekes, M., Nowosad, J., Gombin, J., Jeworutzki, S., Russell, K., Zijdeman, R., Clouse, J., Lovelace, R., & Muenchow, J. (2020). *tmap: Thematic Maps* (R package version 3.2). https://cran.r-project.org/web/packages/tmap/

Teucher, A., Russell, K., & Bloch, M. (2022). *rmapshaper: Client for 'mapshaper' for 'Geospatial' Operations* (R package version 0.4.6). https://cran.r-project.org/web/packages/rmapshaper/

Thiam, A. K. (1998). *Geographic information systems and remote sensing methods for assessing and monitoring land degradation in the Sahel region: The case of southern Mauritania.* Clark University.

Thuillier, G., Labs, D., Foujols, T., Peetermans, W., Gillotay, D., Simon, P. C., & Mandel, H. (2003). The solar spectral irradiance from 200 to 2400 nm as measured by the solspec spectrometer from the atlas and eureca missions. *Solar Physics, 214*, 1–22. https://doi.org/10.1023/A:1024048429145

Title, P. O., & Bemmels, J. B. (2018). ENVIREM: An expanded set of bioclimatic and topographic variables increases flexibility and improves performance of ecological niche modeling. *Ecography, 41*(2), 291–307. https://doi.org/10.1111/ecog.02880

Title, P. O., & Bemmels, J. B. (2021). *envirem: Generation of ENVIREM Variables* (R package version 2.3). https://cran.r-project.org/web/packages/envirem/

Tucker, C. J. (1979). Red and photographic infrared linear combinations for monitoring vegetation. *Remote Sensing of Environment, 8*(2), 127–150.

Tucker, C. J., Townshend, J. R. G., & Goff, T. E. (1985). African land-cover classification using satellite data. *Science, 227*(4685), 369–375. https://doi.org/10.1126/science.227.4685.369

Turbek, S. P., Chock, T. M., Donahue, K., Havrilla, C. A., Oliverio, A. M., Polutchko, S. K., Shoemaker, L. G., & Vimercati, L. (2016). Scientific writing made easy: A step-by-step guide to undergraduate writing in the biological sciences. *The Bulletin of the Ecological Society of America, 97*(4), 417–426. https://doi.org/10.1002/bes2.1258

Tyukavina, A., Hansen, M. C., Potapov, P. V., Stehman, S. V., Smith-Rodriguez, K., Okpa, C., & Aguilar, R. (2017). Types and rates of forest disturbance in Brazilian Legal Amazon, 2000-2013. *Science Advances, 3*(4), e1601047. https://doi.org/10.1126/sciadv.1601047

USDA. (1999). *Soil taxonomy. A basic system of soil classification for making and interpreting soil surveys* (No. 436; 2nd ed., p. 886). United States Department of Agriculture.

USDA. (2014). *Keys to soil taxonomy* (12th ed., p. 372). United States Department of Agriculture; USDA.

USGS. (2021). *Earth Explorer.* https://earthexplorer.usgs.gov

USGS. (2022). *USGS EROS Archive - Digital Elevation - Shuttle Radar Topography Mission (SRTM) 1 Arc-Second Global.* https://www.usgs.gov/centers/eros/science/usgs-eros-archive-digital-elevation-shuttle-radar-topography-mission-srtm-1

Vasques, G. M., Dart, R. O., Baca, J. F. M., Ceddia, M. B., & Mendonça Santos, M. L. (2017). *Mapa de estoque de carbono orgânico do solo (COS) a 0-30 cm do Brasil.* Embrapa Solos. http://geoinfo.cnps.embrapa.br/documents/1115

Vermote, E. F., Tanré, D., Deuze, J. L., Herman, M., & Morcette, J.-J. (1997). Second simulation of the satellite signal in the solar spectrum, 6S: An overview. *IEEE Transactions on Geoscience and Remote Sensing, 35*(3), 675–686. https://doi.org/10.1109/36.581987

Vicente, G. A., Davenport, J. C., & Scofield, R. A. (2002). The role of orographic and parallax corrections on real time high resolution satellite rainfall rate distribution. *International Journal of Remote Sensing, 23*(2), 221–230. https://doi.org/10.1080/01431160010006935

Vicente, G. A., Scofield, R. A., & Menzel, W. P. (1998). The operational GOES infrared rainfall estimation technique. *Bulletin of the American Meteorological Society*, *79*(9), 1883–1898. https://doi.org/10.1175/1520-0477(1998)079%3C1883:TOGIRE%3E2.0.CO;2

Wang, P., Huang, C., Brown de Colstoun, E. C., Tilton, J., & Tan, B. (2017). *Global human built-up and settlement extent (HBASE) dataset from Landsat*. NASA Socioeconomic Data; Applications Center (SEDAC). https://doi.org/10.7927/H4DN434S

WEBforSCIENCE. (2016). *Dissemination*. http://www.webforscience.com/dissemination/

Whittaker, R. H. (1969). New concepts of kingdoms of organisms. *Science*, *163*(3863), 150–160.

Wickham, H. (2020). *reshape2: Flexibly Reshape Data: A Reboot of the Reshape Package* (R package version 1.4.4). https://cran.r-project.org/web/packages/reshape2/

Wickham, H., Chang, W., Henry, L., Pedersen, T. L., Takahashi, K., Wilke, C., Woo, K., Yutani, H., Dunnington, D., & RStudio. (2022). *ggplot2: Create Elegant Data Visualisations Using the Grammar of Graphics* (R package version 3.4.0). https://cran.r-project.org/web/packages/ggplot2/

Wickham, H., François, R., Henry, L., Müller, K., & RStudio. (2022). *dplyr: A Grammar of Data Manipulation* (R package version 1.0.3). https://cran.r-project.org/web/packages/dplyr/

Wickham, H., Hester, J., Chang, W., & RStudio. (2021). *devtools: Tools to Make Developing R Packages Easier* (R package version 2.4.2). https://cran.r-project.org/web/packages/devtools/

Wickham, H., & RStudio. (2021). *tidyverse: Easily Install and Load the 'Tidyverse'* (R package version 1.3.1). https://cran.r-project.org/web/packages/tidyverse/

Wikipedia. (2020a). *Carta de solos do Brasil*. https://pt.wikipedia.org/w/index.php?title=Carta_de_Solos_do_Brasil&oldid=52571327

Wikipedia. (2020b). *Rompimento de barragem em Mariana*. https://pt.wikipedia.org/wiki/Rompimento_de_barragem_em_Mariana

Wilson, J. P., & Gallant, J. C. (2000). *Terrain analysis: Principles and applications* (1st ed., p. 520). Wiley Online Library.

Witten, I. H., Frank, E., Hall, M. A., & Pal, C. J. (2016). *Data mining: Practical machine learning tools and techniques* (4th ed., p. 654). Morgan Kaufmann.

Wong, T.-T. (2015). Performance evaluation of classification algorithms by k-fold and leave-one-out cross validation. *Pattern Recognition*, *48*(9), 2839–2846. https://doi.org/10.1016/j.patcog.2015.03.009

Xu, H. (2006). Modification of normalised difference water index (NDWI) to enhance open water features in remotely sensed imagery. *International Journal of Remote Sensing*, *27*(14), 3025–3033. https://doi.org/10.1080/01431160600589179

YARA. (2020). *Deficiências - café*. https://www.yarabrasil.com.br/nutricao-de-plantas/cafe/deficiencias-cafe/

Yarbrough, L. D., Easson, G., & Kuszmaul, J. S. (2005). QuickBird 2 tasseled cap transform coefficients: A comparison of derivation methods. *Ecora 16 Global Priorities in Land Remote Sensing*, 1–9.

Zakeri, H., Yamazaki, F., & Liu, W. (2017). Texture analysis and land cover classification of Tehran using polarimetric synthetic aperture radar imagery. *Applied Sciences*, *7*(5), 452. https://doi.org/10.3390/app7050452

Zambrano-Bigiarini, M. (2020). *hydroTSM: Time Series Management, Analysis and Interpolation for Hydrological Modelling* (R package version 0.6-0). https://cran.r-project.org/web/packages/hydroTSM/

Zarco-Tejada, P. J., Berjón, A., López-Lozano, R., Miller, J. R., Martín, P., Cachorro, V., González, M. R., & Frutos, A. (2005). Assessing vineyard condition with hyperspectral indices: Leaf and canopy reflectance simulation in a row-structured discontinuous canopy. *Remote Sensing of Environment*, *99*(3), 271–287. https://doi.org/10.1016/j.rse.2005.09.002

Zevenbergen, L. W., & Thorne, C. R. (1987). Quantitative analysis of land surface topography. *Earth Surface Processes and Landforms*, *12*(1), 47–56. https://doi.org/10.1002/esp.3290120107

Zhou, B. (2015). Image segmentation using SLIC superpixels and affinity propagation clustering. *International Journal of Science and Research*, *4*(4), 1525–1529.

Zhu, Z., & Woodcock, C. E. (2012). Object-based cloud and cloud shadow detection in Landsat imagery. *Remote Sensing of Environment, 118*, 83–94. https://doi.org/10.1016/j.rse.2011.10.028

Zuur, A., Ieno, E. N., Walker, N., Saveliev, A. A., & Smith, G. M. (2009). *Mixed effects models and extensions in ecology with R* (p. 574). Springer.

Zvoleff, A. (2020). *glcm: Calculate Textures from Grey-Level Co-Occurrence Matrices (GLCMs)* (R package version 1.6.5). https://cran.r-project.org/web/packages/glcm/

Index